Reading the World

[CONNECTIONS] LITERATURE

Reading the World

THIRD EDITION

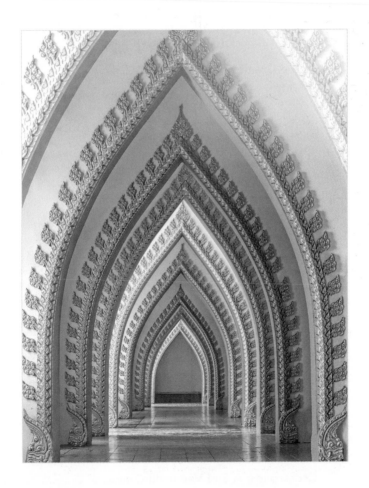

Perfection Learning®

Table of Contents

UNIT ONE The Americas

Ⓝ indicates Nobel laureate

UNIT THREE Africa

UNIT FOUR The Middle East & South Asia

UNIT FIVE East Asia & the Pacific Rim

Ⓝ indicates Nobel laureate

Where in the World?

In *Reading the World,* you will read stories and poems in English with the flavor of elsewhere. The writers come from all over the world—Mexico, Ireland, Nigeria, Iraq, China—and include many Nobel Prize winners. In addition, the book includes an older "classic" selection from each region of the world. *Reading the World*'s focus on research, with numerous research activities and a Research Handbook, will help you appreciate world literature as you develop your research skills.

Many of the writers in this book have lived lives as intriguing as their poetry or prose. Like South African Nobel Laureate Wole Soyinka, they have been imprisoned for being of the wrong race, faith, or political belief. Many were born in one country, but eventually made their home in another—so that they could write and express themselves in freedom.

No matter what a writer's origins, common themes and universal events dominate all the literature in this anthology. Injustice still permeates countries with histories of colonial rule and civil war or with stark divisions between rich and poor. Devastation from war and environmental disasters has led to massive worldwide emigration. Millions of people are struggling to find where they fit in this globalized world.

Other themes are ever present, everywhere. Women in many cultures struggle to find freedom and respect. Family and community life bring both solace and conflict. Love, beauty, and laughter are necessary components for a fulfilling life.

Reading a single story or poem from a country is unlikely to teach you everything there is to know about a culture. No culture or community can be represented by a single story. But it may help you consider which differences among cultures actually matter. The Pulitzer Prize-winning poet Gwendolyn Brooks, a champion of ordinary people, said, "I believe that we should all know each other, we human carriers of so many pleasurable differences. To not know is to doubt, to shrink from, sidestep or destroy."

For the curious and open-minded, literature is one of the best places to find answers to the tantalizing question: Who are my neighbors on this shrinking planet Earth?

The Art of Translation

Khaled Mattawa

Professor of Creative Writing, The University of Michigan, Ann Arbor

While there is a grain of truth in the phrase "lost in translation," its opposite is much truer. Without translation, the English language would be missing many great works, such as Homer's *Odyssey* (originally in Greek) and Tolstoy's *War and Peace* (originally in Russian). Clearly we gain a great deal from translation.

What are the necessary skills of a translator? The translator must have mastery in reading the original language (the language from which the text is being translated) as well as mastery in the host language (the language into which it is being translated). Translation experts have argued through the ages as to which is more important.

I think both skills are essential. A good poet in her own language with weak command of the original language may be able to translate a poem in very readable fashion, but it may have glaring errors. And a person with excellent command of the original language but poor skills in the host language may deliver a very accurate but literal poem—one that doesn't "sing."

In every act of creativity, bad execution will mar a brilliant idea. Most translations are collaborative projects between a scholar of the original language and a poet skilled in the poetic techniques of his or her own language.

And translations do not take place in a political and social vacuum. When we read a translated poem, we bring with us assumptions—often unconscious—about the culture of the original poem. This happens to translators as well. As in any dialogue, if you're not listening to what a person is saying, you are likely to assume something based on what you already think of that person.

You aim, as a translator, to understand why it is being said the way it is being said. And then you do your best to paraphrase what you hear, keeping all the nuances intact.

When I translate Arabic poetry, I create various renditions of a poem. In my lap will be an English dictionary, an Arabic dictionary, and a thesaurus. If I still don't understand a word or a line, I ask the poet (if he or she is available). I check with scholars of Arabic and have them go through my renditions. And finally, I show it to poets who don't know the original language to see if the poem is coherent in English and if it has a musical quality. I leave the poem alone for a few days or weeks, and go over it again and again until I feel I have satisfied both my concerns about accuracy and about the quality of the result.

Translated poems tend to sound slightly unfamiliar, but they have a logic all their own. In a sense, that is what other cultures are like. When translating, I avoid informal American English and allow the poem's own images and metaphors to present its ideas. Some poems refuse translations: they possess linguistic qualities and word play unique to the original language. They are like plants that will not grow outside their native soil or climate. An overly simplified or unskillful attempt at translating them might rob them of the originality and brilliance they possess in their original language.

Translation is a process that requires fidelity, devotion, open-mindedness, and creativity. And this too is how we should speak to each other—with empathy and attention. We have much to gain from reading translations that abide by these principles.

The Literature of the Americas

Kimberly Koza Harris
Retired Professor of English, Central College, Pella, Iowa

Canada, the Caribbean, and Latin America are our neighbors, yet many Americans are more familiar with the entertainment they offer us—from food and dance to music and vacation spots—than with their literature. Although geographically and culturally unique, they share a common history of European conquest and colonization.

Canada's literature began with its native people, the North American Indians, and was further influenced by two very different colonial cultures: French and British. Contemporary Canada is further energized by the more recent arrival of immigrants from former British colonies in Asia, Africa, and the Caribbean.

The Caribbean, a scattering of islands in the Caribbean Sea, is also called the West Indies. Because of how these islands were colonized, Spanish, French, English, Dutch, Haitian Creole, and Papiamento are spoken along with several other languages. The Caribbean also has a lively mix of different cultures. A majority of modern Caribbean people are ancestors of the African enslaved peoples once forced to work there, on huge plantations of sugar, tobacco, and bananas. Many others are descended from indentured servants brought by European colonizers from India.

Latin America encompasses Mexico and the countries of Central and South America, as well as some islands on the Caribbean Sea. The primary languages spoken—Spanish, Portuguese, and French—all developed from Latin, giving the region its name. Needless to say, Latin America is multicultural, with European descendants, Native indigenous peoples, and *mestizo* people, meaning racially mixed people.

Naturally, literature from Canada, the Caribbean, and Latin America reflects the huge diversity of cultures in each region.

A prominent concern of Canadian literature is the search for a national identity. Canadian writers often explore what makes Canada distinct—especially in comparison with the United States. A former Canadian prime minister, Pierre Trudeau, is famously quoted as saying to a U.S. audience, "Living next to you is in some ways like sleeping with an elephant. No matter how friendly and even-tempered the beast, one is affected by every twitch and grunt."

The same could probably be said by politicians and writers from the Caribbean and Latin America. Twentieth-century Caribbean authors strive for a distinct Caribbean identity. These writers highlight the hybrid culture of this region, sometimes using pidgin and Creole languages to give voice to everyday people. A related theme of cultural displacement—the sense of rootlessness—is also prominent in Caribbean literature.

Long influenced by European literary traditions, many 20th-century Latin American authors began to experiment with literary modes such as surrealism and magical realism. Surrealism stresses the importance of dreams and the unconscious mind and often juxtaposes bizarre or startling images. Magic realism, made famous by authors such as Gabriel García Márquez, blends reality with fantasy, portraying fantastic occurrences as a matter of fact. All of a sudden, animals can speak and human beings can levitate. After all, what could be stranger than life itself? Especially in a region with such extreme divides between its rich and poor, forms of government (totalitarian and democratic), cultures, and climates. In the 1960s—a period known as the "Latin American Boom"—this bold and innovative style brought worldwide attention to Latin American authors.

The vibrant literature of Canada, the Caribbean, and Latin America is valuable for introducing us to new cultures as well as for illuminating the multicultural nature of American society. By discovering the literature of our neighbors, we may also learn about ourselves.

CANADA

Saul Bellow
Alice Munro
Margaret Atwood

MEXICO

Octavio Paz
Juan Rulfo
Aztecs
Carlos Solórzano

Literary Map of
The Americas

JAMAICA

James Berry

COLOMBIA

Gabriel García Márquez

PERU

Mario Vargas Llosa

CHILE

Isabel Allende
Gabriela Mistral

CUBA
Herberto Padilla

PUERTO RICO
Rosario Ferré

ST. LUCIA
Derek Walcott

TRINIDAD & TOBAGO
Samuel Selvon

BRAZIL
João Guimarães Rosa

ARGENTINA
Jorge Luis Borges
Luisa Valenzuela

Aztec Creation Story

Background

The god Quetzalcoatl, whose name means "Feathered Serpent," is usually the hero of the Aztec creation stories. Like creator gods in stories from many other cultures, Quetzalcoatl cleverly defied other gods to create human beings—and he suffered for his deed. Also like similar gods elsewhere, he gave precious gifts to humankind, including calendars and books. Such a deity is often referred to as a "culture hero."

The god of the morning and evening star, Quetzalcoatl was humane and kind. He was said to have been forced to leave Mexico because he objected to human sacrifice. According to one story, he fled across the Atlantic on a raft made of snakes and was long expected by the Aztecs to return.

Some historians believe Aztec Emperor Moctezuma II thought that the Spanish conquistador Hernán Cortés was the returned Quetzalcoatl when he arrived in Mexico in 1519. If so, Moctezuma's mistake helped make Cortés's conquest of Mexico possible.

Aztecs and the United States

Throughout Mexico today, children often stand outside at night looking at the rabbit in the moon. The Aztec story of the creation of the sun and the moon explains how the rabbit got there.

The continuing influence of the Aztec stories reflects an important historical difference between the United States and its southern neighbors. As colonists and settlers swept across today's United States, they seldom blended with indigenous populations. In Mexico and parts of Central and South America, however, Europeans and their descendents often intermarried with Indians, forming a distinct cultural and racial blend called *mestizaje*. In these parts of America, most people feel a kinship with the ancient cultures of their lands.

Research: Summarize Findings

The Mexican coat of arms, featured on the Mexican flag, is based on an Aztec legend. Research this legend and summarize it in an oral report. Explain why the story was incorporated into the coat of arms.

Aztec Creation Story

Oral Tradition

Before You Read

Where did the first people on Earth come from? How did people learn to grow crops, use fire, and protect themselves from natural elements? Why do animals look as they do? The Aztecs, like people around the world, handed down creation stories that provided answers to such questions. These stories, or myths, also reflect basic moral principles of the society that created them.

World Context

Following is the Aztec account of how the gods formed the earth, the sun, and the moon. This story mentions many Aztec gods but focuses on just two: Tecuciztecatl, who is proud, wealthy, and handsome, and Nanahuatzin, who is humble, poor, and suffers from sores all over his body.

 LITERARY LENS Stories sometimes use **juxtaposition**, or placing two things side by side in an unexpected combination. Juxtaposition can often be used to reveal a text's theme.

The great gods, Tezcatlipoca and Quetzalcoatl, brought the Earth Goddess down from the heavens. She was an enormous monster full of eyes and mouths. Each of the joints in her body contained a mouth, and these innumerable mouths bit like wild beasts. The world was already full of water, although no one knows its origin.

When the gods saw the huge monster moving back and forth across the water, they said to each other: "We must create the earth." So they transformed themselves into two large serpents. One of them gripped the goddess from her right hand down to her left foot, while the other took her left hand and right foot. Holding on to her, they turned and twisted with such force that she finally tore in two. They lifted her lower half and made the sky. From the upper part they formed the earth. The rest of the gods looked on and felt ashamed that they had not made anything comparable to this.

Then, in order to make **amends** for the immense damage inflicted on the Earth Goddess, the other gods came down to console her and give her gifts. As a compensation they declared that out of her body would come all that humans need to sustain themselves and live on the earth. From her hair they made wild grasses, trees and flowers. Her skin was changed into delicate greens and ornamental plants. Her eyes were transformed into small hollows, wells and fountains, her mouths into large caves, her nose into mountains and valleys.

Earth Goddess

amends: compensation for an injury

This is the same goddess who sometimes weeps in the night, longing to eat human hearts. She refuses to be silent if she is denied them, and she won't produce fruit unless she is watered with human blood.

It is said that before there was day in the world, when all was in darkness, the gods gathered together in Teotihuacán.[1] They counseled together and said: "O gods, who will accept the burden of lighting the world? Who will be the sun and the moon?"

Then a god named Tecuciztecatl responded to these words and said: "I will take on the burden of lighting the world."

The gods spoke once again and said: "Who will be the other?" So they looked at each other and discussed who would be the other. None of them dared to offer himself for that task. All of them were afraid and made excuses.

One of the gods, Nanahuatzin, who was covered with sores, went unnoticed. He did not speak, but listened to what the other gods were saying. And the other gods spoke to him and said: "O Nanahuatzin, you be the one who gives light." Willingly he consented to their commands, and replied: "Gratefully, I accept what you have asked of me. So be it!"

Then the two of them began to do **penance** lasting four days. A fire was lit in a hearth which was built on a **precipice**—a place now called *Teotexcalli*.

penance: an act of self-punishment to show sorrow for wrongdoing

precipice: a steep cliff

---

1 **Teotihuacán:** an ancient Middle American city, located near where Mexico City is today

The god Tecuciztecatl's offerings—all of them—were expensive. Instead of branches he offered precious feathers called *quetzalli,* and instead of balls of hay, he offered balls of gold. And instead of maguey spines,[2] he offered spines made from precious stones. In place of spines stained with blood, he offered spines made from red coral. And the copal incense[3] which he offered was excellent.

Instead of branches, the god of **pustules,** Nanahuatzin, offered green reeds, which were tied in bundles of three, with a total of nine. He offered balls of hay and maguey spines stained with his own blood. And for incense, instead of copal, he offered scabs from his sores.

pustules: pimples

For each of these gods a tower was erected, like a mountain. On these same mountains they did penance for four nights. Today these mountains are called *tzaqualli* and are the Pyramids of the Sun and the Moon at Teotihuacán.

After they finished the four nights of their penance, they threw away the branches and everything else that they used in the performance of the penance.

This was done at the conclusion of their penance, since on the following night they began to perform the rites of office. Just before midnight the other gods gave their adornments to the one called Tecuciztecatl; they gave him a feather headdress and a linen jacket. As for Nanahuatzin, they covered his head with a paper headdress and dressed him in a paper **stole** and a paper loincloth. With the approach of midnight, all the gods took their places around the hearth called *Teotexcalli,* where the fire had burned for four days.

stole: a scarf

The gods arranged themselves in two rows, some on one side of the fire and some on the other. And then the two, Tecuciztecatl and Nanahuatzin, took their places in front of the fire, facing the hearth, in between the two rows of gods.

All of them were standing when the gods spoke and said to Tecuciztecatl: "Now then, Tecuciztecatl! Cast yourself into the fire!" And he readied himself to leap into the fire. But the flames were so fierce that when he felt the unbearable heat he became terrified, and was afraid to throw himself into the fire. So he turned back.

Again he turned to cast himself into the flames which leaped even higher, but he stopped, not daring to cast himself into the fire. Two more

---

2 **maguey spines:** the stiff leaves of a plant known as the century plant
3 **copal incense:** a material made from a thick liquid produced by plants that gives off pleasant-smelling smoke when burned

times he tried, but each time he lost his nerve. It was tradition that no one could try more than four times.

Since Tecuciztecatl had tried four times the gods then spoke to Nanahuatzin and said to him: "Now then, Nanahuatzin! You try!" When the gods had spoken to him, he gathered his courage and, closing his eyes, rushed forth and cast himself into the fire, where he began to crackle and sizzle like someone being roasted. When Tecuciztecatl saw that he had leaped into the flames, he gathered his nerve, rushed forward and threw himself into the fire.

They say that an eagle then flew into the fire and also burned; for this reason it has dark or blackish feathers. Finally a jaguar entered. He wasn't burned, but only singed; and for this reason he continued to be stained black and white. From this came the custom of calling men who are skilled in war *cuauhtlocelotl. Cuauhtli* is said first because the eagle entered the fire first; *ocelotl* is said last because the jaguar entered the fire after the eagle.

After these two gods had flung themselves into the fire, and after both had burned, the remaining gods seated themselves, waiting to see from which direction Nanahuatzin would begin to rise. After they had waited a long time, the sky began to redden, and the light of dawn appeared all around them. And they say that after this the gods knelt down, waiting to see where on the horizon the Sun Nanahuatzin would rise.

As they looked in each direction they turned in a circle, but not one could guess or say the place where he would appear. They could not make up their minds about a single thing. Some thought he would appear in the north, and they fixed their attention there. Others fixed on the south. Some suspected that he would emerge in all directions at once, because the radiance of dawn was everywhere. Others got in a position to look east and said: "Here, in this direction, the sun is to rise." The word of these gods was true.

They say that those who looked east were Quetzalcoatl, who is also called Ehecatl; and another called Totec, and by another name Anahuatlitecu, and by another name Tlátlahuic Tezcatlipoca. And others called Mimixcoa, who are innumerable. And four women: one named Tiacapan, the other Teicu, the third Tlacoyehua, and the fourth Xocoyotl.

When the sun began to rise, he looked very red and appeared to sway from side to side. No one could look directly at him because his powerful light would blind them. His rays streamed out in a magnificent way and were scattered in all directions.

Afterwards the moon appeared in the east, in the same direction as the sun. First the sun arose, and afterwards the moon. The order that they entered the fire was the order in which they appeared, and were made sun and moon.

And the storytellers say that the light coming from them was of equal intensity. And when the gods saw that they shone equally they discussed it among themselves again and said: "O gods, what shall come of this? Will it actually work if both are alike and move together? Will it be good that they shine with the same intensity?"

The gods made a judgment and said: "Let it be this way, let it thus be done." Then one of them ran up and threw a rabbit into the face of Tecuciztecatl, darkening his face and obscuring the light. And his face remained as it is today.

After both had risen over the earth, the sun and moon stayed in one place without moving. And the gods once more spoke and said: "How are we going to live when the sun doesn't move? Are we to live among the **peons**? Let us all die and give him vitality with our deaths."

peons: servants

And immediately Ehecatl, the Wind, took charge of slaying all the gods, and he killed them. It is said that one named Xolotl refused to die and said to the gods: "O gods, don't kill me!" He wept so intensely that his eyes swelled from crying.

When the executioner arrived, he ran away and hid in the **maize** fields, and changed himself into the base of the maize plant with two stalks, which field hands call *xolotl*. He was discovered among the bottoms of the maize plant. Again he ran away and hid among the maguey, turning into a maguey with two bodies, which is called *mexolotl*. Again he was spotted. He ran away and hid in the water, changing himself into a fish, which is named *axolotl*. There they took him and killed him.

maize: corn

And they say that even though the gods were dead, the sun still did not move. And then Ehecatl, the Wind, began to blow. Blowing like a monsoon, he caused the sun to move and get on his way. After the sun began to travel, the moon remained in the place where he was.

After the sun had set, the moon began to move. In this manner they have their separate ways, coming forth at different times. The sun carries on during the day and the moon works or illuminates the night. And from this comes the saying: that Tecuciztecatl would have been the sun if had been the first to leap into the fire, because he was named first and offered precious things in his penance.

Translated by David M. Johnson

After You Read

Critical Reading

1. The story states that the gods gave Nanahuatzin a paper headdress, a paper stole, and a paper loincloth. Do you think these items represent, or **symbolize**, the sun? Explain.

2. Compare Tecuciztecatl and Nanahuatzin. How are they similar? How do their differences influence the outcome of the story?

3. In the story, Tecuciztecatl and Nanahuatzin completed four days of penance. What is the motivation for these characters to complete penance? How are they changed by the process of penance?

4. What is the **theme**, or moral lesson, that this creation story teaches?

5. Of the two gods, Nanahuatzin and Tecuciztecatl, who do you think more thoroughly embodies the values of the Aztecs? Cite passages from the myth to support your choice.

Literary Lens: Juxtaposition

This myth contains many instances of unexpected **juxtapositions**. First, identify several examples of juxtaposition, then identify the things that are being combined, and lastly infer what meaning or theme is revealed through these juxtapositions. Create the following graphic organizer and fill it in with examples from the text. Under the Theme head, explain the theme each juxtaposition reveals.

Juxtaposition 1		Theme
Object or Thing	Object or Thing	

Juxtaposition 2		Theme
Object or Thing	Object or Thing	

Focus on Research: Summarize Findings

Sacrifices to the gods were important to the Aztecs. Conduct research on this topic, finding three reliable sources. Then write a two- or three-sentence summary of each source. Remember to use your own words and to include key ideas instead of minor details.

The Literature of
Canada

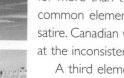

Background

Canada's vast size, impressive mountains, and broad prairies have inspired writers for more than two centuries. Nature—its beauty and its danger—has been a common element in Canadian literature. Another common element has been satire. Canadian writers such as Stephen Leacock became famous by poking fun at the inconsistencies of people and governments.

A third element has shaped Canadian literature increasingly in the last four decades: ethnic diversity. While authors such as Margaret Atwood and Alice Munro were born in Canada, many were born elsewhere and moved to Canada. Among the Canadian writers in this book are people born in Sri Lanka, India, Spain, and the United States.

Canada and the United States

Like the United States, Canada is a large, democratic country shaped by immigrants and the conquest of a frontier. In both countries, English is the most widely used language. Not surprisingly, then, themes such as confronting nature, living on a frontier, and the interaction of ethnic groups are common concerns for writers in both countries.

However, Canada and the United States have some key differences. Canada includes a large French-speaking minority and very few people of African or Latin American descent. The United States is nine times larger in population and immensely more influential in global affairs. Canadians have always wrestled with their attitudes toward the United States. Is it a great neighbor or a bully? The perception of Canada as the smaller, less powerful of the pair of friends may explain why the tradition of Canadian humor is so strong.

As you read the following selections by Canadian writers, consider this question: Are the settings, plots, and themes ones that a U.S. author might use?

Research: Synthesize Multiple Sources

Some Canadian authors, including Margaret Atwood, have suggested that Canadian writers have a "garrison mentality." Use at least two sources to research the meaning of this term. Then write a one-paragraph synthesis of your findings. Include references to authors and works that exemplify the mentality.

from Herzog

Saul Bellow

Before You Read

Saul Bellow (1915–2005), born in Canada and raised in the United States by Russian émigré parents, became a major force in literature, publishing multiple short story collections and novels. *The Adventures of Augie March, Herzog,* and *Mr. Sammler's Planet* won National Book Awards, and *Humboldt's Gift* won a Pulitzer Prize for Fiction. Bellow was awarded the Nobel Prize in Literature in 1976. Over the years many critics have noted the reoccurring themes of Jewish life and identity. Additionally, his work is noted for his complex portrayal of otherness or alienation in his characters and a fascination with the wide-ranging vibrancy of life.

World Context

Bellow's parents fled anti-Semitism and religious persecution in Russia to come to Canada. However, Bellow and his family experienced the costs of freedom, including poverty and discrimination. The challenges of being an immigrant informed many of Bellow's award-winning works.

LITERARY LENS An **interior monologue** is when the unspoken thoughts and feelings of a character are revealed in a text. Consider the reasons Bellow begins his novel with interior monologue.

If I am out of my mind, it's all right with me, thought Moses[1] Herzog.[2] Some people thought he was cracked and for a time he himself had doubted that he was all there. But no, though he still behaved oddly, he felt confident, cheerful, clairvoyant, and strong. He had fallen under a spell and was writing letters to everyone under the sun. He was so stirred by these

---

1 **Moses:** The character is probably named after the prophet Moses, an important figure in Jewish tradition.

2 **Herzog:** a historical German title used to describe a status that is somewhere between that of a count and of a king

letters that from the end of June he moved from place to place with a **valise** full of papers. He had carried this valise from New York to Martha's Vineyard,[3] but returned from the Vineyard immediately; two days later he flew to Chicago, and from Chicago he went to a village in western Massachusetts. Hidden in the country, he wrote endlessly, fanatically to the newspapers, to the people in public life, to friends and relatives and at last to the dead, his own obscure dead, and finally the famous dead.

valise:
a small type
of suitcase

It was the peak of summer in the Berkshires.[4] Herzog was alone in the big old house. Normally particular about food, he now ate Silvercup bread from the paper package, beans from the can, and American cheese. Now and then he picked raspberries in the overgrown garden, lifting up the thorny canes with absent-minded caution. As for sleep, he slept on a mattress without sheets—it was his abandoned marriage bed—or in the hammock, covered by his coat. Tall bearded grass and locust and maple seedlings surrounded him in the yard. When he opened his eyes in the night, the stars were near like spiritual bodies. Fires, of course; gases— minerals, heat, atoms, but eloquent at five in the morning to a man lying in a hammock, wrapped in his overcoat.

When some new thought gripped his heart he went to the kitchen, his headquarters, to write it down. The white paint was scaling from the brick walls and Herzog sometimes wiped mouse droppings from the table with his sleeve, calmly wondering why field mice should have such a passion for wax and paraffin. They made holes in the paraffin-sealed preserves; they gnawed birthday candles down to the wicks. A rat chewed into a package of bread, leaving the shape of its body in the layers of slices. Herzog ate the other half of the loaf spread with jam. He could share with rats too.

All the while, one corner of his mind remained open to the external world. He heard the crows in the morning. Their harsh call was delicious. He heard the thrushes at dusk. At night there was a barn owl. When he walked in the garden, excited by a mental letter, he saw roses winding about the rain spout; or mulberries—birds gorging in the mulberry tree. The days were hot, the evenings flushed and dusty. He looked keenly at everything but he felt half blind.

His friend, his former friend, Valentine, and his wife, his ex-wife Madeleine, had spread the rumor that his sanity had collapsed. Was it true?

He was taking a turn around the empty house and saw the shadow of his

---

3 **Martha's Vineyard:** an island off the coast of Massachusetts known for the wealth of its residents

4 **Berkshires:** a mountainous region of western Connecticut and Massachusetts well-known for its tourism

face in a gray, webby window. He looked weirdly tranquil. A radiant line went from mid-forehead over his straight nose and full, silent lips.

Late in spring Herzog had been overcome by the need to explain, to have it out, to justify, to put in perspective, to clarify, to make amends.

At that time he had been giving adult-education lectures in a New York night school. He was clear enough in April but by the end of May he began to ramble. It became apparent to his students that they would never learn much about The Roots of Romanticism but that they would see and hear odd things. One after another, the academic formalities dropped away. Professor Herzog had the unconscious frankness of a man deeply preoccupied. And toward the end of the term there were long pauses in his lectures. He would stop, muttering "Excuse me," reaching inside his coat for his pen. The table creaking, he wrote on scraps of paper with a great pressure of eagerness in his hand; he was absorbed, his eyes darkly circled. His white face showed everything—everything. He was reasoning, arguing, he was suffering, he had thought of a brilliant alternative—he was wide-open, he was narrow; his eyes, his mouth made everything silently clear—longing, bigotry, bitter anger. One could see it all. The class waited three minutes, five minutes, utterly silent.

At first there was no pattern to the notes he made. They were fragments—nonsense syllables, exclamations, twisted proverbs and quotations or, in the Yiddish[5] of his long-dead mother, *Trepverter*[6]—retorts that came too late, when you were already on your way down the stairs.

He wrote, for instance, *Death—die—live again—die again—live.*
No person, no death.
And, *On the knees of your soul? Might as well be useful. Scrub the floor.*
Next, *Answer a fool according to his folly lest he be wise in his own conceit.*
Answer not a fool according to his folly, lest though be like until him.
Choose one.
He noted also, *I see by Walter Winchell*[7] *that J. S. Bach*[8] *put on black gloves to compose a requiem mass.*

Herzog scarcely knew what to think of this scrawling. He yielded to the excitement that inspired it and suspected at times that it might be as a symptom of disintegration. That did not frighten him.

---

5 **Yiddish:** the language of Jewish people from northern Europe

6 *Trepverter:* a Yiddish word meaning "stepwords," used to describe the words that come up on the way to trying to recall a specific word

7 **Walter Winchell:** an American journalist (1897–1972) known for his celebrity gossip and later for criticizing Nazi sympathizers

8 **J. S. Bach:** a German composer (1685–1750) considered one of the foremost musical composers

After You Read

Read Critically

1. The story states that Herzog "looked keenly at everything but he felt half blind" (page 17). Infer what you think Bellow hoped to reveal about Herzog by saying that Herzog felt "half blind"?

2. Bellow once wrote that "people don't realize how much they are in the grip of ideas. . . . We live among ideas much more than we live in nature." Do you think this does or does not describe the character Herzog? Support your answer with details from the excerpt.

3. This excerpt describes Herzog writing letters and notes. What do you think these letters and notes symbolize? Support your answer with details from the excerpt.

Literary Lens: Interior Monologue

Identify examples of interior monologue from the excerpt. Then consider the effects of the interior monologue on the story.

Interior monologue	Quotation of interior monologue	Effect of interior monologue on the story
1st example	"I am out of my mind, it's all right with me."	
2nd example		
3rd example		

Focus on Research: Quote Sources

Bellow was a major literary force. Conduct research to find out how he influenced other authors, such as Philip Roth. Then write a brief analysis of your findings. Be sure to quote from these sources directly in your analysis. Be sure to use quotation marks to correctly punctuate the quotations. In addition, note your sources. For example, you might write this: According to critic Zachary Leader at *The Guardian*, Philip Roth thought Bellow should be considered "the sturdy backbone of 20th-century literature."

At the Tourist Centre in Boston

Margaret Atwood

Before You Read

Margaret Atwood (1939–) is a Canadian author of fiction, poetry, social history, criticism, and children's books. Atwood writes with a sharp sense of irony, often directed toward specific political and cultural notions. Her political positions, she noted in an interview, developed out of "looking into things . . . out of that comes your view—not that you have the view first and then squash everything to make it fit."

World Context

Many Americans mistake Canada for a quieter, colder version of the United States. Margaret Atwood and other Canadians resent Americans' ignorance of their homeland. The second-largest country in the world, Canada has a wilderness terrain of stunning variety and is equally notable for its diverse population. Unlike the United States, with its "melting pot" credo, Canada has not made assimilation the goal of citizenship for new immigrants.

 LITERARY LENS In literature, **tone** is the attitude of the author toward his or her subject. What tone can you identify in this poem?

There is my country under glass,
a white relief-
map with red dots for the cities,
reduced to the size of a wall
and beside it 10 blownup snapshots   5
one for each province,
in purple-browns and odd reds,
the green of the trees dulled;

all blues however
of an assertive purity.   10

Mountains and lakes and more lakes
(though Quebec[1] is a restaurant and Ontario[2] the empty
interior of the parliament buildings),
with nobody climbing the trails and hauling out
the fish and splashing in the water   15
but arrangements of grinning tourists—
look here, Saskatchewan[3]
is a flat lake, some convenient rocks
where two children pose with a father

Vente Trottoir Fin de Soirée | Raphael Montpetit

---

1 **Quebec:** a French-speaking province in eastern Canada
2 **Ontario:** a Canadian province bordering the Great Lakes
3 **Saskatchewan:** a western province of Canada

and the mother is cooking something 20
in immaculate slacks by a smokeless fire,
her teeth white as detergent.

Whose dream is this, I would like to know:
is this a manufactured
hallucination, a cynical fiction, a lure 25
for export only?
I seem to remember people,
at least in the cities, also slush,
machines and assorted garbage. Perhaps
that was my private mirage 30

which will just evaporate
when I go back. Or the citizens will be gone,
run off to the peculiarly-
green forests
to wait among the brownish mountains 35
for the platoons of tourists
and plan their odd red massacres.

Unsuspecting
window lady, I ask you:

Do you see nothing 40
watching you from under the water?

Was the sky ever that blue?

Who really lives there?

After You Read

Critical Reading

1. Identify two examples from the poem when the narrator compares her experiences in her country with the way the country is presented in pictures on the tourist map. What differences are revealed from these comparisons?

2. In this poem, the narrator asks multiple questions. Identify several examples of questions the narrator asks. How does the use of questions reveal the underlying theme of the poem?

3. What is the main **conflict** of the poem? Support your answer with details from the poem.

 ## Literary Lens: Tone

Cite three lines from the poem that reveal the speaker's tone. Then summarize the speaker's attitude in a sentence.

Quotation	What this reveals about the speaker's tone
Summary:	

Focus on Research: Conduct a Survey

There are many ways to gather information. One way is by conducting a survey. Use an online program, such as Google Forms or Survey Monkey, to survey your classmates about an issue related to your neighborhood, city, or state. Examples of questions you might ask include the following:

- Which of the following local parks have you visited in the last year? [Participants choose from a list of parks.]
- Which new services would you most like to see in our city? [Participants choose from a list of services.]

Compile the results into a format that best communicates the data, for example, a pie chart or bar graph. Share your results with your classmates.

Day of the Butterfly

Alice Munro

Before You Read

Alice Munro (1931–), who began publishing her stories as a teenager, is one of the most celebrated contemporary short story writers in the English-speaking world. "Day of the Butterfly" reveals some of her ongoing subject matters and themes: small-town life in provincial Canada, girls coming of age, and the mysteries of ordinary life.

World Context

The central Canadian province of Ontario, where Munro has spent much of her life, is often the setting in which she explores frustration, loneliness, and moral breakdown.

Depicting rural communities allows Munro to demonstrate how close people can be without really knowing each other at all. She has said, "In small towns, you have no privacy at all. You have a role, a character, but one that other people have made up for you." In the following story, the truth of that remark can easily be seen.

 LITERARY LENS The **theme** of a work of literature is the underlying meaning or message of the piece. A theme may be stated explicitly by the narrator or a character. More often, however, the theme is implicit and requires the power of interpretation to determine. As you read, watch for statements, character actions, and images that might reveal the theme.

I do not remember when Myra Sayla came to town, though she must have been in our class at school for two or three years. I start remembering her in the last year, when her little brother Jimmy Sayla was in Grade One. Jimmy Sayla was not used to going to the bathroom by himself and he would have to come to the Grade Six door and ask for Myra and she would take him downstairs. Quite often he would not get to Myra in time and there would be a big dark stain on his little button-on cotton pants. Then Myra had to come and ask the teacher: "Please may I take my brother home, he has wet himself?"

That was what she said the first time and everybody in the front seats heard her—though Myra's voice was the lightest singsong—and there was a muted giggling which alerted the rest of the class. Our teacher, a cold gentle girl who wore glasses with thin gold rims and in the stiff **solicitude** of certain poses resembled a giraffe, wrote something on a piece of paper and showed it to Myra. And Myra recited uncertainly: "My brother has had an accident, please, teacher."

Everybody knew of Jimmy Sayla's shame and at recess (if he was not being kept in, as he often was, for doing something he shouldn't in school) he did not dare go out on the school grounds, where the other little boys, and some bigger ones, were waiting to chase him and corner him against the back fence and thrash him with tree branches. He had to stay with Myra. But at our school there were the two sides, the Boys' Side and the Girls' Side, and it was believed that if you so much as stepped on the side that was not your own you might easily get the strap. Jimmy could not go out on the Girls' Side and Myra could not go out on the Boys' Side, and no one was allowed to stay in the school unless it was raining or snowing. So Myra and Jimmy spent every recess standing in the little back porch between the two sides. Perhaps they watched the baseball games, the tag and skipping and building of leaf houses in the fall and snow forts in the winter; perhaps they did not watch at all. Whenever you happened to look at them their heads were slightly bent, their narrow bodies hunched in, quite still. They had long smooth oval faces, **melancholy** and **discreet**— dark, oily shining hair. The little boy's was long, clipped at home, and Myra's was worn in heavy braids coiled on top of her head so that she looked, from a distance, as if she was wearing a turban too big for her. Over their dark eyes, the lids were never fully raised; they had a weary look. But it was more than that. They were like children in a medieval painting, they were like small figures carved of wood, for worship or magic, with faces smooth and aged, and meekly, **cryptically** uncommunicative.

• • • • •

Most of the teachers at our school had been teaching for a long time and at recess they would disappear into the teachers' room and not bother us. But our own teacher, the young woman of the fragile gold-rimmed glasses, was apt to watch us from a window and sometimes come out, looking brisk and uncomfortable, to stop a fight among the little girls or start a running

solicitude:
concern; care

melancholy:
sad;
downhearted

discreet:
cautious;
guarded

cryptically:
mysteriously;
secretively

game among the big ones, who had been huddled together playing Truth or Secrets. One day she came out and called, "Girls in Grade Six, I want to talk to you!" She smiled persuasively, earnestly, and with dreadful unease, showing fine gold rims around her teeth. She said, "There is a girl in Grade Six called Myra Sayla. She is in your grade, isn't she?"

We mumbled. But there was a coo from Gladys Healey. "Yes, Miss Darling!"

"Well, why is she never playing with the rest of you? Every day I see her standing in the back porch, never playing. Do you think she looks happy standing back there? Do you think you would be very happy, if *you* were left back there?"

Nobody answered; we faced Miss Darling, all respectful, self-possessed, and bored with the unreality of her question. Then Gladys said, "Myra can't come out with us, Miss Darling. Myra has to look after her little brother!"

"Oh," said Miss Darling dubiously. "Well you ought to try to be nicer to her anyway. Don't you think so? Don't you? You will try to be nicer, won't you? I *know* you will." Poor Miss Darling! Her campaigns were soon confused, her persuasions turned to bleating and uncertain pleas.

When she had gone Gladys Healey said softly, "You will try to be nicer, won't you? I know you will," and then drawing her lip back over her big teeth she yelled exuberantly, "I don't care if it rains or freezes."[1] She went through the whole verse and ended it with a spectacular twirl of her Royal Stuart tartan[2] skirt. Mr. Healey ran a Dry Goods and Ladies' Wear, and his daughter's leadership in our class was partly due to her flashing plaid skirts and organdie blouses and velvet jackets with brass buttons, but also to her early-maturing bust and the fine brutal force of her personality. Now we all began to imitate Miss Darling.

We had not paid much attention to Myra before this. But now a game was developed; it started with saying, "Let's be nice to Myra!" Then we would walk up to her in formal groups of three or four and at a signal, say together, "Hel-lo Myra, Hello My-ra!" and follow up with something like, "What do you wash your hair in, Myra, it's so nice and shiny, My-ra." "Oh she washes it in cod-liver oil, don't you, Myra, she washes it in cod-liver oil, can't you smell it?"

And to tell the truth there was a smell about Myra, but it was a rotten-sweetish smell as of bad fruit. That was what the Saylas did, kept a little fruit store. Her father sat all day on a stool by the window, with his shirt open

---

1 "I don't care . . . freezes.": lyrics from a popular song
2 **Royal Stuart tartan**: a red Scottish plaid

over his swelling stomach and tufts of black hair showing around his belly button; he chewed garlic. But if you went into the store it was Mrs. Sayla who came to wait on you, appearing silently between the limp print curtains hung across the back of the store. Her hair was crimped in black waves and she smiled with her full lips held together, stretched as far as they would go; she told you the price in a little rapping voice, daring you to challenge her and, when you did not, handed you the bag of fruit with open mockery in her eyes.

• • • • •

One morning in the winter I was walking up the school hill very early; a neighbour had given me a ride into town. I lived about half a mile out of town, on a farm, and I should not have been going to the town school at all, but to a country school nearby where there were half a dozen pupils and a teacher a little demented since her change of life.[3] But my mother, who was an ambitious woman, had prevailed on the town trustees to accept me and my father to pay the extra tuition, and I went to school in town. I was the only one in the class who carried a lunch pail and ate peanut-butter sandwiches in the high, bare, mustard-coloured cloakroom, the only one who had to wear rubber boots in the spring, when the roads were heavy with mud. I felt a little danger, on account of this; but I could not tell exactly what it was.

I saw Myra and Jimmy ahead of me on the hill; they always went to school very early—sometimes so early that they had to stand outside waiting for the janitor to open the door. They were walking slowly, and now and then Myra half turned around. I had often loitered in that way, wanting to walk with some important girl who was behind me, and not quite daring to stop and wait. Now it occurred to me that Myra might be doing this with me. I did not know what to do. I could not afford to be seen walking with her, and I did not even want to—but, on the other hand, the flattery of those humble, hopeful turnings was not lost on me. A role was shaping for me that I could not resist playing. I felt a great pleasurable rush of self-conscious benevolence; before I thought what I was doing I called, "Myra! Hey, Myra, wait up, I got some Cracker Jack!" and I quickened my pace as she stopped.

Myra waited, but she did not look at me; she waited in the withdrawn and rigid attitude with which she always met us. Perhaps she thought I was

---

3 **change of life:** menopause, a time when women experience the hormonal changes of midlife

playing a trick on her, perhaps she expected me to run past and throw an empty Cracker Jack box in her face. And I opened the box and held it out to her. She took a little. Jimmy ducked behind her coat and would not take any when I offered the box to him.

"He's shy," I said reassuringly. "A lot of little kids are shy like that. He'll probably grow out of it."

"Yes," said Myra.

"I have a brother four," I said. "He's awfully shy." He wasn't. "Have some more Cracker Jack," I said. "I used to eat Cracker Jack all the time but I don't any more. I think it's bad for your complexion."

There was silence.

"Do you like Art?" said Myra faintly.

"No. I like Social Studies and Spelling and Health."

"I like Art and Arithmetic." Myra could add and multiply in her head faster than anyone else in the class.

"I wish I was as good as you. In Arithmetic," I said, and felt magnanimous.

"But I am no good at Spelling," said Myra. "I make the most mistakes, I'll fail maybe." She did not sound unhappy about this, but pleased to have such a thing to say. She kept her head turned away from me staring at the dirty snowbanks along Victoria Street, and as she talked she made a sound as if she was wetting her lips with her tongue.

"You won't fail," I said. "You are too good in Arithmetic. What are you going to be when you grow up?"

She looked bewildered. "I will help my mother," she said. "And work in the store."

"Well I am going to be an airplane hostess," I said. "But don't mention it to anybody. I haven't told many people."

"No, I won't," said Myra. "Do you read Steve Canyon in the paper?"

"Yes." It was queer to think that Myra, too, read the comics, or that she did anything at all, apart from her role at the school. "Do you read Rip Kirby?"

"Do you read Orphan Annie?"

"Do you read Betsy and the Boys?"

"You haven't had hardly any Cracker Jack," I said. "Have some. Take a whole handful."

Myra looked into the box. "There's a prize in there," she said. She pulled it out. It was a brooch, a little tin butterfly, painted gold with bits of coloured glass stuck onto it to look like jewels. She held it in her brown hand, smiling slightly.

I said, "Do you like that?"

Myra said, "I like them blue stones. Blue stones are sapphires."

"I know. My birthstone is sapphire. What is your birthstone?"

"I don't know."

"When is your birthday?"

"July."

"Then yours is ruby."

"I like sapphire better," said Myra. "I like yours." She handed me the brooch.

"You keep it," I said. "Finders keepers."

It was a brooch, a little tin butterfly, painted gold with bits of coloured glass stuck onto it to look like jewels.

Myra kept holding it out, as if she did not know what I meant. "Finders keepers." I said.

"It was your Cracker Jack," said Myra, scared and solemn. "You bought it."

"Well you found it."

"No—" said Myra.

"Go on!" I said. "Here, I'll *give* it to you." I took the brooch from her and pushed it back into her hand.

We were both surprised. We looked at each other; I flushed but Myra did not. I realized the pledge as our fingers touched; I was panicky, but *all right.* I thought, I can come early and walk with her other mornings. I can go and talk to her at recess. Why not? *Why not?*

Myra put the brooch in her pocket. She said, "I can wear it on my good dress. My good dress is blue."

I knew it would be. Myra wore out her good dresses at school. Even in midwinter among the plaid wool skirts and serge tunics, she glimmered sadly in sky-blue taffeta, in dusty turquoise crepe, a grown woman's dress made over, weighted by a big bow at the V of the neck and folding empty over Myra's narrow chest.

And I was glad she had not put it on. If someone asked her where she got it, and she told them, what would I say?

It was the day after this, or the week after, that Myra did not come to school. Often she was kept at home to help. But this time she did not come back. For a week, then two weeks, her desk was empty. Then we had a moving day at school and Myra's books were taken out of her desk and put on a shelf in the closet. Miss Darling said, "We'll find a seat when she comes back." And she stopped calling Myra's name when she took attendance.

Jimmy Sayla did not come to school either, having no one to take him to the bathroom.

·····

In the fourth week or the fifth, that Myra had been away, Gladys Healey came to school and said, "Do you know what—Myra Sayla is sick in the hospital."

It was true. Gladys Healey had an aunt who was a nurse. Gladys put up her hand in the middle of Spelling and told Miss Darling. "I thought you might like to know," she said. "Oh yes," said Miss Darling, "I do know."

"What has she got?" we said to Gladys.

And Gladys said, "Akemia,[4] or something. And she has blood transfusions." She said to Miss Darling, "My aunt is a nurse."

So Miss Darling had the whole class write Myra a letter, in which everybody said, "Dear Myra, We are all writing you a letter. We hope you will soon be better and be back to school, Yours truly . . . ." And Miss Darling said, "I've thought of something. Who would like to go up to the hospital and visit Myra on the twentieth of March, for a birthday party?"

I said, "Her birthday's in July."

"I know," said Miss Darling. "It's the twentieth of July. So this year she could have it on the twentieth of March, because she's sick."

"But her *birthday* is July."

"Because she's sick," said Miss Darling, with a warning shrillness. "The cook at the hospital would make a cake and you could all give a little present, twenty-five cents or so. It would have to be between two and four, because that's visiting hours. And we couldn't all go, it'd be too many. So who wants to go and who wants to stay here and do supplementary reading?"

We all put up our hands. Miss Darling got out the spelling records and picked out the first fifteen, twelve girls and three boys. Then the three boys did not want to go so she picked out the next three girls. And I do not know when it was, but I think it was probably at this moment that the birthday party of Myra Sayla became fashionable.

Perhaps it was because Gladys Healey had an aunt who was a nurse, perhaps it was the excitement of sickness and hospitals, or simply the fact that Myra was so entirely, impressively set free of all the rules and conditions of our lives. We began to talk of her as if she were something we owned, and her party became a cause; with womanly heaviness we discussed it at recess, and decided that twenty-five cents was too low.

---

4 **Akemia:** a mispronunciation of "leukemia"

We all went up to the hospital on a sunny afternoon when the snow was melting, carrying our presents, and a nurse led us upstairs, single file, and down a hall past half-closed doors and dim conversations. She and Miss Darling kept saying, "Sh-sh," but we were going on tiptoe anyway; our hospital demeanor was perfect.

At this small country hospital there was no children's ward, and Myra was not really a child; they had put her in with two grey old women. A nurse was putting screens around them as we came in.

Myra was sitting up in bed, in a bulky stiff hospital gown. Her hair was down, the long braids falling over her shoulders and down the coverlet. But her face was the same, always the same.

She had been told something about the party, Miss Darling said, so the surprise would not upset her; but it seemed she had not believed, or had not understood what it was. She watched us as she used to watch in the school grounds when we played.

"Well, here we are!" said Miss Darling. "Here we are!"

And we said, "Happy birthday, Myra! Hello, Myra, happy birthday!" Myra said, "My birthday is in July." Her voice was lighter than ever, drifting, expressionless.

"Never mind when it is, really," said Miss Darling. "Pretend it's now! How old are you, Myra?"

"Eleven," Myra said. "In July."

Then we all took off our coats and emerged in our party dresses, and laid our presents, in their pale flowery wrappings on Myra's bed. Some of our mothers had made immense, complicated bows of fine satin ribbon, some of them had even taped on little bouquets of imitation roses and lilies of the valley. "Here Myra," we said, "here Myra, happy birthday." Myra did not look at us, but at the ribbons, pink and blue and speckled with silver, and the miniature bouquets; they pleased her, as the butterfly had done. An innocent look came into her face, a partial, private smile.

"Open them, Myra," said Miss Darling. "They're for you!"

Myra gathered the presents around her, fingering them, with this smile, and a cautious realization, an unexpected pride. She said, "Saturday I'm going to London[5] to St. Joseph's Hospital."

"That's where my mother was at," somebody said. "We went and saw her. They've got all nuns there."

---

5 **London:** a city in Ontario, central Canada

The Americas

"My father's sister is a nun," said Myra calmly.

She began to unwrap the presents, with an air that not even Gladys could have bettered, folding the tissue paper and the ribbons, and drawing out books and puzzles and cutouts as if they were all prizes she had won. Miss Darling said that maybe she should say thank you, and the person's name with every gift she opened, to make sure she knew whom it was from, and so Myra said, "Thank you, Mary Louise, thank you, Carol," and when she came to mine she said, "Thank you, Helen." Everyone explained their presents to her and there was talking and excitement and a little gaiety, which Myra presided over, though she was not gay. A cake was brought in with *Happy Birthday Myra* written on it, pink on white, and eleven candles. Miss Darling lit the candles and we all sang Happy Birthday to You, and cried, "Make a wish, Myra, make a wish—" and Myra blew them out. Then we all had cake and strawberry ice cream.

•••••

At four o'clock a buzzer sounded and the nurse took out what was left of the cake and the dirty dishes, and we put on our coats to go home. Everybody said, "Goodbye, Myra," and Myra sat in bed watching us go, her back straight, not supported by any pillow, her hands resting on the gifts. But at the door I heard her call; she called, "Helen!" Only a couple of the others heard; Miss Darling did not hear, she had gone out ahead. I went back to the bed.

Myra said, "I got too many things. You take something."

"What?" I said. "It's for your birthday. You always get a lot at a birthday."

"Well you take something," Myra said. She picked up a leatherette case with a mirror in it, a comb and a nail file and a natural lipstick and a small handkerchief edged with gold thread. I had noticed it before. "You take that," she said.

"Don't you want it?"

"You take it." She put it into my hand. Our fingers touched again.

"When I come back from London," Myra said, "you can come and play at my place after school."

"Okay," I said. Outside the hospital window there was a clear carrying sound of somebody playing in the street, maybe chasing with the last snowballs of the year. This sound made Myra, her triumph and her bounty, and most of all her future in which she had found this place for me, turn shadowy, turn dark. All the presents on the bed, the folded paper and ribbons, those guilt-tinged offerings, had passed into this shadow, they were no longer innocent objects to be touched, exchanged, accepted without danger. I didn't want to take the case now but I could not think how to get out of it, what lie to tell. I'll give it away, I thought, I won't ever play with it. I would let my little brother pull it apart.

The nurse came back, carrying a glass of chocolate milk.

"What's the matter, didn't you hear the buzzer?"

So I was released, set free by the barriers which now closed about Myra, her unknown, **exalted**, ether-smelling[6] hospital world, and by the treachery of my own heart. "Well thank you," I said. "Thank you for the thing. Goodbye."

Did Myra ever say goodbye? Not likely. She sat in her high bed, her delicate brown neck, rising out of a hospital gown too big for her, her brown carved face immune to treachery, her offering perhaps already forgotten, prepared to be set apart for legendary uses, as she was even in the back porch at school.

exalted:
elevated;
glorified

---

6 **ether-smelling:** smelling like ether, the chemical compound used to anesthetize patients

After You Read

Critical Reading

1. Consider the scene beginning on the bottom of page 27 where Helen catches up to Myra and Myra's brother as they walk to school. In the past, Helen would have "loitered . . . wanting to walk with some important girl." What does this reveal about Helen's point of view of her social status at school? And why did Helen change and choose to walk with Myra this time? Support your response with details from the story.

2. **Pathos** is an element in literature that evokes pity or compassion. Identify different events or scenes that the author uses to develop pathos. Explain how each one develops pathos for the characters.

3. Describe an **internal conflict** and an **external conflict** faced by Helen. Explain why you think each instance is internal or external.

 ## Literary Lens: Theme

The **theme** of a work is often expressed as a short statement or saying. For example, the theme of a story about someone who tries something new but fails might be "nothing ventured, nothing gained." Write two short sayings that express the theme of "Day of the Butterfly." Support each statement with details from the story.

Supporting details		Theme
Imagery		
Setting		
Conflict		
Characterization		

Focus on Research: Use a Variety of Sources

One of the issues Alice Munro touches on in this story is how children can be cruel to each other. She describes how the girls develop a game of teasing Myra, walking up to her in "groups of three or four" and saying things intended to be hurtful. In schools today, bullying is a major concern. Use a variety of sources, such as online, print, and multimedia sources, to find out more about the issue of bullying. Compile a list of sources that provide accurate information on the topic. Rate the sources on a scale according to which provide the most useful and up-to-date information if you were inquiring into the topic of bullying.

The Literature of
Mexico

Background

On July 12, 1562, in the area now known as Mexico, a cultural disaster occurred. The Spanish Catholic missionary Bishop Diego de Landa feared the beliefs of the local Mayan people. So he burned every Mayan codex (book) he could find. A staggering amount of Mexico's poetry, storytelling, history, mythology, and religion was lost that day. Only one great Mayan epic, the Popol Vuh, survived. This codex and the stories shared by oral tradition were all that remained of the great literary traditions of this region's indigenous cultures.

Mexican literature rose up from this catastrophe. Bishop Landa's bonfires introduced one theme that haunts Mexican literature—fierce cultural conflict. Mexican history has been marked by clashes of race, class, religion, and political power. A second great theme of Mexican history and literature, though, is blending. Unlike the United States, where only a small percentage of people can trace their ancestry to Native Americans, most Mexicans have both indigenous and European ancestors. Many Mexican writers draw upon both aspects of their heritage when they write.

Mexico and the United States

At the end of the Mexican-American War (1846–1848), the United States seized more than half of Mexico's territory. The two countries have had uneasy relations ever since. Today, controversies over immigration and trade between the United States and Mexico remain heated.

Mexican literature offers a valuable window into the lives of the people and culture of Mexico. As you read the following selections by Mexican writers, consider this question: What can you learn that you didn't know about Mexico?

Research: Use Literary Texts

In his book The Labyrinth of Solitude, Octavio Paz (1914–1998) argues that Mexico's identity is marked by a sense of solitude. "Solitude is the profoundest fact of the human condition," wrote Paz. "Man is the only being who knows he is alone, and the only one who seeks out another." Identify three works of Mexican literature that reveal this theme of human loneliness and solitude.

You Don't Hear Dogs Barking

Juan Rulfo

Before You Read

Juan Rulfo (1918–1986) was born into a wealthy Mexican family, but the Mexican Revolution (1926–1929) swept away his parents' fortunes. By 1927, Rulfo was an orphan. Educated in religious schools, he later moved to Mexico City, where he wrote two novels, a collection of short stories, and several film scripts. Rulfo's most famous novel, *Pedro Páramo* (1955), is narrated by the dead inhabitants of a mythical village. Rulfo contributed to the Latin American style known as magic realism, in which ordinary events can blend into the fantastical.

World Context

Each November, Mexicans celebrate El Día de los Muertos—The Day of the Dead—during which people pay homage to the deceased with homemade altars, prayer vigils, and processions to cemeteries. Papier-mâché skeletons, called *calaveras*, sprout up everywhere, mocking death and satirizing the living.

 LITERARY LENS In this short story, the **imagery** associated with the night journey creates an overall emotional impression. Note your responses to the images as you read.

Y ou up there, Ignacio! Don't you hear something or see a light somewhere?"

"I can't see a thing."

"We ought to be near now."

"Yes, but I can't hear a thing."

"Look hard. Poor Ignacio."

The long black shadow of the men kept moving up and down, climbing over rocks, diminishing and increasing as it advanced along the edge of the arroyo.[1] It was a single, reeling shadow.

---

1 **arroyo:** a narrow gulch, dry except during heavy rains

The moon came out of the earth like a round flare.

"We should be getting to that town, Ignacio. Your ears are uncovered, so try to see if you can't hear dogs barking. Remember they told us Tonaya was right behind the mountain. And we left the mountain hours ago. Remember, Ignacio?"

"Yes, but I don't see a sign of anything."

"I'm getting tired."

"Put me down."

The old man backed up to a thick wall and shifted his load but didn't let it down from his shoulders. Though his legs were buckling on him, he didn't want to sit down, because then he would be unable to lift his son's body, which they had helped to sling on his back hours ago. He had carried him all this way.

"How do you feel?"

"Bad."

Ignacio didn't talk much. Less and less all the time. Now and then he seemed to sleep. At times he seemed to be cold. He trembled. When the trembling seized him, his feet dug into his father's flanks like spurs. Then his hands, clasped around his father's neck, clutched at the head and shook it as if it were a rattle.

The father gritted his teeth so he wouldn't bite his tongue, and when the shaking was over, he asked, "Does it hurt a lot?"

"Some," Ignacio answered.

First Ignacio had said, "Put me down here—leave me here—you go on alone. I'll catch up with you tomorrow or as soon as I get a little better." He'd said this some fifty times. Now he didn't say it.

There was the moon. Facing them. A large red moon that filled their eyes with light and stretched and darkened its shadow over the earth.

"I can't see where I'm going anymore," the father said.

No answer.

The son up there was illumined by the moon. His face, discolored, bloodless, reflected the opaque light. And he here below.

"Did you hear me, Ignacio? I tell you, I can't see very well."

No answer.

Falteringly, the father continued. He hunched his body over, then straightened up to stumble on again.

"This is no road. They told us Tonaya was behind the hill. We've passed the hill. And you can't see Tonaya or hear any sound that would tell us it is close. Why won't you tell me what you see up there, Ignacio?"

"Put me down, Father."

"Do you feel bad?"

"Yes."

"I'll get you to Tonaya. There I'll find somebody to take care of you. They say there's a doctor in the town. I'll take you to him. I've already carried you for hours, and I'm not going to leave you lying here now for somebody to finish off."

He staggered a little. He took two or three steps to the side, then straightened up again.

"I'll get you to Tonaya."

"Let me down."

His voice was faint, scarcely a murmur. "I want to sleep a little."

"Sleep up there. After all, I've got a good hold on you."

The moon was rising, almost blue, in a clear sky. Now the old man's face, drenched with sweat, was flooded with light. He lowered his eyes so he wouldn't have to look straight ahead, since he couldn't bend his head, tightly gripped in his son's hands.

"I'm not doing all this for you. I'm doing it for your dead mother. Because you were her son. That's why I'm doing it. She would've haunted me if I'd left you lying where I found you and hadn't picked you up and carried you to be cured as I'm doing. She's the one who gives me courage, not you. From the first you've caused me nothing but trouble, humiliation, and shame."

He sweated as he talked. But the night wind dried his sweat. And over the dry sweat, he sweated again.

"I'll break my back, but I'll get to Tonaya with you so they can ease those wounds you got. I'm sure as soon as you feel well, you'll go back to your bad ways. But that doesn't matter to me anymore. As long as you go far away, where I won't hear anything more of you. As long as you do that— because as far as I'm concerned, you aren't my son anymore. I've cursed the blood you got from me. My part of it I've cursed. I said, 'Let the blood I gave him rot in his kidneys.' I said it when I heard you'd taken to the roads, robbing and killing people—good people. My old friend Tranquilino, for instance. The one who baptized you. The one who gave you your name. Even he had the bad luck to run into you. From that time on I said, 'That one cannot be my son.'

"See if you can't see something now. Or hear something. You'll have to do it from up there, because I feel deaf."

"I don't see anything."

"Too bad for you, Ignacio."

"I'm thirsty."

"You'll have to stand it. We must be near now. Because it's now very late at night, they must've turned out the lights in the town. But at least you should hear dogs barking. Try to hear."

"Give me some water."

"There's no water here. Just stones. You'll have to stand it. Even if there was water, I wouldn't let you down to drink. There's nobody to help me lift you up again, and I can't do it alone."

"I'm awfully thirsty and sleepy."

"I remember when you were born. You were that way then. You woke up hungry and ate and went back to sleep. Your mother had to give you water because you'd finished all her milk. You couldn't be filled up. And you were always mad and yelling. I never thought that in time this madness would go to your head. But it did. Your mother, may she rest in peace, wanted you to grow up strong. She thought when you grew up, you'd look after her. She only had you. The other child she tried to give birth to killed her. And you would've killed her again if she'd lived till now."

The man on his back stopped gouging with his knees. His feet began to swing loosely from side to side. And it seemed to the father that Ignacio's head, up there, was shaking as if he were sobbing.

On his hair he felt thick drops fall.

"Are you crying, Ignacio? The memory of your mother makes you cry, doesn't it? But you never did anything for her. You always repaid us badly. Somehow your body got filled with evil instead of affection. And now you see? They've wounded it. What happened to your friends? They were all killed. Only they didn't have anybody. They might well have said, 'We have nobody to be concerned about.' But you, Ignacio?"

At last, the town. He saw roofs shining in the moonlight. He felt his son's weight crushing him as the back of his knees buckled in a final effort. When he reached the first dwelling, he leaned against the wall by the sidewalk. He slipped the body off, dangling, as if it had been wrenched from him.

With difficulty he unpried his son's fingers from around his neck. When he was free, he heard the dogs barking everywhere.

"And you didn't hear them, Ignacio?" he said. "You didn't even help me listen."

Translated by George D. Schade

After You Read

Critical Reading

1. Several times in this story, Ignacio's father asks him if he can hear dogs barking, but Ignacio does not seem to hear anything. Compare and contrast Ignacio and his father. Why doesn't Ignacio seem to hear anything or tell his father he doesn't hear them? What does this reveal about Ignacio? Use details from the story to support your answer.

2. Identify an example of **irony** in the story. Is it situational, dramatic, or verbal? Support your answer with details from the story.

3. Identify several references in the story to "not hearing" or "not seeing" something. What can you infer about the relationship between Ignacio and his father based on these details?

Literary Lens: Imagery

Consider the **imagery** Rulfo includes about the moon. How do the changing descriptions of the moon reveal changes in the mood of the story and in the relationship between Ignacio and his father? Use a graphic organizer like the one below to help you.

Imagery about the moon	What might this suggest about the mood and relationship between Ignacio and his father?

Focus on Research: Generate Questions

One way to find out more about Juan Rulfo's life is to conduct a research project. An important early step in planning a research project is developing a list of questions. Write five or more questions you have about Rulfo's life and his writing. Then refine your questions to be ones that could be used to guide research.

Two Bodies

Octavio Paz

Before You Read

Octavio Paz (1914–1998) said he grew up in a house near Mexico City with a "jungle-like garden and a great room full of books." Paz studied modernist poetry in the United States and later served as ambassador to India. In his acceptance speech for the 1990 Nobel Prize in Literature, Paz said, "Modernity led me to the source of my beginning. . . . I thus found out that the poet is a pulse in the rhythmic flow of generations."

World Context

In his most famous work, *The Labyrinth of Solitude,* Paz asserts that the Mexican soul is split between a pre-Columbian Indian past and the Spanish Conquistador heritage.

 LITERARY LENS A **metaphor** is a figure of speech that imaginatively links two objects. Watch for metaphors in the following poem.

T wo bodies face to face
are at times two waves
and night is an ocean.

Two bodies face to face
are at times two stones
and night a desert.

Two bodies face to face
are at times two roots
laced into night.

5

Two bodies face to face   10
are at times two knives
and night strikes sparks.

Two bodies face to face
are two stars falling
in an empty sky.   15

Translated by Muriel Rukeyser

Abismo |
Fernando Holguin
Cereceres

After You Read

Critical Reading

1. In this poem, Paz repeats several different words and phrases. Identify three examples of **repetition** in "Two Bodies." How do these instances of repetition contribute to the meaning of the poem?

2. Consider Paz's use of sound devices in the poem. Identify any examples of **end rhyme, consonance**, or **assonance**. Explain how each example of a sound device contributes to the mood of the poem.

3. Identify a **theme** conveyed by the poem. Then identify examples of **enjambment**. How does Paz's use of enjambment emphasize the theme of the poem?

Literary Lens: Metaphor

Identify examples of metaphor in two or more of the stanzas and then interpret what these metaphors suggest about human relationships. Use the following graphic organizer to help you.

Stanza number	Metaphor	What it suggests about human relationships

Focus on Research: Develop a Thesis Statement

In his book *The Labyrinth of Solitude*, Octavio Paz writes the following:

> The Mexican, whether young or old, criollo or mestizo, general or laborer or lawyer, seems to me to be a person who shuts himself away to protect himself: his face is a mask and so is his smile. In his harsh solitude, which is both barbed and courteous, everything serves him as a defense: silence and words, politeness and disdain, irony and resignation. . . . He passes through life like a man who has been flayed; everything can hurt him, including words and the very suspicion of words. . . . He builds a wall of indifference and remoteness between reality and himself, a wall that is no less impenetrable for being invisible. The Mexican is always remote, from the world and from other people. And also from himself.

Whether you are of Mexican heritage or not, you may be able to relate to Paz's words. Write a thesis statement in which you respond to Paz's thoughts on self-enforced solitude. Make sure your thesis statement clearly states a main idea and references the work to which you are responding.

Crossroads:
A Sad Vaudeville

Carlos Solórzano

Before You Read

Carlos Solórzano (1922–2011), a native Guatemalan, became a protégé of the famous French writer Albert Camus while living in Europe as a young man. He left Europe for Mexico, where he taught and wrote plays employing the artistic and philosophical trends of the European avant-garde, including surrealism and existentialism. "Crossroads: A Sad Vaudeville" was produced for the first time in 1966. The play exemplifies the author's use of symbolism and concern with humans striving to live with dignity and love in an unfeeling world.

World Context

Like Carlos Solórzano, many Latin American authors were drawn to European cultural centers, where they absorbed the latest artistic trends. Upon their return to Latin America, they would practice and teach the new ideas. Some critics believe that magic realism, the uniquely Latin American art form, resulted from the mixing of the Latin American sensibility with the new ideas imported from Europe.

 LITERARY LENS Dramatic irony occurs when the audience knows something that one or more characters do not know. Watch for dramatic irony in this play.

Characters

THE FLAGMAN   THE TRAIN   THE MAN   THE WOMAN

Setting

Stage empty, dark. At one end, a semaphore[1] that alternately flashes a green light and a red one. In the center, hanging from the ceiling, a big clock

---

1 **semaphore:** a simple traffic signal that flashes red or green lights

whose hands show five o'clock sharp.

(The characters will move mechanically, like characters in the silent movies. The MAN in fast motion; the WOMAN, in slow motion. As the curtain rises, the FLAGMAN is at the end of the stage, opposite the semaphore, with a lighted lantern in his hand. He is standing very stiffly and indifferently.)

FLAGMAN *(staring into space, in an impersonal voice)*. The trains from the North travel toward the South, the trains from the North travel toward the South, the trains from the North travel toward the South. *(He repeats the refrain several times while the train crosses the back of the stage. The train will be formed by three men dressed in gray. As they pass by, they each mechanically perform a pantomime with one arm extended, the hand on the shoulder of the man in front, and the other arm making a circular motion, synchronized with the rhythm of the FLAGMAN's words.)* The trains from the North travel toward the South (etc.). *(Loud train whistle. The MAN who comes at the end of the train breaks free of it by making a movement as though he were jumping off. The train disappears on the right.)*

MAN *(carrying a small valise. He glances around the place, then looks at the clock, which he compares with his watch. He is young, serene of face, approximately twenty-five years old. He addresses the FLAGMAN.)* Good afternoon. *(As a reply, he receives the latter's refrain.)* Is this the place this ticket indicates? *(He places it in front of the FLAGMAN's eyes. The FLAGMAN nods.)* A train stops here, just about now, doesn't it?

FLAGMAN *(without looking at him)*. Trains never stop here.

MAN. Are you the flagman?

FLAGMAN. They call me by many names.

MAN. Then, perhaps you've seen a woman around here.

FLAGMAN. I've seen no one.

MAN *(approaching him)*. Do you know? The woman I'm looking for is . . .

FLAGMAN *(interrupting)*. They all look alike.

MAN. Oh, no! She's different. She's the woman that I've been waiting for for many years. She'll be wearing a white flower on her dress. Or is it yellow? *(He searches nervously in his pockets and takes out a paper that he reads.)* No, it's white . . . that's what she says in her letter. *(The* FLAGMAN *takes a few steps, feeling ill at ease.)* Pardon me for telling you all this, but now you'll be able to understand how important it is for me to find this woman, because . . .

FLAGMAN *(interrupting again)* What woman?

MAN. The one that I'm looking for.

FLAGMAN. I don't know what woman you're looking for.

MAN. The one that I've just told you about.

FLAGMAN. Ah . . . .

MAN. Perhaps she has passed by and you didn't see her. *(The* FLAGMAN *shrugs his shoulders.)* Well, I guess that I have to tell you everything to see if you can remember. She's tall, slender, with black hair and big blue eyes. She's wearing a white flower on her dress . . . . *(Anxiously)* Hasn't she been around here?

FLAGMAN. I can't know if someone I don't know has been around.

MAN. Excuse me. I know that I'm nervous but I have the impression that we aren't speaking the same language, that is, that you aren't answering my questions . . . .

FLAGMAN. That's not my job.

MAN. Nevertheless, I believe that a flagman ought to know how to answer questions. *(Transition.)* She wrote to me that she'd be here at five, at the railroad crossing of . . . *(He reads the ticket.)* I'll never know how to pronounce this name, but I know that it's here. We chose this point because it's halfway between our homes. Even for this kind of date, a romantic one, one must be fair. *(The* FLAGMAN *looks at him without understanding.)* Yes, romantic. *(With ingenuous pride)* Maybe I'll bore you, but I must tell you that one day I saw an ad in a magazine. It was hers. How well written that ad was! She said that she needed a young man like me, to establish relations with so as not to live so alone. *(Pause.)* I wrote to her and she answered me. Then I sent her my photo and she sent me hers. You can't imagine what a beauty!

FLAGMAN *(who has not heard most of the account).* Is she selling something?

MAN *(surprised).* Who?

FLAGMAN. The woman who placed the ad?

MAN. No, for heaven's sake! She placed that ad because she said that she was shy, and she thought it might help and . . .

FLAGMAN. Everyone sells something.

MAN *(impatiently).* You just don't understand me.

FLAGMAN. It's possible . . . .

MAN. Well, I mean . . . understand how excited I am on coming to meet someone whom I don't know but who . . .

FLAGMAN. How's that?

MAN *(upset).* That is, I know her well, but I haven't seen her.

FLAGMAN. That's very common.

MAN. Do you think so?

FLAGMAN. The contrary's also common.

MAN. I don't understand.

FLAGMAN. It isn't necessary.

MAN. But you only speak nonsense! I should warn you that although I've an inclination toward romantic things, I'm a man who isn't pleased by jokes in bad taste. *(The* FLAGMAN *shrugs his shoulders again.)* Besides, this delay upsets me as does this dark place with that clock that doesn't run. It seems like a timeless place.

(Suddenly a loud train whistle is heard. The semaphore comes to life flashing the green light. The FLAGMAN again adopts his rigid posture; staring into space, he repeats his refrain.)

FLAGMAN *(loudly).* The trains from the South travel toward the North. The trains from the South travel toward the North. The trains from the South travel toward the North *(etc.).*

(The train passes across the back of the stage, from right to left.)

MAN *(shouting).* There, on that train! . . . She should be on it. *(He rushes to meet the train which passes by without stopping, almost knocking him down. The MAN remains at stage center, his arms at his sides. Disillusioned:)* She wasn't on it.

FLAGMAN. It's only natural.

MAN. What do you mean?

FLAGMAN. He's never coming . . .

MAN. Who?

FLAGMAN. The man we're waiting for.

MAN. But it's a question of a woman.

FLAGMAN. It's the same.

MAN. How is a man going to be the same as a woman?

FLAGMAN. He isn't the same, but in a certain way he is.

MAN. You change your mind quickly.

FLAGMAN. I don't know.

MAN *(furiously).* Then, what is it that you do know?

FLAGMAN (*indifferently*). Where they're going.

MAN. The trains?

FLAGMAN. They all go to the same place.

MAN. What do you mean?

FLAGMAN. They come and go, but they end by meeting one another . . . .

MAN. That would be impossible.

FLAGMAN. But it's true. The impossible is always true.

MAN (*as if these last words brought him back to reality, he abandons his furious attitude and calms down*). You're right in what you say. (*Hesitating.*) For example, my meeting with that woman seems impossible and it's the only certain thing of my whole existence. (*Suddenly, with an unexpected tone of anguish:*) But it's five ten. (*He looks at his watch.*) And she isn't coming. (*He takes the arm of the* FLAGMAN *who remains indifferent.*) Help me, do all that is possible to remember! I'm sure that if you want to, you can tell me if you saw her or not . . . .

FLAGMAN. One can't know by just seeing a person whether it was the one who placed an ad in newspaper.

MAN (*once again containing his ill humor*). But I already described what she's like to you! . . .

FLAGMAN (*imperturbably*). I'm sorry. I forgot . . . .

(*Meanwhile a* WOMAN *dressed in black has come in behind the* MAN. *She is tall and slim. Her face is covered by a heavy veil. She walks softly with a pantomime motion. On her dress she wears a very large white flower. On seeing her the* FLAGMAN *raises his lantern and examines her. The* MAN, *blinded by light, covers his eyes. On seeing herself discovered, the* WOMAN *tears the white flower violently from her dress. She puts it in her purse and turns her back, remaining motionless.*)

MAN (*still covering his eyes*). Ooh! You're going to blind me with that lantern.

FLAGMAN (*returning to his habitual stiffness*). I beg your pardon . . . .

MAN (*to the* FLAGMAN). Someone has come in, right?

FLAGMAN. It's not important.

MAN (*recovering from the glare, he notices the presence of the* WOMAN *and runs toward her. He stops suddenly*). Ah . . . (*Timidly*) I beg you to . . . .

WOMAN (*her back turned*). Yes?

MAN (*embarrassed*). I thought that you . . . were someone . . .

WOMAN. Yes . . .

MAN (*with determination*). Someone I'm looking for. (*She does not move. Pause.*) Will you permit me to see you from the front?

WOMAN. From the front?

MAN (*upset*). Yes . . . it's absolutely necessary that I see you . . .

WOMAN (*without turning*). But . . . why? (*She begins to turn slowly.*)

MAN. Well . . . in order to . . . (*On seeing that her face is covered, he backs away.*) You aren't wearing anything on your dress . . . and nevertheless . . .

WOMAN (*trembling*). And nevertheless?

MAN. You have the same stature and build . . . .

WOMAN (*with a jesting tone*). Really?

MAN (*with distrust*). Could you tell me how you got here? I didn't see a train.

WOMAN (*interrupting, stammering*). I arrived . . . ahead of time . . . and I waited.

MAN. Ahead of what time?

WOMAN. We all wait for a time. Aren't you waiting for it?

MAN *(sadly)*. Yes.

WOMAN. I believe that there is but one moment to recognize one another, to extend our hands. One musn't let it pass by.

MAN. What do you mean by that? Who are you?

WOMAN. Now I'm the woman I've always wanted to be.

MAN *(timidly)*. Will you let me see your face?

WOMAN *(frightened)*. Why?

MAN. I need to find that one face, the special one, the different one.

WOMAN *(moving away)*. I am sorry. I can't.

MAN *(following her with a tortured motion)*. Excuse me. I'm stupid, I know. For a moment I thought that you could be she. But it's absurd. If it were so, you'd come straight to me, for we have called one another from afar.

WOMAN *(trembling)*. Perhaps she's more afraid of finding the one she seeks than of letting him pass by without stopping.

MAN. No, that would also be absurd. *(Transition.)* In any case, I beg your pardon. *(He moves away and sits down on his small suitcase, his back to the* WOMAN.*)* I'll wait here.

(In the meantime, while the man is not looking at her, the WOMAN *has raised her veil with long slow movements. When she uncovers her face, it is obvious that she is old. Her forehead is furrowed by deep wrinkles. She is like the mask of old age. This face contrasts obviously with her body, still slender, ageless.)*

WOMAN *(to the* FLAGMAN *who stares at her)*. You saw me from the beginning, didn't you? Why didn't you tell him?

FLAGMAN *(indifferently)*. Whom?

WOMAN *(pointing to the* MAN*)*. Him, the only one.

FLAGMAN. I'd forgotten him.

WOMAN (*in a surge of anguish*). Shall I tell him that I'm that woman he's waiting for? Will he recognize in this old face the unsatisfied longing still in this body of mine? How can I tell him that I need him even more than when I was young, as young as I am in that touched-up photo that he's looking at?

(*In the meantime, the man studies the photograph with fascination. The* WOMAN *covers her face again with the veil and goes up to the* MAN.)

WOMAN. Is she very late?

MAN (*his back turned*). Of course . . . .

WOMAN. It would hurt you a great deal if she wouldn't come!

MAN (*turning forcefully*). She has to come.

WOMAN. Nevertheless, you must realize that perhaps she's afraid to reveal herself, that maybe she's waiting for you to discover her.

MAN. I don't understand.

WOMAN (*very close to the* MAN). I have a friend . . . who always lived alone, thinking nevertheless that the best thing for her was to get together with someone. (*She pauses. The* MAN *listens to her, interested.*) She was ugly, very ugly, perhaps that was why she dreamed of a man instead of looking for him. She liked to have her pictures taken. She had the photographs touched up, so that the picture turned out to be hers, but at the same time it was someone else's. She used to write to young men, sending them her photograph. She called them close to her house, with loving words . . . . When they arrived, she'd wait behind the windows; she wouldn't let herself be seen. . . .

MAN. Why are you telling me all this?

WOMAN (*without hearing*). She'd see them. She knew that they were there on account of her. Each day, a different one. She accumulated many memories, the faces, the bodies of those strong men who had waited for her.

MAN. How absurd! I think . . . .

WOMAN. You're also strong and young.

MAN *(confused)*. Yes, but . . .

WOMAN. And today she's one day older than yesterday.

MAN *(after allowing a pause)*. Really I don't see what relation all this can have to . . .

WOMAN *(drawing near and placing her hand on the* MAN's *head)*. Perhaps you'll understand now. Close your eyes. *(She passes her hand over the eyes of the* MAN *in a loving manner.)* Have you never felt fear?

MAN. Fear? Of what?

WOMAN. Of living, of being . . . as if all your life you'd been waiting for something that never comes?

MAN. No . . . . *(He opens his eyes.)*

WOMAN. Tell me the truth. Close your eyes, those eyes that are separating us now. Have you been afraid?

(The MAN *closes his eyes.)*

MAN *(hesitatingly)*. Well, a little . . . .

WOMAN *(with an absent voice)*. A suffering . . . in solitude . . .

MAN. Yes, at times . . . . *(He takes the* WOMAN's *hand.)*

WOMAN. Above all when you begin to fall asleep. The solitude of your body, a body alone, that inevitably ages.

MAN. Yes, but . . .

WOMAN. The solitude of the heart that tries hard every night to prolong its cry against silence.

MAN. I've felt something like that . . . but . . . not so clearly . . . not so pointedly.

WOMAN. It's that . . . perhaps you were waiting for that voice, the one of someone invented by you, to your measure. . . .

MAN. Yes . . . I think that's it.

WOMAN. Would you be able to recognize that voice with your eyes open?

MAN. I'm sure that I could . . . .

WOMAN. Even if it were a voice invented many years before, in the dark inmost recesses of time?

MAN. It wouldn't matter. I'd know how to recognize it.

WOMAN. Then, is that what you're waiting for?

MAN. Yes. I'm here for her sake, looking for her.

WOMAN. She's waiting for you also. *(The WOMAN raises the veil little by little until she leaves her withered face in the open.)* She'll be only a memory for you, if you don't allow yourself to be overcome by time. Time is her worst enemy. Will you fight it?

(They are seated very close to one another.)

MAN. Yes.

WOMAN. All right . . . . Open your eyes.

*(The MAN opens his eyes slowly and is surprised to find himself held by the WOMAN's two hands. He stands up with a **brusque** movement.)*

> **brusque:**
> abrupt; curt

MAN *(bewildered)*. Excuse me, I'm confused . . .

WOMAN *(**entreatingly**)*. Oh, no! . . . Don't tell me that . . .

> **entreatingly:**
> pleadingly;
> persuasively

MAN. It was a stupidity of mine . . .

imploringly:
beseechingly;
begging
urgently

WOMAN *(imploringly)*. But you said . . .

MAN. It's ridiculous! For a moment I thought that you were she. Understand me. It was a wild dream.

WOMAN *(grieved)*. Yes, yes . . .

MAN. I don't know how I could . . .

WOMAN *(calming herself)*. I understand you. A wild dream and nothing more . . .

MAN. You're really very kind to pardon me. . . . *(Looking at his watch, astonished:)* It's five thirty! . . . *(Pause.)*

WOMAN *(sadly)*. Yes . . . . Now I believe that she won't come.

MAN. How would that be possible?

WOMAN. It's better that way.

MAN. Who are you to tell me that?

WOMAN. No one. *(She opens her purse.)* Do you want this white flower?

MAN *(snatching it from her)*. Where did you get it? Why are you giving it to me?

WOMAN. I picked it up . . . in passing . . .

MAN *(with great excitement)*. But then, she has been here. Perhaps she has gotten lost or mistaken the place. Or perhaps, while I was here talking with you, she has passed by without stopping.

WOMAN *(covering her face)*. I already told you that there is but a moment to recognize oneself, to close one's eyes . . .

MAN. But now . . . what can I do in order to . . . find her?

WOMAN. Wait . . . as everyone does . . . Wait . . . *(She takes the flower again.)*

MAN. But, what about you?

WOMAN. I'll continue searching, calling them, seeing them pass by. When you're old, you'll understand. *(The train whistle is heard. The* WOMAN *moves away from the* MAN, *with sorrowful movements.)* Good-bye, good-bye . . .

MAN *(to himself).* Who can this woman be who speaks to me as if she knew me? *(He runs toward her. He checks himself.)* Good-bye . . .

(The semaphore flashes the green light. The FLAGMAN *becomes stiff in order to repeat his refrain.)*

FLAGMAN. The trains from the North travel toward the South, the trains from the North travel toward the South, the trains from the North travel toward the South, the trains from the North travel toward the South *(etc.).*

(The train crosses the back of the stage. The WOMAN *waves the flower sadly and with long movements approaches the train. She gets on it. The* FLAGMAN *repeats his refrain while the train leaves dragging the* WOMAN, *who goes off with writhing and anguished pantomime movements.)*

MAN *(with a certain sadness, to the* FLAGMAN *who remains indifferent).* There was something in her that . . . anyhow, I believe it's better that that woman has left.

FLAGMAN. Which one, sir?

MAN. That one, the one who had picked up a white flower . . .

FLAGMAN. I didn't notice that . . . .

MAN. No? *(He looks at the* FLAGMAN *dejectedly.)* But, really, haven't you seen the other one?

FLAGMAN. What other one?

MAN. The one that I'm looking for.

FLAGMAN. I don't know who it can be . . . .

MAN. One who is wearing a white flower, but who isn't the one that you saw a moment ago.

FLAGMAN *(harshly)*. I saw the one that you aren't looking for, and the one you're looking for I didn't see!

MAN *(irritated)*. Can't you be useful for anything? What the devil are you good for?

(Loud train whistle.)

FLAGMAN. What did you say?

MAN *(shouting)*. What the devil are you good for!

(Green light of the semaphore. The train crosses the back of the stage very slowly.)

FLAGMAN *(in a distant voice)*. The trains from the North travel toward the South, the trains from the North travel toward the South, the trains from the North travel toward the South, the trains from the North travel toward the South *(etc.)*.

(The MAN covers his head with his hands, desperate. The FLAGMAN repeats his refrain while the train passes by slowly. Before it leaves the stage, the curtain falls gently.)

Curtain

Translated by Francesca Colecchia and Julio Matas

After You Read

Critical Reading

1. One of the **themes** of this play is the conflict between conformity and freedom. Cite speeches or stage directions that illustrate this theme.

2. Throughout the play, the **characters** repeatedly refer to a "white flower." What does the white flower symbolize for the man? What does it symbolize for the woman? Support your explanation with details from the text.

3. The characters in this play repeatedly misunderstand each other. Identify an excerpt of dialogue that illustrates this and then infer what the playwright's purpose or goal was by highlighting misunderstandings. Support your response with details from the play.

 ## Literary Lens: Dramatic Irony

Dramatic irony occurs when the audience knows more than one or more of the characters. Identify a scene of dramatic irony. Then identify what the characters know and what the readers know. Lastly, infer the purpose the example of dramatic irony serves. Use the following graphic organizer to help you identify ironic elements.

Summary of scene	What character(s) know	What readers know
Purpose:		

Focus on Research: Paraphrase Information

While in France, Solórzano was influenced by the literary and philosophical movements known as surrealism and existentialism. Conduct research to find out more about the literary techniques associated with one of these movements. As you take notes on your research, paraphrase the information you find. In other words, write the most important facts and information you find in your own words. Avoid merely changing a few words; instead capture the main ideas using your own words and writing style.

The Literature of
The Caribbean

Background

Following the first voyage of Christopher Columbus in 1492, European colonization reshaped life on the Caribbean islands. European diseases and the forced labor nearly wiped out the Native populations and indigenous cultures of the West Indies. The people who now live there are largely descendants of African slaves or European colonists.

Not until the early 1900s did distinctively Caribbean literature thrive. During the 1920s, French- and Spanish-speaking Caribbean writers began to forge a distinct literary culture. Cuba's Alejo Carpentier (1904–1980) is often credited with founding the Latin American literary movement of magic realism. This movement inserts the supernatural and physically improbable into literature in ways that make it seem like it really could be happening.

The Caribbean and the United States

With their range of cultures and their political and social turmoil, the islands of the West Indies have fascinated U.S. intellectuals. One of these was the American author Ernest Hemingway (1899–1961), who lived in Cuba on and off for years. He remains something of a hero in that country, where his home has been turned into a museum.

Hemingway might even be said to have made his own contribution to Caribbean literature. His 1952 novella *The Old Man and the Sea* tells the story of an ill-fated Cuban fisherman. The book helped earn Hemingway the Nobel Prize in Literature in 1954.

Research: Develop a Research Plan

Because of the West Indies' scattered islands and multiple languages, its peoples did not feel much cultural connection to one another for centuries. With a partner, develop a research plan to explore how this changed during the 20th century, especially as colonization waned. Include the kinds of questions you might ask and the types of sources you might consult. Share your plan with the rest of the class and compare approaches.

Love After Love

Derek Walcott

Before You Read

Derek Walcott (1930–2017) was born in St. Lucia and spent much of his life in Trinidad. Although he wrote in English, Walcott's poetry reflects the rhythms of Caribbean speech. Of Dutch, English, and African ancestry, Walcott made diversity one of his most important themes; he quotes sources ranging from Homer to the Beatles.

World Context

Poetry critic Helen Vendler described Derek Walcott as "a black descended from both European and black ancestors; a St. Lucian, yet educated beyond the island norm; a painter-poet deeply attached to the Caribbean landscape, yet living for much of the year in New England; a rebellious colonial, yet deeply involved, imaginatively, in English poetry."

 LITERARY LENS A **paradox** is a statement that appears to contradict itself. Identify paradoxes in this poem.

The time will come
when, with elation,
you will greet yourself arriving
at your own door, in your own mirror,
and each will smile at the other's welcome,   5

and say, sit here. Eat.
You will love again the stranger who was your self.
Give wine. Give bread. Give back your heart
to itself, to the stranger who has loved you

Still Life With Ham | André Dunoyer de Segonzac, 1924

all your life, whom you ignored   10
for another, who knows you by heart.
Take down the love letters from the bookshelf,

the photographs, the desperate notes,
peel your own image from the mirror.
Sit. Feast on your life.   15

After You Read

Critical Reading

1. Derek Walcott's work has been noted for capturing the style of everyday language and everyday speech. Consider the common, everyday word choices of this poem. Infer Walcott's purpose in choosing these words.

2. **Setting** is the time and place in which the action of a text occurs. What is the setting of this poem? How does this setting affect the **mood**? Cite details from the poem in your answer.

3. **Conflict** is a term used to describe the main struggle or problem in a literary work. What is the primary conflict in the poem? Support your answer with details from the poem.

Literary Lens: Paradox

Consider the following paradox from the poem: "the stranger who was yourself." Analyze this paradox by identifying details from the beginning, middle, and end of the poem that reveal the stranger and the present self.

	The stranger	The present self
At the beginning of the poem		
In the middle of the poem		
At the end of the poem		

Focus on Research: Identify Gaps in Research

Conduct research into the life of Derek Walcott. Discover details about his birth, childhood, education, places of residence, and travels. As you conduct this research, identify when you encounter gaps in the information. For example, you might find information about when he was born and then later information about his adult success as an author, which means you have a gap of information. To help you identify gaps in research, create a timeline showing major dates and events from Walcott's life. Conduct further, more targeted research to fill in the missing details on your timeline.

When Greek Meets Greek

Samuel Selvon

Before You Read

Samuel Selvon (1923–1994) was born in Trinidad to East Indian parents. He served in the Royal Navy Reserve during World War II, after which he began publishing in Caribbean magazines. In 1950, Selvon moved to England, became a freelance writer, and was soon internationally famous. Selvon treats important themes—nationality, cultural blending, and rootlessness—with humor and affection, employing dialect to enhance the humor.

World Context

Like the characters in this story, Selvon lived in England before eventually becoming a Canadian citizen. In the late 1950s and early 1960s, more than 113,000 immigrants from the former British colonies of India, Pakistan, and the West Indies came to Great Britain for jobs. As their numbers grew, so did racial tension, and in 1958 there were race riots in England between West Indians and the local white population.

LITERARY LENS Notice the ways that Selvon creates and develops **characters** through the use of exposition, dialogue, and action.

One morning Ramkilawansingh (after this, we calling this man Ram) was making a study of the noticeboards along Westbourne Grove what does advertise rooms to let. Every now and then he writing down an address or a telephone number, though most of the time his eyes colliding up with *No Colours, Please,* or *Sorry, No Kolors.*

"Red, white and blue, all out but you," Ram was humming a little ditty what children say when they playing whoop. Just as he get down by Bradley's Corner he met Fraser.

"You look like a man who looking for a place to live," Fraser say.

"You look like a man who could tell me the right place to go," Ram say.

"You try down by Ladbroke Grove?"[1] Fraser ask.

"I don't want to go down in that criminal area," Ram say, "at least, not until they find the man who kill Kelso."

"Then you will never live in the Grove," Fraser say.

"You are a contact man,"[2] Ram say, "Which part you think I could get a room, boy?"

Fraser scratch his head. "I know of a landlord up the road who vow that he ain't ever taking anybody who come from the West Indies.[3] But he don't mind taking Indians. He wouldn't know the difference when he see you is a Indian . . . them English people so foolish they believe every Indian come from India."

"You think I stand a chance?" Ram ask.

"Sure, you stand a chance. All you have to do is put on a turban."

"I never wear a turban in my life; I am a born Trinidadian,[4] a real Creole.[5] All the same, you best hads give me the address, I will pass around there later."

So Fraser give him the address, and Ram went on reading a few more boards, but he got discourage after a while and went to see the landlord.

The first thing the landlord ask him was: "What part of the world do you come from?"

"I am an Untouchable from the heart of India." Ram say. "I am looking for a single room. I dwelt on the banks of the Ganges. Not too expensive."

"But you are not in your national garments," the landlord say.

"When you are in Rome," Ram say, making it sound like an original statement, "do as the Romans do."

While the landlord sizing up Ram, an Indian tenant come up the steps to go inside. This fellar was Chandrilaboodoo (after this, we calling this man Chan) and he had a big beard with a hairnet over it, and he was

---

1 **Westbourne Grove . . . Ladbroke Grove:** municipal districts in London, England

2 **contact man:** a go-between; someone "in the know"

3 **West Indies:** the Caribbean islands made up of the Greater Antilles, the Lesser Antilles, and the Bahamas

4 **Trinidadian:** a citizen of the West Indies republic of Trinidad and Tobago

5 **Creole:** In the West Indies, *Creole* refers to anyone from the Caribbean island cultures.

wearing a turban. When he see Ram, he clasp his hands with the palms touching across his chest by way of greeting.

The old Ram catch on quick and do the same thing. *"Acha, Hindustani,"*[6] Chan say.

"Acha, pilau, papadom, chickenvindaloo,"[7] Ram say desperately, hoping for the best.

Chan nod his head, say good morning to the landlord and went inside.

"That was a narrow shave," Ram thought, "I have to watch out for that man."

"That was Mr. Chan," the landlord say, "he is the only other Indian tenant I have at the moment. I have a single room for two pounds. Are you a student?"

"Who is not a student?" Ram say, getting into the mood of the thing. "Man is forever studying ways and means until he passes into the hands of Allah."[8]

Well, to cut a long story short, Ram get a room on the first floor, right next door to Chan, and he move in that same evening.

But as the days going by, Ram had to live like cat-and-mouse with Chan. Every time he see Chan, he have to hide in case this man start up this Hindustani talk again, or start to ask him questions about Mother India. In fact, it begin to get on Ram nerves, and he decide that he had to do something.

"This house too small for the two of we," Ram say to himself, "one will have to go."

So Ram went down in the basement to see the landlord.

occult:
supernatural;
magic arts

"I have the powers of the **occult**," Ram say, "and I have come to warn you of this man Chan. He is not a good tenant. He keeps the bathroom dirty, he does not tidy up his room at all, and he is always chanting and saying his prayers loudly and disturbing the other tenants."

"I have had no complaints," the landlord say.

"But I am living next door to him," Ram say, "and if I concentrate my powers I can see through the wall. That man is a menace, and the best thing you can do is to give him notice. You have a good house here and it would be a pity to let one man spoil it for the other tenants."

"I will have a word with him about it," the landlord say.

---

6 *Acha, Hindustani:* Hindi for "Yes, I'm Indian."

7 *pilau, papadom, chickenvindaloo:* a rice dish, a type of cracker, a spicy chicken dish

8 **Allah:** the Supreme Being in the Islamic religion

Well, the next evening Ram was in his room when he hear a knock at the door. He run in the corner quick and stand upon his head, and say, "Come in."

The landlord come in.

"I am just practicing my yogurt," Ram say.

"I have had a word with Mr. Chan," the landlord say, "and I have reason to suspect that you have deceived me. You are not from India, you are from the West Indies."

Ram turn right-side up. "I am a citizen of the world," he say.

"You are flying false colors," the landlord say. "You do not burn incense like Mr. Chan, you do not dress like Mr. Chan, and you do not talk like Mr. Chan."

"Give me a break, old man," Ram say, falling back on the good old West Indian dialect.

"It is too late. You have already started to make trouble. You must go."

Well, the very next week find Ram out scouting again, giving the boards a **perusal**, and who he should chance to meet but Fraser.

He start to tell how life hard, how he had to keep dodging from this Chan fellar all the time, and it was pure torture.

"Listen," Fraser say, "you don't mean a big fellar with a beard, and he always wearing a turban?"

"That sound like him," Ram say. "You know him?"

"Know him!" Fraser say. "Man, that is a fellar from Jamaica who I send to that house to get a room!"

perusal: close look; study

After You Read

Critical Reading

1. Authors can use many techniques to develop humor in their pieces, including the techniques of **satire** and **irony**. Identify one passage from the story that contains humor. Then explain whether you think this humor stems from satire or irony. Support your answer with details from the story.

2. Consider the **dialect** used in the story. Infer how the use of dialect affects reader's understanding of the characters.

3. A **hero** is a main character who often does noble things or lives an exemplary life. An anti-hero is a main character who displays qualities or completes actions that are not heroic. Is Ram a hero or an **anti-hero**? Support your answer with details from the story.

 ## Literary Lens: Characterization

Consider the character of Ram. Then identify the ways Selvon reveals the character using exposition, dialogue, and action. Cite quotations to support your ideas.

	Quotation	What does this reveal about Ram?
Exposition		
Dialogue		
Action		

Focus on Research: Consider Multiple Viewpoints

Samuel Selvon uses realistic dialogue to reveal character and create cultural setting. However, other authors feel that writing in dialect may promote racial stereotypes. Research the technique of using dialect. Find sources that argue for the strengths and sources that suggest problems of writing in dialect. Then write a paragraph that synthesizes the viewpoints you found.

Girls Can We Educate We Dads?

James Berry

Before You Read

James Berry (1924–2017) was born in Jamaica, spent a few years in the United States, and then settled in Britain. In London, he first wrote short stories and then poetry. In 1990, Berry was awarded the O.B.E. (Officer of the British Empire, an honor similar to knighthood) for his contributions to poetry.

World Context

James Berry wrote with an expressive, lyrical voice about ordinary Caribbeans. His special forte is the reproduction and use of Jamaican dialect, which gives his writing a distinctive lilt, energy, and authenticity.

LITERARY LENS Diction refers to the style, intonation, accent, and word choice of a speaker or writer. Note the diction of this poem as you read.

Listn the male chauvinist in mi dad—
a girl walkin night street mus be bad.
He dohn sey, the world's a free place
for a girl to keep her unmolested space.

Instead he sey—a girl is a girl.   5
He sey a girl walkin swingin hips about
call boys to look and shout.
He dohn sey, if a girl have style
she wahn to sey, look

I okay from top to foot. 10
Instead he sey—a girl is a girl.

Listn the male chauvinist in mi dad—
a girl too laughy-laughy look too glad-glad
jus like a girl too looky-looky roun
will get a pretty satan at her side. 15
He dohn sey—a girl full of go
dohn wahn stifle talent comin on show.
Instead he sey—a girl is a girl.

Nubian Knots |
Samere Tansley

After You Read

Critical Reading

1. Identify examples of rhyming **couplets** in this poem. Then infer how these rhyming couplets affect the reader's experience of the poem.

2. Describe a **conflict** the speaker experiences in this poem. Then identify whether this conflict is an **internal conflict** or **external conflict**.

3. Each stanza ends with the same line: "Instead he sey—a girl is a girl." Identify the impact of this repeated line.

Literary Lens: Diction

James Berry was known for using a mixture of standard English and Jamaican Patois in his poetry. Consider the use of **dialect** in the poem "Girls Can We Educate We Dads?" Identify quotations that reveal dialect and then consider what this dialect adds to the poem (tone, mood, conflict, or theme).

Example of dialect	Write the meaning in standard English	What does this dialect add to the poem (tone, mood, conflict, or theme)?

Focus on Research: Synthesize Information

James Berry wrote stories, poetry, and books for children. Find and gather together several reviews of Berry's books. These can be several reviews of the same book or reviews of different books. Reviews are available at publishersweekly.com and websites that sell books. Consider if the reviews note common strengths or common criticisms. After reading them, write a two- to three-sentence summary of the common strengths and common criticisms you found in the reviews.

In Trying Times

Heberto Padilla

Before You Read

Heberto Padilla (1932–2000), Cuban poet and novelist, was a supporter of the Castro revolution, but later he became critical of the Communist government. In 1971, Padilla was accused of treason and jailed. His arrest aroused international protest. After Gabriel García Márquez, Octavio Paz, Jean-Paul Sartre, and other writers appealed to Castro, Padilla was allowed to leave Cuba in 1981. He moved to the United States, where his work published in English includes his memoir, *Self-Portrait of the Other.*

World Context

In 1956, the Cuban Revolution, led by Fidel Castro, overthrew the unpopular dictatorship of Fulgencio Batista. Once in power, however, the revolutionary government quickly became more oppressive than that of the Batista regime, quashing dissent through imprisonment, torture, and executions.

LITERARY LENS Writers use **repetition** to place emphasis on a theme or idea. Watch for the use of repetition in this poem.

T hey asked that man for his time
so that he could link it to History.
They asked him for his hands,
because for trying times
nothing is better than a good pair of hands.   5
They asked him for his eyes
that once had tears
so that he should see the bright side
(the bright side of life, especially)
because to see horror one startled eye is enough.   10

They asked him for his lips,
parched and split, to affirm,
to belch up, with each affirmation, a dream
(the great dream)
they asked him for his legs   15
hard and knotted
(his wandering legs)
because in trying times
is there anything better than a pair of legs
for building or digging ditches?   20
They asked him for the grove that fed him as a child,
with its obedient tree.
They asked him for his breast, heart, his shoulders.
They told him
that that was absolutely necessary.   25
they explained to him later
that all this gift would be useless
unless he turned his tongue over to them,
because in trying times
nothing is so useful in checking hatred or lies.   30
and finally they begged him,
please, to go take a walk.
Because in trying times
that is, without debate, the decisive test.

Translated by Alastair Reid and Andrew Hurley

After You Read

Critical Reading

1. Padilla uses the word "they" repeatedly throughout the poem. Identify two or three examples of the use of "they." Who is "they," and why does Padilla use this general pronoun instead of naming specific people or organizations? Support your answer with details from the poem.

2. What is the underlying message or **theme** of this poem? Use details from the poem to support your response.

3. The word "History" in the second line is capitalized. Why do you think the author chose to capitalize this word? How does this affect reader's understanding of this word?

 ## Literary Lens: Repetition

Identify two or more instances of **repetition** in this poem. Then consider how this repetition creates the distinctive voice of the poem.

Example of repetition	How does this repetition affect the voice of the poem?

Focus on Research: Find Primary and Secondary Sources

In 1971, Herberto Padilla was arrested by the Cuban government and forced to read a public confession in which he admitted to promoting ideas contrary to Castro's regime. Conduct research on this event, sometimes called the Padilla Affair. Find two primary sources and two secondary sources on the topic. Primary sources were written at the time of the events by the people directly involved. Examples include journals, letters, reports, memos, autobiographies, and newspaper articles. Secondary sources are written after an event or by people who heard about an event but were not directly involved.

The Literature of
Puerto Rico

Background

In 1806, the first printing press arrived on the island of Puerto Rico. Before then, the island's Spanish rulers had forbidden written works by Puerto Ricans. Just as it had almost everywhere else in the world, the printing press released a flood of thoughts and ideas. Puerto Rican authors began to protest against Spanish rule of their islands, as well as to forge a literary tradition from their Spanish, African American, and indigenous roots. Poet, playwright, and fiction writer Alejandro Tapia y Rivera (1826–1882) is regarded as the founder of Puerto Rican literature. Twentieth-century authors include Julia de Burgos (1914–1953), who is one of Puerto Rico's greatest poets.

Puerto Rico and the United States

One result of the Spanish-American War of 1898 was that the United States acquired control of Puerto Rico from Spain. Puerto Rico is considered a U.S. territory, not a U.S. state, and as such it is self-governing and its people are U.S. citizens. Puerto Rican literature often deals with Puerto Rican–United States relations, which have been by turns friendly and uneasy for more than a century.

Beginning in the early 1900s, many Puerto Ricans migrated to the United States. One result of this migration was an artistic movement of people who called themselves "Nuyoricans"—Puerto Ricans who had immigrated to New York City and found unique creative voices there. Founded in the 1970s, the hub of this movement is New York City's Nuyorican Poets Café.

Jesús Colón (1901–1974), author of *A Puerto Rican in New York*, is regarded as the founder of Nuyorican literature. Nuyorican playwright Miguel Piñero (1946–1988) achieved international fame for his hard-hitting prison drama *Short Eyes*.

Research: Prepare Interview Questions

Some Puerto Rican authors write in "Spanglish"—a mixture of Spanish and English. They do this for many reasons, such as to comment on how the U.S. presence in Puerto Rico has made the Spanish written and spoken in Puerto Rico different from the Spanish written and spoken in other Latin American countries. Write a series of five questions you might ask a Puerto Rican native about changes in the island's language.

The Youngest Doll

Rosario Ferré

Before You Read

Rosario Ferré (1938–2016) was a Puerto Rican poet, novelist, and literary critic. She was born into one of Puerto Rico's wealthiest families. Ferré studied and taught in the United States and in her home country and wrote novels in Spanish as well as English. Her decision to publish in English as well as her belief that the Commonwealth of Puerto Rico should become the United States' 51st state made her a controversial figure in Puerto Rico.

World Context

Ferré is notable for writing about the role of women in Latin America, where historically men have held positions of power. Her family background gave her firsthand knowledge of the immense power of the South American elites. "The Youngest Doll" comes from Ferré's first book, which is a response to the Pandora story, a myth she considered anti-female.

 LITERARY LENS Magical realism combines elements of realism and fantasy. Watch for elements of this genre, or type of literature, in the story that follows.

Early in the morning the maiden aunt took her rocking chair out onto the porch facing the cane fields, as she always did whenever she woke up with the urge to make a doll. As a young woman, she had often bathed in the river, but one day when the heavy rains had fed the dragontail current, she had a soft feeling of melting snow in the marrow of her bones. With her head nestled among the black rocks' reverberations, she could hear the slamming of salty foam on the beach rolled up with the sound of waves, and she suddenly thought that her hair had poured out to sea at last. At that very moment, she felt a sharp bite in her calf. Screaming, she was pulled out of the water and, writhing in pain, was taken home on a stretcher.

The doctor who examined her assured her it was nothing, that she had probably been bitten by an angry river prawn.[1] But days passed and the scab wouldn't heal. A month later the doctor concluded that the prawn had worked its way into the soft flesh of her calf and had nestled there to grow. He prescribed a mustard plaster[2] so that the heat would force it out. The aunt spent a whole week with her leg covered with mustard from thigh to ankle, but when the treatment was over, they found that the ulcer had grown even larger and that it was covered with a slimy, stonelike substance that couldn't be removed without endangering the whole leg. She then resigned herself to living with the prawn permanently curled up in her calf.

She had been very beautiful, but the prawn hidden under the long, gauzy folds of her skirt stripped her of all vanity. She locked herself up in her house, refusing to see any suitors. At first she devoted herself entirely to bringing up her sister's children, dragging her enormous leg around the house, quite nimbly. In those days, the family was nearly ruined; they lived surrounded by a past that was breaking up around them with the same impassive musicality with which the dining room chandelier crumbled on the frayed linen cloth of the dining room table. Her nieces adored her. She would comb their hair, bathe and feed them, and when she read them stories, they would sit around her and **furtively** lift the starched ruffle of her skirt so as to sniff the aroma of ripe sweetsop[3] that oozed from her leg when it was at rest.

As the girls grew up, the aunt devoted herself to making dolls for them to play with. At first they were just plain dolls, with cotton stuffing from the gourd tree and stray buttons sewn on for eyes. As time passed, though, she began to refine her craft, gaining the respect and admiration of the whole family. The birth of a doll was always cause for a ritual celebration, which explains why it never occurred to the aunt to sell them for profit, even when the girls had grown up and the family was beginning to fall into need. The aunt had continued to increase the size of the dolls so that their height and other measurements conformed to those of each of the girls. There were nine of them, and the aunt made one doll for each per year, so it became necessary to set aside a room for the dolls alone. When the eldest turned eighteen, there were one hundred and twenty-six dolls of all ages in the room. Opening the door gave the impression of entering a dovecote or the

---

1 **prawn:** a shellfish resembling shrimp
2 **plaster:** a covering for a wound
3 **sweetsop:** an aromatic tropical fruit

ballroom in the Czarina's[4] palace or a warehouse in which someone had spread out a row of tobacco leaves to dry. But the aunt did not enter the room for any of these pleasures. Instead, she would unlatch the door and gently pick up each doll, murmuring a lullaby as she rocked it: "This is how you were when you were a year old, this is you at two, and like this at three," measuring out each year of their lives against the hollow they left in her arms.

The day the eldest had turned ten, the aunt sat down in her rocking chair facing the cane fields and never got up again. She would rock away entire days on the porch, watching the patterns of rain shift in the cane fields, coming out of her stupor only when the doctor paid a visit or whenever she awoke with the desire to make a doll. Then she would call out so that everyone in the house would come and help her. On that day, one could see the hired help making repeated trips to town like cheerful Inca[5] messengers, bringing wax, porcelain clay, lace, needles, spools of thread of every color. While these preparations were taking place, the aunt would call the niece she had dreamt about the night before into her room and take her measurements. Then she would make a wax mask of the child's face, covering it with plaster on both sides, like a living face wrapped in two dead ones. She would draw out an endless flaxen thread of melted wax through a pinpoint on its chin. The porcelain of the hands and face was always translucent; it had an ivory tint to it that formed a great contrast with the curdled whiteness of the bisque faces. For the body, the aunt would send out to the garden for twenty glossy gourds. She would hold them in one hand, and with an expert twist of her knife, would slice them up against the railing of the balcony, so that the sun and breeze would dry out the cottony *guano*[6] brains. After a few days, she would scrape off the dried fluff with a teaspoon and, with infinite patience, feed it into the doll's mouth.

The only items the aunt would agree to use that were not made by her were the glass eyeballs. They were mailed to her from Europe in all colors, but the aunt considered them useless until she had left them submerged at the bottom of the stream for a few days, so that they could learn to recognize the slightest stirring of the prawns' antennae. Only then would she carefully rinse them in ammonia water and place them, glossy as gems and nestled in a bed of cotton, at the bottom of one of her Dutch cookie tins. The dolls were always dressed in the same way, even though the girls were growing up.

---

4 **Czarina:** the czar's wife; the wife of a dictator
5 **Inca:** the South American Indians who ruled before the Spanish conquest
6 *guano*: a kind of palm tree

She would dress the younger ones in Swiss embroidery and the older ones in silk *guipure*,[7] and on each of their heads she would tie the same bow, wide and white and trembling like the breast of a dove.

The girls began to marry and leave home. On their wedding day, the aunt would give each of them their last doll, kissing them on the forehead and telling them with a smile, "Here is your Easter Sunday." She would reassure the grooms by explaining to them that the doll was merely a sentimental ornament, of the kind that people used to place on the lid of grand pianos in the old days. From the porch, the aunt would watch the girls walk down the staircase for the last time. They would carry a modest checkered cardboard suitcase in one hand, the other hand slipped around the waist of the exuberant doll made in their image and likeness, still wearing the same old-fashioned kid slippers and gloves, and with Valenciennes[8] bloomers barely showing under their snowy, embroidered skirts. But the hands and faces of these new dolls looked less transparent than those of the old: they had the consistency of skim milk. This difference concealed a more subtle one: the wedding doll was never stuffed with cotton but filled with honey.

> . . . the wedding doll was never stuffed with cotton but filled with honey.

All the older girls had married and only the youngest was left at home when the doctor paid his monthly visit to the aunt, bringing along his son, who had just returned from studying medicine up north. The young man lifted the starched ruffle of the aunt's skirt and looked intently at the huge, swollen ulcer which oozed a perfumed sperm from the tip of its greenish scales. He pulled out his stethoscope and listened to her carefully. The aunt thought he was listening for the breathing of the prawn to see if it was still alive, and she fondly lifted his hand and placed it on the spot where he could feel the constant movement of the creature's antennae. The young man released the ruffle and looked fixedly at his father. "You could have cured this from the start," he told him. "That's true," his father answered, "but I just wanted you to come and see the prawn that has been paying for your education these twenty years."

From then on it was the young doctor who visited the old aunt every month. His interest in the youngest was evident from the start, so the aunt was able to begin her last doll in plenty of time. He would always show up

---

7 *guipure:* lace
8 *Valenciennes:* lace from Valenciennes, France

wearing a pair of brightly polished shoes, a starched collar, and an **ostentatious** tiepin of extravagantly poor taste. After examining the aunt, he would sit in the parlor, lean his paper silhouette against the oval frame of the chair and, each time, hand the youngest an identical bouquet of purple forget-me-nots. She would offer him ginger cookies, taking the bouquet squeamishly with tips of her fingers, as if she were handling a sea urchin turned inside out. She made up her mind to marry him because she was intrigued by his sleepy profile and also because she was deathly curious to see what the dolphin flesh was like.

On her wedding day, as she was about to leave the house, the youngest was surprised to find that the doll her aunt had given her as a wedding present was warm. As she slipped her arm around its waist, she looked at it curiously, but she quickly forgot about it, so amazed was she at the excellence of its craft. The doll's face and hands were made of the most delicate Mikado porcelain.[9] In the doll's half-open and slightly sad smile she recognized her full set of baby teeth. There was also another notable detail: the aunt had embedded her diamond eardrops inside the doll's pupils.

The young doctor took her off to live in town, in a square house that made one think of a cement block. Each day he made her sit out on the balcony, so that passersby would be sure to see that he had married into high society. Motionless inside her cubicle of heat, the youngest began to suspect that it wasn't only her husband's silhouette that was made of paper, but his soul as well. Her suspicions were soon confirmed. One day, he pried out the doll's eyes with the tip of his scalpel and pawned them for a fancy gold pocket watch with a long embossed chain. From then on the doll remained seated on the lid of the grand piano, but with her gaze modestly lowered.

A few months later, the doctor noticed the doll was missing from her usual place and asked the youngest what she'd done with it. A sisterhood of pious ladies had offered him a healthy sum for the porcelain hands and face, which they thought would be perfect for the image of the Veronica in the next Lenten procession.[10]

The youngest answered that the ants had at last discovered the doll was filled with honey and, streaming over the piano, had devoured it in a single night. "Since its hands and face were of Mikado porcelain," she said, "they

---

9 **Mikado porcelain:** ceramic material from Japan

10 **the Veronica . . . procession:** The Veronica is the image of Jesus's bloody face on a cloth offered to him by Saint Veronica on his way to the Crucifixion. The Lenten procession is a spectacle held to mark Lent, the forty days on the Christian calendar leading up to Easter.

must have thought they were made of sugar and at this very moment they are most likely wearing down their teeth, gnawing furiously at its fingers and eyelids in some underground burrow." That night the doctor dug up all the ground around the house, to no avail.

As the years passed, the doctor became a millionaire. He had slowly acquired the whole town as his clientele, people who didn't mind paying **exorbitant** fees in order to see a genuine member of the extinct sugar cane aristocracy up close. The youngest went on sitting in her rocking chair on the balcony, motionless in her muslin and lace, and always with lowered eyelids. Whenever her husband's patients, draped with necklaces and feathers and carrying elaborate canes, would seat themselves beside her, shaking their self-satisfied rolls of flesh with a jingling of coins, they would notice a strange scent that would involuntarily remind them of a slowly oozing sweetsop. They would then feel an uncomfortable urge to rub their hands together as though they were paws.

There was only one thing missing from the doctor's otherwise perfect happiness. He noticed that although he was aging, the youngest still kept that same firm, porcelained skin she had had when he would call on her at the big house on the plantation. One night he decided to go into her bedroom to watch her as she slept. He noticed that her chest wasn't moving. He gently placed his stethoscope over her heart and heard a distant swish of water. Then the doll lifted her eyelids, and out of the empty socket of her eyes came the frenzied antennae of all those prawns.

Translated by Diana Velez

exorbitant: excessive; unreasonably high

The Youngest Doll   81

After You Read

Critical Reading

1. What specific materials does the aunt use to create the marriage dolls? What might the materials **symbolize**? What might the dolls symbolize?

2. Prawns play a key role in the story. Review the story and identify where prawns are mentioned. What might they symbolize?

3. The characters in this story are driven by clashing motivations. Identify the motivations of the aunt, the doctor, and the doctor's son, citing details from the text to support your inferences.

Literary Lens: Magical Realism

Magical (or **magic**) **realism** in literature originated in Latin America and is heavily associated with Latin American literature to this day. Analyze the story to find two or three details that represent realism and two or three details that represent the magical aspect of the genre. Re-create the chart below to help you organize your analysis. Then respond to the following question: What truth about humans, families, or culture does the author convey through joining realism with the fantastic?

Realistic details	"Magical" or "fantastic" details

Focus on Research: Evaluate Sources for Bias

Biased sources present only one side of an argument. Bias is revealed through the author's selection and omission of facts and the use of positive or negative words that reveal a certain attitude toward the subject matter. When researching a topic, carefully evaluate sources for bias by considering the following:

- Does the source present multiple opinions on the topic?
- Does the source fairly represent data and facts?
- Does the source rely heavily on emotional appeals instead of presenting logical arguments?
- Is the source funded by a group with a specific purpose or agenda? (For a website, check the About tab.)

Find three sources on the topic of Puerto Rico becoming the 51st state. Evaluate each source using the questions above. Write a short explanation of any examples of bias.

The Literature of
Colombia

Background

The people of Colombia claim with pride that they have had more poets than soldiers as presidents—something few, if any, other countries can claim. The country has a centuries-old tradition of excellent writers, for example, Hernando Domínguez Camargo (1606–1659) was a Jesuit priest who wrote poetry mostly about religious issues. Since then, a myriad of Colombian authors have documented life in a vibrant nation marked by blended races and cultures, as well as by conflicts of class, politics, and economic injustice.

One of the authors carrying on this tradition of literary excellence today is Max Vergara Poeti (1983–). His first book of short stories, *El Mar* (1999), was published when he was only 16 years old. He is also a highly regarded poet and essayist.

Colombia and the United States

By far the Colombian author with the most fame and recognition in the United States is the Nobel Prize-winning Gabriel García Márquez (1928–2014). His 1967 book *One Hundred Years of Solitude* is revered as one of the greatest novels of the 20th century.

García Márquez considered himself deeply indebted to U.S. literature. He was especially influenced by the fiction of fellow Nobel Prize-winner William Faulkner (1897–1962). In such novels as *The Sound and the Fury,* Faulkner sought to capture the experience of the U.S. South. Through his stories, novels, and journalism, García Márquez strove to do the same for Latin America. Faulkner based the fictional Yoknapatawpha County on his home region in Mississippi; García Márquez set many of his works in the fictional village of Macondo, based on his childhood town of Aracataca, Colombia.

Research: Use the Internet

Colombian writers, especially García Márquez, often employ the technique of magic realism. Use a search engine to find online sources that define magic realism in literature and write a short paragraph explaining the meaning of this term. In your paragraph, explain how magic realism differs from conventional realism and also from fantasy fiction. Consider García Márquez's observation that many readers fail to see that "reality isn't limited to the price of tomatoes and eggs."

The Handsomest Drowned Man in the World

A Tale for Children

Gabriel García Márquez

Before You Read

Gabriel García Márquez (1928–2014) was born in Colombia and lived in many parts of the Spanish-speaking world. His early years of poverty led to his lifelong sympathy with Marxism. A longtime friend of Fidel Castro, García Márquez quietly used his influence with the Cuban dictator to free political prisoners and help dissidents leave Cuba. His works have made him the best-known writer of the magic realist movement. His use of the fantastic helps to convey the troubled realities of Latin America. As he explained upon accepting the Nobel Prize in 1982, "Our crucial problem has been a lack of conventional means to render our lives believable."

World Context

Traditionally in this region, women have been expected to be submissive and nurturing and men to be virile and authoritative. In García Márquez's most famous book, *One Hundred Years of Solitude*, he employs the idea of the handsome and charismatic man—the born leader—whose spirit attracts women and garners the admiration of men, a theme that is echoed in the following story.

 LITERARY LENS The **setting** of a story is the time and place of the action. As you read, pay close attention to changes in the setting.

The first children who saw the dark and slinky bulge approaching through the sea let themselves think it was an enemy ship. Then they saw it had no flags or masts and they thought it was a whale. But when it washed up on the beach, they removed the clumps of seaweed, the jellyfish tentacles, and the remains of fish and flotsam, and only then did they see that it was a drowned man.

They had been playing with him all afternoon, burying him in the sand and digging him up again, when someone chanced to see them and spread the alarm in the village. The men who carried him to the nearest house noticed that he weighed more than any dead man they had ever known, almost as much as a horse, and they said to each other that maybe he'd been floating too long and the water had got into his bones. When they laid him on the floor they said he'd been taller than all other men because there was barely enough room for him in the house, but they thought that maybe the ability to keep on growing after death was part of the nature of certain drowned men. He had the smell of the sea about him and only his shape gave one to suppose that it was the corpse of a human being, because the skin was covered with a crust of mud and scales.

They did not even have to clean off his face to know that the dead man was a stranger. The village was made up of only twenty-odd wooden houses that had stone courtyards with no flowers and which were spread about on the end of a desertlike cape. There was so little land that mothers always went about with the fear that the wind would carry off their children and the few dead that the years had caused among them had to be thrown off the cliffs. But the sea was calm and bountiful and all the men fit into seven boats. So when they found the drowned man they simply had to look at one another to see that they were all there. That night they did not go out to work at sea. While the men went to find out if anyone was missing in neighboring villages, the women stayed behind to care for the drowned man. They took the mud off with grass swabs, they removed the underwater stones entangled in his hair, and they scraped the crust off with tools used for scaling fish. As they were doing that they noticed that the vegetation on him came from faraway oceans and deep water and that his clothes were in tatters, as if he had sailed through **labyrinths** of coral. They noticed too that he bore his death with pride, for he did not have the lonely look of other drowned men who came out of the sea or that **haggard**, needy look of men who drowned in rivers. But only when they finished cleaning him off did they become aware of the kind of man he was and it left them breathless. Not only was he the tallest, strongest, most **virile**, and best built man they had ever seen, but even though they were looking at him there was no room for him in their imagination.

They could not find a bed in the village large enough to lay him on nor was there a table solid enough to use for his wake. The tallest men's holiday

labyrinths:
mazes; complex passageways

haggard:
gaunt; excessively thin

virile:
manly; potent

pants would not fit him, nor the fattest ones' Sunday shirts, nor the shoes of the one with the biggest feet. Fascinated by his huge size and his beauty, the women then decided to make him some pants from a large piece of sail and a shirt from some bridal brabant linen[1] so that he could continue through his death with dignity. As they sewed, sitting in a circle and gazing at the corpse between stitches, it seemed to them that the wind had never been so steady nor the sea so restless as on that night and they supposed that the change had something to do with the dead man. They thought that if that magnificent man had lived in the village, his house would have had the widest doors, the highest ceiling, and the strongest floor, his bedstead would have been made from a midship frame held together by iron bolts, and his wife would have been the happiest woman. They thought that he would have had so much authority that he could have drawn fish out of the sea simply by calling their names and that he would have put so much work into his land that springs would have burst forth from among the rocks so that he would have been able to plant flowers on the cliffs. They secretly compared him to their own men, thinking that for all their lives theirs were incapable of doing what he could do in one night, and they ended up dismissing them deep in their hearts as the weakest, meanest, and most useless creatures on earth. They were wandering through that maze of fantasy when the oldest woman, who as the oldest had looked upon the drowned man with more compassion than passion, sighed:

"He has the face of someone called Esteban."

It was true. Most of them had only to take another look at him to see that he could not have any other name. The more stubborn among them, who were the youngest, still lived for a few hours with the illusion that when they put his clothes on and he lay among the flowers in patent leather shoes his name might be Lautaro. But it was a vain illusion. There had not been enough canvas, the poorly cut and worse sewn pants were too tight, and the hidden strength of his heart popped the buttons on his shirt. After midnight the whistling of the wind died down and the sea fell into its Wednesday drowsiness. The silence put an end to any last doubts: he was Esteban. The women who had dressed him, who had combed his hair, had cut his nails and shaved him were unable to hold back a shudder of pity when they had to resign themselves to his being dragged along the ground. It was then that they understood how unhappy he must have been with that

---

1 **brabant linen:** linen from what is now southern Netherlands and northern Belgium

huge body since it bothered him even after death. They could see him in life, condemned to going through doors sideways, cracking his head on crossbeams, remaining on his feet during visits, not knowing what to do with his soft, pink, sea lion hands while the lady of the house looked for her most resistant chair and begged him, frightened to death, sit here, Esteban, please, and he, leaning against the wall, smiling, don't bother, ma'am, I'm fine where I am, his heels raw and his back roasted from having done the same thing so many times whenever he paid a visit, don't bother, ma'am, I'm fine where I am, just to avoid the embarrassment of breaking up the chair, and never knowing perhaps that the ones who said don't go, Esteban, at least wait till the coffee's ready, were the ones who later on would whisper

Village Scene: on the River |
Montas Antoine

the big boob finally left, how nice, the handsome fool has gone. That was what the women were thinking beside the body a little before dawn. Later, when they covered his face with a handkerchief so that the light would not bother him, he looked so forever dead, so defenseless, so much like their men that the first furrows of tears opened in their hearts. It was one of the younger ones who began the weeping. The others, coming to, went from sighs to wails, and the more they sobbed the more they felt like weeping, because the drowned man was becoming all the more Esteban for them, and so they wept so much, for he was the most destitute, most peaceful, and most obliging man on earth, poor Esteban. So when the men returned with the news that the drowned man was not from the neighboring villages either, the women felt an opening of jubilation in the midst of their tears.

"Praise the Lord," they sighed, "he's ours!"

The men thought the fuss was only womanish **frivolity**. Fatigued because of the difficult nighttime inquiries, all they wanted was to get rid of the bother of the newcomer once and for all before the sun grew strong on that arid, windless day. They improvised a litter with the remains of foremasts and gaffs,[2] tying it together with rigging[3] so that it would bear the weight of the body until they reached the cliffs. They wanted to tie the anchor from a cargo ship to him so that he would sink easily into the deepest waves, where fish are blind and divers die of nostalgia, and bad currents would not bring him back to shore, as had happened with other bodies. But the more they hurried, the more the women thought of ways to waste time. They walked about like startled hens, pecking with the sea charms on their breasts, some interfering on one side to put a scapular[4] of the good wind on the drowned man, some on the other side to put a wrist compass on him, and after a great deal of *get away from there, woman, stay out of the way,*

. . . since when has there ever been such a fuss over a drifting corpse, a drowned nobody, a piece of cold Wednesday meat.

look, you almost made me fall on top of the dead man, the men began to feel mistrust in their livers and started grumbling about why so many main-altar decorations for a stranger, because no matter how many nails and holy-water jars he had on him, the sharks would chew him all the same, but the

---

2 **foremasts and gaffs:** The foremast is in the ship's bow, or forward area, and gaffs are attachments to the mast.

3 **rigging:** a ship's sails and masts

4 **scapular:** a band of cloth

women kept piling on their junk relics, running back and forth, stumbling, while they released in sighs what they did not in tears, so that the men finally exploded with *since when has there ever been such a fuss over a drifting corpse, a drowned nobody, a piece of cold Wednesday meat.* One of the women, **mortified** by so much lack of care, then removed the handkerchief from the dead man's face and the men were left breathless too.

    He was Esteban. It was not necessary to repeat it for them to recognize him. If they had been told Sir Walter Raleigh,[5] even they might have been impressed with his gringo[6] accent, the macaw[7] on his shoulder, his cannibal-killing blunderbuss,[8] but there could be only one Esteban in the world and there he was, stretched out like a sperm whale, shoeless, wearing the pants of an undersized child, and with those stony nails that had to be cut with a knife. They only had to take the handkerchief off his face to see that he was ashamed, that it was not his fault that he was so big or so heavy or so handsome, and if he had known that this was going to happen, he would have looked for a more **discreet** place to drown in, seriously, I even would have tied the anchor off a galleon[9] around my neck and staggered off a cliff like someone who doesn't like things in order not to be upsetting people now with this Wednesday dead body, as you people say, in order not to be bothering anyone with this filthy piece of cold meat that doesn't have anything to do with me. There was so much truth in his manner that even the most mistrustful men, the ones who felt the bitterness of endless nights at sea fearing that their women would tire of dreaming about them and begin to dream of drowned men, even they and others who were harder still shuddered in the marrow of their bones at Esteban's sincerity.

    That was how they came to hold the most splendid funeral they could conceive of for an abandoned drowned man. Some women who had gone to get flowers in the neighboring villages returned with other women who could not believe what they had been told, and those women went back for more flowers when they saw the dead man, and they brought more and more until there were so many flowers and so many people that it was hard to walk about. At the final moment it pained them to return him to the waters as an orphan and they chose a father and mother from among the best people, and aunts and uncles and cousins, so that through him

mortified: ashamed; chagrined

discreet: unobtrusive; convenient

---

5 **Sir Walter Raleigh:** (1522–1618), an English writer and explorer
6 **gringo:** a disparaging term for an English or American foreigner
7 **macaw:** a parrot from Central or South America
8 **blunderbuss:** an old-fashioned firearm
9 **galleon:** a large sailing ship used at war and for cargo by the Spanish

all the inhabitants of the village became kinsmen. Some sailors who heard weeping from a distance went off course and people heard of one who had himself tied to the mainmast, remembering ancient fables about sirens.[10] While they fought for the privilege of carrying him on their shoulders along the steep escarpment[11] by the cliffs, men and women became aware for the first time of the desolation of their streets, the dryness of their courtyards, the narrowness of their dreams as they faced the splendor and beauty of their drowned man. They let him go without an anchor so that he could come back if he wished and whenever he wished, and they all held their breath for the fraction of centuries the body took to fall into the **abyss**. They did not need to look at one another to realize that they were no longer all present, that they would never be. But they also knew that everything would be different from then on, that their houses would have wider doors, higher ceilings, and stronger floors so that Esteban's memory could go everywhere without bumping into beams and so that no one in the future would dare whisper the big boob finally died, too bad, the handsome fool has finally died, because they were going to paint their house fronts gay colors to make Esteban's memory eternal and they were going to break their backs digging for springs among the stones and planting flowers on the cliffs so that in future years at dawn the passengers on great liners would awaken, suffocated by the smell of gardens on the high seas, and the captain would have to come down from the bridge in his dress uniform, with his astrolabe,[12] his pole star,[13] and his row of war medals and, pointing to the **promontory** of roses on the horizon, he would say in fourteen languages, look there, where the wind is so peaceful now that it's gone to sleep beneath the beds, over there, where the sun's so bright that the sunflowers don't know which way to turn, yes, that's Esteban's village.

Translated by Gregory Rabassa and S. J. Bernstein

abyss:
gulf; depths

promontory:
headland;
high point

---

10 **sirens:** in Greek mythology, female creatures whose seductive songs lured sailors to their deaths

11 **escarpment:** a cliff or slope

12 **astrolabe:** an instrument that was used to measure the heavenly bodies

13 **pole star:** the North or guiding star

After You Read

Critical Reading

1. What might you infer from this story about the villagers' attitudes toward death? Use details from the story to support your response.

2. A **foil** is a character who has characteristics that are in sharp contrast to another character, usually the protagonist. How does the drowned man act like a foil in the story?

3. Describe an example of **irony** from the story. Then explain whether this is situational, dramatic, or verbal irony. Support your answer with details from the story.

Literary Lens: Setting

Setting is the time and location in which a story occurs. The setting of this story is transformed by the events in the story. Consider different aspects of the setting. Then consider how these aspects of the setting were changed by the arrival and funeral of the drowned man.

	Before the drowned man washed ashore		After the funeral
The weather		→	
The houses and streets		→	
The vegetation and soil		→	

Focus on Research: Generate and Answer Inquiry Questions

The story "The Handsomest Drowned Man in the World" includes several allusions to mythical and historic figures. With a partner, create a list of three to five questions related to one of the story's allusions. For example, *What does a siren look like?* or *Are all sirens female?* Then conduct research to answer the questions. Record any further questions and answers you discover during your research.

The Literature of
Brazil

Background

Brazil, the most vast and populous country in Latin America, has a unique heritage. When Spain lost colonial control over the Americas, Spanish-speaking territories broke down into many different countries. However, when Portugal's rule in South America ended during the 1820s, the Portuguese-speaking region remained intact as the independent nation of Brazil. Brazil's literature reflects this remarkable unity.

Poet, novelist, and short story writer Joaquim Maria Machado de Assis (1839–1908) is a towering figure in Brazilian literature. His masterpiece is a witty but pessimistic novel of jealousy titled *Dom Casmurro*. In it, he both comments on Brazilian society and accurately portrays universal human emotions such as trust and revenge. Later Brazilian writers, and other writers in Latin America and the United States, were influenced by his use of a narrator whose actions are shaped by fantasy as well as reality.

Brazil and the United States

Like peoples of many developing countries, Brazilians often feel overwhelmed by the influence of United States culture. But instead of responding to this influence with resentment, Brazilian authors tend to treat it with humor and satire.

For example, in the farcical novel *Sangue De Coca Cola* (Coca-Cola Blood) by Roberto Drummond (1933–2002), a character describes Brazilians as trained animals in "A Great North American Circus." Bobby J. Chamberlain, a U.S. scholar in Brazilian literature, regards such playful lampooning as "a healthier way of assimilating imported culture than outright rejection."

Research: Develop a Thesis

Brazilian Portuguese has diverged from the language spoken and written in Portugal. Some Brazilians find it easier to understand Spanish-language movies than those spoken in European Portuguese. Write a thesis statement for a research paper about how Brazil's evolving language has affected its literature.

The Third Bank of the River

João Guimarães Rosa

Before You Read

João Guimarães Rosa (1908–1967) was born in rural Brazil. He studied medicine and then returned to work as a physician in the sparsely populated *sertao* (backcountry) where he grew up. He later became a Brazilian diplomat, serving in several world capitals. Guimarães Rosa was a polyglot, mastering several languages as diverse as Russian and Japanese. The unique voice of his fiction has presented such a challenge to translators that his reputation has been slow to build in the English-speaking world.

Guimarães Rosa's novel *The Devil to Pay in the Backlands* somewhat anticipates the theme of the following story. In this sprawling novel, characters make a pact with Satan and wrestle with the forces of God and the Devil.

World Context

Like many of his fellow Latin American authors, Guimarães Rosa is a metaphysical writer. He explores through his fiction the nature of existence and what it means to be human.

LITERARY LENS A **symbol** is an object used to represent a more abstract or general concept. For example, a rose might symbolize love. As you read this story, consider the possible symbolic meanings of objects and actions.

My father was a dutiful, orderly, straightforward man. And according to several reliable people of whom I enquired, he had had these qualities since adolescence or even childhood. By my own recollection, he was neither jollier nor more melancholy than the other men we knew. Maybe a little quieter. It was Mother, not Father, who ruled the house. She scolded us daily—my sister, my brother, and me. But it happened one day that Father ordered a boat.

He was very serious about it. It was to be made specially for him, of mimosa[1] wood. It was to be sturdy enough to last twenty or thirty years and just large enough for one person. Mother carried on plenty about it. Was her husband going to become a fisherman all of a sudden? Or a hunter? Father said nothing. Our house was less than a mile from the river, which around there was deep, quiet, and so wide you couldn't see across it.

I can never forget the day the rowboat was delivered. Father showed no joy or other emotion. He just put on his hat as he always did and said goodbye to us. He took along no food or bundle of any sort. We expected Mother to rant and rave, but she didn't. She looked very pale and bit her lip, but all she said was: "If you go away, stay away. Don't ever come back!"

Father made no reply. He looked gently at me and motioned me to walk along with him. I feared Mother's wrath, yet I eagerly obeyed. We headed towards the river together. I felt bold and exhilarated, so much so that I said: "Father, will you take me with you in your boat?"

He just looked at me, gave me his blessing, and, by a gesture, told me to go back. I made as if to do so but, when his back was turned, I ducked behind some bushes to watch him. Father got into the boat and rowed away. Its shadow slid across the water like a crocodile, long and quiet.

Father did not come back. Nor did he go anywhere, really. He just rowed and floated across and around, out there in the river. Everyone was appalled. What had never happened, what could not possibly happen, was happening. Our relatives, neighbours, and friends came over to discuss the phenomenon.

Mother was ashamed. She said little and conducted herself with great composure. As a consequence, almost everyone thought (though no one said it) that Father had gone insane. A few, however, suggested that Father might be fulfilling a promise he had made to God or to a saint, or that he might have some horrible disease, maybe leprosy, and that he left for the sake of the family, at the same time wishing to remain fairly near them.

Travellers along the river and people living near the bank on one side or the other reported that Father never put foot on land, by day or night. He **derelict:** just moved about on the river, solitary, aimless, like a **derelict**. Mother and **vagrant; drifter** our relatives agreed that the food which he had doubtless hidden in the boat would soon give out and that then he would either leave the river and travel off somewhere (which would be at least a little more respectable) or he would repent and come home.

---

1 **mimosa:** a type of tree or shrub from the tropics

How far from the truth they were! Father had a secret source of provisions: me. Every day I stole food and brought it to him. The first night after he left, we all lit fires on the shore and prayed and called to him. I was deeply distressed and felt a need to do something more. The following day I went down to the river with a loaf of corn bread, a bunch of bananas, and some bricks of raw brown sugar. I waited impatiently a long, long hour. Then I saw the boat, far off, alone, gliding almost imperceptibly on the smoothness of the river. Father was sitting in the bottom of the boat. He saw me but he did not row towards me or make any gesture. I showed him the food and then I placed it in a hollow rock on the river bank; it was safe there from animals, rain, and dew. I did this day after day, on and on and on. Later I learned, to my surprise, that Mother knew what I was doing and left food around where I could easily steal it. She had a lot of feelings she didn't show.

Mother sent for her brother to come and help on the farm and in business matters. She had the schoolteacher come and tutor us children at home because of the time we had lost. One day, at her request, the priest put on his vestments,[2] went down to the shore, and tried to **exorcise** the devils that had got into my father. He shouted that Father had a duty to cease his unholy obstinacy. Another day she arranged to have two soldiers come and try to frighten him. All to no avail. My father went by in the distance, sometimes so far away he could barely be seen. He never replied to anyone and no one ever got close to him. When some newspapermen came in a launch to take his picture, Father headed his boat to the other side of the river and into the marshes, which he knew like the palm of his hand but in which other people quickly got lost. There in his private maze, which extended for miles, with heavy foliage overhead and rushes[3] on all sides, he was safe.

We had to get accustomed to the idea of Father's being out on the river. We had to but we couldn't, we never could. I think I was the only one who understood to some degree what our father wanted and what he did not want. The thing I could not understand at all was how he stood the hardship. Day and night, in sun and rain, in heat and in terrible mid-year cold spells, with his old hat on his head and very little other clothing, week after week, month after month, year after year, unheedful of the waste and emptiness in which his life was slipping by. He never set foot on earth or grass, on isle or mainland shore. No doubt he sometimes tied up the boat

exorcise: banish; send away

2 **vestments:** religious garments
3 **rushes:** grasslike plants found in marsh areas

at a secret place, perhaps at the tip of some island, to get a little sleep. He never lit a fire or even struck a match and he had no flashlight. He took only a small part of the food that I left in the hollow rock—not enough, it seemed to me, for survival. What could his state of health have been? How about the continual drain on his energy, pulling and pushing the oars to control the boat? And how did he survive the annual floods, when the river rose and swept along with it all sorts of dangerous objects—branches of trees, dead bodies of animals—that might suddenly crash against his little boat?

He never talked to a living soul. And we never talked about him. We just thought. No, we could never put our father out of mind. If for a short time we seemed to, it was just a lull from which we would be sharply awakened by the realization of his frightening situation.

My sister got married, but Mother didn't want a wedding party. It would have been a sad affair, for we thought of him every time we ate some especially tasty food. Just as we thought of him in our cosy beds on a cold, stormy night—out there, alone and unprotected, trying to bail out the boat with only his hands and a gourd. Now and then someone would say that I was getting to look more and more like my father. But I knew that by then his hair and beard must have been shaggy and his nails long. I pictured him thin and sickly, black with hair and sunburn, and almost naked despite the articles of clothing I occasionally left for him.

He didn't seem to care about us at all. But I felt affection and respect for him, and, whenever they praised me because I had done something good, I said: "My father taught me to act that way."

It wasn't exactly accurate but it was a truthful sort of lie. As I said, Father didn't seem to care about us. But then why did he stay around there? Why didn't he go up the river or down the river, beyond the possibility of seeing us or being seen by us? He alone knew the answer.

My sister had a baby boy. She insisted on showing Father his grandson. One beautiful day we all went down to the riverbank, my sister in her white wedding dress, and she lifted the baby high. Her husband held a parasol[4] above them. We shouted to Father and waited. He did not appear. My sister cried; we all cried in each other's arms.

My sister and her husband moved far away. My brother went to live in a city. Times changed, with their usual **imperceptible** rapidity. Mother finally moved too; she was old and went to live with her daughter. I remained behind, a leftover. I could never think of marrying. I just stayed there with

imperceptible: unobservable; untraceable

---

4 **parasol:** a type of umbrella used for sun protection

The Americas

the impedimenta[5] of my life. Father, wandering alone and forlorn on the river, needed me. I knew he needed me, although he never even told me why he was doing it. When I put the question to people bluntly and insistently, all they told me was that they heard that Father had explained it to the man who made the boat. But now this man was dead and nobody knew or remembered anything. There was just some foolish talk, when the rains were especially severe and persistent, that my father was wise like Noah and had the boat built in anticipation of a new flood; I dimly remember people saying this. In any case, I would not condemn my father for what he was doing. My hair was beginning to turn grey.

I have only sad things to say. What bad had I done, what was my great guilt? My father always away and his absence always with me. And the river, always the river, perpetually renewing itself. The river, always. I was beginning to suffer from old age, in which life is just a sort of lingering. I had attacks of illness and of anxiety. I had a nagging rheumatism.[6] And he? Why, why was he doing it? He must have been suffering terribly. He was so old. One day, in his failing strength, he might let the boat capsize; or he might let the current carry it downstream, on and on, until it plunged over the waterfall to the boiling turmoil below. It pressed upon my heart. He was out there and I was forever robbed of my peace. I am guilty of I know not what, and my pain is an open wound inside me. Perhaps I would know—if things were different. I began to guess what was wrong.

No one called anybody crazy, for nobody is crazy. Or maybe everybody.

Out with it! Had I gone crazy? No, in our house that word was never spoken, never through all the years. No one called anybody crazy, for nobody is crazy. Or maybe everybody. All I did was go there and wave a handkerchief so he would be more likely to see me. I was in complete command of myself. I waited. Finally he appeared in the distance, there, then over there, a vague shape sitting in the back of the boat. I called to him several times. And I said what I was so eager to say, to state formally and under oath. I said it as loud as I could:

"Father, you have been out there long enough. You are old . . . Come back, you don't have to do it anymore . . . Come back and I'll go instead. Right now, if you want. Any time. I'll get into the boat. I'll take your place."

And when I had said this my heart beat more firmly.

---

5 **impedimenta:** things that get in the way

6 **rheumatism:** a health condition marked by muscle and joint pain

manoeuvred:
handled; moved
skillfully

He heard me. He stood up. He **manoeuvred** with his oars and headed the boat towards me. He had accepted my offer. And suddenly I trembled, down deep. For he had raised his arm and waved—the first time in so many, so many years. And I couldn't . . . In terror, my hair on end, I ran, I fled madly. For he seemed to come from another world. And I'm begging forgiveness, begging, begging.

I experienced the dreadful sense of cold that comes from deadly fear, and I became ill. Nobody ever saw or heard about him again. Am I a man, after such a failure? I am what never should have been. I am what must be silent. I know it is too late. I must stay in the deserts and unmarked plains of my life, and I fear I shall shorten it. But when death comes I want them to take me and put me in a little boat in this perpetual water between the long shores; and I, down the river, lost in the river, inside the river . . . the river . . .

Translated by William L. Grossman

After You Read

Critical Reading

1. At the end of the story, the son tells the father that he will "get into the boat" (page 97) and take the father's place, at which point the father begins to head the boat toward the shore. What does this reveal about the father and the relationship between the father and the son?

2. In some ways, this story could be considered a **parable**, designed to reveal a moral lesson or general truth. What is the general truth revealed by this story?

3. The story ends with the repetition of the phrase "the river." What mood does the repetition of this phrase convey?

Literary Lens: Symbolism

Guimaraes Rosa uses many different symbols in this story, such as the boat, the river, and more. Select an object or event from the story that you consider to be a symbol. Explain what the object or event might symbolize. Support your interpretation by citing at least one detail from the story.

Symbol	What this symbol stands for	Details from the story

Focus on Research: Use In-Text Citations

In-text citations lend credibility to academic writing and curb the urge to plagiarize. In-text citations should be included with direct quotations and also with information that is not common knowledge. They usually include the author's name and a page number or key word in parenthesis and are included in the main flow of the writing. Two popular citation styles are APA and MLA.

Find a source about the life of João Guimarães Rosa. Then write two sentences in your own words expressing information from the source and include in-text citations, using APA for one sentence and MLA for the other sentence.

The Literature of
Argentina

Background

Starting in the late 19th century, a wave of immigrants began to arrive in Argentina. These immigrants came from Italy and several other countries, including France, Poland, Russia, Germany, Great Britain, Lebanon, Syria, and Japan. This variety of peoples has helped create a literary culture that is rich in ideas and stylistically daring. Argentine literature also reflects the beauty and variety of the country's rural and urban landscapes—the vast lowlands of the countryside and the winding alleys of the cities.

Many Argentine authors are quite experimental and philosophical in their work. An example is the fiction writer Julio Cortázar (1914–1984). His most famous novel is *Hopscotch*, which the reader is invited to read in nonchronological order. Most of its chapters are actually described as "expendable," and the reader may even choose to read only odd- or even-numbered pages. This eccentric narrative technique comments not only on the nature of fiction but also on the chaotic experience of life itself.

Argentina and the United States

The Argentinian poet, essayist, and short story writer Jorge Luis Borges (1899–1986) was a voracious reader. He read Argentinian literature, European literature, U.S. literature, and more. He was deeply influenced by certain U.S. authors, such as Herman Melville, William Faulkner, Walt Whitman, and Edgar Allan Poe. Like Poe, Borges explored inner landscapes of the mind in such famous stories as "The Garden of Forking Paths" and "The Library of Babel."

Borges's work has in turn influenced the works of countless U.S. writers. Among these are the experimental novelist Thomas Pynchon, author of *Gravity's Rainbow*, and the science fiction writer William Gibson, author of *Neuromancer*.

Research: Collaborate with a Partner

Like the United States, Argentina won its freedom from a European country, became home to millions of European immigrants, and had an influential cowboy culture. With a partner, research and prepare a short oral report on one parallel between the literature of Argentina and the United States. Discuss how to divide the work and develop a plan to guide your research.

The Book of Sand

Jorge Luis Borges

Before You Read

Jorge Luis Borges (1899–1986) had an enormous influence on literature, especially in Latin America. He wrote in all genres but preferred short stories because of the way they compress connections and meaning. Like many Latin American writers, he uses fantasy as a way to invest the ordinary with the extraordinary. He wrote about dreams, the connection between reality and the imagination, and the magic of ordinary objects. As a director of the National Library in Buenos Aires, he could indulge his love of books and the notion of the "infinite library," another of his repeated themes.

World Context

The image of the labyrinth, or maze, appears frequently in Latin American literature. Borges once wrote, "Through the years, a man peoples a space with images of provinces, kingdoms, mountains, bays, ships, islands, fishes, rooms, tools, stars, horses, and people. Shortly before his death, he discovers that the patient labyrinth of lines traces the images of his own face."

 LITERARY LENS The **mood,** or atmosphere, of a story communicates a certain feeling to the reader. As you read, identify passages that contribute to the overall mood of the story.

> . . . thy rope of sands . . .
> George Herbert (1593–1623)

The line consists of an infinite number of points; the plane, of an infinite number of lines; the volume, of an infinite number of planes; the hypervolume, of an infinite number of volumes . . . No—this, *more geometrico*, is decidedly not the best way to begin my tale. To say that the story is true is by now a convention of every fantastic tale; mine, nevertheless, is true.

I live alone, in a fifth-floor apartment on Calle Belgrano. One evening a few months ago, I heard a knock at my door. I opened it, and a stranger stepped in. He was a tall man, with blurred, vague features, or perhaps my nearsightedness made me see him that way. Everything about him spoke of honest poverty: he was dressed in gray, and carried a gray valise.[1] I immediately sensed that he was a foreigner. At first I thought he was old; then I noticed that I had been misled by his sparse hair, which was blond, almost white, like the Scandinavians'. In the course of our conversation, which I doubt lasted more than an hour, I learned that he hailed from the Orkneys.[2]

I pointed the man to a chair. He took some time to begin talking. He gave off an air of melancholy, as I myself do now.

"I sell Bibles," he said at last.

pedantic:
professorial;
nitpicking

"In this house," I replied, not without a somewhat stiff, **pedantic** note, "there are several English Bibles, including the first one, Wyclif's.[3] I also have Cipriano de Valera's, Luther's (which is, in literary terms, the worst of the lot), and a Latin copy of the Vulgate.[4] As you see, it isn't exactly Bibles I might be needing."

After a brief silence he replied.

"It's not only Bibles I sell. I can show you a sacred book that might interest a man such as yourself. I came by it in northern India, in Bikaner."

He opened his valise and brought out the book. He laid it on the table. It was a clothbound octavo[5] volume that had clearly passed through many hands. I examined it; the unusual heft of it surprised me. On the spine was printed *Holy Writ*, and then *Bombay*.

"Nineteenth century, I'd say," I observed.

"I don't know," was the reply. "Never did know."

I opened it at random. The characters were unfamiliar to me. The pages, which seemed worn and badly set, were printed in double columns, like a Bible. The text was cramped, and composed into versicles.[6] At the upper corner of each page were Arabic numerals. I was struck by an odd fact: the even-numbered page would carry the number 40,514, let us say, while the odd-numbered page that followed it would be 999. I turned the page; the

---

1 **valise:** a piece of handheld luggage

2 **Orkneys:** a group of islands off northeastern Scotland

3 **Wyclif:** John Wyclif (1328–1384), an English reformer, who inspired the first complete English translation of the Latin Bible

4 **Vulgate:** the Latin Bible used by Roman Catholics

5 **octavo:** a size of book, printed on sheets that fold to form 8 leaves, or 16 pages

6 **versicles:** short verses used in worship services

next page bore an eight-digit number. It also bore a small illustration, like those one sees in dictionaries: an anchor drawn in pen and ink, as though by the unskilled hand of a child.

It was at that point that the stranger spoke again.

"Look at it well. You will never see it again."

There was a threat in the words, but not in the voice.

I took note of the page, and then closed the book. Immediately I opened it again. In vain I searched for the figure of the anchor, page after page. To hide my discomfiture, I tried another tack.

"This is a version of Scripture in some Hindu language, isn't that right?"

"No," he replied.

Then he lowered his voice, as though entrusting me with a secret.

"I came across this book in a village on the plain, and I traded a few rupees and a Bible for it. The man who owned it didn't know how to read. I suspect he saw the Book of Books as an amulet.[7] He was of the lowest caste;[8] people could not so much as step on his shadow without being defiled. He told me his book was called the Book of Sand because neither sand nor this book has a beginning or an end."

He suggested I try to find the first page.

I took the cover in my left hand and opened the book, my thumb and forefinger almost touching. It was impossible: several pages always lay between the cover and my hand. It was as though they grew from the very book.

"Now try to find the end."

I failed there as well.

"This can't be," I stammered, my voice hardly recognizable as my own.

"It can't be, yet it is," the Bible peddler said, his voice little more than a whisper. "The number of pages in this book is literally infinite. No page is the first page; no page is the last. I don't know why they're numbered in this **arbitrary** way, but perhaps it's to give one to understand that the terms of an infinite series can be numbered any way whatever."

arbitrary: random; discretionary

Then, as though thinking out loud, he went on.

"If space is infinite, we are anywhere, at any point in space. If time is infinite, we are at any point in time."

His musings irritated me.

"You," I said, "are a religious man, are you not?"

"Yes, I'm Presbyterian. My conscience is clear. I am certain I didn't cheat

---

7 **amulet:** an object that is supposed to protect against harm
8 **caste:** a person's inherited social class in the Hindu religion

that native when I gave him the Lord's Word in exchange for his **diabolic** book."

I assured him he had nothing to reproach himself for, and asked whether he was just passing through the country. He replied that he planned to return to his own country within a few days. It was then that I learned he was a Scot, and that his home was in the Orkneys. I told him I had great personal fondness of Scotland because of my love for Stevenson[9] and Hume.[10]

"And Robbie Burns,"[11] he corrected.

As we talked I continued to explore the infinite book.

"Had you intended to offer this curious specimen to the British Museum, then?" I asked with feigned indifference.

"No," he replied. "I am offering it to you," and he mentioned a great sum of money.

I told him, with perfect honesty, that such an amount of money was not within my ability to pay. But my mind was working; in a few moments I had devised my plan.

"I propose a trade," I said. "You purchased the volume with a few rupees and the Holy Scripture; I will offer you the full sum of my pension, which I have just received, and Wyclif's black-letter Bible. It was left to me by my parents."

"A black-letter Wyclif!" he murmured.

I went to my bedroom and brought back the money and the book. With a bibliophile's[12] zeal he turned the pages and studied the binding.

"Done," he said.

I was astonished that he did not haggle. Only later was I to realize that he had entered my house already determined to sell the book. He did not count the money, but merely put the bills into his pocket.

We chatted about India, the Orkneys, and the Norwegian jarls[13] that had once ruled those islands. Night was falling when the man left. I have never seen him since, nor do I know his name.

I thought of putting the Book of Sand in the space left by the Wyclif, but I chose at last to hide it behind some imperfect volumes of the *Thousand and One Nights*.[14]

---

9 **Stevenson:** Robert Louis Stevenson (1850–1894), a famous Scottish novelist

10 **Hume:** David Hume (1711–1776), a Scottish philosopher and historian of renown

11 **Robbie Burns:** Robert Burns (1759–1796), the well-known Scottish poet

12 **bibliophile:** one who loves books

13 **jarls:** Scandinavian noblemen

14 *Thousand and One Nights:* a famous collection of Indian, Persian, and Arabic tales, arranged together in about 1450

I went to bed but could not sleep. At three or four in the morning I turned on the light. I took out the impossible book and turned its pages. On one, I saw an engraving of a mask. There was a number in the corner of the page—I don't remember now what it was—raised to the ninth power.

I showed no one my treasure. To the joy of possession was added the fear that it would be stolen from me, and to that, the suspicion that it might not be truly infinite. Those two points of anxiety aggravated my already habitual **misanthropy**. I had but few friends left, and those, I stopped seeing. A prisoner of the Book, I hardly left my house, I examined the worn binding and the covers with a magnifying glass, and rejected the possibility of some artifice. I found that the small illustrations were spaced at two-thousand-page intervals. I began noting them down in an alphabetized notebook, which was very soon filled. They never repeated themselves. At night, during the rare intervals spared me by insomnia, I dreamed of the book.

misanthropy: dislike of humanity

> I felt it was a nightmare thing, an obscene thing, and that it defiled and corrupted reality.

Summer was drawing to a close, and I realized that the book was monstrous. It was cold consolation to think that I, who looked upon it with my eyes and fondled it with my ten flesh-and-bone fingers, was no less monstrous than the book. I felt it was a nightmare thing, an obscene thing, and that it defiled and corrupted reality.

I considered fire, but I feared that the burning of an infinite book might be similarly infinite, and suffocate the planet in smoke.

I remembered reading once that the best place to hide a leaf is in the forest. Before my retirement I had worked in the National Library, which contained nine hundred thousand books; I knew that to the right of the lobby a curving staircase descended into the shadows of the basement, where the maps and periodicals are kept. I took advantage of the librarians' distraction to hide the Book of Sand on one of the library's damp shelves; I tried not to notice how high up, or how far from the door.

I now feel a little better, but I refuse even to walk down the street the library's on.

Translated by Andrew Hurley

After You Read

Critical Reading

1. An **epigraph** is an opening quote. Read the epigraph to the story, which was written by the poet George Herbert, whose metaphysical poetry is concerned with the philosophy of life. What theme is suggested by this epigraph?

2. What is the **internal conflict**, or struggle, the narrator faces in the story?

3. Consider how *The Book of Sand* is a **foil** in the story. What does it reveal about the narrator and how?

Literary Lens: Mood

Borges develops and builds the **mood** in the story using dialogue, descriptive details, characterization, and the setting. Identify examples of each of these details. Then write a brief description of the mood that they convey.

	Example or quotation	Mood conveyed
Dialogue		
Descriptive details		
Characterization		
Setting		

Focus on Research: Use Quotations Effectively

This story might bring to mind the melodramatic tone of Edgar Allan Poe. Select a passage from this story and a passage from your favorite Poe short story. Write a brief paragraph that includes four to five sentences. In this paragraph, compare the two passages, using quotations from both stories. When using quotations, be sure to use commas and quotation marks appropriately.

The Censors

Luisa Valenzuela

Before You Read

Luisa Valenzuela (1938–) is an Argentine journalist and fiction writer. She was born in Buenos Aires, but due to political turmoil, she has spent years in other countries—Spain, Mexico, and the United States. Much of her writing reflects Argentina's strife-torn political and military situations. Her stories are sometimes told with dark humor and a touch of the grotesque.

World Context

This short story captures the spirit of many Argentines during the military dictatorship of the 1970s. The "Process of National Reorganization," as it was euphemistically called, lasted from 1976 to 1983 and was remarkable for its violence. The military filled concentration camps and later mass graves with "enemies of the state." Ordinary citizens lived in terror, and many fled the country in fear of their lives.

 LITERARY LENS Situational irony is a plot twist in which the outcome of a character's intent or action becomes twisted into its opposite. Watch for such an ironic twist in this story.

Poor Juan! One day they caught him with his guard down before he could even realize that what he had taken as a stroke of luck was really one of fate's dirty tricks. These things happen the minute you're careless and you let down your guard, as one often does. Juancito let happiness—a feeling you can't trust—get the better of him when he received from a confidential source Mariana's new address in Paris and he knew that she hadn't forgotten him. Without thinking twice, he sat down at his table and wrote her a letter. The letter that keeps his mind off his job during the day and won't let him sleep at night (what had he scrawled, what had he put on that sheet of paper he sent to Mariana?).

Juan knows there won't be a problem with the letter's contents, that it's **irreproachable**, harmless. But what about the rest? He knows that they examine, sniff, feel, and read between the lines of each and every letter, and check its tiniest comma and most accidental stain. He knows that all letters pass from hand to hand and go through all sorts of tests in the huge censorship offices and that, in the end, very few continue on their way. Usually it takes months, even years, if there aren't any snags; all this time the freedom, maybe even the life, of both sender and receiver is in jeopardy. And that's why Juan's so down in the dumps: thinking that something might happen to Mariana because of his letters. Of all people, Mariana, who must finally feel safe there where she always dreamed she'd live. But he knows that the *Censor's Secret Command* operates all over the world and cashes in on the discount in air rates; there's nothing to stop them from going as far as that hidden Paris neighborhood, kidnapping Mariana, and returning to their cozy homes, certain of having fulfilled their noble mission.

Well, you've got to beat them to the punch, do what everyone tries to do: sabotage the machinery, throw sand in its gears, get to the bottom of the problem so as to stop it.

This was Juan's sound plan when he, like many others, applied for a censor's job—not because he had a calling or needed a job: no, he applied simply to intercept his own letter, a consoling but unoriginal idea. He was

hired immediately, for each day more and more censors are needed and no one would bother to check on his references.

Ulterior motives couldn't be overlooked by the *Censorship Division*, but they needn't be too strict with those who applied. They knew how hard it would be for those poor guys to find the letter they wanted and even if they did, what's a letter or two when the new censor would snap up so many others? That's how Juan managed to join the *Post Office's Censorship Division*, with a certain goal in mind.

The building had a festive air on the outside which contrasted with its inner staidness. Little by little, Juan was absorbed by his job and he felt at peace since he was doing everything he could to get his letter for Mariana. He didn't even worry when, in his first month, he was sent to *Section K*, where envelopes were very carefully screened for explosives.

It's true that on the third day, a fellow worker had his right hand blown off by a letter, but the division chief claimed it was sheer negligence on the victim's part. Juan and the other employees were allowed to go back to their work, albeit feeling less secure. After work, one of them tried to organize a strike to demand higher wages for unhealthy work, but Juan didn't join in; after thinking it over, he reported him to his superiors and thus got promoted.

You don't form a habit by doing something once, he told himself as he left his boss's office. And when he was transferred to *Section J*, where letters are carefully checked for poison dust, he felt he had climbed a rung in the ladder.

By working hard, he quickly reached *Section E* where the work was more interesting, for he could now read and analyze the letters' contents. Here he could even hope to get hold of his letter which, judging by the time that had elapsed, had gone through the other sections and was probably floating around in this one.

Soon his work became so absorbing that his noble mission blurred in his mind. Day after day he crossed out whole paragraphs in red ink, pitilessly chucking many letters into the censored basket. These were horrible days when he was shocked by the subtle and conniving ways employed by people to pass on subversive messages; his instincts were so sharp that he found behind a simple "the weather's unsettled" or "prices continue to soar" the wavering hand of someone secretly scheming to overthrow the Government.

His zeal brought him swift promotion. We don't know if this made him happy. Very few letters reached him in *Section B*—only a handful passed the other hurdles—so he read them over and over again, passed them under a magnifying glass, searched for microprint with an electronic microscope, and tuned his sense of smell so that he was beat by the time he made it home. He'd barely manage to warm up his soup, eat some fruit, and fall into bed, satisfied with having done his duty. Only his darling mother worried, but she couldn't get him back on the right road. She'd say, though it wasn't always true: Lola called, she's at the bar with the girls, they miss you, they're waiting for you. Or else she'd leave a bottle of red wine on the table. But Juan wouldn't overdo it: any distraction could make him lose his edge and the perfect censor had to be alert, keen, attentive, and sharp to nab cheats. He had a truly patriotic task, both self-denying and uplifting.

His basket for censored letters became the best fed as well as the most cunning basket in the whole *Censorship Division*. He was about to congratulate himself for having finally discovered his true mission, when his letter to Mariana reached his hands. Naturally, he censored it without regret. And just as naturally, he couldn't stop them from executing him the following morning, another victim of his devotion to his work.

Translated by David Unger

After You Read

Critical Reading

1. An **anti-hero** is a character who displays qualities opposite of those usually associated with a hero. Do you consider Juan to be a hero or anti-hero? Support your response with details from the story.

2. What is the attitude of the narrator toward the character Juan? What words or descriptions reveal this **tone**?

3. What is the message, or **theme**, of the story?

Literary Lens: Situational Irony

Analyze the use of **situational irony** in the story. Begin by identifying several examples of situational irony. Then for each example, describe the difference between appearances (or what readers and characters expect will happen) and reality (what actually turns out to happen in the story).

Example:	
Appearances/Expectations	**Reality/What Actually Happens**

Example:	
Appearances/Expectations	**Reality/What Actually Happens**

Focus on Research: Develop Research Questions

The plot of the story "The Censors" is focused on government-sponsored censorship. Develop research questions on the topic of government-sponsored censorship in Argentina or another Latin American country. Write three to five sentences describing what you want to learn more about. Then turn these into questions that could guide your research on the topic.

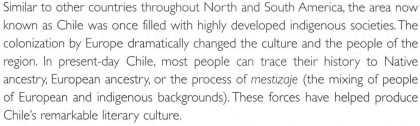

The Literature of
Chile

Background

Similar to other countries throughout North and South America, the area now known as Chile was once filled with highly developed indigenous societies. The colonization by Europe dramatically changed the culture and the people of the region. In present-day Chile, most people can trace their history to Native ancestry, European ancestry, or the process of *mestizaje* (the mixing of people of European and indigenous backgrounds). These forces have helped produce Chile's remarkable literary culture.

Chile is known around the world for its poetry. In 1945, poet Gabriela Mistral (1896–1973) became the first Latin American writer to win the Nobel Prize in Literature. An artist of overpowering passion, perhaps her most famous poem is "Dolor," which translates in English to *pain* or *grief*. The poem is a response to the suicide of her lover. Another Chilean poet, Pablo Neruda (1904–1973), won the Nobel Prize in 1971. Neruda always felt the influence of the high mountains and immense deserts that separate Chile from its neighbors: "I come from a dark region, from a land separated from all others by the steep contours of its geography." Chilean fiction has also rapidly become known around the world.

Chile and the United States

Novelist and short story writer Isabel Allende (1942–) brought Chilean fiction to international prominence. Her best-known novels include *Eva Luna* and *Daughter of Fortune*. English translations of Allende's work have made her a celebrity in the United States. She has lived in the United States since the 1990s and became a U.S. citizen in 2003. Her novel *The House of the Spirits* was adapted into a U.S.-made movie in 1993.

Research: Do Preliminary Research

In 1973, Isabel Allende's uncle, President Salvador Allende of Chile, was assassinated, and the dictatorial rule of Augusto Pinochet began. During the turbulent years that followed, Isabel Allende endured exile and death threats. Conduct preliminary research on Allende's reaction to her uncle's assassination and how it affected her life and writings. Then write a thesis statement for a paper examining political themes in Allende's work.

Serenity

Gabriela Mistral

Before You Read

Gabriela Mistral (1889–1957) was born Lucila Godoy Alcayaga in Chile. After the suicide of her lover, she began writing poetry under the pseudonym Gabriela Mistral. She is credited with founding the modern poetry movement in Chile and was a mentor to the great Pablo Neruda. In later life she became a pioneer in modernizing public education throughout Latin America.

World Context

In a land that prizes its poets, Mistral is viewed with special affection for her strong identity with the poor and the indigenous peoples of South America.

 LITERARY LENS Tone refers to the attitude of the author toward the subject of the writing. Be aware of the tone in the following poem.

When I am singing to you,
on earth all evil ends:
as smooth as your forehead
are the gulch and the bramble.

When I am singing to you,   5
for me all cruel things end:
as gentle as your eyelids,
the lion with the jackal.

Translated by Doris Dana

After You Read

Critical Reading

1. Authors can convey **mood** through various techniques, such as **setting**, **symbols**, and **imagery**. Choose two of these techniques. Identify words, phrases, or lines from the poem that use these techniques to reveal mood. Analyze how the poem uses these techniques and identify what mood is conveyed.

2. In this poem, Mistral uses **juxtaposition**, or the placing of two unexpected things side by side. Identify an instance of juxtaposition in the poem. Infer what Mistral hoped to convey through this juxtaposition.

3. Describe the character of the **speaker** in the poem. Cite examples of what the speaker says as well as how the speaker acts in your description.

Literary Lens: Tone

Cite two or three words or phrases that reveal the tone of the poem. Then analyze what this reveals about the narrator's attitude or perspective. Lastly, describe the tone.

Word or phrase	What this reveals about the speaker's attitude or perspective	Description of the tone

Focus on Research: Create an Annotated Bibliography

For some research papers, you may be asked to write an annotated bibliography. An annotated bibliography includes information about a source (author, title, publishing date, etc.) and also a summary or evaluation of the source written in paragraph form. The format of annotated bibliographies varies depending on which research type you are following (for example, MLA or APA).

Find a source about the life of Gabriela Mistral and write an annotated bibliography using either MLA or APA style. Be sure to check an online style guide to ensure your format is correct.

And of Clay
Are We Created

Isabel Allende

Before You Read

Isabel Allende (1942–) was a journalist in Chile until she was forced into exile in 1973 when her uncle, Chilean president Salvador Allende, was assassinated. She has traveled to many parts of the world and now lives in the United States. At various times, Allende found herself in frightening situations. But as she said in an interview for *Mother Jones*, "The wonderful quality of human beings is that we can overcome even absolute terror, and we do."

Allende resides among the front ranks of Latin American authors, bringing a woman's perspective to matters of class, family, and sexual politics. Her books include *Eva Luna* and the international best seller *The House of the Spirits*.

World Context

Like other Latin American authors, Allende often uses magic realism in her fiction, a technique that seems to go naturally with the fantastic and tumultuous events in Latin America.

Allende's inspiration for this story came from the ordeal of a 13-year-old Colombian girl trapped in the mud after a 1985 avalanche. The author watched on television as a reporter comforted the dying girl.

 LITERARY LENS Trace the development of Rolf Carlé's **character** from the beginning of the tragedy to the end.

T hey discovered the girl's head protruding from the mud pit, eyes wide open, calling soundlessly. She had a First Communion name,[1] Azucena. Lily. In that vast cemetery where the odor of death was already

---

1 **First Communion name:** the name a Roman Catholic child takes when receiving this religious sacrament

attracting vultures from far away, and where the weeping of orphans and wails of the injured filled the air, the little girl obstinately clinging to life became the symbol of the tragedy. The television cameras transmitted so often the unbearable image of the head budding like a black squash from the clay that there was no one who did not recognize her and know her name. And every time we saw her on the screen, right behind her was Rolf Carlé, who had gone there on assignment, never suspecting that he would find a fragment of his past, lost thirty years before.

First a **subterranean** sob rocked the cotton fields, curling them like waves of foam. Geologists had set up their seismographs[2] weeks before and knew that the mountain had awakened again. For some time they had predicted that the heat of the eruption could detach the eternal ice from the slopes of the volcano, but no one heeded their warnings; they sounded like the tales of frightened old women. The towns in the valley went about their daily life, deaf to the moaning of the earth, until that fateful Wednesday night in November when a prolonged roar announced the end of the world, and walls of snow broke loose, rolling in an avalanche of clay, stones, and water that descended on the villages and buried them beneath unfathomable meters of telluric[3] vomit. As soon as the survivors emerged from the paralysis of that first awful terror, they could see that houses, plazas, churches, white cotton plantations, dark coffee forests, cattle pastures—all had disappeared. Much later, after soldiers and volunteers had arrived to rescue the living and try to assess the magnitude of the **cataclysm**, it was calculated that beneath the mud lay more than twenty thousand human beings and an indefinite number of animals **putrefying** in a **viscous** soup. Forests and rivers had also been swept away, and there was nothing to be seen but an immense desert of mire.

When the station called before dawn, Rolf Carlé and I were together. I crawled out of bed, dazed with sleep, and went to prepare coffee while he hurriedly dressed. He stuffed his gear in the green canvas backpack he always carried, and we said goodbye, as we had so many times before. I had no **presentiments**. I sat in the kitchen, sipping my coffee and planning the long hours without him, sure that he would be back the next day.

He was one of the first to reach the scene, because while other reporters were fighting their way to the edges of that **morass** in jeeps, bicycles, or on foot, each getting there however he could, Rolf Carlé had the advantage of the television helicopter, which flew him over the avalanche. We watched

subterranean: underground; below the surface

cataclysm: disaster; catastrophe

putrefying: rotting; decaying

viscous: sticky; gluey

presentiments: foreshadowing; premonitions

morass: swamp; quagmire

---

2 **seismographs:** instruments for measuring earth tremors
3 **telluric:** earthly

on our screens the footage captured by his assistant's camera, in which he was up to his knees in muck, a microphone in his hand, in the midst of a **bedlam** of lost children, wounded survivors, corpses, and devastation. The story came to us in his calm voice. For years he had been a familiar figure in newscasts, reporting live at the scene of battles and catastrophes with awesome **tenacity**. Nothing could stop him, and I was always amazed at his **equanimity** in the face of danger and suffering; it seemed as if nothing could shake his fortitude or deter his curiosity. Fear seemed never to touch him, although he had confessed to me that he was not a courageous man, far from it. I believe that the lens of a camera had a strange effect on him; it was as if it transported him to a different time from which he could watch events without actually participating in them. When I knew him better, I came to realize that this **fictive** distance seemed to protect him from his own emotions.

Rolf Carlé was in on the story of Azucena from the beginning. He filmed the volunteers who discovered her, and the first persons who tried to reach her; his camera zoomed in on the girl, her dark face, her large desolate eyes, the plastered-down tangle of her hair. The mud was like quicksand around her, and anyone attempting to reach her was in danger of sinking. They threw a rope to her that she made no effort to grasp until they shouted to her to catch it; then she pulled a hand from the mire and tried to move but immediately sank a little deeper. Rolf threw down his knapsack and the rest of his equipment and waded into the **quagmire**, commenting for his assistant's microphone that it was cold and that one could begin to smell the stench of corpses.

"What's your name?" he asked the girl, and she told him her flower name. "Don't move, Azucena," Rolf Carlé directed, and kept talking to her, without a thought for what he was saying, just to distract her, while slowly he worked his way forward in mud up to his waist. The air around him seemed as murky as the mud.

It was impossible to reach her from the approach he was attempting, so he retreated and circled around where there seemed to be firmer footing. When finally he was close enough, he took the rope and tied it beneath her arms, so they could pull her out. He smiled at her with that smile that crinkles his eyes and makes him look like a little boy; he told her that everything was fine, that he was here with her now, that soon they would have her out. He signaled the others to pull, but as soon as the cord tensed, the girl screamed. They tried again, and her shoulders and arms appeared, but they could move her no farther; she was trapped. Someone suggested

bedlam:
chaos; place of uproar

tenacity:
persistence; mental toughness

equanimity:
calm; poise

fictive:
imaginary; fictional

quagmire:
bog; quicksand

that her legs might be caught in the collapsed walls of her house, but she said it was not just rubble, that she was also held by the bodies of her brothers and sisters clinging to her legs.

"Don't worry, we'll get you out of here," Rolf promised. Despite the quality of the transmission, I could hear his voice break, and I loved him more than ever. Azucena looked at him but said nothing.

During those first hours Rolf Carlé exhausted all the resources of his ingenuity to rescue her. He struggled with poles and ropes, but every tug was an intolerable torture for the imprisoned girl. It occurred to him to use one of the poles as a lever but got no result and had to abandon the idea. He talked a couple of soldiers into working with him for a while, but they had to leave because so many other victims were calling for help. The girl could not move, she barely could breathe, but she did not seem desperate, as if an ancestral resignation allowed her to accept her fate. The reporter, on the other hand, was determined to snatch her from death. Someone brought him a tire, which he placed beneath her arms like a life buoy, and then laid a plank near the hole to hold his weight and allow him to stay closer to her. As it was impossible to remove the rubble blindly, he tried once or twice to dive toward her feet but emerged frustrated, covered with mud, and spitting gravel. He concluded that he would have to have a pump to drain the water, and radioed a request for one but received in return a message that there was no available transport and it could not be sent until the next morning.

"We can't wait that long!" Rolf Carlé shouted, but in the pandemonium no one stopped to commiserate. Many more hours would go by before he accepted that time had **stagnated** and reality had been irreparably distorted.

stagnated: stilled; stopped moving

A military doctor came to examine the girl and observed that her heart was functioning well and that if she did not get too cold she could survive the night.

"Hang on, Azucena, we'll have the pump tomorrow," Rolf Carlé tried to console her.

"Don't leave me alone," she begged.

"No, of course I won't leave you."

Someone brought him coffee, and he helped the girl drink it, sip by sip. The warm liquid revived her, and she began telling him about her small life, about her family and her school, about how things were in that little bit of world before the volcano erupted. She was thirteen, and she had never been outside her village. Rolf Carlé, buoyed by a premature optimism, was convinced that everything would end well: the pump would arrive, they would drain the water, move the rubble, and Azucena would be transported by helicopter to a hospital where she would recover rapidly and where he could visit her and bring her gifts. He thought, She's already too old for dolls, and I don't know what would please her; maybe a dress. I don't know much about women, he concluded, amused, reflecting that although he had known many women in his lifetime, none had taught him these details. To pass the hours he began to tell Azucena about his travels and adventures as a news hound, and when he exhausted his memory, he called upon imagination, inventing things he thought might entertain her. From time to time she dozed, but he kept talking in the darkness, to assure her that he was still there and to overcome the menace of uncertainty.

That was a long night.

· · · · ·

Many miles away, I watched Rolf Carlé and the girl on a television screen. I could not bear the wait at home, so I went to National Television, where I often spent entire nights with Rolf editing programs. There, I was near his world, and I could at least get a feeling of what he lived through during those three decisive days. I called all the important people in the city, senators, commanders of the armed forces, the North American ambassador, and the president of National Petroleum, begging them for a pump to remove the silt, but obtained only vague promises. I began to ask for urgent help on radio and television, to see if there wasn't *someone* who could help us. Between calls I would run to the newsroom to monitor the satellite transmissions that periodically brought new details of the catastrophe. While reporters selected scenes with most impact for the new report, I searched for footage that featured Azucena's mud pit. The screen reduced the disaster to a single plane and accentuated the tremendous distance that separated me from Rolf Carlé; nonetheless, I was there with him. The child's every suffering hurt me as it did him; I felt his frustration, his **impotence**. Faced with the impossibility of communicating with him, the fantastic idea came to me that if I tried, I could reach him by force of mind and in that way give him encouragement. I concentrated until I was dizzy—a frenzied and futile activity. At times I would be overcome with compassion and burst out crying; at other times, I was so drained I felt as if I were staring through a telescope at the light of a star dead for a million years.

I watched that hell on the first morning broadcast, **cadavers** of people and animals awash in the current of new rivers formed overnight from the

impotence: powerlessness; helplessness

cadavers: bodies; corpses

melted snow. Above the mud rose the tops of trees and the bell towers of a church where several people had taken refuge and were patiently awaiting rescue teams. Hundreds of soldiers and volunteers from the civil defense were clawing through rubble searching for survivors, while long rows of ragged **specters** awaited their turn for a cup of hot broth. Radio networks announced that their phones were jammed with calls from families offering shelter to orphaned children. Drinking water was in scarce supply, along with gasoline and food. Doctors, resigned to amputating arms and legs without anesthesia, pled that at least they be sent **serum** and painkillers and antibiotics; most of the roads, however, were impassable, and worse were the bureaucratic obstacles that stood in the way. To top it all, the clay contaminated by decomposing bodies threatened the living with an outbreak of epidemics.

Azucena was shivering inside the tire that held her above the surface. Immobility and tension had greatly weakened her, but she was conscious and could still be heard when a microphone was held out to her. Her tone was humble, as if apologizing for all the fuss. Rolf Carlé had a growth of beard, and dark circles beneath his eyes; he looked near exhaustion. Even from that enormous distance I could sense the quality of his weariness, so different from the fatigue of other adventures. He had completely forgotten the camera; he could not look at the girl through a lens any longer. The pictures we were receiving were not his assistant's but those of other reporters who had appropriated Azucena, bestowing on her the pathetic responsibility of embodying the horror of what had happened in that place. With the first light Rolf tried again to dislodge the obstacles that held the girl in her tomb, but he had only his hands to work with; he did not dare use a tool for fear of injuring her. He fed Azucena a cup of the cornmeal mush and bananas the army was distributing, but she immediately vomited it up. A doctor stated that she had a fever but added that there was little he could do: antibiotics were being reserved for cases of gangrene. A priest also passed by and blessed her, hanging a medal of the Virgin around her neck. By evening a gentle, persistent drizzle began to fall.

"The sky is weeping," Azucena murmured, and she, too, began to cry.

"Don't be afraid," Rolf begged. "You have to keep your strength up and be calm. Everything will be fine. I'm with you, and I'll get you out somehow."

Reporters returned to photograph Azucena and ask her the same questions, which she no longer tried to answer. In the meanwhile, more television and movie teams arrived with spools of cable, tapes, film, videos,

---

specters:
ghosts; shadows

serum:
blood serum; the liquid part of blood

precision lenses, recorders, sound consoles, lights, reflecting screens, auxiliary motors, cartons of supplies, electricians, sound technicians, and cameramen: Azucena's face was beamed to millions of screens around the world. And all the while Rolf Carlé kept pleading for a pump. The improved technical facilities bore results, and National Television began receiving sharper pictures and clearer sound, the distance seemed suddenly compressed, and I had the horrible sensation that Azucena and Rolf were by my side, separated from me by impenetrable glass. I was able to follow events hour by hour; I knew everything my love did to wrest the girl from her prison and help her endure her suffering; I overheard fragments of what they said to one another and could guess the rest; I was present when she taught Rolf to pray and when he distracted her with the stories I had told him in a thousand and one nights beneath the white mosquito netting of our bed.

When darkness came on the second day, Rolf tried to sing Azucena to sleep with old Austrian folk songs he had learned from his mother, but she was far beyond sleep. They spent most of the night talking, each in a stupor of exhaustion and hunger and shaking with cold. That night, imperceptibly, the unyielding floodgates that had contained Rolf Carlé's past for so many years began to open, and the torrent of all that had lain hidden in the deepest and most secret layers of memory poured out, leveling before it the obstacles that had blocked his consciousness for so long. He could not tell it all to Azucena; she perhaps did not know there was a world beyond the sea or time previous to her own; she was not capable of imagining Europe in the years of the war. So he could not tell her of defeat, nor of the afternoon the Russians had led them to the concentration camp to bury prisoners dead from starvation. Why should he describe to her how the naked bodies piled like a mountain of firewood resembled fragile china? How could he tell this dying child about ovens and gallows? Nor did he mention the night that he had seen his mother naked, shod in stiletto-heeled red boots, sobbing with humiliation. There was much he did not tell, but in those hours he relived for the first time all the things his mind had tried to erase. Azucena had surrendered her fear to him and so, without wishing it, had obliged Rolf to confront his own. There, beside that hellhole of mud, it was impossible for Rolf to flee from himself any longer, and the **visceral** terror he had lived as a boy suddenly invaded him. He reverted to the years when he was the age of Azucena and younger, and, like her, found himself trapped in a pit without escape, buried in life, his head barely above ground; he saw before his eyes the boots and legs of his father, who had

visceral:
deep; instinctive

removed his belt and was whipping it in the air with the neverforgotten hiss of a viper coiled to strike. Sorrow flooded through him, intact and precise, as if it had lain always in his mind, waiting. He was once again in the armoire[4] where his father locked him to punish him for imagined misbehavior, there where for eternal hours he had crouched with his eyes closed, not to see the darkness, with his hands over his ears to shut out the beating of his heart, trembling, huddled like a cornered animal. Wandering in the mist of his memories he found his sister, Katharina, a sweet, retarded child who spent her life hiding, with the hope that her father would forget the disgrace of her having been born. With Katharina, Rolf crawled beneath the dining room table, and with her hid there under the long white tablecloth, two children forever embraced, alert to footsteps and voices. Katharina's scent melded with his own sweat, with aromas of cooking, garlic, soup, freshly baked bread, and the unexpected odor of **putrescent** clay. His sister's hand in his, her frightened breathing, her silk hair against his cheek, the candid gaze of the eyes. Katharina . . . Katharina materialized before him, floating on the air like a flag, clothed in the white tablecloth, now a winding sheet, and at last he could weep for her death and for the guilt of having abandoned her. He understood then that all his exploits as a reporter, the feats that had won him such recognition and fame, were merely an attempt to keep his most ancient fears at bay, a stratagem for taking refuge behind a lens to test whether reality was more tolerable from that perspective. He took excessive risks as an exercise of courage, training by day to conquer the monsters that tormented him by night. But he had to come face to face with the moment of truth; he could not continue to escape his past. He was Azucena; he was buried in the clayey mud; his terror was not the distant emotion of an almost forgotten childhood, it was a claw sunk in his throat. In the flush of his tears he saw his mother, dressed in black and clutching her imitation-crocodile pocketbook to her bosom, just as he had last seen her on the dock when she had come to put him on the boat to South America. She had not come to dry his tears, but to tell him to pick up a shovel: the war was over and now they must bury the dead.

"Don't cry. I don't hurt anymore. I'm fine," Azucena said when dawn came.

"I'm not crying for you," Rolf Carlé smiled. "I'm crying for myself. I hurt all over."

• • • • •

---

4 **armoire:** a kind of cupboard or wardrobe

The third day in the valley of the cataclysm began with a pale light filtering through storm clouds. The president of the republic visited the area in his tailored safari jacket to confirm that this was the worst catastrophe of the century; the country was in mourning; sister nations had offered aid; he had ordered a state of siege; the armed forces would be merciless; anyone caught stealing or committing other offenses would be shot on sight. He added that it was impossible to remove all the corpses or count the thousands who had disappeared; the entire valley would be declared holy ground, and bishops would come to celebrate a solemn mass for the souls of the victims. He went to the army field tents to offer relief in the form of vague promises to crowds of the rescued, then to the improvised hospital to offer a word of encouragement to doctors and nurses worn down from so many hours of **tribulations**. Then he asked to be taken to see Azucena, the little girl the whole world had seen. He waved to her with a limp statesman's hand, and microphones recorded his emotional voice and paternal tone as he told her that her courage had served as an example to the nation. Rolf Carlé interrupted to ask for a pump, and the president assured him that he personally would attend to the matter. I caught a glimpse of Rolf for a few seconds kneeling beside the mud pit. On the evening news broadcast, he was still in the same position; and I, glued to the screen like a fortuneteller to her crystal ball, could tell that something fundamental had changed in him. I knew somehow that during the night his defenses had crumbled and he had given in to grief; finally he was vulnerable. The girl had touched a part of him that he himself had no access to, a part he had never shared with me. Rolf had wanted to console her, but it was Azucena who had given him consolation.

> tribulations:
> great sufferings;
> afflictions

I recognized the precise moment at which Rolf gave up the fight and surrendered to the torture of watching the girl die. I was with them, three days and two nights, spying on them from the other side of life. I was there when she told him that in all her thirteen years no boy had ever loved her and that it was a pity to leave this world without knowing love. Rolf assured her that he loved her more than he could ever love anyone, more than he loved his mother, more than his sister, more than all the women who had slept in his arms, more than he loved me, his life companion, who would have given anything to be trapped in that well in her place, who would have exchanged her life for Azucena's, and I watched as he leaned down to kiss her poor forehead, consumed by a sweet, sad emotion he could not name. I felt how in that instant both were saved from despair, how they were freed from the clay, how they rose above the vultures and helicopters, how together they flew above the vast swamp of corruption and laments. How, finally, they were able to accept death. Rolf Carlé prayed in silence that she would die quickly, because such pain cannot be borne.

By then I had obtained a pump and was in touch with a general who had agreed to ship it the next morning on a military cargo plane. But on the night of that third day, beneath the unblinking focus of quartz lamps and the lens of a hundred cameras, Azucena gave up, her eyes locked with those of the friend who had sustained her to the end. Rolf Carlé removed the life buoy, closed her eyelids, held her to his chest for a few moments, and then let her go. She sank slowly, a flower in the mud.

•••••

You are back with me, but you are not the same man. I often accompany you to the station, and we watch the videos of Azucena again; you study them intently, looking for something you could have done to save her, something you did not think of in time. Or maybe you study them to see yourself as if in a mirror, naked. Your cameras lie forgotten in a closet; you do not write or sing; you sit long hours before the window, staring at the mountains. Beside you, I wait for you to complete the voyage into yourself, for the old wounds to heal. I know that when you return from your nightmares, we shall again walk hand in hand, as before.

Translated by Margaret Sayers Peden

After You Read

Critical Reading

1. In this story, the tension builds and builds until the story reaches **catharsis**. Catharsis is the point in the story when emotions are released or purged. This is often triggered by the death or downfall of the protagonist or hero of the story. Identify the event that is the catharsis of the story. Then analyze what emotions are brought about through this catharsis.

2. The plot of this story is an example of *in media res*. How does this affect the **mood** of the story?

3. Cite a passage of vivid description, noting the **sensory details** (sight, sound, smell, taste, or touch) and **figurative language** (similes, metaphors, personification). Then describe how these sensory details most likely affect readers.

Literary Lens: Character

Analyze how the character of Rolf Carlé changes over the course of the story. Cite details from the story that reveal the character, including dialogue, action, and imagery.

Story	Details about Rolf Carlé	What this reveals about Rolf Carlé
Beginning of the story (the first night)		
Middle of the story (after the first night until the third day when Rolf speaks to the president)		
End of the story (after Rolf "gave up the fight")		

Focus on Research: Write an Outline

Part of the process of drafting a research paper is writing an outline for the report. Consider how you might write an outline for a report about types of natural disasters, such as the one depicted in this story. Include at least three main points (I, II, III) in your outline and multiple subpoints (A, B, C). As part of your outline, write a general thesis statement.

The Literature of
Peru

Background

The region now known as Peru has one of the longest histories of civilization of any country, with the earliest evidence of human societies dating as far back as 9000 B.C.E. The capital of the Incan Empire, Cuzco, is located in southern Peru. After being conquered by Spanish colonizers, many of the indigenous populations of Peru collapsed. European colonizers brought enslaved people from Africa to Peru, and over time immigrants came to Peru from Europe and Asia, including England, France, Germany, Italy, China, and Japan. Today, Peru is a multiethnic nation of more than 32 million people.

Peruvian literature has a long history, rooted in the oral tradition of its indigenous civilizations. Now, the literature of Peru is influenced by a blend of styles, from European romanticism to Spanish *costumbrismo* and the *indigenismo* movement, which asserts the unique cultural and literary traditions and styles of the indigenous Peruvian people.

Peru and the United States

Several Peruvian authors have influenced literature in the United States and around the world. Cesar Vallejo, a Peruvian poet (1892–1938), is considered by many literary critics to be one of the greatest and most innovative poets. He has been described as "the greatest twentieth-century poet in any language." Mario Vargas Llosa, a leading Peruvian author and recipient of the 2010 Nobel Prize in Literature, is a leading author of the Latin American Boom, a literary movement of the 1960s and 1970s that introduced Latin American novelists to the world. Llosa lists U.S. novelist William Faulkner as an author who greatly influenced his writing.

Research: Use Literary Texts

Although many of Llosa's books focus on Peruvian society, some of his work expands to other parts of the world; for example, his book *The Feast of the Goat* is set in the Dominican Republic in the years following the assassination of a dictator. When Llosa was awarded the Nobel Prize in 2010, the Nobel Prize committee noted his commitment to portraying societal power struggles and the effects of an "individual's resistance" and "revolt." With a partner, develop a research plan to explore the Ucharaccay Massacre in Peru in 1983 and Llosa's efforts to investigate the massacre.

from
The Feast of the Goat

Mario Vargas Llosa

Before You Read

Mario Vargas Llosa (1936–) is an internationally recognized Peruvian author who writes prolifically across multiple genres, including novels and politically focused journalism. Much of his work focuses on entrenched social and political power structures and the effect of resistance and revolution. His skilled development of these themes earned him the Nobel Prize in Literature in 2010.

World Context

Llosa can be considered a part of the Latin American Boom, a literary movement that occurred during the 1960s and 1970s. This movement can be characterized as part of the larger Modernist movement, and they share many of the same aesthetics. But Latin American Boom authors were noted for producing work with a particularly edgy political focus, often questioning national and international politics and exploring national and political identity. Over the span of his career, Llosa's work has at times been considered Modernist and at other times Postmodernist.

   In *The Feast of the Goat,* Llosa explores political issues. The book concerns the effects of the assassination of a dictator in the Dominican Republic. Urania, the protagonist for much of the book, must face memories regarding the dictatorship and her now-ailing father's past involvement. This novel was inspired, in part, by the historical dictatorial regime in the Dominican Republic led by Rafael Trujillo, commonly called *El Jefe* or "the boss," who ruled the country from 1930 until his assassination in 1961. Trujillo's regime was known as one of the most violent eras in the history of the Dominican Republic.

LITERARY LENS A **flashback** can help to reveal characters. What is revealed about the characters through the use of flashback in this excerpt?

U rania. Her parents had done her no favor; her name suggested a planet, a mineral, anything but the slender, fine-featured woman with burnished skin and large, dark, rather sad eyes who looked back at her from the mirror. Urania! What an idea for a name. Fortunately nobody called her that anymore; now it was Uri, Miss Cabral, Ms. Cabral, Dr. Cabral. As far as she could remember, after she left Santo Domingo[1] (or Ciudad Trujillo—when she left they had not yet restored the old name to the capital city), no one in Adrian, or Boston, or Washington, D.C., or New York had called her Urania as they did at home at the Santo Domingo Academy, where the sisters and her classmates pronounced with absolute correctness the ridiculous name inflicted on her at birth. Was it his idea or hers? Too late to find out, my girl; your mother was in heaven and your father condemned to a living death. You'll never know. Urania! As absurd as insulting old Santo Domingo de Guzmán[2] by calling it Ciudad[3] Trujillo.[4] Could that have been her father's idea too?

She waits for the sea to become visible through the window of her room on the ninth floor of the Hotel Jaragua, and at last she sees it. The darkness fades in a few seconds and the brilliant blue of the horizon quickly intensifies, beginning the spectacle she has been anticipating since she woke at four in spite of the pill she had taken, breaking her rule against sedatives. The dark blue surface of the ocean, marked by streaks of foam, extends to a **leaden** sky at the remote line of the horizon, while here, at the shore, it breaks in resounding, whitecapped waves against the Seal Walk, the Malecón,[5] where she can make out sections of the broad road through the palms and almond trees that line it. Back then, the Hotel Jaragua faced the Malecón directly. Now it's to the side. Her memory brings back the image—was that the day?—of the little girl holding her father's hand as they entered the hotel restaurant so the two of them could have lunch together. They were given a table next to the window, and through the sheer lace curtains Uranita could see the spacious garden and the pool with its diving boards and swimmers. In the Patio Español, surrounded by glazed tiles and flowerpots filled with carnations, an orchestra was playing merengues. Was that the day? "No," she says aloud. The Jaragua of those days had been torn down and replaced by this massive shocking-pink structure that had surprised her so much when she arrived in Santo Domingo three days ago.

leaden: the color of lead; dull gray

---

1 **Santo Domingo:** the capital city in the Dominican Republic
2 **Santo Domingo de Guzmán:** the official name for the city of Santo Domingo
3 **Cuidad:** a Spanish word meaning "city"
4 **Trujillo:** a reference to the historic Dominican Republic dictator, Rafael Trujillo
5 **Malecón:** a Spanish word for a stone pier or jetty along a waterfront

Were you right to come back? You'll be sorry, Urania. Wasting a week's vacation, when you never had time to visit all the cities, regions, countries you would have liked to see—the mountain ranges and snow-covered lakes of Alaska, for instance—returning to the island you swore you'd never set foot on again. A symptom of decline? The **sentimentality** of age? Curiosity, nothing more. To prove to yourself you can walk along the streets of this city that is no longer yours, travel through this foreign country and not have it provoke sadness, **nostalgia**, hatred, bitterness, rage in you. Or have you come to confront the ruin of your father? To learn what effect seeing him has on you, after so many years. A shudder runs the length of her body. Urania, Urania! What if after all these years you discover that behind your determined, disciplined mind, **impervious** to discouragement, behind the fortress admired and envied by others, you have a tender, timid, wounded, sentimental heart?

She bursts into laughter. Enough foolishness, my girl.

She puts on sneakers, slacks, a tailored blouse, and pulls back her hair. She drinks a glass of cold water and is about to turn on the television to watch CNN but changes her mind. She remains at the window, looking at the ocean, the Malecón, and then, turning her head, at the city's forest of roofs, towers, domes, belfries, and treetops. It's grown so much! When you left, in 1961, it sheltered three hundred thousand souls. More than a million now. It has filled up with neighborhoods, avenues, parks, hotels. The night before, she felt like a foreigner as she drove a rented car past the condominiums in Bella Vista, and the immense El Mirador Park, where there were as many joggers as in Central Park. When she was a girl, the city ended at the Hotel El Embajador; beyond that point, it was all farms and fields. The Country Club, where her father took her on Sundays to swim in the pool, was surrounded by open countryside, not the asphalt, houses, and streetlights that are there now.

But the colonial city has not been modernized, and neither has Gazcue, her neighborhood. And she is absolutely certain her house has hardly changed at all. It must be the same, with its small garden, old mango tree, and the flamboyán with red flowers bending over the terrace where they used to have lunch outdoors on weekends; the sloping roof and the little balcony outside her bedroom, where she would go to wait for her cousins Lucinda and Manolita, and, during the last year, 1961, spy on the boy who rode past on his bicycle, watching her out of the corner of his eye and not daring to speak. Would it be the same inside? The Austrian clock that sounded the hours had Gothic numerals and a hunting scene. Would her

sentimentality: state of having or expressing strong feelings of love, sadness, etc., in a way that may seem foolish or excessive

nostalgia: wistful yearning for the past

impervious: not capable of being affected or harmed

father be the same? No. You've seen him failing in the photos sent to you every few months or years by Aunt Adelina and other relatives who continued to write even though you never answered their letters.

She drops into an armchair. The rising sun penetrates to the center of the city; the dome of the National Palace and its pale **ochre** walls sparkle gently under a curve of blue. Go now, soon the heat will be unbearable. She closes her eyes, overcome by a rare **inertia**, for she was accustomed to always being active and not wasting time in what, since her return to Dominican soil, has occupied her day and night: remembering. "This daughter of mine is always working, she even repeats her lessons when she's asleep." That's what Senator Agustín Cabral, Minister Cabral, Egghead Cabral used to say about you when he boasted to his friends about the girl who won all the prizes, the student the sisters always held up as an example. Did he boast to the Chief about Uranita's scholarly achievements? "I'd like so much for you to know her, she has won the Prize for Excellence every year since she enrolled at Santo Domingo. It would make her so happy to meet you and shake your hand. Uranita prays every night for God to protect that iron health of yours. And for Doña Julia and Doña Maria as well. Do us this honor. The most loyal of your dogs asks, begs, implores you. You can't refuse: receive her. Excellency! Chief!"

Do you despise him? Do you hate him? Still? "Not anymore," she says aloud. You wouldn't have come back if the **rancor** were still sizzling, the wound still bleeding, the deception still crushing her, poisoning her, the way it did in your youth, when studying and working became an obsessive defense against remembering. Back then you did hate him. With every atom of your being, with all the thought and feeling your body could hold. You wanted him to suffer misfortunes, diseases, accidents. God granted your wish, Urania. Or rather, the devil did. Isn't it enough that the cerebral hemorrhage brought him a living death? A sweet revenge that he has spent the last ten years in a wheelchair, not walking or talking, depending on a nurse to eat, lie down, dress, undress, trim his nails, shave, urinate, defecate? Do you feel avenged? "No."

She drinks a second glass of water and goes out. . . .

ochre:
pale yellow

inertia:
sluggishness, lack of desire to move

rancor:
bitter ill will

After You Read

Critical Reading

1. The **theme** of a work can sometimes be expressed in a short statement or saying. Analyze the main message in *The Feast of the Goat* and then write this theme as a brief statement.

2. The main character, Urania, faces both **internal** and **external conflicts**. Identify one example of each type of conflict that she faces. Explain why you consider the conflicts to be internal or external and support your explanation with details from the excerpt.

3. Analyze the **point of view**. Would you consider this a **third-person limited point of view** or a **third-person omniscient point of view**? Support your analysis with details from the text.

Literary Lens: Flashback

Identify two or more **flashbacks** in the excerpt. Then consider what each flashback reveals about the character Urania.

Flashback	First sentence of flashback and page number	What this reveals about Urania
1st flashback		
2nd flashback		
3rd flashback		

Focus on Research: Use a Variety of Methods to Take Notes

Conduct research to answer the following question: Does *The Feast of the Goat* contain techniques or themes that could be considered Modernism or Postmodernism? As you conduct this research, use a variety of methods to take notes. There are many ways to take notes; for example, you can take notes on note cards, type notes into a computer file, or record them in a notebook. Remember that a note may be a paraphrase of the text or a direct quotation. Record key source information with each note, including author, title, page number, and website name or link.

The Americas

Unit Review

Key Ideas and Details

1. "I am a citizen of the world" (page 67) is a key line in the story "When Greek Meets Greek." What does this line mean to you? How does it fit the events of this story or any other selection in this unit? Cite evidence from the texts to support your position.

Craft and Structure

2. Through an Internet or library search, find a concise definition of **magic realism.** Then select an example of magic realism from this unit. Citing two or three passages, illustrate how the selection manifests (or fails to manifest) the attributes of magic realism.

3. **Tone** is the author's attitude toward the subject he or she is writing about. For example, a writer may express ridicule, longing, or pessimism through a piece of writing. Review one of the selections in this unit and decide on its overall tone. Select two or three passages that you feel best express the author's attitude and support your claim with examples.

4. Many of the poems in this unit share the theme of love—love of self, love of family, love of country, and love of a significant other. Select your favorite poem from the unit. Then decide what kind of love is addressed in your selected poem and list the sensory details the poet uses to evoke this powerful emotion.

5. Rewrite a part of "You Don't Hear Dogs Barking" from a different point of view. You might choose to rewrite this part through the eyes of the son, from the point of view of a stranger observing the father carrying his son across the Mexican landscape at night, or from the perspective of a doctor called to the scene at the end. In addition to choosing your point of view, you can also choose your style: you may choose to fill in facts and details or, like Rulfo, you may choose to keep the story mysterious and not provide clear answers.

Integration of Knowledge and Ideas

6. In the short story "And of Clay Are We Created," Azucena becomes a symbol of the disaster. Such a comparison is called a **synecdoche.** A synecdoche is a type of metaphor in which a part (one victim) represents a larger whole (a catastrophe). Consider a real or imagined catastrophic event. Then imagine a single person who, like Azucena, comes to represent the event. Write a short description or narrative based on your situation and character.

7. Gabriela Mistral believed that artists are to society what the soul is to the individual. Extend this idea in a short essay of your own, answering the question "What functions or roles do artists serve in society?"

Research Projects

Learning Through Book Reviews

Pick a text from this unit that you would like to learn more about. Then conduct research to find three or more book reviews about this text. Read the book reviews and then write two to three sentences sharing what you learned about your chosen text from the book reviews.

Multimedia Project

Find out more about the Mexican celebration known as El Día de Muertos—Day of the Dead. On this day, calaveras—whimsical paper-maché or sugar skulls—spring up everywhere, mocking the dead and satirizing the living. Conduct research about El Día de Muertos. Find a variety of sources including printed text (articles, books, encyclopedia entries, and more), digital sources (websites), images (photos, paintings, and videos), and music. Create a digital presentation that explains the history and modern influence of the holiday.

Publish Written Works

One scholar described the Mayan epic the *Popol Vuh* as "mythistory." The *Popol Vuh* deals with Mayan myths, genealogies, and everyday life. In it, history and myth are not separate but are linked together in a storytelling tradition. Conduct research on the *Popol Vuh*. Then write and publish your research. As part of publishing your research, consider creating a Venn diagram to compare and contrast mythistory with magic realism.

Revising to Improve Organization

Choose three authors from the unit (each author from a different country) and then research each author's life and work. After drafting your research report, focus on revising it to improve organization. You might organize your report by addressing each author in a separate section. Or you might organize your report by addressing the lives of all the authors in one section and the work of all the authors in another section. Ask a classmate to read your paper and offer feedback on the effectiveness of the organization.

Cultural Reflection

Identify a few characters you encountered in this unit who opened your eyes to a new way of seeing the world. Write five to ten sentences identifying these characters and explaining how these characters altered your way of viewing the world. Then revise what you have written to make sure that all of your details are focused on your topic. As you revise your draft, ask yourself questions such as *Does this detail identify an author in the unit?* and *Does this detail clearly state how this author changed my viewpoint?*

UNIT TWO

The Literature of Europe

Petra S. Fiero
Professor of German, Western Washington University,
Bellingham, Washington

In the 20th century, Europe was ravaged by two world wars, saw the rise and fall of Fascism and Communism, and began to live with the threat of the atomic bomb. The impact of these events on all areas of human life, including literature, was enormous.

A movement called *modernism* emerged in the first decades of the 20th century, its representatives seeking a radical break with traditional Western ideas. After the catastrophe of World War I (1914–18) and the collapse of European monarchies, many writers felt they could no longer describe the world's harsh new realities in the time-honored ways. Modernist literature substitutes the traditional techniques of storytelling with innovations such as stream of consciousness, fragmentation, and unconventional ways of representing characters.

The term *postmodernism* is often applied to literature and art after World War II (1939–45). Influences on literature included the experience of the Holocaust; the rapid development of technology, including nuclear weapons; and the continuing spoilage of the natural environment. These things eroded Western morale to a greater degree than the first war had done. Works of postmodern literature blend literary genres and mix the serious with the playful, resisting classification along traditional lines.

The literature of the absurd, one branch of postmodern writing, depicts a world without continuity or meaning. Absurdist writers often use black humor, combining the genres of tragedy and comedy to convey this attitude.

Not all literary works since World War II can be characterized as postmodern. The aim of neorealism, especially prominent in

Italy, was to describe the human condition authentically. Neorealistic works often convey a tragic view of human existence, marked by solitude and alienation.

The 1950s signaled an era of high hopes and deep disappointments. Writers began to attack what they perceived as the materialism, complacency, and shabby values of the middle class. The 1960s saw renewed political and social concern among the young, prompted by the Vietnam War, the emergence of the "third world," and the rise in Western democracies of both liberating and reactionary factions. Well into the 1990s, many postwar writers concentrated on their own time period and its conditions. The contemporary European reading public expects writers to confront the problems of society, not sit in the ivory tower of art.

In Eastern Europe, World War II and its aftermath made a deep impact. The euphoria of liberation was soon followed by radical changes in the political and social structure. Communist regimes were established, with the Cold War well under way by mid-century. The Stalinist doctrine of socialist realism demanded uncritical optimism about progress toward a "classless society." These governments insisted that writers create purely positive heroes who were healthy and active, never questioning their roles in society. This constituted a sharp break with earlier literature, in which protagonists were generally male, alienated from society, and unable to find a useful purpose in life. Many Eastern European writers had trouble adhering to this formula and openly resisted it; as a result, their work was censored and suppressed, some were imprisoned, and others were sent into exile.

Mikhail Gorbachev, president of the former Soviet Union, introduced the policies of *glasnost* (openness) and *perestroika* (reconstruction) in the early '90s, freeing up the Communist societies of Eastern Europe and leading to the demise of Soviet-style communism. Previously suppressed books and new works of long-silenced authors could now be published. The end of the Cold War in the late 1980s brought Eastern and Western European countries much closer together. In the larger picture, how an increasingly global economy and the threat of worldwide terrorism will affect Europe remains to be seen. What is certain is that human tragedy and comedy will continue to shape European literature.

Literary Map of
Europe

SWEDEN
Tomas Tranströmer

ENGLAND
Stevie Smith
T. S. Eliot
W. H. Auden
Graham Greene

GERMANY
Heinrich Böll

CZECH REPUBLIC
Karel Čapek

IRELAND
Frank O'Connor
Seamus Heaney

WALES
Dylan Thomas

FRANCE
Eugène Ionesco

SPAIN
Federico García Lorca

ITALY
Dante Alighieri
Alberto Moravia
Italo Calvino

POLAND

Wislawa Szymborska
Czesław Miłosz
Olga Tokarczuk

REPUBLIC OF ABKHAZIA

Fazil Iskander

RUSSIA

Boris Pasternak
Andrei Voznesensky

A European Classic
The Divine Comedy

Background

At the beginning of *The Divine Comedy*, Dante meets the soul who will be his guide through hell and purgatory—the Roman poet Virgil (70–19 B.C.E.). Virgil's masterpiece was the *Aeneid*, a legendary account of the origins of Rome. The *Aeneid* became Rome's national epic. By choosing Virgil as a guide, the poet Dante is claiming a similar ambition—to capture the essence of the Italy of his time.

Soon after *The Divine Comedy* was completed, Dante's contemporaries acknowledged his success. They recognized that Dante had created a masterpiece that would become Italy's defining epic. In the centuries following its publication, the poem's influence has extended far beyond Italy. Aside from the writings of Shakespeare and Cervantes, few works are referred to as often in Western culture as *The Divine Comedy*. Characters and places from Dante's world have even found their way into computer and video games.

Dante and the United States

Many American poets have translated all or parts of *The Divine Comedy* into English. The revered poet Henry Wadsworth Longfellow (1807–1882) was the first American to do so. Longfellow assembled a group of notable American literary figures called the "Dante Club" to help him in this work.

The Dante Club was also the name of a bestselling murder mystery by Matthew Pearl published in 2003. In it, Longfellow and his colleagues notice eerie similarities between an ongoing series of murders and the punishments suffered in Dante's *Inferno*. The members of the Dante Club set out to find the killer.

Research: Use General Reference Works

Use a general reference work, either online or in print, to find a summary of the ways *The Divine Comedy* has found its way into other works of literature, music, art, and popular culture. As a result of that research, choose one of the other works that seems especially interesting. Write a research plan you could follow to learn more about that work and to analyze how the creator drew on and transformed the source material in Dante's original.

from The Divine Comedy

Dante Alighieri

Before You Read

Dante Alighieri (1265–1321) was born in the Italian city of Florence. He studied poetry and Latin literature and as a young man joined in the political battles in his city. When his faction lost, Dante was sentenced to death and banished from Florence. He spent the last two decades of his life living in various Italian cities. In 1312, he began writing an allegorical poem about a spiritual journey. The lead character, named Dante, starts his travels in hell, moves through purgatory, and ends in heaven. The entire work, known as *The Divine Comedy*, is divided into three volumes: *Inferno*, *Purgatorio*, and *Paradiso*. Each volume is divided into thirty-three sections, or cantos. *The Divine Comedy* is Dante's most famous work, but his poetry, especially his love sonnets, are also well known.

The following excerpt is from the beginning of *The Divine Comedy*. Dante meets Virgil, the ancient Roman poet, who volunteers to guide him through the first two realms.

World Context

Like other European writers and scholars of his time, Dante often wrote in Latin. However, he was one of the first to also write in the dialect of his region, which over time became the basis for the language today known as Italian.

 LITERARY LENS This passage is from a translation done in verse by Michael Palma. It uses the same triple-**rhyme scheme** that Dante used in the original. Scan the first dozen lines to determine the pattern. As you read, consider what effect the pattern may have on the poem's meaning.

M idway through the journey of our life, I found
    myself in a dark wood, for I had strayed
    from the straight pathway to this tangled ground.
How hard it is to tell of, overlaid
    with harsh and savage growth, so wild and raw   5
    the thought of it still makes me feel afraid.

Death scarce could be more bitter. But to draw
    the lessons of the good that came my way,
    I will describe the other things I saw.
Just how I entered there I cannot say,   10
    so full of sleep when I began to veer
    that I did not see that I had gone astray
from the one true path. But once I had drawn near
    the bottom of a hill at the far remove
    of the valley that had pierced my heart with fear,   15

mantled: covered

I saw its shoulders **mantled** from above
    by the warm rays of the planet that gives light
    to guide our steps, wherever we may rove.
At least I felt some calming of the fright
    that had allowed the lake of my heart no rest   20
    while I endured the long and piteous night.
And as a drowning man with heaving chest
    escapes the current and, once safe on shore,
    turns back to see the dangers he has passed,
so too my mind, still lost in flight, once more   25
    turned back to see the passage that had never
    let anyone escape alive before.
I paused to let my weary limbs recover,
    and then began to climb the lone hillside,
    my fixed foot always lower than the other.   30
But I had hardly started when I spied

lithe: able to move with effortless grace

    a leopard in my pathway, **lithe** and fleet,
    all covered with a sleek and spotted hide.
And as I faced it, it would not retreat,
    but paced before me and so blocked my way   35
    that more than once I had to turn my feet
to retrace my steps. It was the break of day,
    the sun was mounting in the morning sky

array: an imposing arrangement of elements

    with the same stars as when that whole **array**
of lovely things was first given movement by   40
    divine love. The sweet season of the year
    and the hour made me think that I might try
to evade that bright-skinned beast as it came near,
    but then I felt my good hopes quickly fade
    and in an instant I was numbed with fear   45

Dante and Virgil

to see a lion in my path that made
   straight for me, head held high and **ravenous,**
   and seemed to make the very air afraid.
And a she-wolf too, that in its leanness was
   laden with every craving. Those who seek   50
   fulfillment there find only wretchedness.
The sight of this one made me feel so weak,
   so overcome with dread, that instantly
   I lost all hopes of climbing to the peak.
As a man is eager in prosperity   55
   but when time brings him losses can be found
   giving way to weeping and to misery,
so did I feel as the she-wolf pressed me round
   so relentlessly that bit by bit I stepped
   back where the sun is mute on the low ground.   60
And as I drove myself into the depth,

   a shape was offered to my vision, **wan**
   as if from a long silence it had kept.
Seeing him in that great desert, I began
   to call out *"Miserere*[1]—on me," I cried,   65

   "whatever you are, a **shade** or a solid man!"
"Not man, although I was a man," he replied.
   "My parents were both Mantuans.[2] I descend
   from those of Lombardy[3] on either side.
I was born *sub Julio,*[4] at the latter end.   70
   Under the good Augustus[5] I lived in Rome
   in the days when false and lying gods still reigned.
I was a poet, and I sang of him,
   Anchises' righteous son,[6] who sailed from Troy[7]
   after the burning of proud Ilium.[8]   75

---

1 *Miserere:* a Latin expression meaning "have mercy"
2 **Mantuans:** people from Mantua, a city in what is now northern Italy
3 **Lombardy:** a region in what is now northern Italy
4 *sub Julio:* before the reign of Julius Caesar; the speaker was born in 70 B.C.
5 **Augustus:** the ruler of Rome, 27 B.C. to A.D. 14
6 **Anchises:** a prince in the city of Troy whose son was Aeneas
7 **Troy:** a city in what is now Turkey
8 **Ilium:** another name for Troy

But why do you turn back toward trouble? Why
    do you not ascend the delectable mount instead,
    the origin and cause of every joy?"
"Are you that Virgil then, that fountainhead
    that spills such a mighty stream of eloquence?"   80
    I said this with a shame-filled brow, and said:
"Light and glory of all poets, may my intense
    love and long study of your poetry
    avail me now for my deliverance.
You are my master, my authority,   85
    for it is from you alone that I learned to write
    in the noble style that has so honored me.
You see why I have turned back from the height.
    Illustrious sage, please help me to confound
    this beast that makes my pulses shake with fright."   90
"It were best to go another way around,"
    he answered, seeing tears start from my eyes,
    "if your hope is to escape this savage ground,
because this creature that provokes our cries
    allows no man to get the best of her,   95
    but blocks each one, attacking till he dies.
Of such a vile and vicious character

and greedy appetite, she is never **sated**,	**sated:**
and when she has fed is even hungrier.	satisfied; appeased

Many the animals with whom she has mated.   100
    Her couplings—till her painful deathblow is dealt
    by the greyhound—will continue unabated.
This greyhound will not feed on land or wealth,
    but on virtue, love, and wisdom. He will be
    born in this region between felt and felt.[9]   105
He will restore low-lying Italy,
    for which Eurylaus, Turnus, the maid Camilla,
    and Nisus[10] gave their life's blood. Tirelessly
he will track the beast through every town until
    he comes at last to drive her back into   110

---

9   **between felt and felt:** This may refer to a region of Italy between the towns of
    Feltre and Montefeltro, or it may refer to the pages of a book, which were
    dried between pieces of felt.

10 **Eurylaus, Turnus, Camilla, Nisus:** characters from Virgil's *Aeneid*

that hell from which she sprang at Envy's will.
Therefore I think it would be best for you
  to follow me. I will be your guide, and I
  will lead you out of here and take you through
an eternal place where you will be greeted by   115
  the shriekings of despair and you will see
  ancient tormented spirits as they cry
aloud at the second death. Then you will be
  with those who are content within the fire,
  for they hope to join the blest eventually.   120
You will see those blest, if that is your desire,
  with a worthier soul than I. Into her hands
  I will entrust you when I can go no higher.
That emperor who presides above commands,
  since I did not heed his law, that none may gain   125
  entrance through me to where his city stands.
His rule is everywhere. There is his reign,
  his city, and his throne! Happy are they
  whom he chooses to inhabit that domain!"
"Poet," I said to him, "so that I may   130
  escape this harm and worse that may await,
  in the name of that God you never knew, I pray
you lead me out to see Saint Peter's gate
  and all those souls that you have told me of,
  who must endure their miserable state."   135
I followed him as he began to move.

After You Read

Critical Reading

1. An **allegory** is a story, poem, or picture that can be interpreted to reveal a hidden meaning, often a moral or political one. Find a part of the poem that could be taken as allegorical and analyze what deeper meaning you think it has.

2. What can you infer about the territory beyond the mountain based on the animals Dante encounters? What do you think each animal could **symbolize**? Support your answer with strong textual evidence.

3. According to Virgil, some people that Dante will see are "content within the fire." What is the meaning of that phrase in the context of the text? Why are some people content? Provide evidence to back up your viewpoint.

4. Describe the relationship between the pilgrim and Virgil. Support your answer with textual evidence.

Literary Lens: Rhyme Scheme

It is common for poetry to follow a **rhyme scheme.** *The Divine Comedy* is written in a rhyme scheme called terza rima, or in three-line stanzas that follow the pattern aba, bcb, cdc, etc. This work by Dante, originally written in Italian, is the first known poem in terza rima form. In his English translation, Michael Palma maintained the terza rima form. Review the selection. As you review, pay close attention to the rhyme scheme. Notice the aba, bcb, cdc pattern of the lines. Then choose nine lines (three stanzas) and analyze the effects of the rhyme scheme. Next, write your own three stanzas in terza rima form, as if you are creating a translation of the translation.

Focus on Research: Use General and Specific References

There are two major categories of reference materials: general and subject specific. General reference sources include all subjects and present overviews. Examples include encyclopedias, almanacs, and *Book Review Digest.* Specific reference sources provide in-depth coverage on certain topics, for example, *Encyclopedia of World Art, Political Reference Almanac,* and *Children's Literature Review.* Find one of each type of source that contains information about Dante and compare the type of information you get from each.

The Literature of
Ireland

Background

From the 12th century to the mid-20th century, Ireland's political history was intertwined with that of its more powerful neighbor, England. Irish literature often reflected this relationship. Many of Ireland's greatest writers have protested against England's dominant influence in Ireland.

Resistance to England reached a peak in the late 19th century, and it sparked a literary movement known as the Irish Renaissance. A key figure of this movement was Lady Augusta Gregory (1852–1932), a playwright who founded Dublin's Abbey Theatre, where many original Irish plays premiered. In her effort to celebrate Irish culture, Lady Gregory worked closely with the Nobel Prize-winning poet William Butler Yeats (1865–1939), whose best-known poems include "The Second Coming" and "Sailing to Byzantium."

Ireland and the United States

In the early 1840s, Ireland's population was around 8 million people. Then the Great Potato Famine of 1845 struck. Within a decade, more than one million people had died from malnutrition, and another million had emigrated, many to the United States.

One of these emigrants was the celebrated actor James O'Neill. His son, the playwright Eugene O'Neill (1888–1953), became one of the greatest American dramatists. Especially in his later plays, such as *Long Day's Journey Into Night* and *The Touch of a Poet*, O'Neill touched on the experience of Irish immigrants and their families. *Long Day's Journey Into Night* includes a thinly fictionalized portrait of the playwright's father, forever scarred by the poverty of his Irish childhood. *The Touch of a Poet* tragically portrays a proud but aging Irish immigrant's struggle against class prejudice in Massachusetts.

Research: Take Notes and Represent Graphically

Using at least three sources on British and Irish history, take notes on events that show the rise or decline of British influence in Ireland as well as developments in Irish literary history. Use your notes to create a timeline of Irish history that includes at least twelve entries. Include at least four dates charting British influence in Ireland and at least four dates related to Irish literary history.

First Confession[1]

Frank O'Connor

Before You Read

Michael O'Donovan (1903–1966) wrote fiction, poetry, criticism, and drama and also translated works of Gaelic literature. He used the name Frank O'Connor, possibly to create distance from his alcoholic father. He is best known for his realistic and often humorous short stories, including "My Oedipus Complex" and the more serious "Guests of the Nation." O'Connor said that in his stories he wanted to "lay bare a person's fundamental character in one moment of crisis."

World Context

About 95 percent of citizens in the Irish Republic are Catholic. After centuries of Protestant British rule, the Catholic Church came to be a powerful source of Irish national identity. It also offered spiritual comfort to a country downtrodden by colonialism and crushing poverty. To this day, Catholic ceremonies such as First Confession and First Communion are considered major events in Irish Catholic families. Even the poorest families often manage to afford the fancy white dresses customary for a girl's First Communion.

 LITERARY LENS Identify details that reveal the **historical context** of the story. Consider how this context impacts the characters and events.

All the trouble began when my grandfather died and my grandmother— my father's mother—came to live with us. Relations in the one house are a strain at the best of times, but, to make matters worse, my grandmother was a real old country woman and quite unsuited to the life in town. She had a fat, wrinkled old face, and, to Mother's great indignation, went round the house in bare feet—the boots had her crippled, she said. For dinner she had

---

1 **confession:** one of the Roman Catholic sacraments that involves church members confessing their sins to a priest and receiving forgiveness from God

a jug of porter[2] and a pot of potatoes with—sometimes—a bit of salt fish, and she poured out the potatoes on the table and ate them slowly, with great relish, using her fingers by way of a fork.

Now, girls are supposed to be **fastidious**, but I was the one who suffered most from this. Nora, my sister, just sucked up to the old woman for the penny she got every Friday out of the old-age pension, a thing I could not do. I was too honest, that was my trouble; and when I was playing with Bill Connell, the sergeant-major's son, and saw my grandmother steering up the path with a jug of porter sticking out from beneath her shawl I was **mortified**. I made excuses not to let him come into the house, because I could never be sure what she would be up to when we went in.

When Mother was at work and my grandmother made the dinner I wouldn't touch it. Nora once tried to make me, but I hid under the table from her and took the bread-knife with me for protection. Nora let on to be very indignant (she wasn't, of course, but she knew Mother saw through her, so she sided with Gran) and came after me. I lashed out at her with the bread-knife, and after that she left me alone. I stayed there till Mother came in from work and made my dinner, but when Father came in later Nora said in a shocked voice: "Oh, Dadda, do you know what Jackie did at dinnertime?" Then, of course, it all came out; Father gave me a flaking; Mother interfered, and for days after that he didn't speak to me and Mother barely spoke to Nora. And all because of that old woman! God knows, I was heart-scalded.

Then, to crown my misfortunes, I had to make my first confession and Communion.[3] It was an old woman called Ryan who prepared us for these. She was about the one age with Gran; she was well-to-do, lived in a big house on Montenotte, wore a black cloak and bonnet, and came every day to school at three o'clock when we should have been going home, and talked to us of Hell. She may have mentioned the other place as well, but that could only have been by accident, for Hell had the first place in her heart.

She lit a candle, took out a new half-crown, and offered it to the first boy who would hold one finger—only one finger!—in the flame for five minutes by the school clock. Being always very ambitious I was tempted to volunteer, but I thought it might look greedy. Then she asked were we afraid of holding one finger—only one finger!—in a little candle flame for five

---

2 **porter:** a heavy malt beer

3 **Communion:** sacrament that involves receiving bread and wine that Catholics believe become the body and blood of Christ

minutes and not afraid of burning all over in roasting hot furnaces for all eternity. "All eternity! Just think of that! A whole lifetime goes by and it's nothing, not even a drop in the ocean of your sufferings." The woman was really interesting about Hell, but my attention was all fixed on the half-crown. At the end of the lesson she put it back in her purse. It was a great disappointment; a religious woman like that, you wouldn't think she'd bother about a thing like a half-crown.

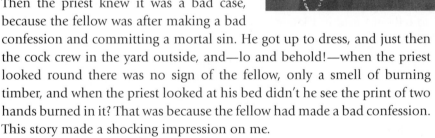

Another day she said she knew a priest who woke one night to find a fellow he didn't recognize leaning over the end of his bed. The priest was a bit frightened—naturally enough—but he asked the fellow what he wanted, and the fellow said in a deep, husky voice that he wanted to go to Confession. The priest said it was an awkward time and wouldn't it do in the morning, but the fellow said that last time he went to Confession, there was one sin he kept back, being ashamed to mention it, and now it was always on his mind. Then the priest knew it was a bad case, because the fellow was after making a bad confession and committing a mortal sin. He got up to dress, and just then the cock crew in the yard outside, and—lo and behold!—when the priest looked round there was no sign of the fellow, only a smell of burning timber, and when the priest looked at his bed didn't he see the print of two hands burned in it? That was because the fellow had made a bad confession. This story made a shocking impression on me.

But the worst of all was when she showed us how to examine our conscience. Did we take the name of the Lord, our God, in vain? Did we honor our father and our mother? (I asked her did this include grandmothers and she said it did.) Did we love our neighbor as ourselves? Did we **covet** our neighbor's goods? (I thought of the way I felt about the penny that Nora got every Friday.) I decided that, between one thing and another, I

covet:
want; desire
what belongs
to another

must have broken the whole Ten Commandments, all on account of that old woman, and so far as I could see, so long as she remained in the house I had no hope of ever doing anything else.

I was scared to death of Confession. The day the whole class went I let on to have a toothache, hoping my absence wouldn't be noticed; but at three o'clock, just as I was feeling safe, along comes a chap with a message from Mrs. Ryan that I was to go to Confession myself on Saturday and be at the chapel for Communion with the rest. To make it worse, Mother couldn't come with me and sent Nora instead.

Now, that girl had ways of tormenting me that Mother never knew of. She held my hand as we went down the hill, smiling sadly and saying how sorry she was for me, as if she were bringing me to the hospital for an operation.

"Oh, God help us!" she moaned. "Isn't it a terrible pity you weren't a good boy? Oh, Jackie, my heart bleeds for you! How will you ever think of all your sins? Don't forget you have to tell him about the time you kicked Gran on the shin."

"Lemme go!" I said, trying to drag myself free of her. "I don't want to go to Confession at all."

"But sure, you'll have to go to Confession, Jackie," she replied in the same regretful tone. "Sure, if you didn't, the parish priest would be up to the house, looking for you. 'Tisn't, God knows, that I'm not sorry for you. Do you remember the time you tried to kill me with the bread-knife under the table? And the language you used to me? I don't know what he'll do with you at all, Jackie. He might have to send you up to the Bishop."[4]

I remember thinking bitterly that she didn't know the half of what I had to tell—if I told it. I knew I couldn't tell it, and understood perfectly why the fellow in Mrs. Ryan's story made a bad confession; it seemed to me a great shame that people wouldn't stop criticizing him. I remember that steep hill down to the church, and the sunlit hillsides beyond the valley of the river, which I saw in the gaps between the houses like Adam's last glimpse of Paradise.

Then, when she had manoeuvered me down the long flight of steps to the chapel yard, Nora suddenly changed her tone. She became the raging malicious devil she really was.

---

4 **Bishop:** one of the highest-ranking members of the Roman Catholic Church

"There you are!" she said with a yelp of triumph, hurling me through the church door. "And I hope he'll give you the penitential psalms,[5] you dirty little caffler."[6]

I knew then I was lost, given up to eternal justice. The door with the colored-glass panels swung shut behind me, the sunlight went out and gave place to deep shadow, and the wind whistled outside so that the silence within seemed to crackle like ice under my feet. Nora sat in front of me by the confession box. There were a couple of old women ahead of her, and then a miserable-looking poor devil came and wedged me in at the other side, so that I couldn't escape even if I had the courage. He joined his hands and rolled his eyes in the direction of the roof, muttering aspirations[7] in an anguished tone, and I wondered had he a grandmother too. Only a grandmother could account for a fellow behaving in that heartbroken way, but he was better off than I, for he at least could go and confess his sins; while I would make a bad confession and then die in the night and be continually coming back and burning people's furniture.

Nora's turn came, and I heard the sound of something slamming, and then her voice as if butter wouldn't melt in her mouth, and then another slam, and out she came. God, the hypocrisy of women! Her eyes were lowered, her head was bowed, and her hands were joined very low down on her stomach, and she walked up the aisle to the side altar looking like a saint. You never saw such an exhibition of devotion; and I remembered the devilish malice with which she had tormented me all the way from our door, and wondered were all religious people like that, really. It was my turn now. With the fear of damnation in my soul I went in, and the confessional door closed of itself behind me.

It was pitch-dark and I couldn't see the priest or anything else. Then I really began to be frightened. In the darkness it was a matter between God

"Bless me, father, for I have sinned; this is my first confession."

and me, and He had all the odds. He knew what my intentions were before I even started; I had no chance. All I had ever been told about Confession got mixed up in my mind, and I knelt to one wall and said: "Bless me,

---

5 **penitential psalms:** verses from the biblical book of Psalms about seeking the Lord's forgiveness
6 **caffler:** Irish slang term for "idiot"
7 **aspirations:** short prayers

father, for I have sinned; this is my first confession." I waited for a few minutes, but nothing happened, so I tried it on the other wall. Nothing happened there either. He had me spotted all right.

It must have been then that I noticed the shelf at about one height with my head. It was really a place for grown-up people to rest their elbows, but in my distracted state I thought it was probably the place you were supposed to kneel. Of course, it was on the high side and not very deep, but I was always good at climbing and managed to get up all right. Staying up was the trouble. There was room only for my knees, and nothing you could get a grip on but a sort of wooden molding a bit above it. I held on to the molding and repeated the words a little louder, and this time something happened all right. A slide was slammed back; a little light entered the box, and a man's voice said: "Who's there?"

"'Tis me, father," I said for fear he mightn't see me and go away again. I couldn't see him at all. The place the voice came from was under the molding, about level with my knees, so I took a good grip of the molding and swung myself down till I saw the astonished face of a young priest looking up at me. He had to put his head on one side to see me, and I had to put mine on one side to see him, so we were more or less talking to one another upside-down. It struck me as a queer way of hearing confessions, but I didn't feel it my place to criticize.

"Bless me, father, for I have sinned; this is my first confession," I rattled off all in one breath, and swung myself down the least shade more to make it easier for him.

"What are you doing up there?" he shouted in an angry voice, and the strain the politeness was putting on my hold of the molding, and the shock of being addressed in such an uncivil tone, were too much for me. I lost my grip, tumbled, and hit the door an unmerciful wallop before I found myself flat on my back in the middle of the aisle. The people who had been waiting stood up with their mouths open. The priest opened the door of the middle box and came out, pushing his biretta back from his forehead; he looked something terrible. Then Nora came scampering down the aisle.

"Oh, you dirty little caffler!" she said. "I might have known you'd do it. I might have known you'd disgrace me. I can't leave you out of my sight for one minute."

Before I could even get to my feet to defend myself she bent down and gave me a clip across the ear. This reminded me that I was so stunned I had even forgotten to cry, so that people might think I wasn't hurt at all, when in fact I was probably maimed for life. I gave a roar out of me.

"What's all this about?" the priest hissed, getting angrier than ever and pushing Nora off me. "How dare you hit the child like that, you little **vixen**?"

vixen:
a bad-tempered
female

"But I can't do my penance with him, father," Nora cried, cocking an outraged eye up at him.

"Well, go and do it, or I'll give you some more to do," he said, giving me a hand up. "Was it coming to Confession you were, my poor man?" he asked me.

"'Twas, father," said I with a sob.

"Oh," he said respectfully, "a big hefty fellow like you must have terrible sins. Is this your first?"

"'Tis, father," said I.

"Worse and worse," he said gloomily. "The crimes of a lifetime. I don't know will I get rid of you at all today. You'd better wait now till I'm finished with these old ones. You can see by the looks of them they haven't much to tell."

"I will, father," I said with something approaching joy.

The relief of it was really enormous. Nora stuck out her tongue at me from behind his back, but I couldn't even be bothered retorting. I knew from the very moment that man opened his mouth that he was intelligent above the ordinary. When I had time to think, I saw how right I was. It only stood to reason that a fellow confessing after seven years would have more to tell than people that went every week. The crimes of a lifetime, exactly as he said. It was only what he expected, and the rest was a cackle of old women and girls with their talk of Hell, the Bishop, and the penitential psalms. That was all they knew. I started to make my examination of conscience, and barring the one bad business of my grandmother it didn't seem so bad.

The next time, the priest steered me into the confession box himself and left the shutter back the way I could see him get in and sit down at the further side of the grille from me.

"Well, now," he said, "what do they call you?"

"Jackie, father," said I.

"And what's a-trouble to you, Jackie?"

"Father," I said, feeling I might as well get it over while I had him in good humor, "I had it all arranged to kill my grandmother."

He seemed a bit shaken by that, all right, because he said nothing for quite a while.

"My goodness," he said at last, "that'd be a shocking thing to do. What put that into your head?"

"Father," I said, feeling very sorry for myself, "she's an awful woman."

"Is she?" he asked. "What way is she awful?"

"She takes porter, father," I said, knowing well from the way Mother talked of it that this was a mortal sin, and hoping it would make the priest take a more favorable view of my case.

"Oh, my!" he said, and I could see he was impressed.

"And snuff, father," said I.

"That's a bad case, sure enough, Jackie," he said.

"And she goes round in her bare feet, father," I went on in a rush of self-pity, "and she knows I don't like her, and she gives pennies to Nora and none to me, and my da sides with her and flakes me, and one night I was so heart-scalded I made up my mind I'd have to kill her."

"And what would you do with the body?" he asked with great interest.

"I was thinking I could chop that up and carry it away in a barrow I have," I said.

"Begor,[8] Jackie," he said, "do you know you're a terrible child?"

"I know, father," I said, for I was just thinking the same thing myself. "I tried to kill Nora too with a bread-knife under the table, only I missed her."

"Is that the little girl that was beating you just now?" he asked.

"'Tis, father."

"Someone will go for her with a bread-knife one day, and he won't miss her," he said rather **cryptically**. "You must have great courage. Between ourselves, there's a lot of people I'd like to do the same to but I'd never have the nerve. Hanging is an awful death."

"Is it, father?" I asked with the deepest interest—I was always very keen on[9] hanging. "Did you ever see a fellow hanged?"

"Dozens of them," he said solemnly. "And they all died roaring."

"Jay!" I said.

"Oh, a horrible death!" he said with great satisfaction. "Lots of the fellows I saw killed their grandmothers too, but they all said 'twas never worth it."

He had me there for a full ten minutes talking, and then walked out of the chapel yard with me. I was genuinely sorry to part with him, because he was the most interesting character I'd ever met in the religious line. Outside,

---

8 **Begor:** short for "begorrah," an Irish oath that stands for "by God"
9 **keen on:** interested in

after the shadow of the church, the sunlight was like a roaring of waves on a beach; it dazzled me; and when the frozen silence melted and I heard the screech of trams on the road my heart soared. I knew now I wouldn't die in the night and come back, leaving marks on my mother's furniture. It would be a great worry to her, and the poor soul had enough.

Nora was sitting on the railing, waiting for me, and she put on a very sour puss when she saw the priest with me. She was mad jealous because a priest had never come out of the church with her.

"Well," she asked coldly, after he left me, "what did he give you?"

"Three Hail Marys,"[10] I said.

"Three Hail Marys," she repeated **incredulously**. "You mustn't have told him anything."

"I told him everything," I said confidently.

"About Gran and all?"

"About Gran and all."

(All she wanted was to able to go home and say I'd made a bad confession.)

"Did you tell him you went for me with a bread-knife?" she asked with a frown.

"I did to be sure."

"And he only gave you three Hail Marys?"

"That's all."

She slowly got down from the railing with a baffled air. Clearly, this was beyond her. As we mounted the steps back to the main road she looked at me suspiciously.

"What are you sucking?" she asked.

"Bullseyes."[11]

"Was it the priest gave them to you?"

"'Twas."

"Lord God," she wailed bitterly, "some people have all the luck! 'Tis no advantage to anybody trying to be good. I might just as well be a sinner like you."

---

10 **Hail Marys:** Catholic prayers devoted to Mary, mother of Jesus
11 **Bullseyes:** a kind of hard candy

After You Read

Critical Reading

1. The **voice** of the narrator in "First Confession" is especially vivid. Use adjectives and details from the story to write a description of the narrator.

2. O'Connor represents **conflict** in his story by portraying division between characters or within a character (Jackie). Using examples from the story, explore the conflict between Jackie and his grandmother, or between Jackie and his sister Nora, or within Jackie.

3. One **theme** of this story is hypocrisy, the practice of claiming to have moral standards or beliefs that one's behavior doesn't follow. Identify at least two examples of hypocrisy and examine what effects these have on the story.

4. How did Jackie's first confession change him? Support your answer with textual evidence.

Literary Lens: Historical Context

Each character in "First Confession" has a unique relationship with and attitude toward the Catholic Church. Understanding these relationships and attitudes can illuminate the role of Catholicism in everyday Irish life.

Use the chart below to examine the relationship each character in "First Confession" has with the Catholic faith. In the third column, cite details that support your analysis of each character's views of Catholicism.

Name of character	Relationship with Catholic faith	Details that support your analysis
The narrator		
Nora		
Gran		
The priest		

Focus on Research: Organize Notes

Choose a historical event or time period in Irish history. (See page 146 for ideas.) Find both print and online sources from which to conduct research. Use a method of taking notes that works best for you, such as using paper notecards or typing notes into a computer file. With each note, include information that identifies the source, including source title, author, page numbers, or website link. Use quotation marks around any information taken directly from the source.

from Clearances

Seamus Heaney

Before You Read

Poet, translator, and essayist Seamus Heaney (1939–2013) was born and raised an Irish Catholic in predominantly Protestant Northern Ireland. He is widely regarded and sometimes called the "laureate of violence" because much of his poetry deals with religious and political bloodshed in his native country. Nevertheless, as he said upon winning the 1995 Nobel Prize in Literature, he always tried "to make space in my reckoning and imagining for the marvelous as well as for the murderous." His books of poetry include *Death of a Naturalist, Field Work,* and *The Spirit Level.* In 2000, his acclaimed translation of the Anglo-Saxon epic *Beowulf* surprised the literary world by appearing on the *New York Times* fiction best-seller list.

World Context

A recurring Irish national image, the potato, features prominently in this poem. The potato famine of the 1840s, made all the more widespread because of changes the British made in Irish farming patterns, helped stir the nationalist movement.

 LITERARY LENS As you read this poem, look for words and images that may have a **double meaning**—both a literal and a figurative meaning.

W hen all the others were away at Mass
I was all hers as we peeled potatoes.
They broke the silence, let fall one by one
Like solder weeping off the soldering iron:[1]
Cold comforts set between us, things to share   5
Gleaming in a bucket of clean water.
And again let fall. Little pleasant splashes
From each other's work would bring us to our senses.

---

1 **solder . . . soldering iron:** the substance and tool used to fuse metals

So while the parish priest at her bedside
Went hammer and tongs at the prayers for the dying   10
And some were responding and some crying
I remembered her head bent towards my head,
Her breath in mine, our fluent dipping knives—
Never closer the whole rest of our lives.

After You Read

Critical Reading

1. The potato is a **symbol** in Ireland because of its value as a food staple and as a reminder of the terrible famine in the 19th century. What symbolic value does the poet place on the potatoes in this poem?

2. Heaney is known for using nontraditional rhyme, such as **internal rhyme, assonance,** and **alliteration.** Find examples of these types of rhyme and evaluate their effects.

3. The poet shows how important peeling potatoes with his mother was by using vivid images, or word pictures. Name the **images** in the poem that you think are most powerful.

 ## Literary Lens: Double Meaning

Writers sometimes describe an image or action that has a double meaning, as Seamus Heaney does in "Clearances." The image or action may have more than one literal meaning, or it may have both a literal and a figurative, or symbolic, meaning. Use the table below to examine the double meanings in "Clearances."

Phrase from poem	One meaning	Second meaning
"peeled potatoes"		
"bring us to our senses"		
"cold comforts"		
"Her breath in mine"		

Focus on Research: Revise Writing

Read opposing views on the causes of the potato famine, especially Britain's role in it, and evaluate the evidence for each. Explain your evaluation in a paragraph. After you draft, revise your paragraph with a focus on its organizational structure, for instance, consider whether compare-contrast, cause-effect, or chronological order better suits your topic.

The Literature of
England and Wales

Background

The history of English literature reflects the history of the English language. England's oldest surviving epic poem is the 8th-century work *Beowulf*. It was written in Old English, a Germanic language also known as Anglo-Saxon. Reading it today requires as much study as learning Italian or Spanish.

In the 14th century, Geoffrey Chaucer wrote his own unfinished epic poem, *The Canterbury Tales*, in Middle English. The language had absorbed a large number of words from French. A modern English speaker trying to read a Middle English document can usually puzzle out the basic meaning; however, its unusual vowel sounds make hearing it a baffling experience.

William Shakespeare (1564–1616) wrote in Early Modern English. This is basically the English we use today, with many vocabulary changes.

Wales covers the western portion of the island of Great Britain, the island that also includes Scotland and England. Some of the oldest tales about the legendary King Arthur can be traced to Welsh writings. Today, Wales maintains its own cultural identity, although many of its authors write in English.

Great Britain and the United States

Because England and the United States have kept close cultural and language ties, many great writers have connections to both countries. For example, the Nobel Prize-winning poet T. S. Eliot (1888–1965) was born and grew up in St. Louis, Missouri, but settled in England in 1914. In his speech, Eliot cultivated an English accent, and his poetry, including "The Love Song of J. Alfred Prufrock," has a distinctly English flavor.

On the other hand, the poet W. H. Auden (1907–1973) was born and raised in England but moved to the United States in 1939. His famous poem "Funeral Blues" is read in the popular movie *Four Weddings and a Funeral*.

Research: Use the Internet

Beginning in the 18th century, British authors were great innovators in the creation of the modern novel. Many of the most important British novelists are women, ranging from Mary Shelley (1797–1851), author of *Frankenstein*, to J. K. Rowling (1965–), author of the Harry Potter books. Use online sources to list five other British women writers, and write two sentences about each.

Do Not Go Gentle into That Good Night

Dylan Thomas

Before You Read

Born in Wales, Dylan Thomas (1914–1953) was a sickly child who preferred reading on his own to attending school. He published his first book of poetry after he moved to London in 1934. Thomas also wrote short stories, film scripts, and radio plays, including the well-known *Under Milkwood*. He lived the life of the Romantic poets—drinking, brawling, and captivating audiences with public readings of his work. After a bout of heavy drinking, Thomas died of alcoholism at age 39.

World Context

Thomas's themes—birth, sex, and death—and his emotional intensity, exuberant language, and mix of surrealistic and realistic images made him a major force in 20th-century poetry. The following poem, written as his father was dying, expresses the poet's "personal religion"—a joy and rage for life.

 LITERARY LENS This poem uses a form called **villanelle**, a traditional rhyming verse that is based on a repeating couplet. Notice this rhyme scheme as you read.

Do not go gentle into that good night,
Old age should burn and rave at close of day;
Rage, rage against the dying of the light.

Though wise men at their end know dark is right,
Because their words had forked no lightning they   5
Do not go gentle into that good night.

Good men, the last wave by, crying how bright
Their frail deeds might have danced in a green bay,
Rage, rage against the dying of the light.

Wild men who caught and sang the sun in flight,   10
And learn, too late, they grieved it on its way,
Do not go gentle into that good night.

Grave men, near death, who see with blinding sight
Blind eyes could blaze like meteors and be gay,
Rage, rage against the dying of the light.   15

And you, my father, there on the sad height,
Curse, bless, me now with your fierce tears, I pray.
Do not go gentle into that good night.
Rage, rage against the dying of the light.

After You Read

Critical Reading

1. Thomas once said, "My poetry is the record of my individual struggle from darkness towards some measure of light." Analyze how light is used metaphorically in this poem.

2. What do you think is the meaning of the phrase in line 5: "Because their words had forked no lightning . . ."?

3. What lessons does the poet try to impart to all the "men" invoked in this poem? What **theme** emerges from these lessons?

Literary Lens: Villanelle

This poem is an example of a **villanelle**, a traditional rhyming verse that is based on a repeating couplet. In this case, Thomas creates a pattern based on rhymes with the words *night* and *day*.

Re-create the chart below, adding columns for the rest of the lines. In the first empty column, write the ending word of each line. In the second empty column, assign that word the letter A if it rhymes with *night* and the letter B if it rhymes with *day*. When you are done, write a few sentences explaining why you think Thomas used this structure.

Line	Ending word	A (rhymes with *night*) or B (rhymes with *day*)?
1		
2		
3		
4		
5		
6		

Focus on Research: Create a Plan for Research

Develop a research plan for an inquiry into world customs related to dying or death. Plot out the steps you would take beginning with writing questions and ending with a published five-page research report. Write out the steps you would take in chronological order, providing a few sentences of explanation with each step.

Not Waving but Drowning

Stevie Smith

Before You Read

Margaret Florence Smith (1902–1971), better known as Stevie Smith, often wrote about the most basic issues: life and death. Many of her poems were illustrated with her own drawings.

World Context

Smith's poetry defies categorization. One critic notes that Smith's verse "sometimes contains [a] disconcerting mixture of wit and seriousness. . . . , making her at once one of the most consistent and most elusive of poets." Smith's voice reflects what she herself called the "age of unrest" in which she lived.

 LITERARY LENS As you read, identify the different **voices** in the poem that represent varying points of view.

Nobody heard him, the dead man,
But still he lay moaning:
I was much further out than you thought
And not waving but drowning.

Poor chap, he always loved larking[1]   5
And now he's dead
It must have been too cold for him his heart gave way,
They said.

Oh, no no no, it was too cold always
(Still the dead one lay moaning)   10
I was much too far out all my life
And not waving but drowning.

1 larking: frolicking

After You Read

Critical Reading

1. Notice the structure the poet uses in this poem: three **quatrains** (four-line stanzas) with lines of varying length. What are the effects of using very short lines and what different effects are achieved by the longer lines?

2. Smith uses **repetition** of certain words in this poem. Find the repeated words and comment on why the poet chose to do this.

3. Do you think the main **theme** of the poem is—misunderstanding or loneliness? Support your conclusion with textual evidence.

Literary Lens: Voice

In the poem "Not Waving but Drowning," Smith presents several different points of view, each with a different voice. Use the chart below to examine the use of voice in the poem. In the first column, identify the three points of view in the poem. In the second column, write a brief quote from each voice. In the last column, use your own words to describe the characteristics or personality of each voice.

Point of view	Quotation	Description of the voice

Focus on Research: Use Literary Criticism

Using authoritative print or online sources, research what one or more literary critics have written about the figurative meaning of the last two lines of the poem. If possible, find at least one source using an online database of literary criticism. These types of databases are often available through your school or public library. Write a summary of your research and include your own analysis of what these lines mean.

The Love Song of J. Alfred Prufrock

T. S. Eliot

Before You Read

Thomas Stearns Eliot (1888–1965) was born in St. Louis, Missouri, but moved permanently to England in 1914. There he transformed himself into an Englishman. In 1917, his first book of poems, *Prufrock and Other Observations*, established him as one of the most important English-language poets. His later poems include *The Waste Land* and *Four Quartets*. A critic, playwright, and editor as well as poet, he won the Nobel Prize in Literature in 1948. His *Old Possum's Book of Practical Cats* later became the basis for the Broadway musical and movie *Cats*.

World Context

Eliot is credited with propelling English poetry into the 20th century. He substituted the "poetic-sounding" language of earlier poetry with the free verse pioneered by French and Italian poets. Eliot approximated the sound of educated but natural speech and replaced abstractions with sensory imagery. Nevertheless, his poetry is intellectual and full of references to classical literature and history.

LITERARY LENS References to other works or events are called **allusions**. As you read, look for allusions and think about their effect.

S'io credesse che mia risposta fosse
a persona che mai tornasse al mondo,
questa fiamma staria senza piu scosse.
Ma per ciò che giammai di questo fondo
non tornò vivo alcun, s'i' odo il vero,   5
senza tema d'infamia ti rispondo.[1]

---

1 *S'io . . . rispondo:* An excerpt from Dante's *Inferno* (Canto 27, lines 61–66):
  If I thought my answer were given to anyone who would ever return to the world, this flame
  would stand still without moving any further. But since never from this abyss has anyone ever
  returned alive, if what I hear is true, without fear of infamy I answer thee.

Let us go then, you and I,
When the evening is spread out against the sky

Like a patient etherised² upon a table;
Let us go, through certain half-deserted streets,   10
The muttering retreats
Of restless nights in one-night cheap hotels
And sawdust restaurants with oyster-shells:
Streets that follow like a tedious argument
Of insidious intent   15
To lead you to an overwhelming question . . .
Oh, do not ask, "What is it?"
Let us go and make our visit.

In the room the women come and go
Talking of Michelangelo.³   20

The yellow fog that rubs its back upon the window-panes,
The yellow smoke that rubs its muzzle on the window-panes
Licked its tongue into the corners of the evening,
Lingered upon the pools that stand in drains,
Let fall upon its back the soot that falls from chimneys,   25
Slipped by the terrace, made a sudden leap,
And seeing that it was a soft October night,
Curled once about the house, and fell asleep.

And indeed there will be time
For the yellow smoke that slides along the street   30
Rubbing its back upon the window-panes;
There will be time, there will be time
To prepare a face to meet the faces that you meet;
There will be time to murder and create,
And time for all the works and days of hands   35
That lift and drop a question on your plate;
Time for you and time for me,
And time yet for a hundred indecisions
And for a hundred visions and revisions,
Before the taking of a toast and tea.   40

---

2 **etherised:** anaesthetized

3 **Michelangelo:** Michelangelo Buonarroti (1475–1564), the famous Italian architect, artist, and
   sculptor, renowned especially for his painting of the Sistine Chapel in the Vatican

In the room the women come and go
Talking of Michelangelo.

And indeed there will be time
To wonder, "Do I dare?" and, "Do I dare?"
Time to turn back and descend the stair, 45
With a bald spot in the middle of my hair—
(They will say: "How his hair is growing thin!")
My morning coat, my collar mounting firmly to the chin,
My necktie rich and modest, but asserted by a simple pin—
(They will say: "But how his arms and legs are thin!") 50
Do I dare
Disturb the universe?
In a minute there is time
For decisions and revisions which a minute will reverse.

For I have known them all already, known them all— 55
Have known the evenings, mornings, afternoons,
I have measured out my life with coffee spoons;
I know the voices dying with a dying fall
Beneath the music from a farther room.
    So how should I presume? 60

And I have known the eyes already, known them all—
The eyes that fix you in a formulated phrase,
And when I am formulated, sprawling on a pin,
When I am pinned and wriggling on the wall,
Then how should I begin 65
To spit out all the butt-ends of my days and ways?
    And how should I presume?

And I have known the arms already, know them all—
Arms that are braceleted and white and bare
(But in the lamplight, downed with light brown hair!) 70
Is it perfume from a dress
That makes me so digress?
Arms that lie along a table, or wrap about a shawl.
    And should I then presume?
    And how should I begin? 75

• • • • •

Shall I say, I have gone at dusk through narrow streets
And watched the smoke that rises from the pipes
Of lonely men in shirt-sleeves, leaning out of windows? . . .

I should have been a pair of ragged claws
Scuttling across the floors of silent seas.   80

• • • • •

And the afternoon, the evening, sleeps so peacefully!
Smoothed by long fingers,
Asleep . . . tired . . . or it malingers,
Stretched on the floor, here beside you and me.
Should I, after tea and cakes and ices,   85
Have the strength to force the moment to its crisis?
But though I have wept and fasted, wept and prayed,
Though I have seen my head (grown slightly bald) brought in
    upon a platter,
I am no prophet—and here's no great matter;
I have seen the moment of my greatness flicker,   90
And I have seen the eternal Footman hold my coat, and snicker
And in short, I was afraid.

And would it have been worth it, after all,
After the cups, the marmalade, the tea,
Among the porcelain, among some talk of you and me,   95
Would it have been worth while,
To have bitten off the matter with a smile,
To have squeezed the universe into a ball
To roll it towards some overwhelming question,
To say: "I am Lazarus,[4] come from the dead,   100
Come back to tell you all, I shall tell you all"—
If one, settling a pillow by her head,
    Should say: "That is not what I meant at all.
    That is not it, at all."

---

4 **Lazarus:** in the Bible, he is resurrected from the dead by Jesus

And would it have been worth it, after all,　　　　　　　　105
Would it have been worth while,
After the sunsets and the dooryards and the sprinkled streets,
After the novels, after the teacups, after the skirts
　　that trail along the floor—
And this, and so much more?—
It is impossible to say just what I mean!　　　　　　　　110
But as if a magic lantern threw the nerves in patterns on a screen:
Would it have been worth while
If one, settling a pillow or throwing off a shawl,
And turning toward the window, should say:
"That is not it at all,　　　　　　　　　　　　　　115
That is not what I meant, at all."

The Narcissistic Man |
Marc Chagall, 1976

• • • • •

No! I am not Prince Hamlet,[5] nor was meant to be;
Am an attendant lord, one that will do
To swell a progress, start a scene or two,
Advise the prince; no doubt, an easy tool,   120
Deferential, glad to be of use,
Politic, cautious, and meticulous;
Full of high sentence, but a bit obtuse;
At times, indeed, almost ridiculous—
Almost, at times, the Fool.   125

I grow old . . . I grow old . . .
I shall wear the bottoms of my trousers rolled.

Shall I part my hair behind? Do I dare to eat a peach?
I shall wear white flannel trousers, and walk upon the beach.
I have heard the mermaids singing, each to each.   130

I do not think that they will sing to me.

I have seen them riding seaward on the waves
Combing the white hair of the waves blown back
When the wind blows the water white and black.

We have lingered in the chambers of the sea   135
By sea-girls wreathed with seaweed red and brown
Till human voices wake us, and we drown.

---

5 **Prince Hamlet:** the young royal from Shakespeare's play of the same name

After You Read

Critical Reading

1. Identify the **similes** in the opening stanza. What comparisons are being made and what do they mean?

2. The third stanza (lines 15–23) contains an elaborate **metaphor**. Identify what is being compared and notice the techniques Eliot uses to create the metaphor.

3. Notice all the references to time in the poem ("I have measured out my life in coffee spoons"). Analyze how these references contribute to the poem's **themes**.

4. If this is a love song, as the **title** claims, where is the evidence of that?

5. Notice how many stanzas begin with a simple conjunction, such as the words *and* or *for*. What are the effects of this **repetition**?

Literary Lens: Allusions

An allusion is a reference to an artistic, historical, or literary figure, work, or event. "The Love Song of J. Alfred Prufrock" contains several artistic and literary allusions. Use the chart below to analyze Eliot's use of allusions. In the first column of the table, identify an artistic or literary figure, work, or event alluded to in the poem. In the second column, analyze what you think the allusion represents. Finally, comment on why you think Eliot used so many allusions in this poem.

Allusion	What it represents
Why do you think Eliot used so many allusions in the poem?	

Focus on Research: Use Credible Sources

With a partner, put together a bibliography of at least three sources you could use to research literary allusions in the poetry of T. S. Eliot. Make sure to evaluate each source for credibility. Consider the author's credentials and the site on which the article is posted. You could also use a database that specializes in scholarly resources, such as Google Scholar.

Refugee Blues

W. H. Auden

Before You Read

Wysten Hugh Auden (1907–1973) was born in England, became an American citizen, and died in Austria. In addition to poetry, he wrote plays, opera librettos, and criticism. An active leftist during his middle years, he fought in the Spanish Civil War. Though openly gay, he married Erika Mann, daughter of the German novelist Thomas Mann, to help her escape Nazi Germany in 1935. He later became disillusioned with leftism and became devoutly religious. Auden always maintained his compassion for human suffering in a troubled century. "We are here on Earth to do good to others," he once observed. "What the others are here for, I don't know."

World Context

Auden addressed head-on the political and cultural crises of the 20th century. He believed that in times of poverty, political extremism can flourish. In his day, Italy and Germany fell under Hitler's spell not only because of hatred for minorities and Jews but because of the economic depression that followed World War I.

 LITERARY LENS Poets and writers create imagery through their use of vivid descriptive details. As you read this poem, consider the effect the use of **sensory details** has on the poem's mood.

S ay this city has ten million souls,
Some are living in mansions, some are living in holes:
Yet there's no place for us, my dear, yet there's no place for us.

Once we had a country and we thought it fair,
Look in the atlas and you'll find it there: 5
We cannot go there now, my dear, we cannot go there now.

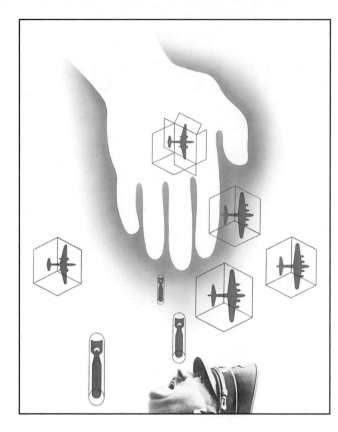

**Gift Packages
for Hitler |
Jean Carlu, 1942**

In the village churchyard there grows an old yew,
Every spring it blossoms anew:
Old passports can't do that, my dear, old passports can't do that.

The consul banged that table and said: 10
"If you've got no passport you're officially dead":
But we are still alive, my dear, but we are still alive.

Went to a committee; they offered me a chair;
Asked me politely to return next year:
But where shall we go to-day, my dear, but where shall we go to-day?   15

Came to a public meeting; the speaker got up and said:
"If we let them in, they will steal our daily bread";
He was talking of you and me, my dear, he was talking of you and me.

Thought I heard the thunder rumbling in the sky;
It was Hitler over Europe, saying: "They must die";   20
We were in his mind, my dear, we were in his mind.

Saw a poodle in a jacket fastened with a pin,
Saw a door opened and a cat let in:
But they weren't German Jews, my dear, but they weren't German Jews.

Went down to the harbour and stood upon the quay,[1]   25
Saw the fish swimming as if they were free:
Only ten feet away, my dear, only ten feet away.

Walked through a wood, saw the birds in the trees;
They had no politicians and sang at their ease:
They weren't the human race, my dear, they weren't the human race.   30

Dreamed I saw a building with a thousand floors,
A thousand windows and a thousand doors;
Not one of them was ours, my dear, not one of them was ours.

Stood on a great plain in the falling snow;
Ten thousand soldiers marched to and fro: 35
Looking for you and me, my dear, looking for you and me.

---

1 **quay:** a walk or landing structure next to water

After You Read

Critical Reading

1. Describe the **speaker** and his situation, giving evidence from the poem to support your analysis.

2. Find examples of **dialogue** in the poem. What is the effect of the one-sided nature of the dialogue? What do you notice about who is speaking and what ideas they are conveying?

3. What do you think is the meaning of lines 22–24: "Saw a poodle in a jacket fastened with a pin, / Saw a door opened and a cat let in: / But they weren't German Jews, my dear, but they weren't German Jews." What do the animals **symbolize**?

4. Notice Auden's use of punctuation. Why do you think the poet uses a colon after the second line in each stanza? Use examples from the poem to support your answer.

Literary Lens: Sensory Details

Vivid and striking descriptions of objects and details in a literary work create imagery. In this poem, Auden creates imagery through the use of vivid verbs and sensory details. Complete the chart below to examine the various methods Auden uses to create imagery in the poem. Write at least two examples in each category.

Example of sensory details	Sense to which it appeals	Effect

Focus on Research: Use Infographics

Infographics are visual representations of information that often use numbers and proportional data. They use images to catch your attention and convey essential information. Find an infographic that provides data on current refugee crises. (One possible source is the United Nations Refugee Agency website.) Pick an infographic, chart, or other visual representation that interests you and evaluate it by considering its layout, main message, content, and visual appeal. Take a note on a piece of data from the graphic and include a works cited or bibliography entry. Indicate which style guide you use to create the entry (MLA, APA, Chicago).

The Destructors

Graham Greene

Before You Read

Henry Graham Greene (1904–1991) was a versatile writer whose work ranged from film criticism to fiction. He specialized in stories that he called "entertainments"—thrillers and mysteries of greater than usual depth and literary quality. One of his best-known novels is *The Third Man,* which was made into an even more famous film in 1949. Greene's fictional world is full of characters making difficult moral choices—a world in which innocence is in scant supply.

World Context

The *blitzkrieg* (German for "lightning war") took its toll on the landscape, health, and psyches of everyday British citizens. Greene often examined the moral chaos and lost opportunities that emanate from war. Among literary critics, the urban wastelands of stories such as "The Destructors" even have a name: "Greeneland."

LITERARY LENS As you read, think about how Greene's **word choice** evokes a sense of setting.

I t was on the eve of August Bank Holiday that the latest recruit became the leader of the Wormsley Common Gang. No one was surprised except Mike, but Mike at the age of nine was surprised by everything. "If you don't shut your mouth," somebody once said to him, "you'll get a frog down it." After that Mike kept his teeth tightly clamped except when the surprise was too great.

The new recruit had been with the gang since the beginning of the summer holidays, and there were possibilities about his brooding silence that all recognized. He never wasted a word even to tell his name until that was required of him by the rules. When he said "Trevor" it was statement of fact, not as it would have been with the others a statement of shame or defiance. Nor did anyone laugh except Mike, who finding himself without support and meeting the dark gaze of the newcomer opened his mouth and was quiet again. There was every reason why T, as he was afterwards referred to, should have been an object of mockery—there was his name (and they substituted the initial because otherwise they had no excuse not to laugh at it), the fact that his father, a former architect and present clerk, had "come down in the world" and that his mother considered herself better than the neighbours. What but an odd quality of danger, of the unpredictable, established him in the gang without any **ignoble** ceremony of initiation?

The gang met every morning in an **impromptu** car-park, the site of the last bomb of the first blitz.[1] The leader, who was known as Blackie, claimed to have heard it fall, and no one was precise enough in his dates to point out that he would have been one year old and fast asleep on the down platform of Wormsley Common[2] Underground Station.[3] On one side of the car-park leant the first occupied house, No. 3, of the shattered Northwood Terrace—literally leant, for it had suffered from the blast of the bomb and the side walls were supported on wooden struts.[4] A smaller bomb and **incendiaries** had fallen beyond, so that the house stuck up like a jagged tooth and carried on the further wall relics of its neighbour, a dado,[5] the remains of a fireplace. T, whose words were almost confined to voting "Yes" or "No" to the plan of operations proposed each day by Blackie, once startled the whole gang by saying broodingly, "Wren[6] built that house, father says."

"Who's Wren?"

"The man who built St. Paul's."[7]

"Who cares?" Blackie said. "It's only Old Misery's."

Old Misery—whose real name was Thomas—had once been a builder and decorator. He lived alone in the crippled house, doing for himself: once a week you could see him coming back across the common with bread and vegetables, and once as the boys played in the car-park he put his head over the smashed wall of his garden[8] and looked at them.

---

1 **first blitz:** the first German air bombardment of London in World War II

2 **Common:** a municipal park or square

3 **Underground Station:** London's subway system

4 **struts:** structural supports

5 **dado:** part of a building column

6 **Wren:** Sir Christopher Wren (1632–1723), one of the most famous English architects; particularly known for the churches he designed

7 **St. Paul's:** the London cathedral designed by Wren, which survived the German blitz in World War II

8 **garden:** the British term for "yard"

"Been to the lav,"[9] one of the boys said, for it was common knowledge that since the bombs fell something had gone wrong with the pipes of the house and Old Misery was too mean to spend money on the property. He could do the redecorating himself at cost price, but he had never learnt plumbing. The lav was a wooden shed at the bottom of the narrow garden with a star-shaped hole in the door: it had escaped the blast which had smashed the house next door and sucked out the window-frames of No. 3.

The next time the gang became aware of Mr. Thomas was more surprising. Blackie, Mike and a thin yellow boy, who for some reason was called by his surname Summers, met him on the common coming back from the market. Mr. Thomas stopped them. He said glumly, "You belong to the lot that play in the car-park?"

Mike was about to answer when Blackie stopped him. As the leader he had responsibilities. "Suppose we are?" he said **ambiguously**.

"I got some chocolates," Mr. Thomas said. "Don't like 'em myself. Here you are. Not enough to go round, I don't suppose. There never is," he added with sombre conviction. He handed over three packets of Smarties.

The gang was puzzled and perturbed by this action and tried to explain it away. "Bet someone dropped them and he picked 'em up," somebody suggested.

"Pinched[10] 'em and then got in a bleeding funk,"[11] another thought aloud.

"It's a bribe," Summers said. "He wants us to stop bouncing balls on his wall."

"We'll show him we don't take bribes," Blackie said, and they sacrificed the whole morning to the game of bouncing that only Mike was young enough to enjoy. There was no sign from Mr. Thomas.

Next day T astonished them all. He was late at the **rendezvous**, and the voting for that day's exploit took place without him. At Blackie's suggestion the gang was to disperse in pairs, take buses at random and see how many free rides could be snatched from unwary conductors (the operation was to be carried out in pairs to avoid cheating). They were drawing lots for their companions when T arrived.

"Where you been, T?" Blackie asked. "You can't vote now. You know the rules."

"I've been *there*," T said. He looked at the ground, as though he had thoughts to hide.

ambiguously: obscurely; unclearly

rendezvous: meeting; appointment

---

9 **lav:** short for *lavatory*, the British term for "bathroom"
10 **pinched:** British slang for "stole"
11 **bleeding funk:** British slang for "worried state"

"Where?"

"At Old Misery's." Mike's mouth opened and then hurriedly closed again with a click. He had remembered the frog.

"At Old Misery's?" Blackie said. There was nothing in the rules against it, but he had a sensation that T was treading on dangerous ground. He asked hopefully, "Did you break in?"

"No. I rang the bell."

"And what did you say?"

"I said I wanted to see his house."

"What did he do?"

"He showed it me."

"Pinch anything?"

"No."

"What did you do it for then?"

The gang had gathered round: it was as though an impromptu court were about to form and try some case of **deviation**. T said, "It's a beautiful house," and still watching the ground, meeting no one's eyes, he licked his lips first one way, then the other.

"What do you mean, a beautiful house?" Blackie asked with scorn.

"It's got a staircase two hundred years old like a corkscrew. Nothing holds it up."

"What do you mean, nothing holds it up. Does it float?"

"It's to do with opposite forces, Old Misery said."

"What else?"

"There's panelling."

"Like in the Blue Boar?"

"Two hundred years old."

"Is Old Misery two hundred years old?"

Mike laughed suddenly and then was quiet again. The meeting was in a serious mood. For the first time since T had strolled into the car-park on the first day of the holidays his position was in danger. It only needed a single use of his real name and the gang would be at his heels.

"What did you do it for?" Blackie asked. He was just, he had no jealousy, he was anxious to retain T in the gang if he could. It was the word "beautiful" that worried him—that belonged to a class world[12] that you could still see parodied at the Wormsley Common Empire by a man wearing a top hat and a monocle, with a haw-haw[13] accent. He was tempted

---

12 **class world:** an upper-class culture

13 **top hat . . . monocle . . . haw-haw:** symbols of England's old aristocracy—the formal hat, the single eyeglass, and the braying laugh

to say, "My dear Trevor, old chap," and unleash his hell hounds. "If you'd broken in," he said sadly—that indeed would have been an **exploit** worthy of the gang.

exploit: adventure; feat

"This was better," T said. "I found out things." He continued to stare at his feet, not meeting anybody's eye, as though he were absorbed in some dream he was unwilling—or ashamed—to share.

"What things?"

"Old Misery's going to be away all tomorrow and Bank Holiday."[14]

Blackie said with relief, "You mean we could break in?"

"And pinch things?" somebody asked.

Blackie said, "Nobody's going to pinch things. Breaking in—that's good enough, isn't it? We don't want any court stuff."

"I don't want to pinch anything," T said. "I've got a better idea."

"What is it?"

T raised eyes, as grey and disturbed as the drab August day. "We'll pull it down," he said. "We'll destroy it."

Blackie gave a single hoot of laughter and then, like Mike, fell quiet, daunted by the serious **implacable** gaze. "What'd the police be doing all the time?" he said.

implacable: inflexible; unrelenting

"They'd never know. We'd do it from inside. I've found a way in." He said with a sort of intensity, "We'd be like worms, don't you see, in an apple. When we came out again there'd be nothing there, no staircase, no panels, nothing but just walls, and then we'd make the walls fall down—somehow."

"We'd go to jug,"[15] Blackie said.

"Who's to prove? and anyway we wouldn't have pinched anything." He added without the smallest flicker of glee, "There wouldn't be anything to pinch after we'd finished."

"I've never heard of going to prison for breaking things," Summers said.

"There wouldn't be time," Blackie said. "I've seen housebreakers at work."

"There are twelve of us," T said. "We'd organize."

"None of us know how . . ."

"I know," T said. He looked across at Blackie. "Have you got a better plan?"

"Today," Mike said tactlessly, "we're pinching free rides . . ."

"Free rides," T said. "Kid stuff. You can stand down, Blackie, if you'd rather . . ."

---

14 **Bank Holiday:** a public holiday in Great Britain
15 **jug:** slang for "prison"

"The gang's got to vote."

"Put it up then."

Blackie said uneasily, "It's proposed that tomorrow and Monday we destroy Old Misery's house."

"Here, here," said a fat boy called Joe.

"Who's in favour?"

T said, "It's carried."

"How do we start?" Summers asked.

"He'll tell you," Blackie said. It was the end of his leadership. He went away to the back of the car-park and began to kick a stone, dribbling it this way and that. There was only one old Morris in the park, for few cars were left there except lorries:[16] without an attendant there was no safety. He took a flying kick at the car and scraped a little paint off the rear mudguard. Beyond, paying no more attention to him than to a stranger, the gang had gathered round T; Blackie was dimly aware of the **fickleness** of favour. He thought of going home, of never returning, of letting them all discover the hollowness of T's leadership, but suppose after all what T proposed was possible—nothing like it had ever been done before. The fame of the Wormsley Common car-park gang would surely reach around London. There would be headlines in the papers. Even the grown-up gangs who ran the betting at the all-in wrestling[17] and the barrow-boys[18] would hear with respect of how Old Misery's house had been destroyed. Driven by the pure, simple and **altruistic** ambition of fame for the gang, Blackie came back to where T stood in the shadow of Old Misery's wall.

T was giving his orders with decision: it was as though this plan had been with him all his life, pondered through the seasons, now in his fifteenth year crystallized with the pain of puberty. "You," he said to Mike, "bring some big nails, the biggest you can find, and a hammer. Anybody who can, better bring a hammer and a screwdriver. We'll need plenty of them. Chisels too. We can't have too many chisels. Can anybody bring a saw?"

"I can," Mike said.

fickleness: changeability; inconstancy

The fame of the Wormsley Common car-park gang would surely reach around London.

altruistic: unselfish; without thought of personal gain

---

16 **lorries:** British English for "trucks"

17 **all-in wrestling:** submission wrestling, or when opponents wrestle using submission moves such as choke holds, armbars, and leg locks

18 **barrow-boys:** British street hawkers who sold things from wheelbarrows

"Not a child's saw," T said. "A real saw."

Blackie realized he had raised his hand like any ordinary member of the gang.

"Right, you bring one, Blackie. But now there's a difficulty. We want a hacksaw."

"What's a hacksaw?" someone asked.

"You can get 'em at Woolworth's," Summers said.

The fat boy called Joe said gloomily, "I knew it would end in a collection."

"I'll get one myself," T said. "I don't want your money. But I can't buy a sledge-hammer."

Blackie said, "They are working on No. 15. I know where they'll leave their stuff for Bank Holiday."

"Then that's all," T said. "We meet here at nine sharp."

"I've got to go to church," Mike said.

"Come over the wall and whistle. We'll let you in."

<h1 style="text-align:center">2</h1>

On Sunday morning all were punctual except Blackie, even Mike. Mike had a stroke of luck. His mother felt ill, his father was tired after Saturday night, and he was told to go to church alone with many warnings of what would happen if he strayed. Blackie had difficulty in smuggling out the saw, and then in finding the sledge-hammer at the back of No. 15. He approached the house from a lane at the rear of the garden, for fear of the policeman's beat along the main road. The tired evergreens kept off a stormy sun: another wet Bank Holiday was being prepared over the Atlantic, beginning in swirls of dust under the trees. Blackie climbed the wall into Misery's garden.

There was no sign of anybody anywhere. The lav stood like a tomb in a neglected graveyard. The curtains were drawn. The house slept. Blackie lumbered nearer with the saw and the sledge-hammer. Perhaps after all nobody had turned up: the plan had been a wild invention: they had woken wiser. But when he came close to the back door he could hear a confusion of sound hardly louder than a hive in swarm: a clickety-clack, a bang bang, a scraping, a creaking, a sudden painful crack. He thought: it's true, and whistled.

They opened the back door to him and he came in. He had at once the impression of organization, very different from the old happy-go-lucky

La Poitrine | Rene Magritte, 1961

ways under his leadership. For a while he wandered up and down stairs looking for T. Nobody addressed him: he had a sense of great urgency, and already he could begin to see the plan. The interior of the house was being carefully demolished without touching the walls. Summers with hammer and chisel was ripping out the skirting-boards in the ground-floor dining-room: he had already smashed the panels of the door. In the same room Joe was heaving up the parquet blocks, exposing the soft wood floorboards over the cellar. Coils of wire came out of the damaged skirting and Mike sat happily on the floor clipping the wires.

On the curved stairs two of the gang were working hard with an inadequate child's saw on the banisters—when they saw Blackie's big saw they signalled for it wordlessly. When he next saw them a quarter of the banisters had been dropped into the hall. He found T at last in the bathroom—he sat moodily in the least cared-for room in the house, listening to the sounds coming up from below.

"You've really done it," Blackie said with awe. "What's going to happen?"

"We've only just begun," T said. He looked at the sledge-hammer and gave his instructions. "You stay here and break the bath and the wash-basin. Don't bother about the pipes. They come later."

Mike appeared at the door. "I've finished the wires, T," he said.

"Good. You've just got to go wandering round now. The kitchen's in the basement. Smash all the china and glass and bottles you can lay hold of. Don't turn on the taps—we don't want a flood—yet. Then go into all the rooms and turn out the drawers. If they are locked get one of the others to break them open. Tear up any papers you find and smash all the ornaments. Better take a carving knife with you from the kitchen. The bedroom's opposite here. Open the pillows and tear up the sheets. That's enough for the moment. And you Blackie, when you've finished in here crack the plaster in the passage up with your sledge-hammer."

"What are you going to do?" Blackie asked.

"I'm looking for something special," T said.

It was nearly lunch-time before Blackie had finished and went in search of T. Chaos had advanced. The kitchen was a shambles of broken glass and china. The dining-room was stripped of parquet, the skirting was up, the door had been taken off its hinges, and the destroyers had moved up a floor. Streaks of light came in through the closed shutters where they worked with the seriousness of creators—and destruction after all is a form of creation. A kind of imagination had seen this house as it had now become.

Mike said, "I've got to go home for dinner."

"Who else?" T asked, but all the others on one excuse or another had brought provisions with them.

They squatted in the ruins of the room and swapped unwanted sandwiches. Half an hour for lunch and they were at work again. By the time Mike returned they were on the top floor, and by six the superficial damage was completed. The doors were all off, all the skirtings raised, the furniture **pillaged** and ripped and smashed—no one could have slept in the house except on a bed of broken plaster. T gave his orders—eight o'clock next morning, and to escape notice they climbed singly over the garden wall, into the car-park. Only Blackie and T were left: the light had

pillaged: destroyed; looted

nearly gone, and when they touched a switch, nothing worked—Mike had done his job thoroughly.

"Did you find anything special?" Blackie asked.

T nodded. "Come over here," he said, "and look." Out of both pockets he drew bundles of pound notes.[19] "Old Misery's savings," he said. "Mike ripped out the mattress, but he missed them."

"What are you going to do? Share them?"

"We aren't thieves," T said. "Nobody's going to steal anything from this house. I kept these for you and me—a celebration." He knelt down on the floor and counted them out—there were seventy in all. "We'll burn them," he said, "one by one," and taking it in turns they held a note upwards and lit the top corner, so that the flame burnt slowly towards their fingers. The grey ash floated above them and fell on their heads like age. "I'd like to see Old Misery's face when we are through," T said.

"You hate him a lot?" Blackie asked.

"Of course I don't hate him," T said. "There'd be no fun if I hated him." The last burning note illuminated his brooding face. "All this hate and love," he said, "it's soft, it's hooey. There's only things, Blackie," and he looked round the room crowded with the unfamiliar shadows of half things, broken things, former things. "I'll race you home, Blackie," he said.

3

Next morning the serious destruction started. Two were missing—Mike and another boy whose parents were off to Southend and Brighton in spite of the slow warm drops that had begun to fall and the rumble of thunder in the estuary[20] like the first guns of the old blitz. "We've got to hurry," T said.

Summers was restive. "Haven't we done enough?" he asked. "I've been given a bob for slot machines. This is like work."

"We've hardly started," T said. "Why, there's all the floors left, and the stairs. We haven't taken out a single window. You voted like the others. We are going to *destroy* this house. There won't be anything left when we've finished."

They began again on the first floor picking up the top floorboards next the outer wall, leaving the joists exposed. Then they sawed through the joists and retreated into the hall, as what was left of the floor heeled and sank. They had learnt with practice, and the second floor collapsed

---

19 **pound notes:** units of British currency
20 **estuary:** where the sea tide meets the river

more easily. By the evening an odd exhilaration seized them as they looked down the great hollow of the house. They ran risks and made mistakes: when they thought of the windows it was too late to reach them. "Cor," Joe said, and dropped a penny down into the dry rubble-filled well. It cracked and span amongst the broken glass.

"Why did we start this?" Summers asked with astonishment; T was already on the ground, digging at the rubble, clearing a space along the outer wall. "Turn on the taps," he said. "It's too dark for anyone to see now, and in the morning it won't matter." The water overtook them on the stairs and fell through the floorless rooms.

It was then they heard Mike's whistle at the back. "Something's wrong," Blackie said. They could hear his urgent breathing as they unlocked the door.

"The bogies?" Summers asked.

"Old Misery," Mike said. "He's on his way," he said with pride.

"But why?" T said. "He told me . . ." He protested with the fury of the child he had never been, "It isn't fair."

"He was down at Southend," Mike said, "and he was on the train coming back. Said it was too cold and wet." He paused and gazed at the water. "My, you've had a storm here. Is the roof leaking?"

"How long will he be?"

"Five minutes. I gave Ma the slip and ran."

"We better clear," Summers said. "We've done enough, anyway."

"Oh no, we haven't. Anybody could do this—" "this" was the shattered hollowed house with nothing left but the walls. Yet walls could be preserved. Façades[21] were valuable. They could build inside again more beautifully than before. This could again be a home. He said angrily, "We've got to finish. Don't move. Let me think."

"There's no time," a boy said.

"There's got to be a way," T said. "We couldn't have got this far . . ."

"We've done a lot," Blackie said.

"No. No, we haven't. Somebody watch the front."

"We can't do any more."

"He may come in at the back."

"Watch the back too." T began to plead. "Just give me a minute and I'll fix it. I swear I'll fix it." But his authority had gone with his ambiguity. He was only one of the gang. "Please," he said.

---

21 **façades:** outer faces of buildings

"Please," Summers mimicked him, and then suddenly struck home with the fatal name. "Run along home, Trevor."

T stood with his back to the rubble like a boxer knocked groggy against the ropes. He had no words as his dreams shook and slid. Then Blackie acted before the gang had time to laugh, pushing Summers backward. "I'll watch the front, T," he said, and cautiously he opened the shutters of the hall. The grey wet common stretched ahead, and the lamps gleamed in the puddles. "Someone's coming, T. No, it's not him. What's your plan, T?"

"Tell Mike to go out to the lav and hide close beside it. When he hears me whistle he's got to count ten and start to shout."

"Shout what?"

"Oh, 'Help', anything."

"You hear, Mike," Blackie said. He was the leader again. He took a quick look between the shutters. "He's coming, T."

"Quick, Mike. The lav. Stay here, Blackie, all of you, till I yell."

"Where are you going, T?"

"Don't worry. I'll see to this. I said I would, didn't I?"

Old Misery came limping off the common. He had mud on his shoes and he stopped to scrape them on the pavement's edge. He didn't want to soil his house, which stood jagged and dark between the bomb-sites, saved so narrowly, as he believed, from destruction. Even the fan-light had been left unbroken by the bomb's blast. Somewhere somebody whistled. Old Misery looked sharply round. He didn't trust whistles. A child was shouting: it seemed to come from his own garden. Then a boy ran into the road from the car-park. "Mr. Thomas," he called, "Mr. Thomas."

"What is it?"

"I'm terribly sorry, Mr. Thomas. One of us got taken short, and we thought you wouldn't mind and now he can't get out."

"What do you mean, boy?"

"He's got stuck in your lav."

"He'd no business . . . Haven't I seen you before?"

"You showed me your house."

"So I did. So I did. That doesn't give you the right to . . ."

"Do hurry, Mr. Thomas. He'll suffocate."

"Nonsense. He can't suffocate. Wait till I put my bag in."

"I'll carry your bag."

"Oh no, you don't. I carry my own."

"This way, Mr. Thomas."

"I can't get in the garden that way. I've got to go through the house."

"But you *can* get in the garden this way, Mr. Thomas. We often do."

"You often do?" He followed the boy with a scandalized fascination. "When? What right . . . ?"

"Do you see . . . ? the wall's low."

"I'm not going to climb walls into my own garden. It's absurd."

"This is how we do it. One foot here, one foot there, and over." The boy's face peered down, an arm shot out, and Mr. Thomas found his bag taken and deposited on the other side of the wall.

"Give me back my bag," Mr. Thomas said. From the loo[22] a boy yelled and yelled. "I'll call the police."

"Your bag's all right, Mr. Thomas. Look. One foot there. On your right. Now just above. To your left." Mr. Thomas climbed over his own garden wall. "Here's your bag, Mr. Thomas."

"I'll have the wall built up," Mr. Thomas said, "I'll not have you boys coming over here, using my loo." He stumbled on the path, but the boy caught his elbow and supported him. "Thank you, thank you, my boy," he murmured automatically. Somebody shouted again through the dark. "I'm coming, I'm coming," Mr. Thomas called. He said to the boy beside him, "I'm not unreasonable. Been a boy myself. As long as things are done regular. I don't mind you playing round the place Saturday mornings. Sometimes I like company. Only it's got to be regular. One of you asks leave and I say Yes. Sometimes I'll say No. Won't feel like it. And you come in at the front door and out at the back. No garden walls."

"Do get him out, Mr. Thomas."

"He won't come to any harm in my loo," Mr. Thomas said, stumbling slowly down the garden. "Oh, my rheumatics," he said. "Always get 'em on Bank Holiday. I've got to be careful. There's loose stones here. Give me your hand. Do you know what my horoscope said yesterday? 'Abstain from any dealings in first half of the week. Danger of serious crash.' That might be on this path," Mr. Thomas said. "They speak in parables and double meanings."[23] He paused at the door of the loo. "What's the matter in there?" he called. There was no reply.

"Perhaps he's fainted," the boy said.

"Not in my loo. Here, you, come out," Mr. Thomas said, and giving a great jerk at the door he nearly fell on his back when it swung easily open.

---

22 **loo:** British slang for "bathroom"

23 **parables and double meanings:** short stories containing moral lessons and words that can be interpreted in multiple ways

A hand first supported him and then pushed him hard. His head hit the opposite wall and he sat heavily down. His bag hit his feet. A hand whipped the key out of the lock and the door slammed. "Let me out," he called, and heard the key turn in the lock. "A serious crash," he thought, and felt dithery and confused and old.

A voice spoke to him softly through the star-shaped hole in the door. "Don't worry, Mr. Thomas," it said, "we won't hurt you, not if you stay quiet."

Mr. Thomas put his head between his hands and pondered. He had noticed that there was only one lorry in the car-park, and he felt certain that the driver would not come for it before the morning. Nobody could hear him from the road in front, and the lane at the back was seldom used. Anyone who passed there would be hurrying home and would not pause for what they would certainly take to be drunken cries. And if he did call "Help," who, on a lonely Bank Holiday evening, would have the courage to investigate? Mr. Thomas sat on the loo and pondered with the wisdom of age.

After a while it seemed to him that there were sounds in the silence—they were faint and came from the direction of his house. He stood up and peered through the ventilation-hole—between the cracks in one of the shutters he saw a light, not the light of a lamp, but the wavering light that a candle might give. Then he thought he heard the sound of hammering and scraping and chipping. He thought of burglars—perhaps they had employed the boy as a scout, but why should burglars engage in what sounded more and more like a **stealthy** form of carpentry? Mr. Thomas let out an experimental yell, but nobody answered. The noise could not even have reached his enemies.

stealthy:
secret; furtive

4

Mike had gone home to bed, but the rest stayed. The question of leadership no longer concerned the gang. With nails, chisels, screwdrivers, anything that was sharp and penetrating, they moved around the inner walls worrying at the mortar between the bricks. They started too high, and it was Blackie who hit on the damp course and realized the work could be halved if they weakened the joints immediately above. It was a long, tiring, unamusing job, but at last it was finished. The gutted house stood there balanced on a few inches of mortar between the damp course and the bricks.

There remained the most dangerous task of all, out in the open at the edge of the bomb-site. Summers was sent to watch the road for passers-by, and Mr. Thomas, sitting on the loo, heard clearly now the sound of sawing. It no longer came from the house, and that a little reassured him. He felt less concerned. Perhaps the other noises too had no significance.

A voice spoke to him through the hole. "Mr. Thomas."

"Let me out," Mr. Thomas said sternly.

"Here's a blanket," the voice said, and a long grey sausage was worked through the hole and fell in **swathes** over Mr. Thomas's head.

"There's nothing personal," the voice said. "We want you to be comfortable tonight."

"Tonight," Mr. Thomas repeated incredulously.

"Catch," the voice said. "Penny buns—we've buttered them, and sausage-rolls. We don't want you to starve, Mr. Thomas."

Mr. Thomas pleaded desperately. "A joke's a joke, boy. Let me out and I won't say a thing. I've got rheumatics. I got to sleep comfortable."

"You wouldn't be comfortable, not in your house, you wouldn't. Not now."

"What do you mean, boy?" But the footsteps receded. There was only the silence of night: no sound of sawing. Mr. Thomas tried one more yell, but he was **daunted** and **rebuked** by the silence—a long way off an owl hooted and made away again on its muffled flight through the soundless world.

At seven next morning the driver came to fetch his lorry. He climbed into the seat and tried to start the engine. He was vaguely aware of a voice shouting, but it didn't concern him. At last the engine responded and he backed the lorry until it touched the great wooden shore that supported Mr. Thomas's house. That way he could drive right out and down the street without reversing. The lorry moved forward, was momentarily checked as though something were pulling it from behind, and then went on to the sound of a long rumbling crash. The driver was astonished to see bricks bouncing ahead of him, while stones hit the roof of his cab. He put on his brakes. When he climbed out the whole landscape had suddenly altered. There was no house beside the car-park, only a hill of rubble. He went round and examined the back of his lorry for damage, and found a rope tied there that was still twisted at the other end round part of a wooden strut.

The driver again became aware of somebody shouting. It came from the wooden erection which was the nearest thing to a house in that desolation of broken brick. The driver climbed the smashed wall and unlocked the door. Mr. Thomas came out of the loo. He was wearing a grey blanket to which flakes of pastry adhered. He gave a sobbing cry. "My house," he said. "Where's my house?"

"Search me," the driver said. His eye lit on the remains of a bath and what had once been a dresser and he began to laugh. There wasn't anything left anywhere.

"How dare you laugh," Mr. Thomas said. "It was my house. My house."

"I'm sorry," the driver said, making heroic efforts, but when he remembered the sudden check of his lorry, the crash of bricks falling, he became convulsed again. One moment the house had stood there with such dignity between the bomb-sites like a man in a top hat, and then, bang, crash, there wasn't anything left—not anything. He said, "I'm sorry. I can't help it, Mr. Thomas. There's nothing personal, but you got to admit it's funny."

After You Read

Critical Reading

1. Why do you think the young men behave as they do by destroying this old man's house? What can you infer about their **motivation** when Trevor says "there'd be no fun" in the destruction if he hated Old Misery?

2. "Coming down in the world" is a **theme** in this story. Trace the development of this theme by identifying some of the things that "come down" in this story in addition to the most obvious one, the house.

3. Identify **conflicts** in the story and their causes. Categorize each one as human versus human, human versus society, human versus nature, or human versus self. Which one is the central conflict of the story?

4. What are some ideas the author has about group psychology? Give examples, noting the boys' speech and leadership styles.

Literary Lens: Word Choice

In "The Destructors," Graham Greene uses the colorful language of the boys' dialogue and the descriptions of the dynamics of the gang to make his story come alive. Re-create the charts below and then fill them in to document the unique characteristics of Graham Greene's style. When you are done, write an explanation of how the slang terms and the description of the gang affect your experience of reading the story.

Descriptions of gang dynamics	
Description	What it reveals about dynamics

Focus on Research: Use Databases

In order to understand more about topics such as gang membership, risk factors for joining gangs, and the short and long-term consequences of joining a gang, develop a few research questions and then use databases such as the Social Science Research Network, CORE, and the Directory of Open Access to find answers. After some initial research, modify your research questions as needed. Once you have found answers to your research questions, identify any lingering gaps in your research that would need to be filled if you were to write a full analysis on your topic.

The Literature of
Spain

Background

In 2002, one hundred of the most celebrated authors in the world were asked to name the greatest work of fiction ever written. By a huge margin, they chose *Don Quixote* by Spanish writer Miguel de Cervantes (1547–1616). *Don Quixote* tells the immortal story of a delusional nobleman, who is trying to live the life of a medieval knight. Accompanying Quixote on his adventures is Sancho Panza, who is both loyal to his master and completely in touch with reality.

The influence of Cervantes on literature in Spain and throughout and the world is immense. Perhaps the most internationally famous Spanish writer since Cervantes is the poet and playwright Federico García Lorca (1898–1936). One of his best-known works is the *Romeo and Juliet*-like romantic tragedy *Blood Wedding*.

Spain and the United States

García Lorca died an early death due to the Spanish Civil War (1936–1939). The war began when right-wing forces (the Nationalists) rebelled against those of Spain's democratically elected republican government (the Loyalists). Each side quickly attracted international supporters. German Nazis and Italian Fascists backed the Nationalists, while Soviet Communists and advocates of democracy from around the world backed the Loyalists.

García Lorca's murder by Nationalists helped sway the sympathies of many American authors toward the Loyalist cause. Among these writers, John Dos Passos, Lillian Hellman, Ernest Hemingway, and Archibald Macleish contributed to the pro-Loyalist 1937 film documentary *The Spanish Earth*. Herbert Matthews, Martha Gellhorn, and Dorothy Parker all wrote pro-Loyalist articles during the war.

The war ended in 1939, when the Nationalists were victorious over the Loyalists. Spain suffered under a harsh dictatorship until 1975.

Research: Develop a Thesis

Miguel de Cervantes was an accomplished playwright as well as a pioneering novelist. He wrote during the 17th century, the so-called Golden Age of Spanish drama. Compile a list of major Spanish Golden Age playwrights, including a few key works by each of them. Do some preliminary research to determine what characteristics dramas of Spain's Golden Age might have in common. Express your idea in a working thesis statement.

The Guitar

Federico García Lorca

Before You Read

Possibly the greatest Spanish-language poet and playwright of his century, Federico García Lorca (1898–1936) was also a musician and painter. Because he read his works in public, many of his poems became famous before they were even published. "Verse is made to be recited," he once observed. "In a book it is dead." His most famous works for the stage include a trilogy of "folk plays" about Spanish life: *Blood Wedding, Yerma,* and *The House of Bernarda Alba.* Many of his writings show a deep preoccupation with death, as if he had some premonition that his own life would be cut short. During the early days of the Spanish Civil War, he was executed by right-wing Nationalists, perhaps less for his leftist sympathies than for his homosexuality.

World Context

García Lorca's artistry and intense identification with the landscape, music, and people of Spain make him one of the most important Spanish writers of the 20th century. García Lorca's writing often celebrates the Roma culture of Andalusia in the south of Spain. The mournful guitar music and fiery, stomping flamenco dance are still emblematic of this often romantically depicted region.

 LITERARY LENS A **symbol** is something that stands for or represents something else. What might the guitar symbolize in the following poem?

Now begins the cry
Of the guitar,
Breaking the vaults
Of dawn.
Now begins the cry   5
Of the guitar.
Useless
To still it.
It weeps monotonously

As weeps the water,   10
As weeps the wind
Over snow.
Impossible
To still it.
It weeps   15
For distant things,
Warm southern sands
Desiring white camellias.[1]
It mourns the arrow without a target,
The evening without morning.   20
And the first bird dead
Upon a branch.
O guitar!
A wounded heart,
Wounded by five swords.   25

Translated by Elizabeth du Gué Trapier

---

1 **camellias:** fragrant, roselike flowers

After You Read

Critical Reading

1. Choose one of the **poetic devices** used by the poet, such as **personification**, **repetition**, or **sensory language**. Find examples of the technique and analyze its effects.

2. What is the **tone** of this poem? Find examples in the text to support your answer.

3. What would you say is a main **theme** of this poem? Cite some examples, such as images, words, or poetic devices, that support your answer.

Literary Lens: Symbolism

A **symbol** is something that stands for, or represents, something else. A dove, for example, often symbolizes peace. A hawk, on the other hand, can symbolize war. Since writers usually do not specify what their symbols represent, readers need to infer their meaning. Re-create the chart below and use it to analyze the symbols in the poem.

Symbol	Stands for	Support/Evidence from the text
the guitar		
white camellias		
the arrow		
the dead bird		
five swords		

Focus on Research: Conduct Informal Research

In Spain, the passionate music of flamenco dancers and the Roma people is called *cante jondo,* or "deep song." In his verse and plays, García Lorca tries to suggest *cante jondo* without the benefit of musical notes and rhythm. Conduct informal research on *cante jondo,* finding videos, audio recordings, and art inspired by this music and time period. Based on what you find, do you think this poem has the same feel as *cante jondo*? Explain your answer.

The Literature of
Italy

Background

Italian literature dates from the 14th century. Until then, respected writers in what is now Italy wrote in Latin. In the 14th century, though, three writers often wrote in the Tuscan dialect of what evolved into today's Italian language.

Dante Alighieri (1265–1321) is most famous for his three-part epic poem *The Divine Comedy*, a journey through Hell, Purgatory, and Paradise. Petrarch (1304–1374) mastered many poetic forms but may be best known for his works devoted to a woman named Laura. Petrarch's friend Giovanni Boccaccio (1313–1375) wrote the *Decameron*, a collection of stories told by people trying to escape a deadly plague known as the Black Death.

The influence of these writers stretches across nations and centuries. Dante's epic *The Divine Comedy* made possible *Paradise Lost*, the masterpiece of the English poet John Milton (1609–1674). Shakespeare's sonnets would have been impossible if Petrarch had not developed that poetic form. Geoffrey Chaucer (c. 1340–1400) visited Italy and was inspired by the Tuscan writings of Petrarch and Boccaccio to write such works as *The Canterbury Tales* in his native Middle English.

Italy and the United States

Probably the most widely read Italian author in the United States today is Umberto Eco (1932–2016). A philosophical scholar as well as a novelist, his medieval mystery *The Name of the Rose* was popular in the United States; it was also made into a successful English-language movie in 1986 starring Sean Connery. Another commercial success in the United States was Eco's 1988 novel *Foucault's Pendulum*. Eco's fiction inspired the work of the American writer Dan Brown, author of the worldwide best-selling novel *The Da Vinci Code*.

Research: Synthesize Information

Among the great writers of Italian literature were Vittoria Colonna (1490–1547) and Gaspara Stampa (1523–1554). Their works were largely forgotten until their rediscovery in the 1990s. Research these writers and then think about how they are alike and how they are different. Write an imaginary interview with these women, emphasizing why their works were neglected for so many centuries.

Poor Fish

Alberto Moravia

Before You Read

Italian author Alberto Moravia (1907–1990), pen name for Alberto Pincherle, began writing as a teenager while cooped up at home due to illness. His first novel, *Time of Indifference*, was an immediate sensation. However, Moravia's attacks on fascism led Mussolini, Italy's fascist dictator, to ban his work. After World War II, when Moravia could again publish his short stories and novels, many were adapted for films.

Moravia endeared himself to Italians with his fiction about the common people. "Poor Fish" comes from *Roman Tales*, a collection of stories depicting "low-life" characters in Italy's capital city.

World Context

In Italy, beauty is a virtue. Italians are renowned for beauty in the visual arts—from the architecture of ancient Rome to the paintings and sculpture of the Renaissance. This visual flair extends even to a form of entertainment Italians are credited with creating—the circus. The following story's preoccupation with physical perfection is one of its most Italian characteristics.

 LITERARY LENS Look for **conflict,** the struggle of opposing forces, both internal and external.

People never know very much about who they are, nor about who is inferior to them and who superior. As for me, I went too far in the direction of thinking myself inferior to everybody. It is true that I was not born with a frame as tough as iron; about as tough as earthenware, let us say. But I looked upon myself as being as fragile as glass, as the thinnest glass, in fact; and that was altogether too much. That was debasing myself too far. I used often to say to myself: now let's run over our own qualities. Physical strength, then—**nil**: I am small, crooked, rickety, my arms and legs are like sticks, I'm like a spider. Intelligence—very little above nil, considering that

nil: zero; absolutely nothing

I've never managed, out of all the jobs there are, to rise above that of dish-washer in a hotel. Looks—less than nil: I have a narrow, yellow face, eyes of an indefinite, dirty colour, and a nose that seems to have been made for a face twice as broad as mine; it is big and long, and looks as if it was going straight down, and then, at the tip, it turns up like a lizard raising its snout. Other qualities, such as courage, quickness, personal charm, likeableness—less said about them the better. Quite naturally, then, after coming to such conclusions, I was careful not to make advances to women. The only one I ever attempted to approach—a housemaid in the hotel—put me in my place with a very suitable word—"you poor fish," she said. And so I became gradually convinced that I was worth nothing at all and that the best thing for me to do was to keep quiet, in a corner, so as not to get in anybody's way.

Anyone passing along the street at the back of the Rome hotel where I work, during the early hours of the afternoon, can see a row of windows open at ground level, with a strong smell of washing-up coming from them. If his eyes can pierce the gloom, he will also see piles and piles of plates towering up to the ceiling, on tables and on the marble slab of the sink. Well, that was my corner, the corner of the world I had chosen so as not to be conspicuous. But what a queer thing fate is: the last thing I should have expected was that, in that corner, in that very kitchen, I mean, somebody should come and catch me by surprise and pluck me like a flower that has been hidden in the grass. Ida, it was, Ida, the new scullery-maid[1] who took Giuditta's place when she was going to have a baby. Ida, among women, was just what I was among men: a poor fish. Like me, she was small and twisted, scraggy, insignificant. But she was passionate, restless, gay, a devil. We quickly became friends, owing to the fact that we stood in front of the same dishes and the same greasy water; and then, one thing leading to another, she prevailed upon me to invite her one Sunday to go to the cinema. I invited her out of politeness; and I was surprised when, in the darkness of the cinema, she took my hand, slipping her five fingers in between mine. I thought there was some mistake and even tried to free myself, but she whispered to me to stay still: what harm could there be in holding hands? Then, as we came out, she explained to me that she had been noticing me for some time, from the very day, it might even be said, that she had been

> Ida, among women, was just what I was among men: a poor fish.

---

1 **scullery-maid:** the maid in charge of kitchen dishes and utensils

taken on at the hotel. That, ever since then, she had done nothing but think about me. That she hoped, now, that I was a little fond of her, because she, for her part, could not live without me. It was the first time that a woman, even a woman like Ida, had said things like this to me, and I lost my head. I gave her all the answers she wanted, and a great deal more as well.

But I still felt profoundly astonished, and although she went on repeating that she was mad about me, I failed to be convinced. And so, on other occasions, when we went out together, I couldn't keep from harping on the subject, partly for the pleasure of hearing her say it again, and partly because I found it hard to believe. "Now do tell me, I should like to know what it is you see in me? How do you manage to love me?" And would you believe it? Ida used to cling on to my arm with both hands, raise an adoring face towards me, and answer: "I love you because you have all the good qualities . . . for me you're just living perfection." Incredulously I would repeat: "All the good qualities? Well, I never knew that before." "Yes, all . . . . To begin with, you're so good-looking." I couldn't help laughing, I must confess, and I said: "Me good-looking? but have you taken a proper look at me?" "Yes, indeed I have . . . . I'm doing it all the time." "But what about my nose? Have you ever looked at my nose?" "It's just your nose that I like," she answered; and then, taking hold of my nose between two fingers and shaking it like a bell, "Nose, nose," she went on, "for this nose I don't know what I wouldn't do." Then she added: "Besides, you're so intelligent." "Me intelligent? Why, everyone says I'm an idiot." "They say it out of envy," she replied with feminine logic, "but you are intelligent, extremely intelligent . . . . When you talk, I listen to you open-mouthed . . . . You're the most intelligent person I've ever met." "Well, anyhow," I resumed after a moment, "you won't say I'm strong . . . that you can't say." And she answered, with passion: "Yes, you are strong . . . very, very, strong." This took a little swallowing, and for a moment I was left speechless. Then she started off again: "And besides, if you really want to know, you've got something about you that I just love." So I asked her: "But what is this 'something,' I should like to know?" "I don't quite know how to explain," she replied; "it's your voice, your expression, the way you move . . . . Certainly nobody else has got what you have." Naturally for some time I did not believe her; and I used to make her repeat these speeches to me, simply because it amused me to compare them with what I had always thought about myself. But, as the days went by, I began, I must admit, to get ideas into my head. "Suppose it was really true?" I sometimes said to myself. Not that I really believed that I was any different, essentially, from what I had always thought I was. But Ida's remark about the "something" left me in doubt. In that remark, I felt, lay the explanation of the mystery. On account of that "something," I knew, women liked hunchbacks, dwarfs, old men, even monsters. Why shouldn't somebody like me too? I was neither a hunchback, a dwarf, an old man or a monster.

About this time Ida and I decided to go and see a circus which had pitched its tents opposite the Passeggiata Archeologica. We were both of us feeling very cheerful; and, once inside the big tent, we took our places in the cheap seats, cuddling very close together, arm in arm. Beside me was a tall, fair woman, young and handsome, and with her, one seat farther on, a dark young man, big and strong too, a tough, athletic-looking type. I thought of them as what is called "a handsome pair"; and then I thought no more of them and gave all my attention to the circus. The yellow-sanded arena was still empty, but at the far end there was a platform with a band in red uniforms, entirely of brass instruments and flutes, that never stopped playing warlike marches, one after another. At last four clowns came in, two of them dwarfs and two bigger, with whitened faces and large loose trousers, and they cut capers and made jokes, slapping and kicking each other, and Ida laughed so much that she started coughing. Then the band struck up a lively march and it was the turn of the horses—six in all, three dappled grey and three white—which started circling round the ring, as good as could be, while their trainer, all dressed in red and gold, stood in the middle of the arena and cracked his long whip. A woman in a tulle[2] skirt and white tights came dancing in, took hold of the saddle of one of the horses and ran beside it, mounting and dismounting, up and down, while the horses still went round and round, first at a trot and then at a gallop. When the horses had gone, the clowns came back and turned somersaults and kicked each other's behinds, and then came a family of trapezists, father, mother and their little boy, all three wearing blue tights, and all three very muscular, especially the boy. They clapped their hands up and then, houp la! up a knotted rope they climbed, up and up, right to the roof of the tent. There they began to send the trapezes flying backwards and forwards, hanging on now with their hands and now with their feet and throwing the little boy to each other like a ball. Filled with admiration, I said to Ida: "Look at that! How I should like to be a trapezist! I should like to launch myself into the air and then catch hold of the trapeze with my legs!" Ida, in her usual way, nestled up close beside me and answered in a tone of adoration: "It's all a matter of practice . . . . If you practiced, you could do it too." The fair

---

2 **tulle:** a sheer silk or synthetic material often used for ballet costumes

woman looked at us and whispered something to her companion, and they both started laughing. After the trapezists came the number one attraction— the lions. A number of young men in red-tail coats came in and rolled up the carpet used by the trapezists. As they carried it away, without noticing they rolled up one of the clowns inside it; and again Ida, seeing his white face poking out of the roll of carpet, almost fell off her chair with laughing. Very nimbly and quickly the young men put up a big nickelled cage in the middle of the arena, and then, to a roll of drums, the great blond head of the first lion appeared through a little door. There entered, in all, five of them, as well as a lioness who looked thoroughly ill-tempered and at once began to roar. Last of all came the lion-tamer, an agreeable, ceremonious little man in a green coat with gold braid on it, who at once started bowing to the public, waving a riding-master's whip in one hand and in the other a stick with a hook on the end, like the ones they use for pulling down the roller-blinds of shops. The lions went circling round him, roaring; he went on bowing, calmly and smilingly; then at last he turned toward them, and, by poking them in the backside with the hook, forced them to climb up, one after another, on to some little stools—really quite small ones—which were arranged in a row at the back of the cage. The lions, **cowering**, poor beasts, on top of these cat-sized seats, roared and showed their teeth; two or three of them, as the trainer passed within range, put out a paw in his direction, which he avoided with a pirouette. "What if they eat him?" Ida whispered to me, clinging to my arm. There was a roll of drums; the trainer went up to one of the lions which was older than the rest and which looked three-quarters asleep and was not roaring, opened its mouth and put his head inside, three times in succession. I said to Ida, amid the bursts of applause which followed: "You won't believe me . . . but I should just love to go into that cage and put my head in the lion's mouth too." Filled with admiration, and cuddling up against me, she replied. "I know you'd be quite capable of it." At these words, the fair young woman and the athletic young man burst out laughing, looking significantly at us. This time we could not ignore the fact that they were laughing at us, and Ida grew angry and muttered to me: "They're laughing at us . . . . Why don't you tell them how rude they are?" But at that moment a bell rang and everyone got up, while the lions went off with their heads down, through the usual little door. The first part of the show was over.

As we left the tent the other two were walking in front of us. Ida went on doggedly whispering to me: "You've got to tell them how rude they are . . . if you don't you're a coward"; and I, **piqued** in my pride, made up my mind

cowering:
shrinking from; showing fear

piqued:
irritated; bothered

to accost them. Outside the big tent, and in the shelter of it, was a shed where you could pay extra to visit the zoo belonging to the circus: it contained a row of cages on one side, with the wild animals, and on the other a space with straw on the floor where the tame ones were kept loose—that is to say, zebras, elephants, horses and dogs. It was almost dark inside the shed, but, as we came in, we could see, in the gloom, the other two standing in front of the bear's cage. The fair woman was leaning forward to look at the bear, which was curled up fast asleep, its furry back against the bars; and the man was pulling her away by the arm. I went straight up to the man and said in a firm voice: "Tell me . . . were you laughing at us?"

He turned slightly and answered without hesitation: "No, we were laughing at a frog pretending to be an ox."

"The frog, I suppose, being me?"

"If the cap fits, wear it."

Ida was pushing me forward with her hand on my arm. Raising my voice, I replied: "You know what you are? You're just an ignorant cad."

He retorted, brutally: "Ah, so the frog's beginning to croak now, is he?"

At this, the woman started to laugh, and Ida, hissing like a viper, broke in: "There's nothing to laugh at . . . instead of laughing, you'd better stop rubbing yourself up against my husband . . . . I suppose you think I didn't see you. . . . You've been rubbing your arm up against him the whole time."

I was astonished, because I hadn't noticed it: at most, since she was sitting beside me, she might have perhaps just touched me with her elbow. Indeed she answered indignantly: "My dear girl, you're crazy . . . . "

"No, I'm not crazy; I saw you rubbing up against him."

"But why d'you think I should worry about a poor fish like your husband?" she spoke now with the utmost scorn. "If I had to rub up against anyone, I should choose a real man . . . . Here's a real man for you." As she said this she took hold of her boy friend's arm as a pork-butcher might take up a ham to show it off to a customer. "This is the arm I'd rub up against . . . Look what muscles . . . look how strong he is."

And now in turn, the man came up to me and said threateningly: "That's enough . . . get along with you . . . better for you if you do."

"Who says so?" I cried in exasperation, raising myself on tiptoe to be on a level with him.

The scene that followed I shall remember as long as I live. He made no reply to my remark, but, all of the sudden, took me under the arms and lifted me up in the air like a feather. On the other side from the cages, as I have said, there was a straw-covered space where the tame animals were kept. Just behind us there was a family of elephants—father, mother, and baby, the latter comparatively small but still about the size of a horse. They were standing in a dark corner, poor creatures, with drooping ears and trunks, with their huge dark rumps pressed close together. And so he lifted me up, this great bully, and suddenly dumped me down on the back of the smallest elephant. The animal perhaps thought the moment had come for it to go into the circus-ring, and started trotting, with me on its back, along the gangway beside the cages. People rushed in all directions, Ida was running along behind me, screaming, and I, after sitting astride the little elephant and trying in vain to snatch hold of it by the ears, when we reached the end of the gangway, slipped off and fell to the ground, hitting the back of my head. What happened then, I don't know, because I fainted, and when I came round I found myself at the First Aid post, with Ida sitting beside me holding my hand. Later, as soon as I felt better, we went home without seeing the second part of the show.

Next day I said to Ida: "It was your fault . . . you put such ideas into my head, making me think I was goodness knows what . . . . But that woman was perfectly right: I'm just a poor fish and nothing more."

But Ida, taking me by the arm and gazing at me, "You were magnificent," she said. "He was frightened, and that was why he put you on to the elephant . . . . And then, riding along on the elephant, you looked really splendid . . . . It was a pity you fell off."

So there was nothing to be done. For her I was one thing, for other people, another. But can you ever tell what women see, when they're in love?

Translated by Angus Davidson

After You Read

Critical Reading

1. What **connotations** does the phrase "poor fish" have for you? How do those connotations affect your feelings toward the narrator?

2. What is the significance of the **setting** of the story, a circus?

3. Do you agree that one **theme** of this story could be the idea that love is blind? If not, what do you think the theme is? For either position, use textual evidence to support your conclusion.

4. Does the narrator change by the end of the story? Defend your answer with details from the story.

Literary Lens: Conflict

Conflict, the struggle between opposing forces, may be external or internal. In "Poor Fish," the narrator's internal conflict, his struggle to decide if he is an inferior person, is paralleled by external conflicts. Re-create the chart below. In the center box, record three quotes from the story that show the narrator's internal conflict. Then identify two examples of external conflict in the story. Draw a conclusion about how the narrator's internal struggle impacts his external ones.

Conflict	Quotes	Internal or external?

Focus on Research: Use Literary Criticism

Literary criticism is the evaluation, analysis, or interpretation of literary works. Using your school or public library website, find a source of literary criticism for Alberto Moravia's "Poor Fish." Databases such as Literature Online (LION), Literary Reference Center, or JSTOR are all good places to start. For most of these sites, you will need to type the title of the work in quotation marks in the search box, as well as the author's name (sometimes in quotes also). Find at least one literary criticism of Moravia's story and write a summary of it. Paraphrase or quote the source as needed and use appropriate in-text citations.

The Black Sheep

Italo Calvino

Before You Read

Born in Cuba, Italo Calvino (1923–1985) moved to Italy as a youth. As a teenager during World War II, Calvino fought in the Resistance movement against fascist Italian dictator Benito Mussolini and Hitler's occupying German troops. He became fascinated with storytelling as a young soldier, swapping stories around the fire.

Calvino is as famous for his novels as for his collections of short stories. Though one of his first novels was a realistic depiction of wartime, he later employed a wide variety of styles, switching back and forth between realism and fantasy. Calvino was especially fond of fables—the form of the following story—believing them to be "true."

World Context

In his later works, Calvino moved away from modernist themes and experimented with narrative. *If on a Winter's Night a Traveller* (1979) treats the reader as the central character. Calvino's work was widely known and influential in Europe and beyond.

 LITERARY LENS In an **allegory,** characters stand for abstract qualities. As you read, consider what those qualities might be.

There was a country where they were all thieves. At night everybody would leave home with skeleton keys and shaded lanterns and go and burgle a neighbor's house. They'd get back at dawn, loaded, to find their own house had been robbed. So everybody lived happily together, nobody lost out, since each stole from the other, and that other from another again, and so on and on until you got to a last person who stole from the first. Trade in the country inevitably involved cheating on the parts both of buyer and seller. The government was a criminal organization that stole from its subjects, and the subjects for their part were only interested in defrauding the government. Thus life went on smoothly, nobody was rich and nobody was poor.

One day, how we don't know, it so happened that an honest man came to live in the place. At night, instead of going out with his sack and his lantern, he stayed home to smoke and read novels.

The thieves came, saw the light on and didn't go in.

This went on for a while: then they were obliged to explain to him that even if he wanted to live without doing anything, it was no reason to stop others from doing things. Every night he spent at home meant a family would have nothing to eat the following day.

The honest man could hardly object to such reasoning. He took to going out in the evening and coming back the following morning like they did, but he didn't steal. He was honest, there was nothing you could do about it. He went as far as the bridge and watched the water flow by beneath. When he got home he found he had been robbed.

In less than a week the honest man found himself penniless, he had nothing to eat and his house was empty. But this was hardly a problem, since it was his own fault; no, the problem was that his behavior upset everything else. Because he let the others steal everything he had without stealing anything from anybody; so there was always someone who got home at dawn to find their house untouched; the house he should have robbed. In any event after a while the ones who weren't being robbed found themselves richer than the others and didn't want to steal anymore. To make matters worse, the ones who came to steal from the honest man's house found it was always empty; so they became poor.

Meanwhile, the ones who had become rich got into the honest man's habit of going to the bridge at night to watch the water flow by beneath. This increased the confusion because it meant lots of others became rich and lots of others became poor.

Now, the rich people saw that if they went to the bridge every night they'd soon be poor. And they thought: "Let's pay some of the poor to go and rob for us." They made contracts, fixed salaries, percentages: they were still thieves of course, and they still tried to swindle each other. But, as tends to happen, the rich got richer and richer and the poor got poorer and poorer.

Some of the rich people got so rich that they didn't need to steal or have others steal for them so as to stay rich. But if they stopped stealing they would get poor because the poor stole from them. So they paid the very poorest of the poor to defend their property from the other poor, and that meant setting up a police force and building prisons.

So it was that only a few years after the appearance of the honest man, people no longer spoke of robbing and being robbed, but only of the rich and the poor; but they were still all thieves.

The only honest man had been the one at the beginning, and he died in very short order, of hunger.

Translated by Tim Parks

Backyards | Hugo Robus

After You Read

Critical Reading

1. What do you think is the meaning of the story's title, "The Black Sheep"? Explain why it is **ironic**.

2. **Hyperbole**—a literary device using exaggeration for effect—is used often in this story. Find some examples and analyze their effect.

3. **Satire** is a literary form that ridicules human vices and foibles. What is the point of Calvino's satire?

Literary Lens: Allegory

An **allegory** is a literary work in which characters, objects, and events represent universal philosophies or historical events. Use the table below to examine the meaning of "The Black Sheep" as an allegory. Re-create it on another piece of paper and then fill in the columns by writing the larger meaning of the character, object, or event.

Character	What it/ they represent	Object	What it/ they represent	Event	What it represents
Thieves		Bridge		Honest man arrives	
Honest man		Money		Rich hire the poor	
Rich people		Prisons		People speak only of rich and poor	

Focus on Research: Evaluate Evidence

Search for a list of Italo Calvino's novels and read summaries of them. Choose a title that interests you the most. Then find two book reviews. As you read, consider any conflicting points of view. Evaluate the evidence that each reviewer provides in support of their opinion of the book. Which reviewer provides stronger evidence in support of their position? Write a short evaluation of the evidence provided.

The Literature of
Germany

Background

In the early 1800s, no country called "Germany" existed. Rather, the German-speaking people were divided among hundreds of small kingdoms, duchies, and principalities. Throughout the century, the desire of these people to unify into one country—into a nation—was powerful. Two influential writers who benefited from and advanced German nationalism were a pair of friends, Johann Wolfgang von Goethe (1749–1832) and Friedrich von Schiller (1759–1805). Goethe, besides being a poet, playwright, and novelist, was an able scientist whose studies of plants influenced Charles Darwin. His masterpiece was a massive, two-part poetic drama *Faust*, which tells about the man who trades his soul to the devil in return for knowledge.

Schiller, a poet, playwright, and historian, is widely remembered for his poem "Ode to Joy." This was set to music in the last movement of Ludwig van Beethoven's 9th Symphony.

Germany and the United States

Among the many costs of a dictatorship is that it often drives a country's most talented intellectuals into exile. Germany under Nazi rule during the 1930s and 1940s was no exception. As the Nazis tightened their control, scientists, musicians, filmmakers, and writers sought refuge in other countries. Thomas Mann, the Nobel Prize-winning author of *The Magic Mountain*, fled Germany and eventually settled in the United States. So did Franz Werfel (1890–1945), author of the novel *The Song of Bernadette*. Bertolt Brecht (1898–1956), perhaps the 20th century's most significant playwright, also spent time in American exile.

Research: Summarize

Few, if any, works of German literature are as deeply revered as the anonymous epic poem the *Nibelungenlied,* written around 1200. It tells the tragic story of the legendary dragon-killer Siegfried. Adaptations include *The Ring of the Nibelung,* a mammoth four-part opera composed between 1848 and 1874 by Richard Wagner, and Fritz Lang's classic, two-part silent movie of the epic, which premiered in 1924. Find a concise synopsis of this epic. Then, briefly summarize its story in a one-minute oral report.

The Balek Scales

Heinrich Böll

Before You Read

As a young man, Heinrich Böll (1917–1985) was conscripted as a German soldier during World War II. He was later taken as a POW by the Americans. Horrified both by war and Nazism, Böll faced the "frightful fate of being a soldier and having to wish that the war might be lost." He described his wartime experience in his first novel, *The Train Was on Time*. After this he began to explore the spiritual and moral emptiness of postwar Germany in works like *Billiards at Half-Past Nine* and *The Clown*. A committed pacifist and anti-authoritarian, Böll believed that literature plays a critical role in shaping human society. As he wrote upon winning the Nobel Prize in Literature in 1972, "Art is always a good hiding place, not for dynamite, but for intellectual explosives and social time bombs."

World Context

Like his famous compatriot Günter Grass, Böll is known for the social criticism and antimilitarism in his writing. He fervently believed that Germany had a mandate to remember its terrible past. He also criticized the corruption in Germany's Catholic Church.

 LITERARY LENS As you read, identify the **theme**, or underlying message of the story.

W here my grandfather came from, most of the people lived by working in the flax[1] sheds. For five generations they had been breathing in the dust which rose from the crushed flax stalks, letting themselves be killed off by slow degrees, a race of long-suffering, cheerful people who ate goat cheese, potatoes, and now and then a rabbit; in the evening they would sit at home spinning and knitting; they sang, drank mint tea and were happy. During the day they would carry the flax stalks to the antiquated machines, with no protection from the dust and at the mercy

---
1 **flax:** a crop cultivated mostly for its fiber and seed

from the heat which came pouring out of the drying kilns. Each cottage contained only one bed, standing against the wall like a closet and reserved for the parents, while the children slept all round the room on benches. In the morning the room would be filled with the odor of thin soup; on Sundays there was stew, and on feast days the children's faces would light up with pleasure as they watched the black acorn coffee turning paler and paler from the milk their smiling mother poured into their coffee mugs.

The parents went off early to the flax sheds; the housework was left to the children: they would sweep the room, tidy up, wash the dishes and peel the potatoes, precious pale-yellow fruit whose thin peel had to be produced afterwards to dispel any suspicion of extravagance or carelessness.

As soon as the children were out of school they had to go off into the woods and, depending on the season, gather mushrooms and herbs: woodruff and thyme, caraway, mint and foxglove, and in summer, when they had brought in the hay from their meager fields, they gathered hayflowers. A kilo[2] of hayflowers was worth one pfennig,[3] and they were sold by the apothecaries[4] in town for twenty pfennigs a kilo to highly strung ladies. The mushrooms were highly prized: they fetched twenty pfennigs a kilo and were sold in the shops in town for one mark[5] twenty. The children would crawl deep into the green darkness of the forest during the autumn when dampness drove the mushrooms out of the soil, and almost every family had its own places where it gathered mushrooms, places which were handed down in whispers from generation to generation.

The woods belonged to the Baleks, as well as the flax sheds, and in my grandfather's village the Baleks had a château,[6] and the wife of the head of the family had a little room next to the dairy where mushrooms, herbs, and hayflowers were weighed and paid for. There on the table stood the great Balek scales, an old-fashioned, ornate bronze-gilt contraption, which my grandfather's grandparents had already faced when they were children, their grubby hands holding their little baskets of mushrooms, their paper bags of hayflowers, breathlessly watching the number of weights Frau Balek had to throw on the scale before the swinging pointer came to rest exactly over the black line, that thin line of justice which had to be redrawn every

---

2 **kilo:** a kilogram, a unit for measuring
3 **pfennig:** a German monetary unit comparable to a penny
4 **apothecaries:** pharmacists
5 **mark:** a German monetary unit
6 **château:** French word for a large house in the countryside

year. Then Frau Balek would take the big book covered in brown leather, write down the weight, and pay out the money, pfennigs or ten-pfennig pieces and very, very occasionally, a mark. And when my grandfather was a child there was a big glass jar of lemon drops standing there, the kind that cost one mark a kilo, and when Frau Balek—whichever one happened to be presiding over the little room—was in a good mood, she would put her hand into this jar and give each child a lemon drop, and the children's faces would light up with pleasure, the way they used to when on feast days their mother poured milk into their coffee mugs, milk that made the coffee turn paler and paler until it was as pale as the flaxen pigtails of the little girls.

One of the laws imposed by the Baleks on the village was: No one was permitted to have scales in the house. The law was so ancient that nobody gave a thought as to when and how it had arisen, and it had to be obeyed, for anyone who broke it was dismissed from the flax sheds, he could not sell his mushrooms or his thyme or his hayflowers, and the power of the Baleks was so far-reaching that no one in the neighboring villages would give him work either, or buy his forest herbs. But since the days when my grandfather's parents had gone out as small children to gather mushrooms and sell them in order that they might season the meat of the rich people of Prague or be baked into game pies, it had never occurred to anyone to break this law: flour could be measured in cups, eggs could be counted, what they had spun could be measured by the yard, and besides, the old-fashioned bronze-gilt, ornate Balek scales did not look as if there was anything wrong with them, and five generations had entrusted the swinging black pointer with what they had gone out as eager children to gather from the woods.

True, there were some among these quiet people who **flouted** the law, **poachers** bent on making more money in one night than they could earn in a whole month in the flax sheds, but even these people apparently never thought of buying scales or making their own. My grandfather was the first person bold enough to test the justice of the Baleks, the family who lived in the château and drove two carriages, who always maintained one boy from the village while he studied **theology** at the **seminary** in Prague, the family with whom the priest played taroc[7] every Wednesday, on whom the local reeve,[8] in his carriage emblazoned with the Imperial coat of arms,[9]

flouted: disregarded; defied

poachers: trespassers; people who hunt illegally

theology: study of religious belief and practice

seminary: school that trains priests, ministers, or rabbis

---

7 **taroc:** a kind of card game
8 **reeve:** an administrative official
9 **Imperial coat of arms:** the royal symbol or emblem

made an annual New Year's Day call and on whom the Emperor conferred a title on the first day of the year 1900.

My grandfather was hardworking and smart: he crawled further into the woods than the children of his clan had crawled before him, he penetrated as far as the thicket where, according to legend, Bilgan the Giant was supposed to dwell, guarding a treasure. But my grandfather was not afraid of Bilgan: he worked his way deep into the thicket, even when he was quite little, and brought out great quantities of mushrooms; he even found truffles, for which Frau Balek paid thirty pfennigs a pound. Everything my grandfather took to the Baleks he entered on the back of a torn-off calendar page: every pound of mushrooms, every gram of thyme, and on the right-hand side, in his childish handwriting, he entered the amount he received for each item; he scrawled in every pfennig, from the age of seven to the age of twelve, and by the time he was twelve the year 1900 had arrived, and because the Baleks had been raised to the aristocracy by the Emperor, they gave every family in the village a quarter of a pound of real coffee, the Brazilian kind; there was also free beer and tobacco for the men, and at the château there was a great banquet; many carriages stood in the avenue of poplars leading from the entrance gates to the château.

But the day before the banquet the coffee was distributed in the little room which had housed the Balek scales for almost a hundred years, and the Balek family was now called Balek von Bilgan because, according to legend, Bilgan the Giant used to have a great castle on the site of the present Balek estate.

My grandfather often used to tell me how he went there after school to fetch the coffee for four families: the Cechs, the Weidlers, the Vohlas, and his own, the Brüchers. It was the afternoon of New Year's Eve: there were the front rooms to be decorated, the baking to be done, and the families did not want to spare four boys and have each of them go all the way to the château to bring back a quarter of a pound of coffee.

And so my grandfather sat on the narrow wooden bench in the little room while Gertrud the maid counted out the wrapped four-ounce packages of coffee, four of them, and he looked at the scales and saw that the pound weight was still lying on the left-hand scale; Frau Balek von Bilgan was busy with preparations for the banquet. And when Gertrud was about to put her hand into the jar with the lemon drops to give my grandfather one, she discovered it was empty: it was refilled once a year, and held one kilo of the kind that cost a mark.

Gertrud laughed and said: "Wait here while I get the new lot," and my grandfather waited with the four four-ounce packages which had been wrapped and sealed in the factory, facing the scales on which someone had left the pound weight, and my grandfather took the four packages of coffee, put them on the empty scale, and his heart thudded as he watched the black finger of justice come to rest on the left of the black line: the scale with the pound weight stayed down, and the pound of coffee remained up in the air; his heart thudded more than if he had been lying behind a bush in the forest waiting for Bilgan the Giant, and he felt in his pocket for the pebbles he always carried with him so he could use his catapult to shoot the sparrows which pecked away at his mother's cabbage plants—he had to put three, four, five pebbles beside the packages of coffee before the scale with the pound weight rose and the pointer at last came to rest over the black line. My grandfather took the coffee from the scale, wrapped the five pebbles in his kerchief, and when Gertrud came back with the big kilo bag of lemon drops which had to last for another whole year in order to make the children's faces light up with pleasure, when Gertrud let the lemon drops rattle into the glass jar, the pale little fellow was still standing there, and nothing seemed to have changed. My grandfather only took three of the packages, then Gertrud looked in startled surprise at the white-faced child who threw the lemon drop onto the floor, ground it under his heel, and said: "I want to see Frau Balek."

"Balek von Bilgan, if you please," said Gertrud.

"All right, Frau Balek von Bilgan," but Gertrud only laughed at him, and he walked back to the village in the dark, took the Cechs, the Weidlers, and the Vohlas their coffee, and said he had to go and see the priest.

Instead he went out into the dark night with his five pebbles in his kerchief. He had to walk a long way before he found someone who had scales, who was permitted to have them; no one in the villages of Blaugau and Bernau had any, he knew that, and he went straight through them till, after two hours' walking, he reached the little town of Dielheim where Honig the apothecary lived. From Honig's house came the smell of fresh pancakes, and Honig's breath, when he opened the door to the half-frozen boy, already smelled of punch, there was a moist cigar between his narrow lips, and he clasped the boy's cold hands firmly for a moment, saying: "What's the matter, has your father's lung got worse?"

"No, I haven't come for medicine, I wanted . . ." My grandfather undid his kerchief, took out the five pebbles, held them out to Honig and said: "I wanted to have these weighed." He glanced anxiously into Honig's face, but

Market |
George Tooker
1949

when Honig said nothing and did not get angry, or even ask him anything, my grandfather said: "It is the amount that is short of justice," and now, as he went into the warm room, my grandfather realized how wet his feet were. The snow had soaked through his cheap shoes, and in the forest the branches had showered him with snow which was now melting, and he was tired and hungry and suddenly began to cry because he thought of the quantities of mushrooms, the herbs, the flowers, which had been weighed on the scales which were short five pebbles' worth of justice. And when Honig, shaking his head and holding the five pebbles, called his wife, my grandfather thought of the generations of his parents, his grandparents, who had all had to have their mushrooms, their flowers, weighed on the scales, and he was overwhelmed by a great wave of injustice, and began to sob louder than ever, and, without waiting to be asked, he sat down on a chair, ignoring the pancakes, the cup of hot coffee which nice plump Frau Honig put in front of him, and did not stop crying till Honig himself came out from the shop at the back and, rattling the pebbles in his hand, said in a low voice to his wife: "Fifty-five grams, exactly."

The Balek Scales

My grandfather walked the two hours home through the forest, got a beating at home, said nothing, not a single word, when he was asked about the coffee, spent the whole evening doing sums on the piece of paper on which he had written down everything he had sold to Frau Balek, and when midnight struck, and the cannon could be heard from the château, and the whole village rang with shouting and laughter and the noise of rattles, when the family kissed and embraced all round, he said into the New Year silence: "The Baleks owe me eighteen marks and thirty-two pfennigs." And again he thought of all the children there were in the village, of his brother Fritz who had gathered so many mushrooms, of his sister Ludmilla; he thought of the many hundreds of children who had all gathered mushrooms for the Baleks, and herbs and flowers, and this time he did not cry but told his parents and brothers and sisters of his discovery.

When the Baleks von Bilgan went to High Mass on New Year's Day, their new coat of arms—a giant crouching under a fir tree—already emblazoned in blue and gold on their carriage, they saw the hard, pale faces of the people all staring at them. They had expected garlands in the village, a song in their honor, cheers and hurrahs, but the village was completely deserted as they drove through it, and in church the pale faces of the people were turned toward them, mute and hostile, and when the priest mounted the pulpit to deliver his New Year's sermon he sensed the chill in those otherwise quiet and peaceful faces, and he stumbled painfully through his sermon and went back to the altar drenched in sweat. And as the Baleks von Bilgan left the church after Mass, they walked through a lane of mute, pale faces. But young Frau Balek von Bilgan stopped in front of the children's pews, sought out my grandfather's face, pale little Franz Brücher, and asked him, right there in the church: "Why didn't you take the coffee for your mother?" And my grandfather stood up and said: "Because you owe me as much money as five kilos of coffee would cost." And he pulled the five pebbles from his pocket, held them out to the young woman and said: "This much, fifty-five grams, is short in every pound of your justice"; and before the woman could say anything the men and women in the church lifted up their voices and sang: "The justice of this earth, O Lord, hath put Thee to death . . . ."

While the Baleks were at church, Wilhelm Vohla, the poacher, had broken into the little room, stolen the scales and the big fat leather-bound book in which had been entered every kilo of mushrooms, every kilo of hayflowers, everything bought by the Baleks in the village, and all afternoon of that New Year's Day the men of the village sat in my great-grandparents' front room and calculated, calculated one tenth of everything that had been bought—but when they had calculated many thousands of talers[10] and had still not come to an end, the reeve's gendarmes[11] arrived, made their way into my great-grandfather's front room, shooting and stabbing as they came, and removed the scales and the book by force. My grandfather's little sister Ludmilla lost her life, a few men were wounded, and one of the gendarmes was stabbed to death by Wilhelm Vohla the poacher.

Our village was not the only one to rebel: Blaugau and Bernau did too, and for almost a week no work was done in the flax sheds. But a great many gendarmes appeared, and the men and women were threatened with prison, and the Baleks forced the priest to display the scales publicly in the school and demonstrate that the finger of justice swung to and fro accurately. And the men and women went back to the flax sheds—but no one went to the school to watch the priest: he stood there all alone, helpless and forlorn with his weights, scales, and packages of coffee.

And the children went back to gathering mushrooms, to gathering thyme, flowers, and foxglove, but every Sunday, as soon as the Baleks entered the church, the hymn was struck up: "The justice of this earth, O Lord, hath put Thee to death," until the reeve ordered it proclaimed in every village that the singing of the hymn was forbidden.

My grandfather's parents had to leave the village, and the new grave of their little daughter; they became basket weavers, but did not stay long anywhere because it pained them to see how everywhere the finger of justice swung falsely. They walked along behind their cart, which crept slowly over the country roads, taking their thin goat with them, and passers-by could sometimes hear a voice from the cart singing: "The justice of this earth, O Lord, hath put Thee to death." And those who wanted to listen could hear the tale of the Baleks von Bilgan, whose justice lacked a tenth part. But there were few who listened.

Translated by Leila Vennewitz

---

10 **talers:** silver coins
11 **gendarmes:** law-enforcing soldiers

After You Read

Critical Reading

1. Examine the methods the author uses to **characterize** the narrator's grandfather. Using evidence from the story, how would you describe him?

2. Why do you suppose the author chooses to use a **first-person narrator** to relate this story? Explain what he gains by doing so.

3. How does the **mood** of the story change from the beginning to the end of the story? Use textual evidence to support your answer.

4. What other institutions are bound to the power of the Baleks, according to Böll? Think about whether such relationships continue in any modern societies, especially your own.

Literary Lens: Theme

The **theme** of a literary work is the underlying meaning or message. The theme may be stated explicitly or it may be inferred through details of the text. Re-create the chart below. First, write a sentence or phrase that you think best describes the theme of "The Balek Scales." Then fill in the columns with answers to each question.

Theme:			
How does the plot contribute to the theme?	How does the setting contribute to the theme?	How does characterization contribute to the theme?	What sections of the passage demonstrate the theme?

Focus on Research: Use a Direct Quotation

Böll was part of a literary movement called *trümmerliteratur*. Use a literary dictionary or other sources to define this term and explain the movement's characteristics. Take notes on these characteristics and then evaluate the ways in which "The Balek Scales" fits and/or doesn't fit them. Finally, write a paragraph in which you use a direct quotation from one of your sources. Use appropriate in-text citations with the quotation.

The Literature of the
Czech Republic

Background

The most renowned Czech writer of the 20th century is also one of its national political heroes. In the late 1960s, the playwright and essayist Václav Havel (1936–2011) led efforts to demand more freedom in his communist-ruled country, Czechoslovakia. He was imprisoned several times. By 1993, the communists had fallen from power, and the country had peacefully split into two separate republics. In that year, Havel became the first president of the Czech Republic.

During his days as a resistance leader, Havel's plays dramatized the inhumane absurdities imposed by authoritarian rule. For example, in his 1967 play *The Memorandum*, a totalitarian government imposes an artificial language too nonsensical for anyone to understand. Havel's plays are often linked with the Theater of the Absurd, a movement that includes the works of Eugène Ionesco, Samuel Beckett, and Harold Pinter.

The Czech Republic and the United States

The term "robot" is so common in the United States that people might assume that it is originally an English word. Actually, it was first introduced in the 1921 science fiction play *R.U.R.* by the Czech writer Karel Čapek (1890–1938), who based it on the Czech word for forced labor. *R.U.R.* is a terrifying story of how robots, originally docile, turn on their human masters and exterminate them.

Robots have been endlessly portrayed in U.S. popular culture. They were popularized in the *Star Wars* and *Terminator* movies and television shows such as *Lost in Space* and *Dr. Who*. In a series of novels, the Russian-born American science fiction writer Isaac Asimov (1920–1992) seriously considered the role robots might play in human society.

Research: Develop a Thesis

The unfinished satirical novel *The Good Soldier Schweik* by Czech writer Jaroslav Hašek (1883–1923) is widely considered to be the first true anti-war novel. Do some preliminary research on this book and then write a thesis statement for a paper describing this novel's influence on later anti-war novels.

The Last Judgment

Karel Čapek

Before You Read

Karel Čapek (1890–1938) was one of the most popular and influential Czech writers of the 20th century. In addition to numerous novels, stories, and essays, Čapek is especially famous for two science fiction plays—*The Life of Insects* and the frightening *R.U.R.: Rossum's Universal Robots*. Devoted to democracy and fearful of totalitarianism, Čapek warned against the impending threat of Nazi Germany. In frail health throughout his life, Čapek died of pneumonia before the Nazis decided to arrest him.

World Context

The land that is now the Czech Republic was once occupied by two dictatorships—the Nazis and the Soviets. Writers opposing the official line risked prison, work camps, or death, so many masked their social criticism as fantasy, science fiction, black humor, or allegory. Čapek's writing fell into many of these categories and so served as a model.

 LITERARY LENS As you read, consider your feelings for the **character** Kugler. Do you sympathize with him?

Pursued by several warrants and a whole army of policemen and detectives, the notorious multiple-killer Kugler swore that they'd never take him, and they didn't—at least not alive. The last of his nine murderous deeds was shooting a policeman who was trying to arrest him. The policeman indeed died, but not before putting a total of seven bullets into Kugler, three of which were definitely fatal. To all appearances he had escaped earthly justice.

Kugler's death came so quickly that he had no time to feel any particular pain. When his soul left his body, it might have been surprised at the oddness of the next world, a world beyond space, gray and infinitely

desolate—but it wasn't. A man who has been jailed on two continents looks upon the next life merely as new surroundings. Kugler expected to charge on through, equipped with a bit of courage, just as he'd done everywhere else.

desolate: deserted; joyless

At length the inevitable Last Judgment got around to Kugler. Heaven being eternally in a state of emergency, he was brought before a special court of three judges and not, as his previous conduct would ordinarily merit, before a jury. The courtroom was furnished simply, like courtrooms on earth, with one exception: there was no provision for swearing in witnesses. The judges were old and worthy councilors with austere, weary faces. The formalities were somewhat tedious: Kugler, Ferdinand; unemployed; born on such-and-such a date; died . . . At this point it was shown that Kugler did not know the date of his own death. Immediately he realized that his failure to remember was damaging in the eyes of the judges, and his attitude hardened.

"Of what do you consider yourself guilty?" the presiding judge asked.

"Nothing," Kugler replied obstinately.

"Bring in the witness," the judge sighed.

In front of Kugler there appeared an extraordinary gentleman, stately, bearded, and clothed in a blue robe strewn with golden stars; at his entrance the judges rose, and even Kugler stood up, reluctant but fascinated. Only when the old gentleman took a seat did the judges sit down again.

"Witness," began the presiding judge, "Omniscient God, this court has summoned You in order to hear Your testimony in the matter of Kugler, Ferdinand. As You are the Supreme Truth, You need not take the oath. We ask only that, in the interest of the proceedings, You keep to the subject at hand and not branch out into particulars that have no legal bearing on the case. And you, Kugler, don't interrupt the Witness. He knows everything, so there's no use denying anything. And now, Witness, if You would please begin."

That said, the presiding judge took off his spectacles and leaned comfortably on the bench before him, evidently in preparation for a long speech by the witness. The oldest of the three judges nestled down in sleep. The recording angel opened the Book of Life.

The Witness, God, cleared his throat and began:

"Yes, Kugler, Ferdinand. Ferdinand Kugler, son of a factory official, was a bad, unmanageable child from his earliest days. He loved his mother dearly but was ashamed to show it; that's why he was unruly and defiant. Young man, you infuriated everyone! Do you remember how you bit your father on the thumb when he tried to spank you because you'd stolen a rose from the notary's[1] garden?"

"That rose was for Irma, the tax collector's daughter," Kugler recalled.

"I know," said God. "Irma was seven years old then. And do you know what happened to her later?"

"No, I don't."

"She got married; she married Oskar, the son of the factory owner. But she contracted a venereal disease from him and died of a miscarriage. You remember Rudy Zaruba?"

"What happened to him?"

"Why, he joined the navy and died in Bombay. You two were the worst boys in the whole town. Kugler, Ferdinand was a thief before his tenth year and an **inveterate** liar. He kept bad company, the drunken beggar Dlabola, for instance, with whom he shared his food."

inveterate: habitual; confirmed

The presiding judge motioned with his hand, as if perhaps this was unnecessary information; but Kugler himself asked shyly, "And . . . what happened to his daughter?"

"Marka?" said God. "She lowered herself considerably. In her fourteenth year she prostituted herself; in her twentieth year she died, remembering you in the agony of her death. By your fourteenth year you were nearly a drunkard yourself, and you often ran away from home. Your father died from grief and worry, and your mother nearly cried her eyes out. You brought dishonor on your home, and your little sister, your pretty sister Marticka, never married: no young man would come calling at the home of a thief. She's still living alone and in poverty, exhausted from sewing each night and humiliated by her scant earnings from people who take pity on her."

"What's happening right now?"

"This very minute she is at Vlcak's, buying thread. Do you remember that shop? Once, when you were six years old, you bought a colored glass marble there; and that very same day you lost it and never ever found it. Do you remember how sad and angry you were then, and how you blubbered?"

"Where did it roll away to?" Kugler asked eagerly.

"Down the drain and into the gutter. As a matter of fact, it's still there, after thirty years. Right now it's raining on earth, and your marble is shivering in a gush of cold water."

---

1 **notary:** the clerk who certifies public mail

Kugler bent his head, overcome. But the presiding judge fitted his spectacles back on his nose and said mildly, "Witness, we are obliged to get on with the case. Has the accused committed murder?"

The Witness nodded his head. "He murdered nine people. The first one he killed in a brawl, and while in prison for it he was completely corrupted. The second was an unfaithful sweetheart. For that he was sentenced to death, but he escaped. The third was an old man, whom he robbed. The fourth was a night watchman."

"Then he died?" Kugler shouted.

"He died after three days of terrible pain," God said, "and he left six children behind. The fifth and sixth people were an old married couple; he finished them off with an axe and found practically no money, although they had more than twenty thousand hidden away."

Kugler jumped up: "Where? Tell me!"

"In the straw mattress," God said. "In a linen sack inside the mattress. That's where they stored the money they got from **usury** and penny-pinching. The seventh man he killed in America; he was an immigrant, a countryman, helpless as a child."

usury:
lending money
at a high rate of
interest

"So it was in the mattress," Kugler whispered in amazement.

"Yes," the Witness continued. "The eighth man was a passerby who happened to be in the way when Kugler was trying to outrun the police. Kugler had periostitis[2] then and was delirious from the pain. Young man, you were suffering terribly. The last was the policeman who killed Kugler, whom Kugler felled just as he himself was dying."

"And why did the accused commit murder?" queried the presiding judge.

"For the same reasons others do," answered God. "From anger, from greed, deliberately and by chance, sometimes with pleasure and other times from necessity. He was generous and sometimes he helped people. He was kind to women, he loved animals, and he kept his word. Should I tell about his good deeds?"

"Thank You," the presiding judge said, "it isn't necessary. Does the accused have anything to say in his defense?"

"No," Kugler replied with honest indifference; it was all the same to him.

"The court will now take this case under advisement," the presiding judge declared, and the councilors withdrew. God and Kugler remained in the courtroom.

---

2 **periostitis:** an inflammation of the connective tissue of the bone

"Who are they?" Kugler asked, inclining his head toward the three who were leaving.

"People like you," said God. "They were judges on earth, so they're judges here as well."

Kugler nibbled at his fingertips. "I thought . . . I mean, I didn't worry about it or anything, but . . . I figured that You would judge, since . . . since . . ."

"Since I'm God," finished the **stately** gentleman. "But that's just it, don't you see? Because I know everything, I can't possibly judge. That wouldn't do at all. By the way, do you know who turned you in this time?"

"No, I don't," said Kugler, surprised.

"Lucka, the waitress. She did it out of jealousy."

"Excuse me," Kugler ventured, feeling bolder, "but You forgot to mention that no-good Teddy I shot in Chicago."

"You're wrong there," God objected. "He recovered and is alive this very minute. I know he's an informer, but otherwise he's a good man and truly fond of children. You shouldn't think of anyone as being completely worthless."

"But really, why don't You . . . why don't You Yourself do the judging?" Kugler asked **pensively**.

"Because I know everything. If judges knew everything, absolutely everything, they couldn't judge, either: they would understand everything, and their hearts would ache. How could I possibly judge you? Judges know only about your crimes; but I know everything about you. Everything, Kugler. And that's why I cannot judge you."

"But why are those same people judges . . . even here in heaven?"

"Because people belong to each other. As you see, I'm only a witness; it's people who determine the verdict—even in heaven. Believe me, Kugler, this is the way it should be. The only justice people deserve is human justice."

At that moment, the judges returned from their deliberations. In stern tones the presiding judge announced: "For repeated crimes of first-degree murder, manslaughter, robbery, illegal re-entry, concealment of weapons, and the theft of a rose, Kugler, Ferdinand is sentenced to lifelong punishment in hell. The sentence begins immediately. Next case, please. Is the accused, Machat, Frantisek present in court?"

Translated by Norma Comrada

After You Read

Critical Reading

1. What purpose do the **anecdotes** (brief stories) about the people in Kugler's life serve? Evaluate their effectiveness.

2. Reread the paragraph on page 226 that begins "Because I know everything. If judges knew everything, absolutely everything, they couldn't judge, either. . . ." What is meant by this?

3. Why do you think the story ends with a summons to the next criminal? What effect does this have?

Literary Lens: Character

A sympathetic **character** is a fictional character whom the writer expects a reader to care about. Some would say that if an author provides enough information about a character, he or she can create a sympathetic character no matter how badly the character behaves. Analyze Kugler in "The Last Judgment" using the table below. Reread the sections of the story listed in the first column. Then fill in the second and third columns by answering the questions about Kugler.

	Reread the first two paragraphs of the story	Reread the section page 225 that starts with "For the same reasons others do . . . good deeds?"	Go back and trace Kugler through the entire story. Do your feelings about him change?
Essential facts and information about Kugler			
Your impressions of Kugler			

Focus on Research: Develop a Thesis Statement

A thesis statement is a statement of your main idea. Often in a research paper, it is a claim you make and prove through research. A good thesis statement is clear, specific, and arguable. With a partner, brainstorm questions about a literary element of "The Last Judgment," such as theme, characterization, or writing style. Then write a thesis statement on which a literary analysis could be written. Consider whether you can find credible sources to support your argument.

The Literature of

Poland

Background

During the roughly 1,000 years of Polish history, Poles have had eras of great military and political power. However, in the past 250 years, Poland has suffered under its more powerful neighbors: Austria, Germany, and Russia.

Not surprisingly, then, one of Poland's greatest recent writers was one who protested tyranny. Czesław Miłosz (1911–2004) was a Nobel Prize-winning poet, novelist, essayist, and translator. During World War II, when Nazi Germany occupied Poland, he fought in the Polish resistance movement. After the war, the Soviet Union dominated the Polish government, and he sought political asylum in France. Miłosz eventually became a U.S. citizen. After the fall of communism, Miłosz returned to Poland.

In his 1953 collection of essays *The Captive Mind*, Miłosz ruthlessly examined why so many intellectuals surrender their minds to totalitarian rule. His 1957 *Treatise on Poetry* was described by the American critic Helen Vendler as "the most comprehensive and moving poem" of its time.

Poland and the United States

One of Poland's most influential authors was Stanisław Lem (1921–2006), who wrote science fiction. Like the best science fiction writers, Lem explored philosophical themes, including the nature of technology and the potential of human beings. Lem's depth of thought placed him in high esteem among U.S. science fiction writers, who made him an honorary member of the Science Fiction Writers of America in 1973. However, Lem had a poor opinion of U.S. science fiction writers and said so in writing. As a result, his membership to the SFWA was withdrawn in 1976.

Research: Synthesize

Regarding his role as a political dissident, Czesław Miłosz wrote, "My own decision proceeded not from the functioning of the reasoning mind, but from a revolt of the stomach." Dissidents, he said, were less likely to have strong minds than weak stomachs. Synthesizing what you have learned about other European dissidents in this unit, write a short paragraph explaining why a "weak stomach" might promote dissent. Use examples to back up your synthesis.

A Contribution to Statistics

Wislawa Szymborska

Before You Read

Wislawa Szymborska (1923–2012) published her first poem in 1945. Her poems have won many international awards. Collections have been published in more than a dozen languages. In 1996, Szymborska won the Nobel Prize in Literature. In her acceptance speech, she said that "inspiration is not the exclusive privilege of poets or artists generally." Inspired people include any "who've consciously chosen their calling and do their job with love and imagination."

World Context

Szymborska's poems, which often use irony to comment on society, are frequently direct and pointed. She appreciated clear language in poetry. The great Czech writer Czeslaw Milosz wrote that Szymborska's poetry, like other European contemporaries, was "grim" but that she offered "a world where one can breathe."

 LITERARY LENS After you have read this poem once, read it a second time and try to "hear" the poet's **tone**.

O ut of a hundred people
those who always know better
—fifty-two,

doubting every step
—nearly all the rest,   5

glad to lend a hand
if it doesn't take too long
—as high as forty-nine,

Zero Through Nine |
Jasper Johns, 1961

always good
because they can't be otherwise   10
—four, well maybe five,

able to admire without envy,
—eighteen,

suffering illusions
induced by fleeting youth   15
—sixty, give or take a few,

not to be taken lightly
—forty and four,

living in constant fear
of someone or something   20
—seventy-seven,

capable of happiness
—twenty-something tops,

harmless singly,
savage in crowds   25
—half at least,

cruel
when forced by circumstances
—better not to know even ballpark figures,

wise after the fact   30
—just a couple more
than wise before it,

taking only things from life
—thirty
(I wish I were wrong),   35
hunched in pain,
no flashlight in the dark
—eighty-three
sooner or later,

righteous   40
—thirty-five, which is a lot,

righteous
and understanding
—three,

worthy of compassion   45
—ninety-nine,

mortal
—a hundred out of a hundred.
Thus far this figure still remains unchanged.

Translated by Stanislaw Baranczak and Clare Cavanagh

After You Read

Critical Reading

1. Write a **summary** of this poem. Limit your summary to five sentences or less and write in simple, plain language.

2. Analyze the poet's use of percentages to define the characteristics of human behavior. What **theme** does she develop? Use examples from the poem to support your answer.

3. An **aside** is a comment made by the author that is outside the regular flow of the text, such as the comment in parentheses in stanza 13. Find other examples of asides in the poem and comment on the purpose they serve.

Literary Lens: Tone

Tone is a poet's attitude toward their writing. Elements such as word choice, structure, syntax, use of figurative language, and rhyme contribute to tone. Use the table below to identify a few lines of the poem that reveal tone. In the second column, make observations about the aspects of the lines that contribute to tone. In the third column, use an adjective to describe the tone.

Lines or phrases from poem	Notes on word choice, structure, syntax, poetic devices, etc.	Tone (attitude or feeling conveyed)

Focus on Research: Write an Outline

Find several more poems written by Wislawa Szymborska. Consider looking at the library for some of her poetry collections such as *People on a Bridge*, *View with a Grain of Sand: Selected Poems*, *Miracle Fair,* and *Monologue of a Dog*. After reading several poems, choose one that you can compare and contrast with "A Contribution to Statistics." Compare aspects such as the poem's tone, theme, structure, etc. Create an outline for an essay comparing the two poems. In your outline include at least three main points (I, II, III) with two subpoints (A, B, C) under each main point.

And Yet the Books

Czesław Miłosz

Before You Read

Although Czesław Miłosz (1911–2004) was born in Lithuania, his family moved to Poland after World War I. As a young man, he also lived in Paris, where he became serious about writing poetry. Miłosz returned to Poland just before World War II and wrote for anti-Nazi publications during the German occupation. After the war, political turmoil continued in Poland, and Miłosz moved to the United States. Miłosz's poems and his memoir, *The Worlds Within,* have been published in English. He taught at the University of California, Berkeley, from 1961 to 1978. He won the Nobel Prize in Literature in 1980.

World Context

Miłosz spent his early years in Nazi-occupied Poland, where he was one of the leaders of the avant-garde poetry movement. Like many other writers and intellectuals in the 1930s, Miłosz participated in the Resistance movement against the Nazis.

 LITERARY LENS Notice how the poet often uses a similar pattern, called **parallel structure**, in his listing of phrases.

And yet the books will be there on the shelves, separate beings,
That appeared once, still wet
As shining chestnuts under a tree in autumn,
And, touched, coddled, began to live
In spite of fires on the horizon, castles blown up,   5
Tribes on the march, planets in motion.
"We are," they said, even as their pages
Were being torn out, or a buzzing flame

Licked away their letters. So much more durable
Than we are, whose frail warmth 10
Cools down with memory, disperses, perishes.
I imagine the earth when I am no more:
Nothing happens, no loss, it's still a strange pageant,
Women's dresses, dewy lilacs, a song in the valley.
Yet the books will be there on the shelves, well born, 15
Derived from people, but also from radiance, heights.

Translated by the author and Robert Hass

The Book | Juan Gris, 1913

After You Read

Critical Reading

1. What is a **theme** of this poem? Identify details that support the theme.

2. Where in the poem do you see the books personified? Explain what is gained by the **personification** in this poem.

3. Explain the meaning of the last two lines of the poem.

 ## Literary Lens: Parallel Structure

Parallel structure is the technique of using the same pattern of words to show that ideas are of similar importance. Re-create the chart below to record examples of parallel structure and their effects.

Example from poem	Type of pattern	Effects
Ex. Lines 5–6: "fires on the horizon," "Tribes on the march, planets in motion"	Noun followed by a prepositional phrase	repetition of the obstacles books have faced has a harsh, stark, almost violent feel

Focus on Research: Draft and Revise

Using the ideas from this unit, write a working thesis about how European writers have dealt with the trauma of World War II. Make a list of details from the stories and poems that you could use to support your thesis. Rewrite your thesis statement so that it better reflects ideas from your list of details. Then draft several paragraphs based on your thesis statement, making sure to include appropriate transitions. Ask a partner to read your work and offer suggestions to improve content, organization, and sentence structure.

from Flights

Olga Tokarczuk

Before You Read

Olga Tokarczuk (1962–) is considered one of the most critically acclaimed Polish authors of her generation, having published multiple books across genres and having won major awards including the Nobel Prize in Literature in 2018. Her books span many topics, including what she calls "the dark areas" in Polish history and other reflections on historical and modern policies. Widely published throughout Europe, Tokarczuk's works are just beginning to gain popularity in English-speaking countries. Her book *Flights*, originally published in Polish in 2007, was first translated and published in English in 2017.

World Context

Tokarczuk's paternal family were refugees from an area of Poland that later became part of Ukraine. Tokarczuk has observed that the literature of central Europe is often different from the literature of the West, stating "The first thing is that we don't trust reality as much as you do. Reading English novels I always adore the ability to write without fear about inner psychological things . . . but we don't have this patience. We feel that in every moment something must be wrong because our own story wasn't linear."

LITERARY LENS As you read the selections from *Flights*, consider any recurring **motifs** you may find.

Syndrome

The chronicles of my travels would in fact be chronicles of an ailment. I suffer from a **syndrome** that can easily be found in any atlas of clinical syndromes and that—at least according to the literature—occurs with greater and greater frequency. We had better take a peek at this old edition (published in the seventies) of the *Clinical Syndromes*, which is an encyclopedia of syndromes of sorts. For me, it is also an endless source of inspiration. Is there anyone else who would dare to describe people as

syndrome: disorder; disease

totalities, both objectively and generally? Who would employ with such conviction the notion of personality? Who would build up to a convincing typology of it? I don't think so. The idea of the syndrome fits travel psychology like a glove. A syndrome is small, portable, not weighed down by theory, **episodic**. You can explain something with it and then discard it. A disposable instrument of **cognition**.

Mine is called Recurrent Detoxification Syndrome. Without the bells and whistles, its description boils down to the insistence of one's consciousness on returning to certain images, or even the compulsive search for them. It is a variant of the Mean World Syndrome, which has been described fairly exhaustively in neuropsychological studies as a particular type of infection caused by the media. It's quite a **bourgeois** ailment, I suppose. Patients spend long hours in front of the TV, thumbing at their remote controls through all the channels till they find the ones with the most horrendous news: wars, epidemics, and disasters. Then, fascinated by what they're seeing, they can't tear themselves away.

The symptoms themselves are not dangerous, allowing one to lead a normal life as long as one is able to maintain some emotional distance. This unfortunate syndrome cannot be cured; science is reduced in its case to the regretful **constatation** of its existence. When, sufficiently alarmed by their own behavior, patients end up in the offices of psychiatrists, they'll be told to try healthier living—giving up coffee and alcohol, sleeping in a well-ventilated room, gardening, weaving or knitting.

My set of symptoms revolves around my being drawn to all things spoiled, flawed, defective, broken. I'm interested in whatever shape this may take, mistakes in the making of the thing, dead ends. What was supposed to develop but for some reason didn't; or vice versa, what outstretched the design. Anything that **deviates** from the norm, that is too small or too big, overgrown or incomplete, monstrous and disgusting. Shapes that don't heed symmetry, that grow exponentially, brim over, bud, or on the contrary, that scale back to the single unit. I'm not interested in the patterns so scrutinized by statistics that everyone celebrated with a familiar, satisfied smile on their faces. My weakness is for teratology and for freaks. I believe, unswervingly, agonizingly, that it is in freaks that Being breaks through to the surface and reveals its true nature. A sudden fluke disclosure. An embarrassing oops, the seam of one's underwear from beneath a perfectly pleated skirt. The hideous metal skeleton that suddenly pops out from the velvet upholstery; the eruption of a spring from within a cushioned armchair that shamelessly **debunks** any illusion of softness.

episodic: temporary; limited to short occurrences

cognition: mental processes; thinking

bourgeois: middle-class; conventional or mediocre

constatation: assertion without reason or support

deviates: strays or departs from

debunks: exposes something false

Cabinet of Curiosities

I've never been a big fan of art museums, which I would happily exchange for cabinets of **curiosities**, where collections encompass the rare, the unique, the bizarre, the freakish. The things that exist in the shadows of consciousness, and that, when you do take a look, ark out of your field of vision. Yes. I definitely have this unfortunate syndrome. I'm not drawn to centrally located collections, but rather to the smaller places near hospitals, frequently moved down to basements, since they're deemed unworthy of prized exhibition spots, and since they suggest the questionable tastes of their original collectors. A salamander with two tails, faceup in an oblong jar, awaiting its Judgment Day[1]—for all the specimens in the world will be resurrected in the end. A dolphin's kidney in formaldehyde. A sheep's skull,

a total **anomaly**, with double sets of eyes and ears and mouths, pretty as the figure of an ancient god with a dual nature. A human fetus draped in beads and a label in careful calligraphy saying *"Fetus aethiopis 5 mensium."*[2]

Collected over the years, these freaks of nature, two-headed and no-headed, float lazily in formaldehyde solution. Or take the case of the *"Cephalothoracopagus monosymetro,"*[3] exhibited to this day in a museum in Pennsylvania, where the pathological morphology of a fetus with one head and two bodies calls into questions the foundations of logic by asserting that $1 = 2$. And finally a moving culinary specimen: apples from 1848, resting in alcohol, each of them odd, abnormally shaped. Evidently there was someone who recognized that these freaks of nature were owed

immortality, and that only what is different will survive.

It's this kind of thing I make my way toward on my travels, slowly but surely, trailing the errors and blunders of creation.

I've learned to write on trains and in hotels and waiting rooms. On the tray tables on planes. I take notes at lunch, under the table, or in the bathroom. I write in museum stairwells, in cafes, in the car on the shoulder of the motorway. I jot things down on scraps of paper, in notebooks, on postcards, on my other hand, on napkins, in the margins of books. Usually they're short sentences, little images, but sometimes I copy out quotes from

---

1 **Judgment Day:** a concept found in several religions that proposes humanity will reach its end, and on the last day, humanity will be judged by a god or deity; some religions propose that the dead will be resurrected on this last day to be judged alongside the rest of humanity.

2 *Fetus aethiopis 5 mensium*: Latin, roughly translated to a fetus of five months development

3 *Cephalothoracopagus monosymetro*: Latin, a label used to identify the skeletal remains of two female conjoined twins connected at the head and stomach; an artifact found at the Mütter Museum in Philadelphia

the papers. Sometimes a figure carves itself out of the crowd, and then I deviate from my itinerary to follow it for a moment, start on its story. It's a good method; I excel at it. With the years, time has become my ally, as it does for every woman—I've become invisible, see-through. I am able to move around like a ghost, look over people's shoulders, listen in on their arguments and watch them sleep with their heads on their backpacks or talking to themselves, unaware of my presence, moving just their lips, forming words that I will soon pronounce for them.

Purity of Blood

A certain island-dwelling woman from the other hemisphere, whom I met in a hotel in Prague,[4] told me the following:

People have always slogged around with them millions of bacteria, viruses, and diseases; there's no way to stop it. But we can at least try. After the worldwide panic over mad cow disease[5] some countries introduced new legislation. Any of the residents of her island who went away to Europe could no longer donate blood; it might be said that according to the law they suffered from lifelong contamination. And this would now be her case—she would never be able to give blood now. This was the price of her trip, not included in the cost of the ticket. Lost purity. Lost honor.

I asked her if it was worth it, if it made sense to sacrifice the purity of her blood for the pleasure of looking around a few cities, churches, and museums.

She answered seriously that all things have a price.

---

4 **Prague:** the capital city of the Czech Republic

5 **mad cow disease:** the common name for bovine spongiform encephalopathy (BSE), a type of cattle disease that can spread to humans; the spread of BSE to humans peaked at the end of the 20th century

After You Read

Critical Reading

1. Cite a sentence or series of sentences from the passage that use vivid **sensory details**. Then describe the effect of the sensory details on readers.

2. Pick one of the sections in the excerpt and describe the narrator's **tone**. What words best express this tone and what does this tone reveal about the narrator's point of view on the topic?

3. Tokarczuk frequently uses a technique called **asyndeton** which refers to the omission of conjunctions (*and, or, but,* etc.) that are usually replaced with a series of commas. Find an example of this and explain the effect this has on the writing.

Literary Lens: Motif

A **motif** is a recurring object, image, or idea that has symbolic importance to the theme of the piece. Use the chart below to identify a motif in one or more of the excerpts from *Flights*. Find a few references to it in the text and add these to the first column. Then make observations about the significance of the motif and how it contributes to the theme.

Motif:	
Example of motif in the story	**Observations on its significance**

Focus on Research: Use Geographical Sources

Use an online map to locate Poland and Ukraine. Notice the border between these countries. Then find an article regarding the boundaries of these two countries. Write a short summary of the article and include a screenshot or a link to a map that supports your writing. Include a works cited or bibliographical entry for your map.

The Literature of

France

Background

The first French king was crowned in A.D. 987. Since then, French politicians, philosophers, scientists, and artists have been at the center of European history and culture. Since the end of World War II in 1945, the French have been leaders in integrating the diverse countries of Europe into a united region.

French-speaking writers have produced more literary works that have been recognized as masterpieces in English than any country except England. Among the earliest of these were medieval epics such as *La Chanson de Roland (The Song of Roland,* c. 1100). The playwright Molière (1622–1673) wrote some of the world's finest comedies. The writer and philosopher Voltaire (1694–1778) was one of the most respected thinkers of his time. Victor Hugo (1802–1885) gave the world some of its greatest novels, including *Les Misérables.*

During the 20th century, French writers contributed to all movements of the *avant-garde* (experimental art). These included Surrealism, which replaced logic with an appeal to the unconscious mind. In our own day, living French writers are read and admired all over the world.

France and the United States

Since the days of Benjamin Franklin and Thomas Jefferson, many American thinkers have viewed France as a center of sophistication and intellectual leadership. They have considered a stay in Paris essential to their education.

The American writer with the most impact on French literature was Edgar Allan Poe (1809–1849). Poe's experiments with imagination and scientific progress influenced Jules Verne (1828–1905), who became one of the founders of science fiction. Verne wrote a sequel to Poe's only novel, *The Narrative of Arthur Gordon Pym.* The innovative French poet Charles Pierre Baudelaire (1821–1867) considered himself to be Poe's disciple. Baudelaire's excellent translations of Poe are still read in France today.

Research: Take Notes and Represent Graphically

Research the history of French literature and take notes. Then create a timeline of major works of French literature, from *The Song of Roland* to the present day. Include between 15 and 20 entries.

Rhinoceros

Eugène Ionesco

Before You Read

Born in Romania, Eugène Ionesco (1909–1994) lived in France and wrote in French. In plays like *The Lesson, The Chairs*, and *Rhinoceros*, he helped create the Theater of the Absurd, a movement emphasizing the meaninglessness of existence. Ionesco was especially concerned about the absurdity of human communication. In his first play, *The Bald Soprano,* a man and a woman—apparently strangers—exchange meaningless small talk until they realize they're actually married. Such comical moments thinly disguise Ionesco's tragic viewpoint. Despite that viewpoint, Ionesco's fundamental sympathy with the human predicament has made him one of the most popular of the absurdist writers.

World Context

Rhinoceros—famous foremost as a play—is generally thought to be an allegory about the perils of Nazism.

 LITERARY LENS The **Theatre of the Absurd** was a post World War II literary movement. Absurdist plays communicate a pessimistic view of humans who struggle in vain to find purpose and meaning in the world. As you read this story, which is based on Ionesco's play of the same name, identify details that fit with the Theatre of the Absurd.

We were sitting outside the café, my friend Jean and I, peacefully talking about one thing and another, when we caught sight of it on the opposite pavement, huge and powerful, panting noisily, charging straight ahead and brushing against market stalls—a rhinoceros. People in the street stepped hurriedly aside to let it pass. A housewife uttered a cry of terror, her basket dropped from her hands, the wine from a broken bottle spread over the pavement, and some pedestrians, one of them an elderly man, rushed into the shops. It was all over like a flash of lightning. People emerged from their hiding places and gathered in groups which watched the rhinoceros disappear into the distance, made some comments on the incident and then dispersed.

My own reactions are slowish. I absentmindedly took in the image of the rushing beast, without ascribing any very great importance to it. That morning, moreover, I was feeling tired and my mouth was sour, as a result of the previous night's excesses; we had been celebrating a friend's birthday. Jean had not been at the party; and when the first moment of surprise was over, he exclaimed: "A rhinoceros at large in town! Doesn't that surprise you? It ought not to be allowed."

"True," I said, "I hadn't thought of that. It's dangerous."

"We ought to protest to the Town Council."

"Perhaps it's escaped from the zoo," I said.

"You're dreaming," he replied. "There hasn't been a zoo in our town since the animals were decimated by the plague in the seventeenth century."

"Perhaps it belongs to the circus?"

"What circus? The council has forbidden **itinerant** entertainers to stop on municipal territory. None have come here since we were children."

> **itinerant:** traveling; circuit-riding

"Perhaps it has lived here ever since, hidden in the marshy woods round about," I answered with a yawn.

"You're completely lost in a dense alcoholic haze . . . ."

"Which rises from the stomach . . ."

"Yes. And has pervaded your brain. What marshy woods can you think of round about here? Our province is so arid they call it Little Castile."[1]

"Perhaps it sheltered under a pebble? Perhaps it made its nest on a dry branch?"

"How tiresome you are with your **paradoxes**. You're quite incapable of talking seriously."

> **paradoxes:** seeming contradictions; anomalies

"Today, particularly."

"Today and every other day."

"Don't lose your temper, my dear Jean. We're not going to quarrel about that creature . . . ."

We changed the subject of our conversation and began to talk about the weather again, about the rain which fell so rarely in our region, about the need to provide our sky with artificial clouds, and other **banal** and insoluble questions.

> **banal:** trite; overused

We parted. It was Sunday. I went to bed and slept all day: another wasted Sunday. On Monday morning I went to the office, making a solemn promise to myself never to get drunk again, and particularly not on

---

1 **Castile:** central Spain, notable for its sparse rain

Saturdays, so as not to spoil the following Sundays. For I had one single free day a week and three weeks' holiday in the summer. Instead of drinking and making myself ill, wouldn't it be better to keep fit and healthy, to spend my precious moments of freedom in a more intelligent fashion: visiting museums, reading literary magazines and listening to lectures? And instead of spending all my available money on drink, wouldn't it be preferable to buy tickets for interesting plays? I was still unfamiliar with the avant-garde[2] theater, of which I had heard so much talk; I had never seen a play by Ionesco. Now or never was the time to bring myself up-to-date.

The following Sunday I met Jean once again at the same café.

"I've kept my promise," I said, shaking hands with him.

"What promise have you kept?" he asked.

"My promise to myself. I've vowed to give up drinking. Instead of drinking I've decided to cultivate my mind. Today I am clearheaded. This afternoon I'm going to the Municipal Museum, and this evening I've a ticket for the theater. Won't you come with me?"

"Let's hope your good intentions will last," replied Jean. "But I can't go with you. I'm meeting some friends at the brasserie."[3]

"Oh, my dear fellow, now it's you who are setting a bad example. You'll get drunk!"

"Once in a while doesn't imply a habit," replied Jean irritably. "Whereas you . . ."

The discussion was about to take a disagreeable turn, when we heard a mighty trumpeting, the hurried clatter of some perissodactyl's[4] hoofs, cries, a cat's mewing; almost simultaneously we saw a rhinoceros appear, then disappear, on the opposite pavement, panting noisily and charging straight ahead.

Immediately afterwards a woman appeared holding in her arms a shapeless, bloodstained little object:

"It's run over my cat," she wailed, "it's run over my cat!"

The poor dishevelled woman, who seemed the very embodiment of grief, was soon surrounded by people offering sympathy.

Jean and I got up. We rushed across the street to the side of the unfortunate woman.

"All cats are mortal," I said stupidly, not knowing how to console her.

"It came past my shop last week!" the grocer recalled.

---

2 **avant-garde:** in the arts, especially, refers to the leading edge or the experimental
3 **brasserie:** an informal restaurant serving homecooked, basic fare
4 **perissodactyl:** an order of hoofed mammals that includes rhinoceroses

"It wasn't the same one," Jean declared. "It wasn't the same one: last week's had two horns on its nose—it was an Asian rhinoceros; this one had only one—it's an African rhinoceros."

"You're talking nonsense," I said irritably. "How could you distinguish its horns? The animal rushed past so fast that we could hardly see it; you hadn't time to count them . . . ."

"I don't live in a haze," Jean retorted sharply. "I'm clearheaded, I'm quick at figures."

"He was charging with his head down."

"That made it all the easier to see."

"You're a pretentious fellow, Jean. You're a **pedant**, who isn't even sure of his own knowledge. For in the first place, it's the Asian rhinoceros that has one horn on its nose and the African rhinoceros that has two!"

"You're quite wrong; it's the other way about."

"Would you like to bet on it?"

"I won't bet against you. You're the one who has two horns," he cried, red with fury, "you Asiatic, you!" (He stuck to his guns.)

"I haven't any horns. I shall never wear them. And I'm not an Asiatic, either. In any case, Asiatics are just like other people."

Jean turned his back on me and strode off, cursing.

I felt a fool. I ought to have been more conciliatory and not contradicted him: for I knew he could not bear it. The slightest objection made him foam at the mouth. This was his only fault, for he had a heart of gold and had done me countless good turns. The few people who were there and who had been listening to us had, as a result, quite forgotten about the poor woman's squashed cat. They crowded round me, arguing: some maintained that the Asian rhinoceros was indeed one-horned, and that I was right; others maintained that on the contrary the African rhinoceros was one-horned, and that therefore the previous speaker had been right.

"That is not the question," interposed a gentleman (straw boater,[5] small moustache, eyeglass, a typical logician's head) who had hitherto stood silent. "The discussion turned on a problem from which you have wandered. You began by asking yourselves whether today's rhinoceros is the same as last Sunday's or whether it is a different one. That is what must be decided. You may have seen one and the same one-horned rhinoceros on two occasions, or you may have seen one and the same two-horned rhinoceros on two occasions. Or again, you may have seen first one one-

pedant: person who shows off learning; stickler for details

---

5 **straw boater:** a stiff straw hat

horned rhinoceros and then a second one-horned rhinoceros. Or else, first one two-horned rhinoceros and then a second two-horned rhinoceros. If on the first occasion you had seen a two-horned rhinoceros and on the second a one-horned rhinoceros, that would not be conclusive either. It might be that since last week the rhinoceros had lost one of his horns and that the one you saw today was the same. Or it might be that two two-horned rhinoceroses had each lost one of their horns. If you could prove that on the first occasion you had seen a one-horned rhinoceros, whether it was Asian or African, and today a two-horned rhinoceros, whether it was African or Asian—that doesn't matter—then we might conclude that two different rhinoceroses were involved, for it is most unlikely that a second horn could grow in a few days, to any visible extent, on a rhinoceros's nose; this would mean that an Asian, or African, rhinoceros had become an African, or Asian, rhinoceros, which is logically impossible, since the same creature cannot be born in two places at once or even successively."

"That seems clear to me," I said. "But it doesn't settle the question."

"Of course," retorted the gentleman, smiling with a knowledgeable air, "only the problem has now been stated correctly."

"That's not the problem either," interrupted the grocer, who being no doubt of an emotional nature cared little about logic. "Can we allow our cats to be run over under our eyes by two-horned or one-horned rhinoceroses, be they Asian or African?"

"He's right, he's right," everybody exclaimed. "We can't allow our cats to be run over, by rhinoceroses or anything else!"

The grocer pointed with a theatrical gesture to the poor weeping woman, who still held and rocked in her arms the shapeless, bleeding remains of what had once been her cat.

• • • • •

Next day in the paper, under the heading Road Casualties Among Cats, there were two lines describing the death of the poor creature: "crushed underfoot by a pachyderm"[6] it was said, without further details.

On Sunday afternoon I hadn't visited a museum; in the evening I hadn't gone to the theater. I had moped at home by myself, overwhelmed by remorse at having quarrelled with Jean.

"He's so susceptible, I ought to have spared his feelings," I told myself. "It's absurd to lose one's temper about something like that . . . about the

---

6 **pachyderm:** a hoofed, often thick-skinned mammal, such as a rhinoceros or an elephant

horns of a rhinoceros that one had never seen before . . . a native of Africa or of India, such faraway countries, what could it matter to me? Whereas Jean had always been my friend, a friend who . . . to whom I owed so much . . . and who . . ."

In short, while promising myself to go and see Jean as soon as possible and to make it up with him, I had drunk an entire bottle of brandy without noticing. But I did indeed notice it the next day: a sore head, a foul mouth, an uneasy conscience; I was really most uncomfortable. But duty before everything: I got to the office on time, or almost. I was able to sign the register just before it was taken away.

"Well, so you've seen rhinoceroses too?" asked the chief clerk, who, to my great surprise, was already there.

"Sure I've seen him," I said, taking off my town jacket and putting on my old jacket with the frayed sleeves, good enough for work.

"Oh, now you see, I'm not crazy!" exclaimed the typist Daisy excitedly. (How pretty she was, with her pink cheeks and fair hair! I found her terribly attractive. If I could fall in love with anybody, it would be with her. . . .) "A one-horned rhinoceros!"

"Two-horned!" corrected my colleague Emile Dudard, Bachelor of Law, eminent jurist, who looked forward to a brilliant future with the firm and, possibly, in Daisy's affections.

"*I've* not seen it! And I don't believe in it!" declared Botard, an ex-schoolmaster who acted as **archivist**. "And nobody's ever seen one in this part of the world, except in the illustrations to school textbooks. These rhinoceroses have blossomed only in the imagination of ignorant women. The thing's a myth, like flying saucers."

archivist: person who maintains a collection of documents

I was about to point out to Botard that the expression "blossomed" applied to a rhinoceros, or to a number of them, seemed to me inappropriate, when the jurist exclaimed: "All the same, a cat was crushed, and before witnesses!"

"Collective **psychosis**," retorted Botard, who was a freethinker, "just like religion, the opium of the people!"

psychosis: mental derangement; loss of contact with reality

"I believe in flying saucers myself," remarked Daisy.

The chief clerk cut short our argument:

"That'll do! Enough chatter! Rhinoceros or no rhinoceros, flying saucers or no flying saucers, work's got to be done."

The typist started typing. I sat down at my desk and became engrossed in my documents. Emile Dudard began correcting the proofs of a commentary on the Law for the Repression of Alcoholism, while the chief clerk, slamming the door, retired into his study.

"It's a hoax!" Botard grumbled once more, aiming his remarks at Dudard. "It's your propaganda that spreads these rumors!"

"It's not propaganda," I interposed.

"I saw it myself . . . ," Daisy confirmed simultaneously.

"You make me laugh," said Dudard to Botard. "Propaganda? For what?"

"You know that better than I do! Don't act the simpleton!"

"In any case, *I'm* not paid by the Pontenegrins!"

"That's an insult!" cried Botard, thumping the table with his fist. The door of the chief clerk's room opened suddenly and his head appeared.

"Monsieur Boeuf hasn't come in today."

"Quite true, he's not here," I said.

"Just when I needed him. Did he tell anyone he was ill? If this goes on I shall give him the sack . . . ."

It was not the first time that the chief clerk had threatened our colleague in this way.

"Has one of you got the key to his desk?" he went on.

Just then Madame Boeuf made her appearance. She seemed terrified.

"I must ask you to excuse my husband. He went to spend the weekend with relations. He's had a slight attack of 'flu. Look, that's what he says in his telegram. He hopes to be back on Wednesday. Give me a glass of water . . . and a chair!" she gasped, collapsing onto the chair we offered her.

"It's very tiresome! But it's no reason to get so alarmed!" remarked the chief clerk.

"I was pursued by a rhinoceros all the way from home," she stammered.

"With one horn or two?" I asked.

"You make me laugh!" exclaimed Botard.

"Why don't you let her speak!" protested Dudard.

Madame Boeuf had to make a great effort to be explicit:

"It's downstairs, in the doorway. It seems to be trying to come upstairs."

At that very moment a tremendous noise was heard: the stairs were undoubtedly giving way under a considerable weight. We rushed out onto the landing. And there, in fact, amidst the debris, was a rhinoceros, its head lowered, trumpeting in an agonized and agonizing voice and turning vainly round and round. I was able to make out two horns.

"It's an African rhinoceros . . . ," I said, "or rather an Asian one."

My mind was so confused that I was no longer sure whether two horns were characteristic of the Asian or of the African rhinoceros, whether a single horn was characteristic of the African or the Asian rhinoceros, or whether on the contrary two horns . . . In short, I was floundering mentally, while Botard glared furiously at Dudard.

"It's an infamous plot!" and, with an orator's gesture, he pointed at the jurist: "It's your fault!"

"It's yours!" the other retorted.

"Keep calm, this is no time to quarrel!" declared Daisy, trying in vain to pacify them.

"For years now I've been asking the board to let us have concrete steps instead of that rickety old staircase," said the chief clerk. "Something like this was bound to happen. It was predictable. I was quite right!"

"As usual," Daisy added ironically. "But how shall we get down?"

"I'll carry you in my arms," the chief clerk joked flirtatiously, stroking the typist's cheek, "and we'll jump together!"

"Don't put your horny hand on my face, you pachydermous creature!"

The chief clerk had not time to react. Madame Boeuf, who had got up and come to join us, and who had for some minutes been staring attentively at the rhinoceros, which was turning round and round below us, suddenly uttered a terrible cry:

"It's my husband! Boeuf, my poor dear Boeuf, what has happened to you?"

The rhinoceros, or rather Boeuf, responded with a violent and yet tender trumpeting, while Madame Boeuf fainted into my arms and Botard, raising his to heaven, stormed: "It's sheer lunacy! What a society!"

• • • • •

When we had recovered from our initial astonishment, we telephoned to the fire brigade, who drove up with their ladder and fetched us down. Madame Boeuf, although we advised her against it, rode off on her spouse's back toward their home. She had ample grounds for divorce (but who was the guilty party?), yet she chose rather not to desert her husband in his present state.

At the little bistro[7] where we all went for lunch (all except the Boeufs, of course) we learnt that several rhinoceroses had been seen in various parts of the town: some people said seven, others seventeen, others again said thirty-two. In the face of this accumulated evidence, Botard could no longer deny the rhinoceric facts. But he knew, he declared, what to think about it.

---

7 **bistro:** a small restaurant

He would explain it to us some day. He knew the "why" of things, the "underside" of the story, the names of those responsible, the aim and significance of the outrage. Going back to the office that afternoon, business or no business, was out of the question. We had to wait for the staircase to be repaired.

I took advantage of this to pay a call on Jean, with the intention of making it up with him. He was in bed.

"I don't feel very well!" he said.

"You know, Jean, we were both right. There are two-horned rhinoceroses in the town as well as one-horned ones. It really doesn't matter where either sort comes from. The only significant thing, in my opinion, is the existence of the rhinoceros in itself."

"I don't feel very well," my friend kept on saying without listening to me, "I don't feel very well!"

"What's the matter with you? I'm so sorry!"

"I'm rather feverish, and my head aches."

More precisely, it was his forehead which was aching. He must have had a knock, he said. And in fact a lump was swelling up there, just above his nose. He had gone a greenish color, and his voice was hoarse.

"Have you got a sore throat? It may be tonsillitis."

I took his pulse. It was beating quite regularly.

"It can't be very serious. A few days' rest and you'll be all right. Have you sent for the doctor?"

As I was about to let go of his wrist, I noticed that his veins were swollen and bulging out. Looking closely, I observed that not only were the veins enlarged but the skin all round them was visibly changing color and growing hard.

"It may be more serious than I imagined," I thought. "We must send for the doctor," I said aloud.

"I felt uncomfortable in my clothes, and now my pajamas are too tight," he said in a hoarse voice.

"What's the matter with your skin? It's like leather . . . ." Then, staring at him: "Do you know what happened to Boeuf? He's turned into a rhinoceros."

"Well, what about it? That's not such a bad thing! After all, rhinoceroses are creatures like ourselves, with just as much right to live . . . ."

"Provided they don't imperil our own lives. Aren't you aware of the difference in mentality?"

"Do you think ours is preferable?"

"All the same, we have our own moral code, which I consider incompatible with that of these animals. We have our philosophy, our irreplaceable system of values . . . ."

"**Humanism** is out of date! You're a ridiculous old sentimentalist. You're talking nonsense."

"I'm surprised to hear you say that, my dear Jean! Have you taken leave of your senses?"

It really looked like it. Blind fury had disfigured his face and altered his voice to such an extent that I could scarcely understand the words that issued from his lips.

"Such assertions, coming from you . . . ," I tried to resume.

He did not give me a chance to do so. He flung back his blankets, tore off his pajamas, and stood up in bed, entirely naked (he who was usually the most modest of men!), green with rage from head to foot.

The lump on his forehead had grown longer; he was staring fixedly at me, apparently without seeing me. Or, rather, he must have seen me quite clearly, for he charged at me with his head lowered. I barely had time to leap to one side; if I hadn't, he would have pinned me to the wall.

"You are a rhinoceros!" I cried.

"I'll trample on you! I'll trample on you!" I made out these words as I dashed toward the door.

I went downstairs four steps at a time, while the walls shook as he butted them with his horn, and I heard him utter fearful angry trumpetings.

"Call the police! Call the police! You've got a rhinoceros in the house!" I called out to the tenants who, in great surprise, looked out of their flats as I passed each landing.

On the ground floor I had great difficulty in dodging the rhinoceros, which emerged from the concierge's[8] lodge and tried to charge me. At last I found myself out in the street, sweating, my legs limp, at the end of my tether.

Fortunately there was a bench by the edge of the pavement, and I sat down on it. Scarcely had I more or less got back my breath when I saw a herd of rhinoceroses hurrying down the avenue and nearing, at full speed, the place where I was. If only they had been content to stay in the middle of the street! But they were so many that there was not room for them all there, and they overflowed onto the pavement. I leapt off my bench and flattened myself against the wall: snorting, trumpeting, with a smell of

humanism: philosophy that stresses the power of human reason; way of life centered on human interests or values

---

8 **concierge:** the doorkeeper

leather and of wild animals in heat, they brushed past me and covered me with a cloud of dust. When they had disappeared, I could not go back to sit on the bench; the animals had demolished it, and it lay in fragments on the pavement.

I did not find it easy to recover from such emotions. I had to stay at home for several days. Daisy came to see me and kept me informed as to the changes that were taking place.

The chief clerk had been the first to turn into a rhinoceros, to the great disgust of Botard, who, nevertheless, became one himself twenty-four hours later.

"One must keep up with one's times!" were his last words as a man.

The case of Botard did not surprise me, in spite of his apparent strength of mind. I found it less easy to understand the chief clerk's transformation. Of course it might have been involuntary, but one would have expected him to put up more resistance.

Daisy recalled that she had commented on the roughness of his palms the very day that Boeuf had appeared in rhinoceros shape. This must have made a deep impression on him; he had not shown it, but he had certainly been cut to the quick.

"If I hadn't been so outspoken, if I had pointed it out to him more tactfully, perhaps this would never have happened."

"I blame myself, too, for not having been gentler with Jean. I ought to have been friendlier, shown more understanding," I said in my turn.

Daisy informed me that Dudard, too, had been transformed, as had also a cousin of hers, whom I did not know. And there were others, mutual friends, strangers.

"There are a great many of them," she said, "about a quarter of the inhabitants of our town."

"They're still in the minority, however."

"The way things are going, that won't last long!" she sighed.

"Alas! And they're so much more efficient."

Herds of rhinoceroses rushing at top speed through the streets became a sight that no longer surprised anybody. People would stand aside to let them pass and then resume their stroll, or attend to their business, as if nothing had happened.

"How can anybody be a rhinoceros! It's unthinkable!" I protested in vain.

More of them kept emerging from courtyards and houses, even from windows, and went to join the rest.

There came a point when the authorities proposed to enclose them in huge parks. For humanitarian reasons, the Society for the Protection of Animals opposed this. Besides, everyone had some close relative or friend among the rhinoceroses, which, for obvious reasons, made the project well-nigh impracticable. It was abandoned.

The situation grew worse, which was only to be expected. One day a whole regiment of rhinoceroses, having knocked down the walls of the barracks, came out with drums at their head and poured onto the boulevards.

At the Ministry of Statistics, statisticians produced their statistics: census of animals, approximate reckoning of their daily increase, percentage of those with one horn, percentage of those with two. . . . What an opportunity for learned controversies! Soon there were defections among the statisticians themselves. The few who remained were paid fantastic sums.

One day from my balcony I caught sight of a rhinoceros charging forward with loud trumpetings, presumably to join his fellows; he wore a straw boater impaled on his horn.

"The logician!" I cried. "He's one too? Is it possible?" Just at that moment Daisy opened the door.

"The logician is a rhinoceros!" I told her.

She knew. She had just seen him in the street. She was bringing me a basket of provisions.

"Shall we have lunch together?" she suggested. "You know, it was difficult to find anything to eat. The shops have been ransacked; they devour everything. A number of shops are closed 'on account of transformations,' the notices say."

"I love you, Daisy, please never leave me."

"Close the window, darling. They make too much noise. And the dust comes in."

"So long as we're together, I'm afraid of nothing, I don't mind about anything." Then, when I had closed the window: "I thought I should never be able to fall in love with a woman again."

I clasped her tightly in my arms. She responded to my embrace.

"How I'd like to make you happy! Could you be happy with me?"

"Why not? You declare you're afraid of nothing and yet you're scared of everything! What can happen to us?"

"My love, my joy!" I stammered, kissing her lips with a passion such as I had forgotten, intense and agonizing.

The ringing of the telephone interrupted us.

She broke from my arms, went to pick up the receiver, then uttered a cry: "Listen. . . ."

I put the receiver to my ear. I heard ferocious trumpetings.

"They're playing tricks on us now!"

"Whatever can be happening?" she inquired in alarm.

We turned on the radio to hear the news; we heard more trumpetings. She was shaking with fear.

"Keep calm," I said, "keep calm!"

She cried out in terror, "They've taken over the broadcasting station!"

"Keep calm, keep calm!" I repeated, increasingly agitated myself.

Next day in the street they were running about in all directions. You could watch for hours without catching sight of a single human being. Our house was shaking under the weight of our perissodactylic neighbors' hoofs.

"What must be must be," said Daisy. "What can we do about it?"

"They've all gone mad. The world is sick."

"It's not you and I who'll cure it."

"We shan't be able to communicate with anybody. Can you understand them?"

"We ought to try to interpret their psychology, to learn their language."

"They have no language."

"What do you know about it?"

"Listen to me, Daisy. We shall have children, and then they will have children. It'll take time, but between us we can regenerate humanity. With a little courage . . ."

"I don't want to have children."

"How do you hope to save the world, then?"

"Perhaps after all it's we who need saving. Perhaps we are the abnormal ones. Do you see anyone else like us?"

"Daisy, I can't have you talking like that!"

I looked at her in despair.

"It's we who are in the right, Daisy, I assure you."

"What arrogance! There's no absolute right. It's the whole world that is right—not you or me."

"Yes, Daisy, I *am* right. The proof is that you understand me and that I love you as much as a man can love a woman."

"I'm rather ashamed of what you call love, that **morbid** thing. . . . It cannot compare with the extraordinary energy displayed by all these beings we see around us."

morbid: unhealthy; gloomy

"Energy? Here's energy for you!" I cried, my powers of argument exhausted, giving her a slap.

Then, as she burst into tears: "I won't give in, no, I won't give in."

She rose, weeping, and flung her sweet-smelling arms round my neck.

"I'll stand fast, with you, to the end."

She was unable to keep her word. She grew melancholy and visibly pined away. One morning when I woke up, I saw that her place in the bed was empty. She had gone away without leaving any message.

The situation became literally unbearable for me. It was my fault if Daisy had gone. Who knows what had become of her? Another burden on my conscience. There was nobody who could help me find her again. I imagined the worst and felt myself responsible.

And on every side there were trumpetings and frenzied chargings and clouds of dust. In vain did I shut myself up in my own room, putting cotton wool in my ears: at night I saw them in my dreams.

"The only way out is to convince them." But of what? Were these **mutations** reversible? And in order to convince them, one would have to talk to them. In order for them to relearn my language (which moreover I was beginning to forget), I should first have to learn theirs. I could not

mutations: changes; alterations

distinguish one trumpeting from another, one rhinoceros from another rhinoceros.

One day, looking at myself in the glass, I took a dislike to my long face: I needed a horn, or even two, to give dignity to my flabby features.

And what if, as Daisy had said, it was they who were in the right? I was out of date; I had missed the boat, that was clear.

I discovered that their trumpetings had after all a certain charm, if a somewhat harsh one. I should have noticed that while there was still time. I tried to trumpet: how feeble the sound was, how lacking in vigor! When I made greater efforts, I only succeeded in howling. Howlings are not trumpetings.

It is obvious that one must not always drift blindly behind events and that it's a good thing to maintain one's individuality. However, one must also make allowances for things; asserting one's own difference, to be sure, but yet . . . remaining akin to one's fellows. I no longer bore any likeness to anyone or to anything, except to ancient, old-fashioned photographs which had no connection with living beings.

Each morning I looked at my hands, hoping that the palms would have hardened during my sleep. The skin remained flabby. I gazed at my too-white body, my hairy legs: oh for a hard skin and that magnificent green color, a decent, hairless nudity, like theirs!

My conscience was increasingly uneasy, unhappy. I felt I was a monster. Alas, I would never become a rhinoceros. I could never change.

I dared no longer look at myself. I was ashamed. And yet I couldn't, no, I couldn't.

After You Read

Critical Reading

1. One recurring **motif** in the story is alcohol. Choose an aspect of how alcohol is dealt with the in story and examine how it is used, its effects, and what you think it is meant to represent or mean.

2. A **syllogistic fallacy** is a form of reasoning that connects two premises that result in an incorrect conclusion. Find one conversation that contains this type of reasoning and summarize it. Then explain what you think the purpose of these absurd exchanges is.

3. Consider the **protagonist's** personality. Would you consider Berenger a **hero** or an **antihero** and why?

4. This story could be called a **parable**, a short story that is meant to teach a lesson. What do you think the moral, or lesson, of the story is?

Literary Lens: Theater of the Absurd

"Rhinoceros" falls under the category of Theater of the Absurd, a movement that began in France in the 1950s and grew out of the philosophy of existentialism. Existentialism emphasized the nothingness of human existence. Thus, Absurdist stories usually have illogical plots, ridiculous elements, and scenes that do not fit together. They feature characters who lack motivation and purpose and are out of harmony with the world. In "Rhinoceros" Ionesco creates an allegory for the rise of Nazism and the often unquestioned following of its Fascist ideals.

Absurdist element	Examples from the story
Illogical and/or nonlinear plot	
Ridiculous elements	
Characters who lack motivation/ purpose	
Meaninglessness of human existence	
Other	

Focus on Research: Evaluate Primary Sources

With a partner, brainstorm a list of several types of primary sources you could use to find more information about the political climate that led up to the Holocaust. For instance, how did Nazism and fascism, which seem so wrong in retrospect, permeate society and eventually gain popularity? Choose three to five primary sources and evaluate their usefulness. Examples of primary sources include newspaper articles, letters, speeches, and essays written by people involved in the historical events.

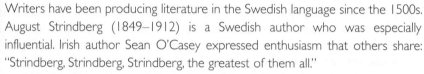

The Literature of
Sweden

Background

Writers have been producing literature in the Swedish language since the 1500s. August Strindberg (1849–1912) is a Swedish author who was especially influential. Irish author Sean O'Casey expressed enthusiasm that others share: "Strindberg, Strindberg, Strindberg, the greatest of them all."

Strindberg was an essayist, novelist, and journalist, but he is best known as an innovative playwright. He wrote plays in both verse and prose, some of which explored Swedish history and folklore. Most significantly, he pioneered dramatic Naturalism (which combines realistic staging with everyday dialogue) and Expressionism (which rejects realism in favor of exaggerated portrayals of inner feelings).

Strindberg struggled with mental health issues, and his relationships with women usually ended in bitterness. Some of his plays, including *The Father* and *Miss Julie*, are intense studies of conflicts between men and women. Others, including *Easter* and *Swanwhite,* explore happier themes of love and forgiveness.

Sweden and the United States

Many Americans were introduced to Swedish literature through the character Pippi Longstocking, the protagonist of a series of children's books by Astrid Lindgren (1907–2002). Pippi is a freckle-faced, strangely dressed, super-strong, highly independent girl who lives with a monkey and a horse. *The Adventures of Pippi Longstocking* was first translated into English in 1950.

More recently, American readers have been captivated by Scandinavian crime fiction, also known as "Nordic noir." Writers of the genre include Henning Mankell, Stieg Larsson, and Camilla Lackberg. Larsson has stated that his anti-heroine Lisabeth Slander (*The Girl With the Dragon Tatoo*) is based on a grown-up Pippi Longstocking who has become "a dysfuntional girl . . . with attention deficit disorder who would have a hard time finding a place in normal society."

Research: Represent Graphically

In 1909, Selma Lagerlöf became the first woman and the first Swede to win the Nobel Prize in Literature. Her style and political leanings stand in sharp contrast to those of Strindberg. Read a short summary of Lagerlöf's life and writings and then create a Venn diagram comparing the authors' styles and philosophies.

Alone

Tomas Tranströmer

Before You Read

Tomas Tranströmer (1931–2015) was both a poet and a psychologist. As a psychologist, he worked with young offenders, the disabled, convicts, and drug addicts. He is known for his experimental verse forms and unusual images.

World Context

Tranströmer's poems have been translated into 30 languages and have won more than 50 international awards.

 LITERARY LENS An **epiphany** is a revelation that brings a deep change. What epiphany occurs in this poem?

I

One evening in February I came near to dying here.
The car skidded sideways on the ice, out
on the wrong side of the road. The approaching cars—
their lights—closed in.

My name, my girls, my job   5
broke free and were left silently behind
further and further away. I was anonymous
like a boy in a playground surrounded by enemies.

The approaching traffic had huge lights.
They shone on me while I pulled at the wheel   10
in a transparent terror that floated like egg white.
The seconds grew—there was space in them—
they grew big as hospital buildings.

You could almost pause
and breathe out for a while   15
before being crushed.

Then something caught: a helping grain of sand
or a wonderful gust of wind. The car broke free
and scuttled smartly right over the road.
A post shot up and cracked—a sharp clang—it   20
flew away in the darkness.

Then—stillness. I sat back in my seat-belt
and saw someone coming through the whirling snow
to see what had become of me.

II

I have been walking for a long time   25
on the frozen Östergötland fields.
I have not seen a single person.

In other parts of the world
there are people who are born, live and die
in a perpetual crowd.   30

To be always visible—to live
in a swarm of eyes—
a special expression must develop.
Face coated with clay.

The murmuring rises and falls   35
while they divide up among themselves
the sky, the shadows, the sand grains.

I must be alone
ten minutes in the morning
and ten minutes in the evening.   40
—Without a program.

Everyone is queuing at everyone's door.

Many.

One.

Translated by Robin Fulton

After You Read

Critical Reading

1. Author Teju Cole commented about Tranströmer's poetry: "There is little elaborate construction evident; rather, the sense is of the sudden arrival of what was already there, as when a whale comes up for air: massive, exhilarating, and evanescent." Find examples of **imagery** that seem to magically appear in his work and comment on the effects of this.

2. In places Tranströmer uses a nontraditional format of line breaks. Some lines are end-stopped, meaning they use **terminal punctuation** (lines 1 and 9), while others are **enjambed,** meaning they do not end with punctuation (lines 2, 5, and 6). What is achieved by these two approaches? Consider how they affect the **rhythm** of the poem.

3. What do you think of the abrupt ending of the poem? Read it aloud and then decide whether you find the ending effective.

Literary Lens: Epiphany

Tranströmer's poetry has been described as being about "intense encounters or moments of revelation when the world seems a bit clearer." An **epiphany** is an event, sometimes mystical in nature, in which a character experiences a profound change caused by a powerful revelation. The effects of the epiphany can be on the character's thoughts, behavior, or both. In Part I of the poem, the narrator seems to be describing an epiphany in his life. Part II may be the aftermath of this event or may actually precede the events in Part I. Re-create the chart below and fill it in to examine the changes that take place as a result of the epiphany in the poem.

Before	During	After
What might have been the narrator's beliefs and lifestyle before the epiphany?	CAUSE: Describe what caused the epiphany. What is the epiphany?	EFFECT: What do you think are the narrator's beliefs and lifestyle after the epiphany?

Focus on Research: Summarize Findings

In 2007, Tranströmer won a Lifetime Achievement Award from the Griffin Trust for Excellence in Poetry, and in 2011 he won the Nobel Prize in Literature. Research what the award committees and other critics have said about why the author was chosen for the awards. Then write a one-paragraph summary that includes examples of his style and philosophy.

The Literature of
Russia

Background

During the 19th century, most Russians lived in dire poverty. The country remained largely rural and had not yet embraced the Industrial Revolution that was reshaping life in most of Europe and the United States. In spite of the suffering that afflicted the country—or possibly because of it—Russia's literary output was impressive. Two of its greatest writers were Fyodor Dostoevsky (1821–1881) and Leo Tolstoy (1828–1910).

Dostoevsky explored the darkest aspects of human psychology, politics, and religion. For example, in *Crime and Punishment*, the protagonist rationalizes and commits a murder, only to suffer unbearable pangs of conscience. In *The Brothers Karamazov*, a buffoonish father is murdered, apparently by one of his sons.

Tolstoy focused more on the role of history, culture, and family in shaping human behavior. His massive novel *War and Peace* is set during the Napoleonic Wars in the early 1800s. *Anna Karenina* centers on the title character's infidelity to her husband and eventual suicide.

Russia and the United States

During the latter part of the 20th century, one of the Russian writers most admired in the United States was Aleksandr Solzhenitsyn (1918–2008). Solzhenitsyn spent eight years in Soviet prison camps under the regime of Joseph Stalin. He emerged as a harsh critic of the government, a view reflected in his novel *One Day in the Life of Ivan Denisovich* and his nonfiction work *The Gulag Archipelago*.

Solzhenitsyn was eventually exiled from the Soviet Union and lived briefly in the United States. While here, he surprised many of his admirers by becoming a harsh critic of the crass materialism he saw in American life. In 1994, he was allowed to return to his homeland, where he remained until his death.

Research: Use Quotes Smoothly

Dostoevsky, Tolstoy, and Solzhenitsyn are only three of the many influential Russian or Soviet writers of the 19th and 20th centuries. Prepare a brief report on another influential Russian author. Use several sources, choosing a worthwhile quotation from each and working it smoothly into the flow of your report.

The Nobel Prize

Boris Pasternak

Before You Read

Boris Pasternak (1890–1960) published poetry in his native Russia, but the Bolshevik regime disapproved of it, feeling it did not fully support the Communist revolution. Pasternak then turned to translation to make his living. After World War II, he wrote *Doctor Zhivago*, a novel about lovers who try to live apart from the political turmoil of their time. It was banned in the Soviet Union, the country that included Russia, but a copy was smuggled out and published in the West. Pasternak was awarded the Nobel Prize in Literature in 1958. The embarrassed Soviets pressured Pasternak, and he eventually turned it down. In 1988, the novel was finally published in Russia; the next year Pasternak's son accepted his father's Nobel Prize.

World Context

The year 1958 was the height of the Cold War, the tension between capitalist countries led by the United States and Communist countries led by the Soviet Union. In general, Soviet writers could not speak or travel freely and were discouraged from communicating with literary outposts in the West, such as universities, conferences, and periodicals.

 LITERARY LENS As you read the poem, identify **images** that are particularly meaningful.

I've fallen beast-like in a snare:
Light, people, freedom, somewhere bide:
But at my back I hear the chase
And there is no escape outside.

Darkest wood and lakeside shore,   5
Gaunt trunk of a levelled tree,
My way is cut off on all sides:
Let what may, come; all's one to me.

Is there some ill I have committed?
Am I a murderer, miscreant?   10
For I have made the whole world weep
Over the beauty of my land.

But even at the very grave
I trust the time shall come to be
When over malice, over wrong,   15
The good will win its victory.

Translated by Henry Kamen

In the Outskirts of Moscow in 1941 | Alexander Deineka

After You Read

Critical Reading

1. Pasternak employs **formal verse** in this poem, meaning he uses a strict **meter** (syllable count) and **rhyme scheme**. Describe the meter and rhyme scheme and what they contribute to the poem. Why do you think the poet chose this approach?

2. How would you describe the **mood** of this poem? Use evidence to support your answer.

3. Choose either the first or second stanza of the poem and explore it further. Analyze the stanza line by line and consider the **metaphor** and the **imagery**. What feelings does the stanza stir up in you?

Literary Lens: Imagery

Censorship is the practice of suppressing information or ideas that are considered objectionable. Boris Pasternak was censored by the Communist Russian government during the Cold War. Pasternak's poem "The Nobel Prize" uses imagery to describe his feelings and ideas concerning censorship. Before completing this activity, conduct research to learn more about why Pasternak was unable to publish *Dr. Zhivago* and his reasons for refusing the Nobel Prize. Use the chart below to find and analyze images in the poem that represent censorship.

Image	How it alludes to censorship

Focus on Research: Synthesize Sources with Multiple Viewpoints

With a partner, find the online article "The Plot Thickens" by Peter Finn from the January 27, 2007 issue of *The Washington Post*. Take notes on the CIA's alleged involvement in the publication of *Dr. Zhivago* and the resulting Nobel Prize. Then find another reputable source and compare it with the *Post* article. Identify any information that does not agree and write a paragraph that synthesizes the information. Include in-text citations in your paragraph.

First Frost

Andrei Voznesensky

Before You Read

Andrei Voznesensky (1933–2010), a friend of Boris Pasternak, often experimented with language, rhythm, and ideas in his poetry.

World Context

Though he clashed with the authorities in the Communist Soviet Union, Voznesensky wrote freely after it dissolved.

 LITERARY LENS Lyricism expresses a personal and emotional point of view. Look for it as you read.

A girl is freezing in a telephone booth,
huddled in her flimsy coat,
her face stained by tears
and smeared with lipstick.

She breathes on her thin little fingers.   5
Fingers like ice. Glass beads in her ears.

She has to beat her way back alone
down the icy street.

First frost. A beginning of losses.
The first frost of telephone phrases.   10

It is the start of winter glittering on her cheek,
the first frost of having been hurt.

Translated by George Reavey

After You Read

Critical Reading

1. What do you think is the speaker's **point of view** about life? Find a quote from the poem to support your answer.

2. In this poem, Voznesensky plays with **syntax**, or the arrangement of words and sentences to create certain effects and meaning. Notice how he uses long and short sentences, clauses (groups of words that contain a subject and a verb), and phrases. What purpose do these varying structures serve? Refer to specific examples from the poem in your answer.

3. This poem, originally written in Russian, was translated into English. Translators must try to find words that best match the original meanings, as well as syntax that retains the rhythm and feel of the poem. In a different translation of "First Frost," called "First Ice," line 2 is "In her draughty overcoat she hides." Line 5 is "Her fingers are icicles. She wears earrings." Line 6 is "She'll have to walk home alone, alone." Compare these translations to the ones in "First Frost" and consider how they differ. Which ones do you think are more effective and why?

 ## Literary Lens: Extended Metaphor

An **extended metaphor**, sometimes called a conceit or a sustained metaphor, is a comparison that an author develops throughout an entire literary work. An extended metaphor often serves to develop the theme of the story or poem. Use the chart below to help you analyze the poem's extended metaphor.

Point of view:			
Quote 1	Quote 2	Quote 3	Quote 4

Focus on Research: Explore Multimedia Sources

Use a variety of sources to find images and audio files about Voznesensky. Create a digital presentation from your sources and include explanatory commentary. Include a slide with a bibliography of your sources. Use correct MLA or APA style.

Forbidden Fruit

Fazil Iskander

Before You Read

Born in the Georgian Republic of Abkhazia, Fazil Iskander (1929–2016) lived most of his life in Russia. He published more than 200 works of poetry and prose in Russian, many of which have been translated into other languages. In his fiction, such as the novel *Sandro from Chegem*, Iskander uses humor and irony to satirize human behavior and society. He has said, "If you want to make subtle humor your tool, you've got to go to the extreme of pessimism, glimpse the dark abyss to make sure there is nothing in it and then slowly come back."

World Context

Since Iskander directed much of his satire and parody at the Soviet government, he often was in conflict with the censors. Twice he was nominated for the prestigious Lenin Prize only to have his nomination turned down by authorities. His playful style and depiction of the Abkhazian culture have made him a unique voice in contemporary prose.

 LITERARY LENS As you read, look for **hyperbole**, or exaggeration. Why does the author use hyperbole? What effect does it have?

---

latitude: freedom; leeway

abstinence: avoidance; voluntary giving up

Neither children nor grownups in our family ever ate pork. Though another of Mohammed's[1] commandments—the one on alcoholic drinks—was broken (and without constraint, as I know now), no **latitude** was allowed with respect to pork.

The ban provoked hot dreams and icy **abstinence**. I dreamt interminably of eating pork. The smell of fried pork made me faint. I would loiter for hours in front of foodstore showcases and contemplate

---

1 **Mohammed:** (also Muhammad), the prophet in the Islamic faith who lived from about 570 to 632

sausages beaded with fat and dappled with pork. I imagined myself skinning these sausages and letting my teeth sink into the juicy, luxuriant meat. I imagined the taste of sausage so accurately that, when I tasted it later, I was surprised at how truly my imagination had anticipated reality.

Of course, in childhood there were occasions when I could have tasted pork in kindergarten or ate at the home of a friend, but I never broke the commandment.

When we had rice and pork in kindergarten, I fished out all the pieces of pork and gave them to my friends. I conquered the agony of yearning by the sweetness of self-denial. I enjoyed my **ideological** superiority. It was pleasant to be an **enigma**, to behave in a way baffling to everyone around. And yet, all the more intensely did I dream of a transgression.

One of our neighbors was a nurse called Auntie Sonya. For some reason or other, we believed Auntie Sonya was a doctor. In general, I notice that as one grows older, the status of people seems to drop.

Auntie Sonya was an elderly woman with bobbed hair and a sorrowing expression never absent from her face. She always spoke in a low voice as though she had long ago realized that there was nothing in life worth speaking up about.

When she quarreled with her neighbors, she rarely raised her voice. That created problems for her adversaries because they could not grasp her last words, lost the thread, and the quarrel flagged disastrously.

Auntie Sonya and our family were friends, and Mother used to say that Auntie Sonya had saved me. I had been very sick, and she and my mother had taken turns looking after me for a whole month. To tell the truth, I did not feel properly grateful for my saved life, but, out of politeness, whenever the incident came up, I wore the expression of a person happy to have been saved.

Auntie Sonya spent evenings with our family and often told us the story of her life, and the principal hero was her first husband, who had been killed in the Civil War.[2] I had heard the story many times, but my heart always dropped when she reached the point where she found her husband among the corpses. Here she would begin to cry, and my mother and older sister would weep too. Then they would comfort her, beg her to have some tea, or bring her a glass of water. I was always astonished at how quickly the

ideological: based on beliefs

enigma: puzzle; mystery

---

2 **Civil War:** also known as the October Revolution, the years following the 1917 revolution in Russia that had toppled the Czar; the revolutionary Bolsheviks, led by Vladimir Lenin, fought the old Russian aristocracy for complete power. The war ended in 1920 with Lenin heading the new Communist state.

women composed themselves and chattered with fresh, and even cheery, animation about all sorts of trifles. Then Auntie Sonya would leave because it was time for her husband, Uncle Shura, to come home.

I liked Uncle Shura. I liked his black hair and that unruly lock over his forehead, his neatly rolled-up sleeves and strong arms. I even liked his stoop. His was not a clerk's stoop but a pleasant old worker's stoop, though Uncle Shura was neither an old man nor a worker.

After hours he would always tinker with something: a desk lamp, or an electric iron, or a radio set, or even a watch which his neighbors brought and which he repaired, charging them nothing.

prodigiously: enormously; excessively

Auntie Sonya sat across the table, smoked **prodigiously**, and poked fun at him, telling him that he was a jack of all trades, that he would never fix what he was trying to fix, and so on and so forth.

"We'll see if I won't fix it," Uncle Shura muttered through his teeth because he had a cigarette in his mouth. He would handle the thing a neighbor had brought with graceful confidence, dust it off, and then suddenly look at it from some unexpected angle.

"I can see them laughing at you," Auntie Sonya would counter with an arrogant puff of smoke, wrapping her robe tighter around her.

Finally, he would wind the watch, or the radio set would crackle snatches of music.

"I like to see them laughing at me. I don't mind a bit," he would say with a wink at me.

I wanted my smile to show that I had nothing to do with his triumph but that I appreciated his trust.

"You brag too much," Auntie Sonya would say. "Lay the table for tea."

In her voice I detected hidden pride, and I wondered if Uncle Shura was of a less heroic mold than that hero of the Civil War whom Auntie Sonya could not forget.

•••••

Once, when I was spending an evening with them, my sister dropped in, and they invited her to tea. Auntie Sonya sliced some pork fat of an unbelievably delicate pink and put a cruet[3] of mustard on the table. They had often eaten pork before and asked me to have some, but I invariably and firmly refused, which always moved Uncle Shura to mirth for some reason or other. This time they also asked me to have some, but they did not insist. Uncle Shura put several slices of pork fat on a chunk of bread and gave it to my sister. After the few no's required by decency, she accepted the horrible sandwich and began to eat it. Indignation stiffened my throat, and I had difficulty getting my tea down.

"That's what it is," said Uncle Shura. "You're a monk, that's what you are!"

I could say nothing. She ate the sandwich with shameless neatness, a vacant look in her eyes. That vacancy was meant to show that she was eating officially, purely out of respect for her hosts. It was meant to suggest that the sacrilege was not to be taken seriously and did not count at all.

"It does count!" I thought maliciously, watching the sandwich becoming smaller at an agonizingly slow rate.

I felt she was enjoying it. It was evident from the way she licked the crumbs, from the way she swallowed each bite—slowed her chewing in the silliest way as though listening to the sound the food made going down her gullet. The slices of fat were thinner at the edge she nibbled, the surest sign that she was enjoying it because all normal children leave the tidbit for last. In other words, all the evidence was there.

Now she was coming to the edge of the sandwich where the piece of pork was thickest. She kept her enjoyment in crescendo. Meanwhile, she was serenely (woman's infinite ability to pretend) telling how my brother jumped out of a window when the teacher called on our parents. The story had a dual purpose: first, to divert attention from what she was doing, and second, to flatter me in a very subtle way since everyone knew that the teacher had no reason to complain of me, and still less had I any reason to flee from her through a window.

As she was telling all this, she would look at me from time to time to see whether I was still watching her or, carried away by her story, was forgetting about her sin. But my expression was not to be doubted: my vigilance never flagged. In self-defense she goggled her eyes like one surprised that so much

---

3 **cruet:** a glass condiment bottle

attention was being paid to a trifling matter. I only smirked, a hint of the retribution to come.

For a moment I thought that it had come already because she began to cough. I watched **transfixed**. Uncle Shura slapped her on the back, and she stopped coughing to indicate that his cure had helped and that her discomfort was insignificant. But I felt that the piece was still stuck in her throat. She pretended she was all right now and took another bite.

"Chew away!" I thought. "Let's see you swallow it."

But evidently, somewhere on high the retribution was rescheduled. My sister swallowed this bite without difficulty, and perhaps it even helped her swallow down its predecessor because she gave a sigh of relief and looked around cheerfully. Now she chewed and licked her lips after each bite with special care, or maybe she was simply sticking out her tongue at me.

She was at the edge of the sandwich with the thickest piece of fat. Before committing it to her mouth, she bit off the last edge of the bread uncovered by fat. That climaxed that last tidbit even more. Then she swallowed it down, too, and licked her lips as though trying to prolong the pleasure and show that there were no traces of the sin left.

All this did not take much time, of course, and was almost imperceptible to an outsider. At any rate, Uncle Shura and Auntie Sonya did not seem to notice anything. Her sandwich finished, my sister proceeded to her tea, still pretending that nothing had happened. As soon as she touched her cup, I gulped mine down. I did not want to share anything with her. A few minutes before, I had refused to eat some cookies so I could run the whole **gamut** of suffering and have no earthly joys in her presence. Besides, I resented Uncle Shura, who had not urged me nearly as much as he had my sister. I would not have accepted the cookies anyway, but his urging would have made my refusal a better lesson in principles for my sister.

In short, I was terribly let down and went home as soon as I finished my tea. They begged me to stay, but I was adamant.

"I have to do my lessons!" I said piously.

My sister asked me to stay with special insistence. She was sure that I would tell on her at home, and, besides, she was afraid to cross the yard alone.

At home, I slipped out of my clothes and into my bed to luxuriate in the contemplation of my sister's apostasy.[4] All kinds of visions rushed through

transfixed:
held
motionless;
spellbound

gamut:
range;
spectrum

---

4 **apostasy:** an abandonment of principle

my mind. Here I was, a Red partisan captured by the Whites,[5] who are forcing me to eat pork. They torture me, but I will not touch it. Surprised, the officers shake their heads: What sort of boy is this? As a matter of fact, I'm surprised myself. I just won't eat pork. Kill me, but eat pork I will not.

The door creaked and my sister came in. She immediately asked about me.

"He's gone to bed," I heard my mother reply. "He came home in the dumps. Anything happen?"

"Why, nothing," my sister answered and went over to my bed. I was afraid she would begin coaxing me and all that. Pardon was out of the question, anyway, and besides I did not want her to change the state of mind I was in. I, therefore, pretended to be asleep. She stood for a while and stroked my hair, but I turned over to show that I knew her treacherous hand even in my sleep. She stood there for a while longer and then went away. I thought she was feeling guilty and did not know how to redeem herself.

I was sorry for her, but, as it turned out, she was not worth it. A minute later she was saying something to mother in a loud whisper; they began to giggle and then stopped, afraid to wake me up. Gradually they settled to a mood fit for going to bed.

Next day we sat at the table waiting dinner for father. He was late and angry at being waited for. Something was wrong on the job, and he was often gloomy and absentminded.

•••••

I was all prepared to divulge my sister's crime, but I realized that this was not a proper time for my exposure. Nevertheless, I looked at my sister from time to time and pretended I was going to tell. I even opened my mouth but said something else instead. As soon as I opened my mouth, she dropped her eyes and bent her head as though expecting a blow. I discovered that keeping her on the verge of exposure was even more fun than exposing her right away could possibly be.

She would turn pale and then blush. From time to time she would toss her head contemptuously, and then her eyes would beg me to forgive her this gesture of wild defiance. She barely touched her soup, but mother insisted that she eat it.

---

5 **Red partisan . . . Whites:** The Reds were the Bolsheviks, or followers of Lenin, and the Whites represented the old guard of power in Russia.

"Of course," I said, "yesterday she ate so much at Uncle Shura's that—"

"What did you eat there?" my brother asked—as always, he understood nothing.

Mother looked at me anxiously and shook her head imperceptibly for father. My sister pulled up the plate and continued eating. I was getting a full taste of it. I fished a boiled onion out of my soup and spooned it into hers; we all hated boiled onions. Mother looked at me severely.

"She likes onions," I said. "You like onions, don't you?" I asked my sister with velvety softness.

She said nothing but her head went down still lower.

"If you like onions, take mine too!" My brother said, and started to transfer his. However, my father looked at him in a way to make his spoon freeze in midair and beat a hasty retreat.

Between the first and second course I invented another diversion. I put some slices of cucumber from the salad on a slice of bread and began to eat it, pausing from time to time as though the sandwich was too delicious to proceed. That was a witty little skit recreating her fall. She looked at me in pretended puzzlement, refusing to recognize the picture or to admit that it was so shameful. That was the limit to which her protest rose.

In short, the dinner was magnificent. Virtue blackmailed, and vice lowered its head in disgrace. Dinner was followed by tea. Father cheered up, and we shared his mood, especially my sister. Her cheeks reddened and her eyes shone. She started telling some school story, calling on me to testify as though nothing had happened. Her familiarity shocked me. It seemed to me that a person with such a record ought to be more **diffident**, more **self-effacing**, ought to wait for worthier people to tell the story. I was on the point of calling her to order, but father produced a package and unwrapped it. It turned out to be a batch of brand-new notebooks.

In those years before the war, it was difficult to get notebooks, just as it was some other things. The notebooks father had brought were of the best kind, made of wonderful paper, cool, heavy, bluish white like skimmed milk, with clear red lines for the margins.

There were nine notebooks in all, and father divided them, three notebooks apiece. My elation went. This **egalitarian** approach seemed to me simply unjust.

diffident: hesitant; unassuming

self-effacing: modest; not seeking attention

egalitarian: equal; fair-minded

> Virtue blackmailed, and vice lowered its head in disgrace.

The fact was that I did well in school and sometimes even got high marks. The family would tell relatives and friends that all my marks were very high, but probably that was done to balance my brother's academic **notoriety**.

At school he was considered one of the laziest and most unruly boys. As his teacher put it, his ability to evaluate his behavior lagged far behind his temperament. I imagined my brother's temperament as a little ruffian running helter-skelter far ahead of him, my brother unable to catch up. It was perhaps to overtake him that my brother had wanted to become a car driver ever since the fourth grade. On every scrap of paper he would write the same text:

"To: Transport Office

Chief Manager

"I hereby request that you employ me at your agency since I am a third-class driver."

Later he realized his childhood dream, but it turned out that he had to exceed speed limits to overtake his temperament and finally had to change his trade.

And here I, with my almost invariably high marks, was equalized with my brother, who would, of course, use those beautiful notebooks to pen his idiotic car-driving applications. And my sister, who gobbled up pork fat yesterday, would receive an undeserved gift today.

I put my notebooks aside. I felt hard and humiliating tears scalding my eyes and a big lump in my throat. Father coaxed and soothed me and promised to take me to a mountain river for fishing. But the more he consoled me, the more acutely I felt the injustice of it all.

"I have two blotters!" my sister suddenly yelled as she opened one of her notebooks. That was the last straw. Everything might have been different if it hadn't been for those two blotters.

I stood up and said in a trembling voice, addressing myself to father, "She ate pork yesterday."

There was a horrible silence. I realized that something was wrong. Perhaps I hadn't expressed myself properly, or maybe Mohammed's great **tenets** and a little urge to capture someone else's notebooks didn't go together.

Father looked at me, his glance growing heavy with wrath. I made the last pathetic attempt to redeem the situation and direct his wrath into the proper channel.

notoriety: disrepute; poor reputation

tenets: principles; teachings

"She ate pork at Uncle Shura's," I said in despair, and felt that everything was lost.

Father grabbed me by my ears, shook my head as though to make sure that it would not come off, and then flung me to the floor. For a fleeting instant I felt a flash of pain and the crunch of pulled ears.

"You little louse!" he yelled. "All I need now is a stool pigeon at home!"

Grabbing his leather coat, he left the room, slamming the door so hard that plaster crumbled off the wall. I was not crushed by the pain or his words but by that expression of hatred and disgust on his face, as though I were a dangerous snake.

I lay on the floor. Mother tried to pick me up while my brother pranced around me in frantic ecstasy.

"He always gets high marks!" he screamed, pointing to my ears.

I liked my father, and this was the first time he had treated me so.

Many years have passed since. I have long been eating pork like everyone else, though perhaps this does not make me any happier. Still, at that time I realized that no principle justifies treachery, and besides, that treachery is always a hairy caterpillar bred of a small butterfly called envy, no matter how lofty the principles involved.

After You Read

Critical Reading

1. Analyze how the narrator develops over the course of the text. What, if anything, does he learn and how does his development support the **theme**?

2. Do you find any parts of the story humorous? If so, name a line or incident in the story that amuses you and explain how the author achieves this effect. If not, use examples of parts of the story that could be intended as humorous but failed to be and explain why.

3. On page 274, the narrator uses **personification** when he states, "Virtue blackmailed, and vice lowered its head in disgrace." What do you think this line means?

4. Based on the title and the father's reaction to his son being an informer, what is the story's **theme**?

Literary Lens: Hyperbole

Hyperbole is a form of comic exaggeration that can highlight a characteristic in a humorous way. Create a visual map of the use of hyperbole in "Forbidden Fruit." In each illustration box, draw a picture of an example of hyperbole from the story. Under each illustration, write the quotation from the story that inspired the illustration.

Illustration:
Quotation:
Illustration:
Quotation:
Illustration:
Quotation:

Focus on Research: Create an Annotated Bibliography

Conduct research on the origins of the title phrase: "forbidden fruit." Find three appropriate sources and create an annotated bibliography for each one, using a style guide such as MLA or APA.

Europe

Unit Review

Key Ideas and Details

1. Review the story "Forbidden Fruit" and then write an objective summary of the **plot**. Are all parts of the story represented in your summary? If not, do the parts missing in your summary serve another purpose besides plot? If so, what is that purpose?

2. Compare the poems by Thomas, Smith, Auden, Szymborska, and Miłosz. All are important 20th-century writers addressing a similar **theme**—death. Which poets address death within the context of historical events (fascism, Nazism) and which address it in a more personal context? Characterize each poet's treatment of this theme, citing evidence from the poems.

Craft and Structure

3. World War II and Nazism influenced many of these European writers. Look at the selections by Auden, Greene, Miłosz, and Ionesco for evidence of such influences. Why is war such a rich theme for writers? Compare the very different **tones** and perspectives these writers bring to this subject.

4. Reread "First Frost" and pay special attention to the specific word choices. Identify any repeated sounds and explain their cumulative effect on the poem's meaning and tone.

5. Compare the word choice in "Clearances" and "Do Not Go Gentle into That Good Night" and the resulting tones. Which poem has a more formal tone? What word choices contribute to this tone?

6. **Irony** and **black humor** are often seen in Western European writing. Which selections in this unit display this sort of humor? Discuss why European writers, in particular, might favor this form of expression.

Integration of Knowledge and Ideas

7. Find paintings or photographs of London after the German bombardments in 1940. Compare these to the description of the rubble in "The Destructors." Analyze how each medium expresses the images and what is emphasized or absent in each treatment.

8. Many of the authors in this unit use vivid imagery in their writing. Find examples in *Flights*, "Refugee Blues," and "The Balek Scales" and comment on how each author uses imagery.

Research Projects

Speaking and Listening

Develop and conduct a survey of your class to find out which selections from this unit were the most popular and why. First create questions and then interview at least five students, each of whom favored a different piece. Decide how to best present these results to the class.

Give an oral report on one aspect of World War II. Use the Research Handbook in the back of this book to help you narrow the focus of your presentation. Use a digital platform and include visuals and sounds that will enhance your presentation.

Multimedia Project

Choose a European cuisine that you would like to learn more about. Demonstrate for your class how to make a dish from this cuisine. Locate cookbooks or cooking blogs that explain background about the dish and how it was made.

Research Follow-Up

In the 20th century, some intellectuals adopted views known as existentialism or absurdism. Research one of these views, and create an infographic describing how it is reflected in this unit.

Synthesizing Through Research and Writing

Choose one writer from this unit who wrote without fear of censorship and one who wrote in fear of it. In a two-page essay, explain how political conditions shaped their works. Review what you learned about developing a thesis, using direct quotations, paraphrasing, using in-text citations, and drafting. Make sure you revise your essay for sufficient content, logical organization, effective word choice, and varied sentence structure.

Cultural Reflection

Write about any new understandings you might have about the cultures represented by the authors in this unit. Consider how the unit texts also impacted your view of your own experience of American culture.

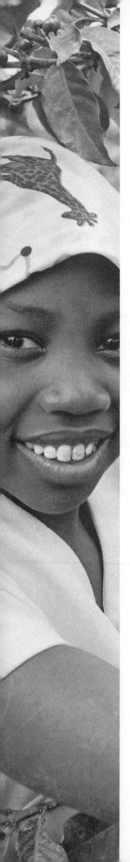

UNIT THREE

The Literature of Africa

Robert M. Baum
Associate Professor of Religion and African and African American Studies
at Dartmouth College

African literature of the 20th century is a unique blend of oral and written forms. It draws on European influences but is rooted in the rich diversity of African cultures. As far back as we know anything about Africa, oral traditions have been handed down from generation to generation. African cultures have always honored literature, giving professional poets the task of composing lengthy epic poems to be sung in honor of kings and other leaders. These traditions continue to be important in Africa today.

From the 10th to the 19th centuries, the literature of this vast continent was written in African languages using Arabic script. That changed, however, with the influence of Europeans who first enslaved African people and then conquered and colonized African societies. In the 19th century, Europeans in Africa established schools in which European languages were taught. There was a practical reason for this: British, French, Portuguese, Belgian, and German administrators wanted to train local people to assist them in running governments and businesses. Missionaries also established schools in order to convert Africans to Christianity. By the early 20th century, an influential group of Western-educated Africans began writing in European languages about the tensions of their role as intermediaries between Europeans and their fellow Africans. They used the literary forms of the novel, short story, play, and essay to examine their lives. Increasingly, they returned to the storytelling tradition of their elders, incorporating its style and power into their writing.

In the late 1920s, a group of students and young professionals from throughout the French-speaking black world began to write about being uprooted. They no longer belonged fully to their home societies in Africa, but they were also not accepted by Europeans in the colonies or France. They began to publish essays, short stories, and plays about their predicament. This early form of black consciousness was dubbed the Negritude movement. Celebrating the contributions of black cultures to world civilization, it had a strong influence on both African and African American writers. Rather than accepting negative European stereotypes about Africa, Negritude writers insisted that the increasingly complex, industrial societies of Europe and America had much to learn from the rich and vibrant cultures of Africa.

Since the 1950s and 1960s, a time when many African countries achieved political independence, African writers began to rediscover their own histories and cultures. They searched through oral traditions and written archives to understand their pasts and build their national futures. They spoke of the obligations of African writers to serve their new nations and help to develop African unity. As the great expectations of political independence and economic development were not met, however, post-colonial writers began to examine the difficulties standing in the way of true political and economic freedom. Nadine Gordimer, Bessie Head, and others have explored the deep-rooted system of racial separation in South Africa known as apartheid. Although apartheid was officially dismantled in 1994, its pervasive effects linger on.

During the last century, Africa's writers have struggled to understand the role of African customs and values within a society that is largely liberated but still not free from European dominance. Living in such a place, African writers have had a unique perspective on the collision of cultures. Some wondered, as Chinua Achebe did, whether things would fall apart. Others hoped new forms of culture would develop out of the long process of national liberation sweeping Africa in the last half of the 20th century. Together, African writers have created a deeply critical, self-reflective, and politically committed literature, one that plays an important role in illuminating what it means to be African at the dawn of the 21st century.

The Literature of Africa

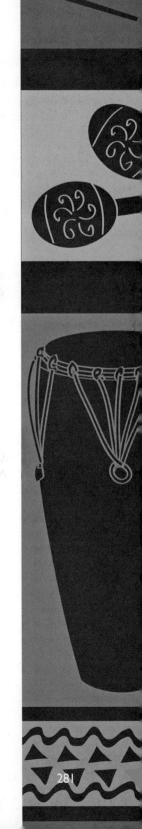

SENEGAL

David Diop
Sembene Ousmane
Léopold Sédar Senghor

WEST AFRICA

Djanka Tassey Condé

NIGERIA

Wole Soyinka
Chinua Achebe
Ben Okri
Adewale Maja-Pearce

Literary Map of
Africa

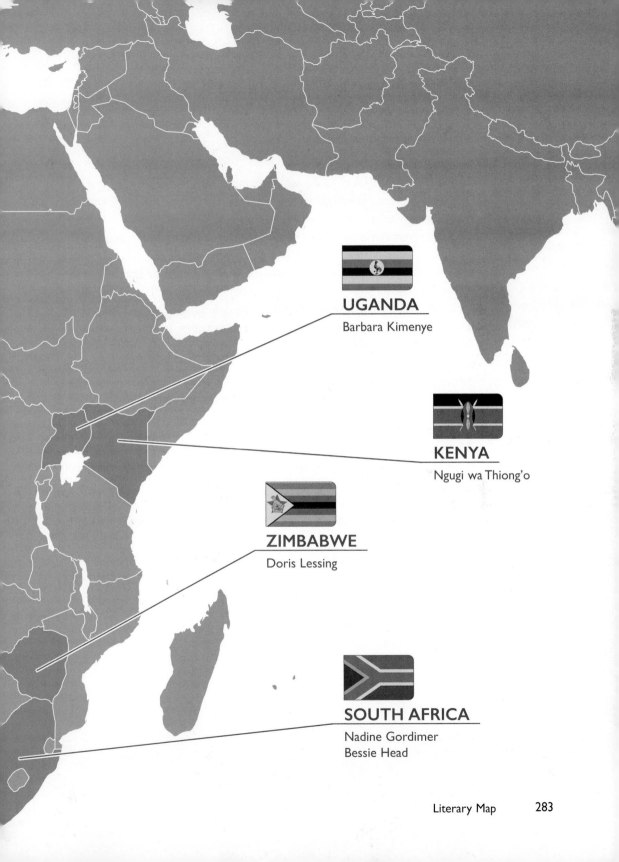

UGANDA

Barbara Kimenye

KENYA

Ngugi wa Thiong'o

ZIMBABWE

Doris Lessing

SOUTH AFRICA

Nadine Gordimer
Bessie Head

An African Classic
Sunjata

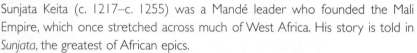

Background

Sunjata Keita (c. 1217–c. 1255) was a Mandé leader who founded the Mali Empire, which once stretched across much of West Africa. His story is told in *Sunjata*, the greatest of African epics.

Sunjata is similar to epics from Europe and the Middle East, such as the Greek *Iliad* and *Odyssey*, the Anglo-Saxon *Beowulf*, and the Babylonian *Gilgamesh*. Each of these epics was composed little by little over centuries by oral storytellers before becoming a single, unified work. In ancient Greece, such storytellers were known as *aoidoi*; in West Africa, storytellers are called *griots*, and they still practice their craft today. There is one major difference between *Sunjata* and the other epics: *Sunjata* has never been put into a final, written form, even after centuries of retelling. Mandé griots continue to tell and retell *Sunjata* today. At least three different griots have published their version of *Sunjata* in English. While these versions tell a single, cohesive story, they also vary in details.

Griots and the United States

When enslaved Africans were brought to America, they were generally forbidden to learn to read or write. So the oral traditions of the griots continued here, creating a wealth of African American storytelling.

Such storytelling was really a form of performance art, often involving verse, song, and dance. Audiences were not passive spectators but were expected to interrupt and comment on the story. As you read this excerpt from *Sunjata*, notice how the narrating griot calls upon the audience to respond, frequently asking, "You heard it?" This tradition of interaction between the speaker and the audience continues in many African American churches today.

Research: Analyze Literary Influences

The 1994 and 2019 movies of *The Lion King* are similar to both Shakespeare's *Hamlet* and *Sunjata*. In a short paragraph, argue whether you think *The Lion King* is based on *Sunjata* or not. Use examples from both works to support your position.

from Sunjata

Retold by Djanka Tassey Condé

Before You Read

The epic *Sunjata* tells the story of the hero named in the title, who founded the Mali Empire in the early 13th century. The story begins with Ma Sogolon Wulen Condé (Sunjata's mother) giving birth to the hero, who is born crippled. As a boy, he shows his strength and virtue by uprooting a baobab tree. When his father dies, Sunjata is denied his inheritance by his half brother, and he and his mother are forced to flee the kingdom. While they are gone, the Susu king Sumanguru overthrows Sunjata's kingdom. Sunjata later returns, uses magic to defeat Sumanguru, and unites various groups in West Africa under the Mali Empire.

World Context

Sunjata is one of the most influential tales in the West African oral tradition. Many versions of the tale exist, but its core—Sunjata's triumph and his commitment to the Mali traditions—remains the same. This version of the story was told by Djanka Tassey Condé, a griot who lives in West Africa. In this excerpt about Sunjata's childhood, he is sometimes referred to as Ma'an Sunjata, Jata, or Simbon.

LITERARY LENS Epics around the world contain common elements. For example, epics are founded in historical fact or legend, they feature a courageous and noble hero who must undertake a dangerous journey or task, and they contain supernatural creatures. Watch for these elements as you read *Sunjata*.

That Ma'an Sunjata,
God made him into a person,
Made him into a human fetus and he was born.
After this son was born,
When the Mande women were told about it,   5
They gathered together again under the Mande **baobab** tree.

baobab:
a species of tree;
its fruit and leaves
are used for food

They said, "It is one thing to give birth to a son,
And another thing for him to survive."
What did they do again?

Through **sorcery** they stretched the tendons of his two feet.   10
They confined him to the ground.
(You heard it?)
His **lameness** forced him to remain on the ground.

One year!
Two years!   15
Three years!
Four years!
Five years!
Six years!
The seventh year!   20
The co-wives provoked Sogolon to anger.
One day—
(Because we are walking on a straight path,
We cannot wander from one side to the other,
We have to take the main road,   25
So we will know how Manden was built,
You heard it?)

In the seventh year there came a day
When Maramajan Tarawelé[1] went and picked some baobab leaves
From the same baobab tree that was already mentioned.   30
While on her way back, Ma Sogolon Wulen Condé said,
She said, "Big sister Maramajan Tarawelé,
Won't you give me a few of your baobab leaves?"
The house in which Ma'an Sunjata was lodged,
This was said under its eaves.   35
Maramajan Tarawelé said, "Ah!"
She said, "Younger sister,
You who are the owner of sons,
If you ask us for baobab leaves, what are we supposed to do?
Your lame son is sitting right there inside the house.   40
You are alone in your search for baobab leaves.

---

1 **Maramajan Tarawelé:** a sister of Sujata's mother

Why don't you tell your son to get up and walk?"
Ma'an Sogolon Wulen Condé said, "Ah, that is not what I meant.
I thought I could depend on sisterhood.
But I did not know you were upset because I had this child."   45
They didn't know Sunjata was listening to them.
After that was said,
When Ma Sogolon Condé was passing by,
Sunjata said, "Mother!
Mother!"   50
She did not answer because she knew he had overheard them.
He said, "Mother, what are they saying?"
She said, "Ah, forget about that talk."
He said, "Ah, how can I ignore that?"
He said, "Mother, I will walk today."   55
(You heard it?)

He said, "What they are talking about,
That you have a lame person in the house,
That you should beg them for a baobab leaf,"
He said, "I will walk today."   60

He said, "Go and get my father's *sunsun*[2] staff,
And bring it to me."
He said, "I will walk today."
Ma Sogolon Condé went and got the *sunsun* staff.
She brought it to Simbon.   65
When the *sunsun* staff was thrust firmly into the ground,
When he attempted to stand holding the staff,
The *sunsun* staff broke.
He said to her, "Ah, mother.
Go and bring my father's iron staff."   70
He said, "They say you have a lame son in the house,
But you gave birth to a real son.
Nothing happens before its time.
Go and bring my father's iron staff."
She went for the iron staff, but he also broke that.   75
He said, "Go and tell my father's blacksmith,

forge:
to form
using heat

Let him **forge** an iron staff so I can walk."
(You heard it?)
The blacksmith carried one load of iron to the bellows,
Forged it and made it into an iron staff.   80
When it was thrust into the ground,
When he attempted to stand, the staff bent.
Where is that iron staff today?
It is in Narena,[3]
The staff of Sunjata.   85
He broke both of his father's staffs.
The one that was forged for him is in Narena.
The one that was bent became a bow.
Therefore, when he stood,
He lifted one foot,   90
Then he lifted the other foot,
Then the other foot.
(You heard it?)
Then his mother said, "Simbon has walked."
The *jeliw*[4] sang this in a song: 95
  "Has walked,

---

2 *sunsun:* a type of extremely strong wood, sometimes called West African ebony
3 **Narena:** a city in what is now Mali
4 *jeliw:* another name for two or more griots

Jata has walked.
Has walked,
Jata has walked."
It was rivalry that caused Jata to walk,   100
Because of the humiliation to his mother.
That is why, when I hear people saying they do not
    love their mother,
They dismiss their mothers, *oof!*

Heh! Jelimori!⁵   105
The father is everybody's, the mother is personal.
When you stand in the crowd,
People do not talk about your father,
It is your mother they will talk about.
After that, God gave him feet.   110
He went into the house and took his bow.
Some people say he made the iron staff into his bow,
But don't repeat that.
His father's quiver and bow were there.
He took the quiver and bow and went out of the town.   115
When he got there, he embraced a baobab tree.
He shook it,
He shook it,
He uprooted it,
And then he put it on his shoulder.   120
He brought it into his mother's yard,
He said, "Now everyone will come here for baobab leaves."
(Aah, Sogolon Condé!
When things are hard for you,
Everyone will abuse you.   125
When things are good for you,
People will say, "We knew this would happen for you."
May God help us to **persevere**.)

Then when the Mande women came, they said,
"Aah, Sogolon Condé!   130
We knew this would happen for you.

persevere:
to continue
despite
opposition

---

5 **Jelimori:** a West African name; the griot is speaking to someone in the audience

The sacrifice that was made by everybody,
It has been answered through you."
That was what they said as they picked the baobab leaves.
Before the time that So'olon Ma'an could walk,   135
His younger brother So'olon Jamori had been born.
While So'olon Ma'an was still on the ground
Manden Bori was born.
After So'olon Ma'an walked,
So'olon Kolonkan was born.   140
Sogolon stopped after four births.

[Sunjata's half brother, Dankaran Tuman, viewed him as a
rival for their father's legacy. Dankaran Tuman and his
mother plotted to have a group of nine sorceresses kill
Sunjata. However, Sunjata had one ally among the sorceresses.]

His ally among the nine sorceresses
Was Jelimusoni Tunku Manyan Diawara.
In the middle of the night, she went and told Simbon.
She said, "Sunjata, we will kill you the day after tomorrow,   145
If God agrees.
You had better do something.
The cows from your father's legacy that you declined from
   your brother,
The big bull that is among them,   150
Dankaran Tuman has called big sister Tasissi Gbandimina,
Called Jonmusoni Manyan,
Called me, Jelimusoni Tunku Manyan Diawara,
Called Nyuma Danba Magasuba,
Called Maramajan Tarawelé,   155
That we should kill you.
If we kill you, he will give us that bull.
Between sorcery and the craving for meat,
We have agreed to it.
Watch out for yourself.   160
If you don't do something about it,
If you don't speak to them about this
And make them an attractive offer,
The day after tomorrow,

Hunting in the bush is very important to you,   165
But if you go out we will kill you.
You are no match for us."
Sunjata took her hand and said, "You have told me the truth."
He said, "Very well, go and tell them
That I, the son of a Condé woman,   170
They must spare me.
You should tell them that one bull
Is not bigger than three male antelope.
Tell them that if they spare me,
And if God is willing,   175
I will give them three male antelope for the one bull.
Tell them to spare me;
They should not do what my brother asks."
When she went and told them,
The sorceresses said, "All we want is meat.   180
Tell him if he does what he has said,
He will have no problem."

That night and the next day passed.
When the following night had passed,
When the *sigbé*[6] bird chirped at dawn,   185
Simbon took his hammock,
Put on his crocodile-mouth hat,
Hung his hunter's whistle on his chest,
Took his quiver and bow,
And left the town.   190
When he got one kilometer away from the town,
He saw an antelope.
He shot at it and knocked it down.
He shot another arrow,
Hit another antelope and knocked it down.   195
Again he shot an arrow,
The sun did not get white before he had killed all three.
God is with the just.
Everybody does what he wants,
But God makes the final decision.   200
The chick destined to be a rooster will eventually crow,

---

6 *sigbé*: a type of sparrow found in West Africa

No matter what is laid in its path.
It will overcome.
After he killed them,
He carried the three antelope to the edge of town. 205
Then he went into the town.
He told Jelimusoni Tunku Manyan Diawara
That she should go and tell the nine sorceresses
That their meat was at the edge of town.
When they were told this, they set out. 210
They went and found the game.
They butchered them;
They roasted some of it,
They boiled some of it,
They fried some of it, 215
And made some of it into meatballs.
What did they say then?
They said, "Ma'an Sunjata,"
They said, "Even a female genie will not harm you,
Much less a human female." 220
What saved him?
His hands.
When you are popular, you must have an open hand.

It is a man's generosity that will save him.
Nothing saved Sunjata but his hands. 225
They blessed him.
They said, "We are with you to the death.
Even a female ant will never sting you.
No female genie will ever even chase you.
No female wild animal will ever harm you, 230
If God agrees,
Or we are not producers of kitchen smoke."
They spared him.

After You Read

Critical Reading

1. How do the Mandé women change their comments to Sogolon Condé after Sunjata learns to walk? What does this imply about their character? Use evidence from the text to support your ideas.

2. The nine sorceresses decide not to kill Sunjata. Summarize the lesson conveyed through this episode.

3. At one point, the griot says, "The chick destined to be a rooster will eventually crow" (page 291). Explain the meaning of this saying in the context of the poem.

Literary Lens: Epics

Like myths, epics reinforce the cultural values of the storyteller as well as the audience. Identify several values represented in the epic. Cite details to support your choices.

Value	Support from the passage

Focus on Research: Gather Sources

Use online and print sources to research the African American tradition known as call-and-response, a form that grew out of the interactive storytelling technique exemplified in *Sunjata*. Identify two print sources and two online sources that you used to research call-and-response. (Your print sources may be ebooks found in an online database.) Ensure someone else can locate these sources by listing the author, publication, publication date, and URL, if applicable. Exchange lists with a partner to see if you are able to find each other's sources.

The Literature of
Senegal

Background

Senegal is a former French colony that achieved independence in 1960. Its literature, and the rest of its arts, have all been shaped by the Negritude movement, which sought to express traditional black African culture through the arts.

The Negritude movement began with a small group of black students born in French colonies in Africa and the Americas who met while studying in Paris in the 1930s. They realized that taking pride in their African heritage was the most effective way to counter the widespread racism that they faced.

One of these students was poet Léopold Senghor (1906–2001) of Senegal. He went on to become one of Africa's greatest writers and intellectuals and a strong advocate of Negritude. In addition, Senghor was unanimously elected Senegal's first president. Guided by the principles of Negritude, Senghor attempted to create a uniquely African merger of socialism and democracy.

Senegal and the United States

The first Senegalese writer of international note became famous in the United States. At the age of seven, Phillis Wheatley (1753–1784) was kidnapped and brought to America as an enslaved person, two centuries before Senegal became a nation. She served in the household of the Wheatley family of Boston, who recognized her precocious brilliance and saw to it that she was exceptionally well educated.

Wheatley's poetry astounded both America and Europe. The slave-owning George Washington admired her poetry, as did the great French writer Voltaire. Wheatley's brilliance led some people to recognize the moral bankruptcy of slavery.

She was freed in 1773, but the harsh climate of New England ruined her health. Despite her fame, she died in poverty at the age of 31.

Research: Use Academic Online Sources

Research the Negritude movement founded by Léopold Senghor along with Martinique's Aimé Césaire (1913–2008) and French Guiana's Léon Damas (1912–1978). Begin by finding websites affiliated with universities or other academic organizations. (Look for .edu and .org in the web address.) Make a list of your sources.

Africa

David Diop

Before You Read

David Diop (1927–1960) was born in France, but he identified with his African heritage. His mother was from Cameroon, his father from Senegal. He had been recognized as a very promising poet when his life was cut short by a plane crash. Most of Diop's work was destroyed with him in the crash. The 22 poems published before his death appear in an English translation in *Hammer Blows and Other Writings*.

World Context

Senegalese writer David Diop was influential in the Negritude (French for "blackness") movement, a literary movement born in the 1930s and celebrating the African cultures.

 LITERARY LENS Personification is a figure of speech in which human qualities are ascribed to nonhuman objects. Watch for personification in this poem.

Africa my Africa
Africa of proud warriors in ancestral savannahs[1]
Africa of whom my grandmother sings
On the banks of the distant river
I have never known you   5
But your blood flows in my veins
Your beautiful black blood that irrigates the fields
The blood of your sweat
The sweat of your work

---

1 **savannahs:** (also *savannas*), a common type of grasslands in parts of Africa where it is rainy in summer, dry in winter

The work of your slavery   10
The slavery of your children
Africa tell me Africa
Is this you this back that is bent
This back that breaks under the weight of humiliation
This back trembling with red scars   15
And saying yes to the whip under the midday sun
But a grave voice answers me
Impetuous son that tree young and strong

That tree there
In splendid loveliness amidst white and faded flowers   20
That is Africa your Africa
That grows again patiently obstinately
And its fruit gradually acquires
The bitter taste of liberty.

Mother of Africa |
Mmakgabo
Mmapula Helen
Sebidi

After You Read

Critical Reading

1. Identify lines from this poem that show it is a good example of the tenets of Negritude. Explain each of your choices.

2. Read this poem aloud, paying special attention to repeated words and phrases. Use examples to illustrate the effect of the **repetition.**

3. Consider the last lines of the poem: "And its fruit gradually acquires / The bitter taste of liberty." Speculate on the reason Diop uses the adjective "bitter" to modify the phrase "taste of liberty." Conduct research to confirm your inferences.

Literary Lens: Personification

In **personification** a nonhuman object is given human attributes. Identify three examples from the poem that show personification and explain the effects it has on the poem.

Example of personification	What effect does it have on the poem?

Focus on Research: Use In-Text Citations

Using the academic sources you found (see page 294), do focused research on the literary movement known as Negritude. Summarize your findings in one or two paragraphs, including at least two direct quotations from your sources. Identify quotations that will have the most impact and incorporate them smoothly into your own writing. Be sure to use quotation marks and in-text citations correctly.

Black Girl

Sembene Ousmane

Before You Read

Sembene Ousmane (1923–2007) produced works in both French and Wolof, the main language of Senegal. After fighting on the side of the French during World War II, he became a dock worker in France, where he wrote his novel *Le Docker Noir (The Black Docker)*. After studying film in Russia, he returned to Senegal to make movies. His "La Noire de . . ." ("Black Girl") won a prize at the 1966 Cannes Film Festival.

World Context

Aware that his readership in Africa was limited by widespread illiteracy, Senegalese Sembene Ousmane decided to rely on film to reach a larger audience. Now he is widely considered to be one of Africa's most important filmmakers.

> **LITERARY LENS Setting** refers to the time and place of a narrative. Watch for details of the two settings, Africa and France.

It was the morning of the 23rd of June in the year of Our Lord nineteen hundred fifty-eight. At Antibes, along the Riviera, neither the fate of the French Republic nor the future of Algeria nor the state of the colonial territories preoccupied those who swarmed across the beaches below La Croisette.

Above, on the road leading to the Hermitage, two old-style Citroens,[1] one behind the other, were moving up the mountain. They stopped and several men quickly got out, rushing down the gravel walk toward a house on which a worn sign spelled out Villa of Green Happiness. The men were

---

1 **Citroen:** a kind of European car

the police chief of the town of Grasse, a medical officer, and two police inspectors from Antibes, flanked by officers in uniform.

There was nothing green about the Villa of Green Happiness except its name. The garden was kept in the French manner, the walks covered with gravel, set off by a couple of palm trees with dropping fronds. The chief looked closely at the house, his eyes stopping at the third window, the broken glass, the ladder.

Inside were other inspectors and a photographer. Three people who seemed to be reporters were looking with rather absentminded interest at the African statues, masks, animal skins, and ostrich eggs set here and there. Entering the living room was like violating the privacy of a hunter's lair.

Two women were hunched together, sobbing. They looked very much alike, the same straight forehead, the same curved nose, the same dark circles about eyes reddened from crying. The one in the pale dress was speaking: "After my nap, I felt like taking a bath. The door was locked from the inside"—blowing her nose—"and I thought to myself, it's the maid taking her bath. I say 'the maid,'" she corrected, "but we never called her anything else but her name, Diouana. I waited for more than an hour, but didn't see her come out. I went back and called, knocking on the door. There was no answer. Then I phoned our neighbor, the Commodore . . ."

She stopped, wiped her nose, and began to cry again. Her sister, the younger of the two, hair cut in a boyish style, sat hanging her head.

"You're the one who discovered the body?" the chief asked the Commodore.

"Yes . . . that is, when Madame Pouchet called and told me that the black girl had locked herself in the bathroom, I thought it was a joke. I spent thirty-five years at sea, you know. I've roamed the seven seas. I'm retired from the Navy."

"Yes, yes, we know."

"Yes, well, when Madame Pouchet called I brought my ladder."

"You brought the ladder?"

"No. It was Mademoiselle Dubois, Madame's sister, who suggested the idea. And when I got to the window, I saw the black girl swimming in blood."

"Where is the key to the door?"

"Here it is, your honor," said the inspector.

"Just wanted to see it."

"I've checked the window," said the other inspector.

"I'm the one who opened it, after breaking the pane," said the retired Navy man.

"Which pane did you break?"

"Which pane?" he repeated. He was wearing white linen trousers and a blue jacket.

"Yes, I saw it, but I'd like to ask precisely."

"The second from the top," answered the sister.

At this, two stretcher-bearers came down, carrying a body wrapped in a blanket. Blood dripped on the steps. The magistrate lifted a corner of the blanket and frowned. A black girl lay dead on the stretcher, her throat cut from one ear to the other.

"It was with this knife. A kitchen knife," said another man, from the top of the stairs.

"Did you bring her from Africa, or did you hire her here?"

"We brought her back from Africa, in April. She came by boat. My husband is with aerial navigation in Dakar, but the company only pays air passage for the family. She worked for us in Dakar. For two and a half or three years."

"How old is she?"

"I don't know exactly."

"According to her passport, she was born in 1927."

"Oh! The natives don't know when they are born," offered the naval officer, plunging his hands into his pockets.

"I don't know why she killed herself. She was well treated here, she ate the same food, shared the same rooms as my children."

"And your husband, where is he?"

"He left for Paris the day before yesterday."

"Ah!" said the inspector, still looking at the knickknacks. "Why do you think it was suicide?"

"Why?" said the retired officer . . . "Oh! Who do you think would make an attempt on the life of a Negro girl? She never went out. She didn't know anyone, except for Madame's children."

The reporters were getting impatient. The suicide of a maid—even if she was black—didn't amount to a hill of beans. There was nothing newsworthy in it.

"It must have been homesickness. Because lately she'd been behaving very strangely. She wasn't the same."

The police magistrate went upstairs, accompanied by one of the inspectors. They examined the bathroom, the window.

"Some boomerang, this story," said the inspector.

The others waited in the living room.

"We'll let you know when the **coroner** is finished," said the inspector, on his way out with the police magistrate an hour after their arrival.

coroner: official who investigates deaths not due to natural causes

The cars and the reporters left. In the Villa of Green Happiness the two women and the retired naval officer remained silent.

Bit by bit, Madame Pouchet searched her memory. She thought back to Africa and her elegant villa on the road to Hann. She remembered Diouana pushing open the iron gate and signaling to the German shepherd to stop barking.

It was there, in Africa, that everything had started. Diouana had made the six-kilometer round trip on foot three times a week. For the last month she had made it gaily—enraptured, her heart beating as if she were in love for the first time. Beginning at the outskirts of Dakar, brand-new houses were scattered like jewels in a landscape of cactus, bougainvillea, and jasmine. The asphalt of the Avenue Gambetta stretched out like a long black ribbon. Joyous and happy as usual, the little maid had no complaints about the road or her employers. Though it was a long way, it had no longer seemed so far the past month, ever since Madame had announced she would take her to France. France! Diouana shouted the word in her head. Everything around her had become ugly, the magnificent villas she had so often admired seemed shabby.

In order to be able to travel, in order to go to France, since she was originally from the Casamance, she had needed an identity card. All her paltry savings went to get one. "So what?" she thought. "I'm on my way to France!"

"Is that you, Diouana?"

"*Viye*, Madame," came her answer in the Senegalese accent. She spoke from the vestibule, nicely dressed in her light-colored cotton, her hair neatly combed.

"Good! Monsieur is in town. Will you look after the children?"

"*Viye*, Madame," she agreed in her childish voice.

Though her identity card read "Born in 1927," Diouana was not yet thirty. But she must have been over twenty-one. She went to find the children. Every room was in the same condition. Parcels packed and tied with string, boxes piled here and there. After ten whole days of washing and ironing, there wasn't much left for Diouana to do. In the proper sense of her duties, she was a laundress. There was a cook, a houseboy, and herself. Three people. The servants.

"Diouana . . . Diouana," Madame called.

"Madame?" she answered, emerging from the children's room.

Madame was standing with a notebook in her hands, making an inventory of the baggage. The movers would be coming at any moment.

"Have you been to see your parents? Do you think they will be happy?"

"*Viye*, Madame. The whole family is agreed. I tell Mama for myself. Also tell Papa Boutoupa," she said.

Her face, which had been radiant with happiness, fixed on the empty walls, and began to fade. Her heartbeat slowed. She would be ill if Madame changed her mind. Diouana's ebony-black face grew gloomy; she lowered her eyes, ready to plead her case.

"You're not going to tell me at the last moment, on this very day, that you're leaving us in the lurch?"

"No, Madame, me go."

They were not speaking the same language. Diouana wanted to see France, this country whose beauty, richness, and joy of living everyone praised. She wanted to see it and make a triumphal return. This was where people got rich. Already, without having left African soil, she could see herself on the dock, returning from France, wealthy to the millions, with gifts of clothes for everyone. She dreamed of the freedom to go where she wished without having to work like a beast of burden. If Madame should change her mind, refuse to take her, it would truly make her ill.

As for Madame, she was remembering the last few holidays she had spent in France. Three of them. And then she had had only two children. In Africa, Madame had acquired bad habits when it came to servants. In France when she hired a maid not only was the salary higher but the maid demanded a day off to boot. Madame had had to let her go and hired another. The next one was no different from the first, if not worse. She answered Madame tit for tat. "Anyone who is capable of having children should take a turn with them herself. I can't live in. I have my own children to take care of and a husband, too," she declared.

Used to being waited on hand and foot, Madame had yielded to her wifely duties, and clumsily fulfilled the role of mother. As for a real vacation, she had hardly had any. She soon persuaded her husband to return to Africa.

On her return, grown thin and thoroughly exasperated, she had conceived a plan for her next vacation. She put want ads in all the newspapers. A hundred young girls answered. Her choice fell on Diouana, newly arrived from her native bush.[2] Producing two more children during the three years that Diouana worked for her, between the last holiday and the one to come, Madame sang the praises of France. For three thousand francs a month, any young African girl would have followed her to the end of the earth. And to top it off, from time to time, especially lately, Madame would give Diouana little gifts of this and that, old clothes, shoes that could be mended.

This was the insurmountable moat that separated the maid and her employer.

"Did you give Monsieur your identity card?"

"*Viye*, Madame."

"You may go back to your work. Tell the cook to give the three of you a good meal."

"*Merci*,[3] Madame," she answered, and went off to the kitchen.

Madame continued her inventory.

Monsieur returned on the stroke of noon, his arrival announced by the barking of the dog. Getting out of his Peugeot 403, he found his wife, **indefatigable**, pencil in hand.

indefatigable: untiring; inexhaustible

"Haven't the baggage men come yet?" she said nervously.

"They'll be here at a quarter to two. Our bags will be on top. That way they'll be out first when we land in Marseilles. And what about Diouana? Diouana!"

The eldest of the children ran to fetch her. She was under the trees with the littlest one.

"*Viye*, Madame."

"It's Monsieur who was calling you."

"That's fine. Here are your ticket and your identity card."

Diouana held out a hand to take them.

"You keep the identity card, I'll take care of the ticket. The Duponts are returning on the same ship, they'll look after you. Are you glad to be going to France?"

"*Viye*, Monsieur."

"Good. Where are your bags?"

"At Rue Escarfait, Monsieur."

"After I've had lunch, we'll go fetch them in the car."

"Bring the children in, Diouana, it's time for their nap."

"*Viye*, Madame."

---

2 **bush:** undeveloped land, often dense with jungle vegetation and other bushy growth
3 *Merci:* French for "thank you"

Diouana wasn't hungry. The cook's helper, two years younger than she, brought the plates and took the empty ones away noiselessly. The cook was sweating heavily. He wasn't happy. He was going to be out of work. This was how the departure affected him. And for this reason he was a bit resentful of the maid. Leaning out the wide window overlooking the sea, transported, Diouana watched the birds flying high above in the immense expanse of blue. In the distance she could barely make out the Island of Gorée. She was holding her identity card, turning it over and over, examining it and smiling quietly to herself. The picture was a gloomy one. She wasn't pleased with the pose or with the exposure. "What does it matter? I'm leaving!" she thought.

"Samba," said Monsieur, who had come to the kitchen, "the meal was excellent today. You outdid yourself. Madame is very pleased with you."

The cook's helper stood at attention. Samba, the cook, adjusted his tall white hat and made an effort to smile.

"Thank you very much, Monsieur," he said. "I too am happy, very happy, because Monsieur and Madame are happy. Monsieur very nice. My family big, unhappy. Monsieur leave, me no more work."

"We'll be back, my good man. And then, with your talent you'll soon find another job!"

Samba, the cook, wasn't so sure. The whites were stingy. And in a Dakar filled with country people each claiming to be a master cook, it wouldn't be easy to find a job.

"We'll be back, Samba. Maybe sooner than you think. The last time we stayed only two and a half months."

To these consoling words from Madame, who had joined her husband in the kitchen, Samba could only answer: "*Merci*, Madame. Madame very nice lady."

Madame was glad. She knew from experience what it meant to have a good reputation with the servants.

"You can go home this afternoon at four with Monsieur. I'll pack up the rest. When we come back I promise to hire you again. Are you pleased?"

"*Merci*, Madame."

Madame and Monsieur were gone. Samba gave Diouana a slap. She hit him back angrily.

"Hey! Careful. Careful. You're going away today. So we shouldn't fight."

"That hurt!" she said.

"And Monsieur, does he hurt you too?"

liaison:
affair; intrigue
Samba suspected a secret **liaison** between the maid and her employer.

"They're calling for you, Diouana. I hear the car starting."

She left without even saying goodbye.

The car moved along the highway. Diouana didn't often have the privilege of being driven by Monsieur. Her very look invited the pedestrians' admiration, though she dared not wave a hand or shout while going past, "I'm on my way to France!" Yes, France! She was sure her happiness was plain to see. The subterranean sources of this **tumultuous** joy made her a bit shaky. When the car stopped in front of the house at Rue Escarfait, she was surprised. "Already?" she thought. Next door to her humble house, at the Gay Navigator Café, a few customers were seated at the tables and several were talking quietly on the sidewalk.

"Is it today you're leaving, little one?" asked Tive Correa. Already tipsy, he steadied himself, legs apart, holding his bottle by the neck. His clothes were rumpled.

Diouana would have nothing to do with the drunkard. She didn't listen to Tive Correa's advice. An old sailor, Tive Correa had come home from Europe after twenty years' absence. He had left, rich with youth, full of ambition, and come home a wreck. From having wanted everything, he had returned with nothing but an excessive love for the bottle. For Diouana he predicted nothing but misfortune. Once, when she had asked his advice, his opinion had been that she shouldn't go. In spite of his serious state of **inebriety**, he made a few steps toward Monsieur, bottle still in hand.

"Is it true that Diouana's leaving with you, Monsieur?"

Monsieur did not answer. He took out a cigarette and lit it, blew the smoke through the car door, and looked Tive Correa over from head to toe. What a bum he was, greasy clothes, stinking of palm wine.

Correa leaned over, putting a hand on the car door. "I was there. I lived in France for twenty years," he began, with a note of pride in his voice. "I, whom you see this way, ruin though I am today, I know France better than you do. During the war I lived in Toulon, and the Germans sent us with the other Africans to Aix-en-Provence, to the mines at Gardanne. I've been against her going."

"We haven't forced her to go! She wants to," Monsieur answered dryly.

"Certainly. What young African doesn't dream of going to France? Unfortunately, they confuse living in France with being a servant in France. I come from the village next to Diouana's, in Casamance. There, we don't say the way you do that it is the light that attracts the moth, but the other way round. In my country, Casamance, we say that the darkness pursues the moth."

> tumultuous: uproarious; wild

> inebriety: drunkenness; intoxication

Pwo mask showing scarification indicating tears |
from the Chokwe Culture, Angola

In the meantime, Diouana returned, escorted by several women. They were chatting along, each begging for a little souvenir. Diouana promised happily; she was smiling, her white teeth gleaming.

"The others are at the dock," said one. "Don't forget my dress."

"For me, some shoes for the children. You've got the size in your suitcase. And remember the sewing machine."

"The petticoats, too."

"Write and tell me how much the hair-straightening irons cost and also the price of a red jacket with big buttons, size 44."

"Don't forget to send a little money to your mother in Boutoupa . . ."

Each one had something to tell her, some request to make of her; Diouana promised. Her face was radiant. Tive Correa took the suitcase, pushing it drunkenly but not roughly into the car.

"Let her go, girls. Do you think money grows on trees in France? She'll have something to say about that when she gets back."

Loud protests from the women.

"Goodbye, little cousin. Take care of yourself. You have the address of the cousin in Toulon. Write to him as soon as you get there, he will help you. Come, give me a kiss."

They all kissed each other goodbye. Monsieur was getting impatient. He started up the motor to indicate politely that he wished they'd be done with it.

The Peugeot was moving. Everyone waved.

At the dock it was the same—relatives, friends, little commissions. Everyone pressed around her. Always under the watchful eye of Monsieur. She embarked.

A week at sea. "No news," she would have written if she'd been keeping a diary, in which case she'd also have had to know how to read and write. Water in front, behind, to port, to starboard.[4] Nothing but a sheet of liquid, and above it, the sky.

When the boat landed, Monsieur was there. After the formalities, they quickly made their way to the Côte d'Azur. She devoured everything with her eyes, marveling, astonished. She packed every detail into her head. It was beautiful. Africa seemed a **sordid** slum by comparison. Towns, buses, trains, trucks went by along the coastal highway. The heaviness of the traffic surprised her.

sordid: dirty; wretched

"Did you have a good crossing?"

"*Viye*, Monsieur," she would have answered, if Monsieur had asked the question.

After a two-hour drive, they were in Antibes.

Days, weeks, and the first month went by. The third month began. Diouana was no longer the joyous young girl with the ready laugh, full of life. Her eyes were beginning to look hollow, her glance was less alert, she no longer noticed details. She had a lot more work to do here than in Africa. At first her fretting was hardly noticeable. Of France, la Belle France, she had only a vague idea, a fleeting vision. French gardens, the hedges of the other villas, the crests of roofs appearing above the green trees, the

---

4 **to port, to starboard:** from left to right

palms. Everyone lived his own life, isolated, shut up in his own house. Monsieur and Madame went out a good deal, leaving her with the four children. The children quickly organized a mafia and persecuted her. "You've got to keep them happy," Madame would say. The oldest, a real scamp, recruited others of like inclination and they played explorer. Diouana was the "savage." The children pestered her. Once in a while the eldest got a good spanking. Having picked up phrases from the conversations of Mama, Papa, or the neighbors back in Africa—phrases in which notions of racial prejudice played a part—he made exaggerated remarks to his pals. Without the knowledge of his parents, they would turn up, chanting, "Black Girl, Black Girl. She's as black as midnight."

Perpetually harassed, Diouana began to waste away. In Dakar she had never had to think about the color of her skin. With the youngsters teasing, she began to question it. She understood that here she was alone. There was nothing that connected her with the others. And it aggravated her, poisoned her life, the very air she breathed.

Everything grew blunt—her old dreams, her contentment eroded. She did a lot of hard work. It was she who did all the cooking, laundry, baby-sitting, ironing. Madame's sister came to stay at the villa, making seven people to look after. At night, as soon as she went up to bed, Diouana slept like a log.

The venom was poisoning her heart. She had never hated anything. Everything became monotonous. Where was France? The beautiful cities she had seen at the movies in Dakar, the rare foods, the interesting crowds? The population of France reduced itself to these spiteful monsters, Monsieur, Madame, and Mademoiselle, who had become strangers to her. The country seemed limited to the immediate surroundings of the villa. Little by little she was drowning. The wide horizons of a short while ago stopped now at the color of her skin, which suddenly filled her with an **invincible** terror. Her skin. Her blackness. Timidly, she retreated into herself.

> Where was France? The beautiful cities she had seen at the movies in Dakar, the rare foods, the interesting crowds?

invincible: unconquerable; unbeatable

With no one from her universe to exchange ideas with, she held long moments of palaver[5] with herself. A week ago, Monsieur and Madame had cleverly taken her along to visit their relatives in Cannes.

---

5 **palaver:** idle speech

"Tomorrow we'll go to Cannes. My parents have never tasted African food. You'll do us African honor with your cooking," Madame had said. She was nearly bare, and getting bronzed from the sun.

"*Viye*, Madame."

"I've ordered some rice and two chickens . . . You'll be careful not to spice it too much?"

"*Viye*, Madame."

Answering this way, she felt her heart harden. It seemed the hundredth time that she'd been trailed from villa to villa. To this one's house and then to that one's. It was at the Commodore's—everyone called him the Commodore—that she had rebelled the first time. Some silly people, who followed her about, hanging on her heels in the kitchen, had been there for dinner. Their presence was an **oppressive** shadow on her slightest movement. She had the feeling of not knowing how to do anything. These strange, self-centered, sophisticated beings never stopped asking her idiotic questions about how African women do their cooking. She kept herself under control.

oppressive: overwhelming; harsh

The three women were still chirping when she waited on them at the table, testing the first spoonful on the tip of their tongues, then gluttonously devouring the rest.

"This time, at my parents', you must outdo yourself."

"*Viye*, Madame."

Restored to her kitchen, she thought of Madame's former kindness. She detested it. Madame had been good to her, but in a self-seeking way. The only reason for her attentiveness had been to wind the strings around Diouana, the better to make her sweat. She loathed everything. Back in Dakar, Diouana used to gather Monsieur and Madame's leftovers to take home to Rue Escarfait. She had taken pride then in working for "important white people." Now she was so alone their meals made her sick to her stomach. The resentment spoiled her relations with her employers. She stood her ground, they stood theirs. They no longer exchanged any remarks but those of a business nature.

"Diouana, will you do the washing today?"

"*Viye*, Madame."

"Last time you didn't do a good job on my slips. The iron was too hot. And the collars of Monsieur's shirts were scorched. Do pay attention to what you're doing, will you?"

"*Viye*, Madame."

"Oh. I forgot. There are some buttons missing on Monsieur's shirts and his shorts."

Every little job was Diouana's. And then Madame started speaking to her in pidgin[6] French, even in front of guests. And this was the only thing she did with honesty. In the end, no one in the house ever spoke to the maid anymore except in terms of "Missie," Senegalese pidgin talk. Bewildered by her inadequacies in French, Diouana closed herself into a sort of solitary confinement. After long, lonely meditation she came to the conclusion first of all that she was nothing but a useful object, and furthermore that she was being put on exhibit like a trophy. At parties, when Monsieur or Madame made remarks about "native" psychology, Diouana was taken as an illustration. The neighbors would say: "It's the Pouchets' black girl . . ." She wasn't "the African girl" in her own right, but theirs. And that hurt.

The fourth month began. Things got worse. Her thoughts grew more **lucid** every day. She had work and work to spare. All week long. Sunday was Mademoiselle's favorite day for asking friends over. There were lots of them. The weeks began and ended with them.

Everything became clear. Why had Madame wanted her to come? Her generosities had been premeditated. Madame no longer took care of her children. She kissed them every morning, that was all. And where was la Belle France? These questions kept repeating themselves. "I am cook, nursemaid, chambermaid; I do all the washing and ironing and for a mere three thousand francs a month. I do housework for six people. What am I doing here?"

Diouana gave way to her memories. She compared her "native bush" to these dead shrubs. How different from the forest of her home in Casamance. The memory of her village, of the community life, cut her off from the others even more. She bit her lip, sorry to have come. And on this film of the past, a thousand other details were projected.

As she returned to these surroundings, where she was doubly an outsider, her feelings hardened. She thought often of Tive Correa. His predictions had come cruelly true. She would have liked to write to him, but couldn't. Since arriving in France, she had had only two letters from her mother. She didn't have the time to answer, even though Madame had promised to write for her. Was it possible to tell Madame what she was thinking? She was angry with herself. Her ignorance made her mute. It was infuriating. And besides, Mademoiselle had made off with her stamps.

A pleasant idea crossed her mind, though, and raised a smile. This evening only Monsieur was at home, watching television. She decided to

---

6 **pidgin:** a simplified form of the language

take advantage of the opportunity. Then, unexpectedly finding Madame there too, Diouana stopped abruptly and left the room.

"Sold, sold. Bought, bought," she repeated to herself. "They've bought me. For three thousand francs I do all this work. They lured me, tied me to them, and I'm stuck here like a slave." She was determined now. That night she opened her suitcase, looked at the objects in it, and wept. No one cared.

Yet she went through the same motions and remained as sealed off from the others as an oyster at low tide on the beach of her native Casamance.

"Douna"—it was Mademoiselle calling her. Why was it impossible for her to say Di-ou-a-na?

Her anger redoubled. Mademoiselle was even lazier than Madame: "Come take this away"—"There is such-and-such to be done, Douna"—"Why don't you do this, Douna?"—"Douna, now and then please rake the garden." For an answer Mademoiselle would receive an **incendiary** glance. Madame complained about her to Monsieur.

"What is the matter with you, Diouana? Are you ill or something?" he asked.

She no longer opened her mouth.

"You can tell me what's the matter. Perhaps you'd like to go to Toulon. I haven't had the time to go, but tomorrow I'll take you with me."

"Anyone would think we disgust her," said Madame.

Three days later Diouana took her bath.

Returning home after a morning of shopping, Madame Pouchet went in the bathroom and quickly emerged.

"Diouana! Diouana!" she called. "You are dirty, in spite of everything. You might have left the bathroom clean."

"No me, Madame. It was the children, *viye*."

"The children! The children are tidy. It may be that you're fed up with them. But to find you telling lies, like a native, that I don't like. I don't like liars and you are a liar!"

Diouana kept silent, though her lips were trembling. She went upstairs to the bathroom and took her clothes off. It was there they found her, dead.

"Suicide," the investigators concluded. The case was closed.

The next day, in the newspaper, on page 4, column 6, hardly noticeable, was a small headline:

"Homesick African Girl Cuts Throat in Antibes."

Translated by Ellen Conroy Kennedy

After You Read

Critical Reading

1. Identify examples of **irony** in this story, taking into account dialogue, setting, and the names of things and places.

2. The **theme** of a work can sometimes be expressed in a short statement or saying. Consider the main message of "Black Girl." Then write a short theme statement.

3. How does Diouana's attitude and behavior change throughout the story? Include examples from the text in your answer.

Literary Lens: Setting

The story takes place in two settings: Senegal and France. Compare and contrast Diouana's life in the two settings.

Re-create the chart below to compare and contrast elements in "Black Girl." In the second and third columns, write words or phrases that describe elements of the story in each of the two settings. In the last column, draw a conclusion about whether that element is similar or different in the two settings. Briefly explain your thinking.

Elements	Setting: Senegal	Setting: France	Similar or different? Explain.
Physical environment			
Society's attitude toward black Africans			
Diouana's work situation			
Diouana's relationship with her employers			
Diouana's relationship with her friends and family			
Diouana's financial situation			

Focus on Research: Create a Visual Representation

Identify statistics you would like to research related to the country of Senegal, such as the types of religions practiced or the level of education of the population. Write an inquiry question you would like to answer and conduct research. If you can't find enough information, change your question. Based on your research, create a graph or chart that communicates the data, such as a pie chart or a bar graph. Publish your visual representation and include your source information using a style such as APA or MLA.

I Will Pronounce Your Name

(for Tama)

Léopold Sédar Senghor

Before You Read

Léopold Sédar Senghor (1906–2001) lived in Paris off and on during his life and joined the French army during World War II. He began writing poems while a prisoner of war. He became the first black man to be inducted into the French Academy, one of France's highest cultural achievements. Senghor also helped to found the Negritude movement, which he felt embodied the cultural values of the black world.

World Context

Senghor considered himself to be a griot. In parts of Africa, griots are the praise-speakers—poets, historians, and musicians who travel and carry on the native oral tradition.

LITERARY LENS As you read, consider the **figurative language**, or figures of speech, the poet uses.

I will pronounce your name, Naëtt, I will declaim you, Naëtt!
Naëtt, your name is mild like cinnamon, it is the fragrance in which
   the lemon grove sleeps,
Naëtt, your name is the sugared clarity of blooming coffee trees
And it resembles the savannah, that blossoms forth under the   5
   masculine ardour of the midday sun.

Name of dew, fresher than shadows of tamarind,[1]
Fresher even than the short dusk, when the heat of the day is
    silenced.
Naëtt, that is the dry tornado, the hard clasp of lightning   10
Naëtt, coin of gold, shining coal, you my night, my sun! . . .
I am your hero, and now I have become your sorcerer, in order
    to pronounce your names.
Princess of Elissa, banished from Futa[2] on the fateful day.

Translated by Gerald Moore and Ulli Beier

---

1 **tamarind:** a large tropical tree
2 **Princess of Elissa . . . Futa:** the Princess of Elissa, also known as Dido, is a mythical figure
  from the epic Roman poem *The Aeneid*; she is said to have founded Carthage (now Tunisia).
  Futa refers to Futa Jallon, a mountainous region in Africa.

After You Read

Critical Reading

1. The author uses **allusions** in the poem. What are they, and why does the author include them?

2. The comparisons in the poem change in tone from the beginning to the end. Trace the change by citing examples. Then speculate on the reason for the change.

3. This poem includes **imagery** related to the senses of smell and taste. Identify at least three images related to these senses and explain how they impact the poem.

Literary Lens: Figurative Language

Identify whether the poem's **tone** is formal or informal. Then list four **similes** or **metaphors** from the poem that help establish the tone. Be prepared to support your choices.

Tone:	
Figurative language	**How does it establish the tone?**

Focus on Research: Evaluate Sources

In many African countries, naming a child is a significant part of the culture. A name is carefully chosen to represent the values of the family and the hopes for the child's future. Conduct research on the importance of names in African culture. Find five sources and evaluate them for accuracy and trustworthiness. Create a rubric that can be used to score your sources. Here are a few questions to get you started:

- What are the author's credentials?
- What is the purpose and who is the intended audience?

In your rubric consider providing a sliding scale to rank the source from not trustworthy to very trustworthy.

The Literature of
Nigeria

Background

Since achieving independence from Great Britain in 1960, Nigeria has been plagued by corruption, violence, military coups, and civil war. Conflicts often pit the country's 250 ethnic groups against each other or divide the Muslim majority and the Christian minority. Other conflicts have flared over natural resources. Though Nigeria is one of the ten largest oil-exporting countries in the world, most of its inhabitants remain mired in poverty.

As tragic as Nigeria's recent history has been, the half century of conflict has inspired great literature. Chinua Achebe's (1930–2013) classic novel *Things Fall Apart* describes the clash between traditional village culture and British colonial ways. Author and environmentalist Ken Saro-Wiwa (1941–1995) penned *Sozaboy: A Novel in Rotten English*, a verbally stunning satire of corruption during the Nigerian Civil War (1967–1970), and *On a Darkling Plain*, his personal diaries of that war. Saro-Wiwa was one of eight activists executed on November 10, 1995.

Nigeria and the United States

As a result of the problems and persecution in Nigeria, many Nigerian writers have moved to the United States. The most celebrated of these is Wole Soyinka (b. 1934), the first black African to win the Nobel Prize in Literature. While his famous play *Death and the King's Horseman* reflects bitterly on the era of British colonialism, Soyinka was also critical of African authoritarianism. Indeed, Soyinka claims that his work condemns "the oppressive boot and the irrelevance of the color of the foot that wears it." During his years in the United States, Soyinka has been a respected professor at several American universities.

Critically acclaimed writer Chimamanda Ngozi Adichie was born in Nigeria in 1977 to parents of Igbo ancestry. Adichie came to the U.S. when she was 19. Her first novel, *Purple Hibiscus,* relates the story of a family caught up in the political turmoil in Nigeria in the late 1990s. In 2013, Adichie published *Americanah,* a socio-political love story that explores the challenges of being a Nigerian immigrant to America.

Research: Use Academic Online Sources

Two Nigerian women writers who have achieved worldwide fame for their writing are Buchi Emecheta (1944–2017) and Flora Nwapa (1931–1993). Choose one of these writers and write a short paragraph about how she portrays women's lives in Africa. Use academic websites for your information.

Telephone Conversation

Wole Soyinka

Before You Read

Akinwande Oluwole Soyinka (1934–) was born in Nigeria and belongs to the Yoruba tribe. He was the first African to win the Nobel Prize in Literature (1986). His multiple talents qualify him as a "Renaissance man": a novelist, playwright, critic, teacher, poet, actor, translator, and politician. According to one critic, Soyinka's writing "blends African with European cultural traditions, the high seriousness of modernist elite literature, and the topicality of African popular theater."

World Context

In 1967, Soyinka was imprisoned for political reasons. While in solitary confinement, a woman prisoner was mistakenly put in the same cell with him. When she recognized him as a famous author, she began to weep. The woman helped him find new strength in himself, Soyinka recalled in an interview, "so she did me a lot more good than she could ever have guessed on that day."

 LITERARY LENS A poet chooses each word in a poem carefully. Consider the **word choice** in this poem.

The price seemed reasonable, location
Indifferent. The landlady swore she lived
Off premises. Nothing remained
But self-confession. "Madam," I warned,
"I hate a wasted journey—I am African."   5
Silence. Silenced transmission of
Pressurized good breeding. Voice, when it came,
Lipstick-coated, long-gold rolled
Cigarette-holder pipped. Caught I was, foully.

"HOW DARK?" . . . I had not misheard . . . "ARE YOU LIGHT   10
OR VERY DARK?" Button B. Button A. Stench
Of rancid breath of public hide-and-speak.
Red booth. Red pillar-box. Red double-tiered
Omnibus squelching tar. It *was* real! Shamed
By ill-mannered silence, surrender   15
Pushed dumbfounded to beg simplification.
Considerate she was, varying the emphasis—
"ARE YOU DARK? OR VERY LIGHT?" Revelation came.
"You mean—like plain or milk chocolate?"
Her assent was very clinical, crushing in its light   20
Impersonality. Rapidly, wave-length adjusted,
I chose. "West African sepia"—and as afterthought,
"Down in my passport." Silence for spectroscopic
Flight of fancy, till truthfulness clanged her accent
Hard on the mouthpiece. "WHAT'S THAT?" conceding   25
"DON'T KNOW WHAT THAT IS." "Like brunette."
"THAT'S DARK, ISN'T IT?" "Not altogether.
Facially, I am brunette, but madam, you should see
The rest of me. Palm of my hand, soles of my feet
Are peroxide blonde. Friction, caused—   30
Foolishly madam—by sitting down, has turned
My bottom raven black—One moment madam!"—sensing
Her receiver rearing on the thunderclap
About my ears—"Madam," I pleaded, "wouldn't you rather
See for youself?"   35

After You Read

Critical Reading

1. In the poem, Soyinka **satirizes** racism. How does the dialogue between the characters reveal Soyinka's attitude toward racism and identity? Include specific examples from the poem in your response.

2. Describe the writer's attitude after he figures out the landlady's "game."

3. Silence is mentioned several times in the poem. Explain the implied message of one of these silent moments. Cite from the poem to support your inference.

Literary Lens: Word Choice

Identify the **setting** of the poem (the time, place, and situation). Then list specific words and phrases that evoke the setting. Write a paragraph in which you explain how the words and phrases you have identified evoke the setting.

Setting:
Words/phrases that evoke the setting

Focus on Research: Paraphrase and Use Quotations Effectively

Wole Soyinka criticized the Negritude movement. Research his views and explain your findings in one or two paragraphs. In your paragraphs paraphrase some information and use at least one direct quotation. Remember that general information should be paraphrased. Quotations are best used to share the words of experts and sentences that are exceptionally well written. Use in-text citations based on a style such as MLA or APA.

Marriage Is a Private Affair

Chinua Achebe

Before You Read

Albert Chinualumogu Achebe (1930–2013), one of the most widely read African writers of the 20th century, was born in Nigeria. His first novel, *Things Fall Apart* (1958), has been called a turning point in African literature. In 1990, a serious automobile accident left Achebe paralyzed from the waist down. After he recuperated, Achebe moved to the United States to write and teach.

World Context

A member of the dominant Ibo ethnic group, Achebe was both a defender and a critic of his people. He decried the disintegration of the Ibo culture due to colonial and missionary influences but acknowledged the problems inherent to some Ibo customs. In the following story, Achebe addresses themes common to his writing: the fragmentation of families and the conflicts between Christians and non-Christians and urban and rural dwellers.

 LITERARY LENS As you read, consider the different characters and their problems. Are their **conflicts** internal or external?

Have you written to your dad yet?" asked Nene one afternoon as she sat with Nnaemeka in her room at 16 Kasanga Street, Lagos.[1]

"No. I've been thinking about it. I think it's better to tell him when I get home on leave!"

"But why? Your leave is such a long way off yet—six whole weeks. He should be let into our happiness now."

---

1 **Lagos:** the capital of Nigeria

Nnaemeka was silent for a while, and then began very slowly as if he groped for his words: "I wish I were sure it would be happiness to him."

"Of course it must," replied Nene, a little surprised. "Why shouldn't it?"

"You have lived in Lagos all your life, and you know very little about people in remote parts of the country."

"That's what you always say. But I don't believe anybody will be so unlike other people that they will be unhappy when their sons are engaged to marry."

"Yes. They are most unhappy if the engagement is not arranged by them. In our case it's worse—you are not even an Ibo."

This was said so seriously and so bluntly that Nene could not find speech immediately. In the **cosmopolitan** atmosphere of the city it had always seemed to her something of a joke that a person's tribe could determine whom he married.

cosmopolitan: sophisticated; worldly

As last she said, "You don't really mean that he will object to your marrying me simply on that account? I had always thought you Ibos were kindly disposed to other people."

"So we are. But when it comes to marriage, well, it's not quite so simple. And this," he added, "is not peculiar to the Ibos. If your father were alive and lived in the heart of Ibibio-land he would be exactly like my father."

"I don't know. But anyway, as your father is so fond of you, I'm sure he will forgive you soon enough. Come on then, be a good boy and send him a nice lovely letter . . ."

"It would not be wise to break the news to him by writing. A letter will bring it upon him with a shock. I'm quite sure about that."

"All right, honey, suit yourself. You know your father."

As Nnaemeka walked home that evening he turned over in his mind different ways of overcoming his father's opposition, especially now that he had gone and found a girl for him. He had thought of showing his letter to Nene but decided on second thoughts not to, at least for the moment. He read it again when he got home and couldn't help smiling to himself. He remembered Ugoye quite well, an Amazon[2] of a girl who used to beat up all the boys, himself included, on the way to the stream, a complete dunce at school.

I have found a girl who will suit you admirably—Ugoye Nweke, the eldest daughter of our neighbour, Jacob Newke. She has a proper Christian upbringing. When she stopped schooling some years ago her father (a man of

---

2 **Amazon:** a large, powerful woman, an allusion to the myth of a race of female warriors

sound judgement) sent her to live in the house of a pastor where she has received all the training a wife could need. Her Sunday School teacher has told me that she reads her Bible very fluently. I hope we shall begin negotiations when you come home in December.

On the second evening of his return from Lagos Nnaemeka sat with his father under a cassia tree. This was the old man's retreat where he went to read his Bible when the parching December sun had set and a fresh, reviving wind blew on the leaves.

"Father," began Nnaemeka suddenly, "I have come to ask for forgiveness."

"Forgiveness? For what, my son?" he asked in amazement.

"It's about this marriage question."

"Which marriage question?"

"I can't—we must—I mean it is impossible for me to marry Nweke's daughter."

"Impossible? Why?" asked his father.

"I don't love her."

"Nobody said you did. Why should you?" he asked.

"Marriage today is different . . ."

"Look here, my son," interrupted his father, "nothing is different. What one looks for in a wife are a good character and a Christian background."

Nnaemeka saw there was no hope along the present line of argument.

"Moreover," he said, "I am engaged to marry another girl who has all of Ugoye's good qualities, and who . . ."

His father did not believe his ears. "What did you say?" he asked slowly and **disconcertingly**.

"She is a good Christian," his son went on, "and a teacher in a Girls' School in Lagos."

"Teacher, did you say? If you consider that a qualification for a good wife I should like to point out to you, Emeka, that no Christian woman should teach. St. Paul in his letter to the Corinthians says that women should keep silence." He rose slowly from his seat and paced forwards and backwards. This was his pet subject, and he condemned vehemently those church leaders who encouraged women to teach in their schools. After he had spent his emotion on a long homily[3] he at last came back to his son's engagement, in a seemingly milder tone.

"Whose daughter is she, anyway?"

"She is Nene Atang."

---

3 **homily:** a short lecture or moralizing speech

"What!" All the mildness was gone again. "Did you say Neneataga, what does that mean?"

"Nene Atang from Calabar. She is the only girl I can marry." This was a very rash reply and Nnaemeka expected the storm to burst. But it did not. His father merely walked away into his room. This was most unexpected and perplexed Nnaemeka. His father's silence was infinitely more menacing than a flood of threatening speech. That night the old man did not eat.

When he sent for Nnaemeka a day later he applied all possible ways of dissuasion. But the young man's heart was hardened, and his father eventually gave him up as lost.

"I owe it to you, my son, as a duty to show you what is right and what is wrong. Whoever put this idea into your head might as well have cut your throat. It is Satan's work." He waved his son away.

> "Whoever put this idea into your head might as well have cut your throat."

"You will change your mind, Father, when you know Nene."

"I shall never see her," was the reply. From that night the father scarcely spoke to his son. He did not, however, cease hoping that he would realize how serious was the danger he was heading for. Day and night he put him in his prayers.

Nnaemeka, for his own part, was very deeply affected by his father's grief. But he kept hoping that it would pass away. If it had occurred to him that never in the history of his people had a man married a woman who spoke a different tongue, he might have been less optimistic. "It has never been heard," was the verdict of an old man speaking a few weeks later. In that short sentence he spoke for all of his people. This man had come with others to commiserate with Okeke when news went round about his son's behaviour. By that time the son had gone back to Lagos.

"It has never been heard," said the old man again with a sad shake of his head.

"What did Our Lord say?" asked another gentleman. "Sons shall rise against their Fathers; it is there in the Holy Book."

"It is the beginning of the end," said another.

The discussion thus tending to become theological, Madubogwu, a highly practical man, brought it down once more to the ordinary level.

"Have you thought of consulting a native doctor about your son?" he asked Nnaemeka's father.

"He isn't sick," was the reply.

"What is he then? The boy's mind is diseased and only a good herbalist can bring him back to his right senses. The medicine he requires is *Amalile*, the same that women apply with success to recapture their husbands' straying affection."

"Madubogwu is right," said another gentleman. "This thing calls for medicine."

"I shall not call in a native doctor." Nnaemeka's father was known to be obstinately ahead of his more superstitious neighbours in these matters. "I will not be another Mrs. Ochuba. If my son wants to kill himself let him do it with his own hands. It is not for me to help him."

"But it was her fault," said Madubogwu. "She ought to have gone to an honest herbalist. She was a clever woman, nevertheless."

"She was a wicked murderess," said Jonathan who rarely argued with his neighbours because, he often said, they were incapable of reasoning. "The medicine was prepared for her husband, it was his name they called in its preparation and I am sure it would have been perfectly beneficial to him. It was wicked to put it into the herbalist's food, and say you were only trying it out."

· · · · ·

Six months later, Nnaemeka was showing his young wife a short letter from his father:

It amazes me that you could be so unfeeling as to send me your wedding picture. I would have sent it back. But on further thought I decided just to cut off your wife and send it back to you because I have nothing to do with her. How I wish that I had nothing to do with you either.

When Nene read through this letter and looked at the mutilated picture her eyes filled with tears, and she began to sob.

"Don't cry, my darling," said her husband. "He is essentially good-natured and will one day look more kindly on our marriage." But years passed and that one day did not come.

For eight years, Okeke would have nothing to do with his son, Nnaemeka. Only three times (when Nnaemeka asked to come home and spend his leave) did he write to him.

"I can't have you in my house," he replied on one occasion. "It can be of no interest to me where or how you spend your leave—or your life, for that matter."

The prejudice against Nnaemeka's marriage was not confined to his little village. In Lagos, especially among his people who worked there, it showed itself in a different way. Their women, when they met at their village meeting, were not hostile to Nene. Rather, they paid her such excessive deference as to make her feel she was not one of them. But as time went on, Nene gradually broke through some of this prejudice and even began to make friends among them. Slowly and grudgingly they began to admit that she kept her home much better than most of them.

The story eventually got to the little village in the heart of the Ibo country that Nnaemeka and his young wife were a most happy couple. But his father was one of the few people in the village who knew nothing about this. He always displayed so much temper whenever his son's name was mentioned that everyone avoided it in his presence. By a tremendous effort of will he had succeeded in pushing his son to the back of his mind. The strain had nearly killed him but he had persevered, and won.

Then one day he received a letter from Nene, and in spite of himself he began to glance through it perfunctorily until all of a sudden the expression on his face changed and he began to read more carefully.

. . . Our two sons, from the day they learnt that they have a grandfather, have insisted on being taken to him. I find it impossible to tell them that you will not see them. I implore you to allow Nnaemeka to bring them home for a short time during his leave next month. I shall remain here in Lagos . . .

The old man at once felt the resolution he had built up over so many years falling in. He was telling himself that he must not give in. He tried to steel his heart against all emotional appeals. It was a re-enactment of that other struggle. He leaned against a window and looked out. The sky was overcast with heavy black clouds and a high wind began to blow filling the air with dust and dry leaves. It was one of those rare occasions when even Nature takes a hand in a human fight. Very soon it began to rain, the first rain in the year. It came down in large sharp drops and was accompanied by the lightning and thunder which mark a change of season. Okeke was trying hard not think of his two grandsons. But he knew he was now fighting a losing battle. He tried to hum a favourite hymn but the pattering of large rain drops on the roof broke up the tune. His mind immediately returned to the children. How could he shut his door against them? By a curious mental process he imagined them standing, sad and forsaken, under the harsh angry weather—shut out from his house.

That night he hardly slept, from remorse—and a vague fear that he might die without making it up to them.

After You Read

Critical Reading

1. In a short paragraph, summarize the collision of modern and traditional ways in this story.

2. Interpret the **symbolic** meaning of rain in this story.

3. Explain the meaning of the title "Marriage Is a Private Affair."

4. Identify at least one inference you can make about each of the three main characters in the story. Cite evidence from the story in your response.

Literary Lens: Conflict

Conflict is the struggle of opposing forces that rage internally within characters and externally against them. Identify the conflicts faced by the characters in the story and determine whether they are internal or external. Then write a few sentences that explain how the conflict reveals the theme of the story.

Character	Conflict(s)
Nnaemeka	
Nene	
Okeke	

Focus on Research: Write a Thesis Statement

Find an article about Chinua Achebe that summarizes the themes he commonly addresses in his fiction. Based on your research, draft a thesis statement for an essay in which you show how "Marriage is a Private Affair" fits into his body of work.

In the Shadow of War

Ben Okri

Before You Read

Ben Okri (1959–) is a Nigerian writer. At 14, he began writing poems, short stories, and essays, and by 18, he had finished his first novel—*Flowers and Shadows*. With the manuscript in his suitcase, he traveled to London to study and work. Although sometimes penniless and homeless, he continued to write. *The Famished Road*, a novel about "spirit children" who are born over and over again, won the British Booker Prize in 1980.

World Context

As a teenager, Okri learned many tales from the oral traditions of his native culture. "We were all told stories as kids in Nigeria," he once said. "We had to tell stories that would keep one another interested, and you weren't allowed to tell stories that everybody else knew."

 LITERARY LENS As you read, follow the **plot** events in the story that show the characters in action.

That afternoon three soldiers came to the village. They scattered the goats and chickens. They went to the palm-frond bar and ordered a calabash[1] of palm wine. They drank amidst the flies.

Omovo watched them from the window as he waited for his father to go out. They both listened to the radio. His father had bought the old Grundig[2] cheaply from a family that had to escape the city when the war broke out. He had covered the radio with a white cloth and made it look like a household fetish.[3] They listened to the news of bombings and air raids in the interior of the country. His father combed his hair, parted it carefully, and slapped some

---

1 **calabash:** a container made out of a gourd
2 **Grundig:** the brand name of a German radio
3 **fetish:** an object thought to have supernatural powers

after-shave on his unshaven face. Then he struggled into the shabby coat that he had long outgrown.

Omovo stared out of the window, irritated with his father. At that hour, for the past seven days, a strange woman with a black veil over her head had been going past the house. She went up the village paths, crossed the Express road, and disappeared into the forest. Omovo waited for her to appear.

The main news was over. The radio announcer said an eclipse of the moon was expected that night. Omovo's father wiped the sweat off his face with his palm and said, with some bitterness:

"As if an eclipse will stop this war."

"What is an eclipse?" Omovo asked.

"That's when the world goes dark and strange things happen."

"Like what?"

His father lit a cigarette.

"The dead start to walk about and sing. So don't stay out late, eh."

Omovo nodded.

"Heclipses hate children. They eat them."

Omovo didn't believe him. His father smiled, gave Omovo his ten kobo[4] allowance, and said:

"Turn off the radio. It's bad for a child to listen to news of war."

Omovo turned it off. His father poured a libation[5] at the doorway and then prayed to his ancestors. When he had finished he picked up his briefcase and strutted out briskly. Omovo watched him as he threaded his way up the path to the bus stop at the main road. When a danfo bus[6] came, and his father went with it, Omovo turned the radio back on. He sat on the windowsill and waited for the woman. The last time he saw her she had glided past with agitated flutters of her yellow smock. The children stopped what they were doing and stared at her. They had said that she had no shadow. They had said that her feet never touched the ground. As she went past, the children began to throw things at her. She didn't flinch, didn't quicken her pace, and didn't look back.

stupefying:
dulling; dazing

The heat was **stupefying**. Noises dimmed and lost their edges. The villagers stumbled about their various tasks as if they were sleepwalking. The three soldiers drank palm wine and played draughts[7] beneath the sun's oppressive glare. Omovo noticed that whenever children went past the bar

---

4 **kobo:** a unit of money in Nigeria
5 **libation:** a liquid poured on the ground to appease the gods
6 **danfo bus:** in this part of Nigeria, a small, dilapidated bus
7 **draughts:** the British term for "checkers"

the soldiers called them, talked to them, and gave them some money. Omovo ran down the stairs and slowly walked past the bar. The soldiers stared at him. On his way back one of them called him.

"What's your name?" he asked.

Omovo hesitated, smiled mischievously, and said:

"Heclipse."

The soldier laughed, spraying Omovo's face with spit. He had a face crowded with veins. His companions seemed uninterested. They swiped flies and concentrated on their game. Their guns were on the table. Omovo noticed that they had numbers on them. The man said:

"Did your father give you that name because you have big lips?"

His companions looked at Omovo and laughed. Omovo nodded.

"You are a good boy," the man said. He paused. Then he asked, in a different voice:

"Have you seen that woman who covers her face with a black cloth?"

"No."

The man gave Omovo ten kobo and said:

"She is a spy. She helps our enemies. If you see her, come and tell us at once, you hear?"

Omovo refused the money and went back upstairs. He repositioned himself on the windowsill. The soldiers occasionally looked at him. The heat got to him and soon he fell asleep in a sitting position. The cocks, crowing dispiritedly, woke him up. He could feel the afternoon softening into evening. The soldiers dozed in the bar. The hourly news came on. Omovo listened without comprehension to the day's casualties. The announcer **succumbed** to the stupor, yawned, apologized, and gave further details of the fighting.

succumbed: yielded; gave in

Omovo looked up and saw that the woman had already gone past. The men had left the bar. He saw them weaving between the eaves of the thatch houses, stumbling through the heat-mists. The woman was further up the path. Omovo ran downstairs and followed the men. One of them had taken off his uniform top. The soldier behind had buttocks so big they had begun to split his pants. Omovo followed them across the Express road. When they got into the forest the men stopped following the woman, and took a different route. They seemed to know what they were doing. Omovo hurried to keep the woman in view.

He followed her through the dense vegetation. She wore faded wrappers and a gray shawl, with the black veil covering her face. She had a red basket on her head. He completely forgot to determine if she had a shadow, or whether her feet touched the ground.

ostentatious: showy; flamboyant

He passed unfinished estates, with their flaking, **ostentatious** signboards and their collapsing fences. He passed an empty cement factory: Blocks lay crumbled in heaps and the workers' sheds were deserted. He passed a baobab[8] tree, under which was the intact skeleton of a large animal. A snake dropped from a branch and slithered through the undergrowth. In the

---

8 **baobab:** a short, broad-trunked tropical tree

distance, over the cliff edge, he heard loud music and people singing war slogans above the noise.

He followed the woman till they came to a rough camp on the plain below. Shadowy figures moved about in the half-light of the cave. The woman went to them. The figures surrounded her and touched her and led her into the cave. He heard their weary voices thanking her. When the woman reappeared she was without the basket. Children with kwashiorkor[9] stomachs and women wearing rags led her halfway up the hill. Then, reluctantly, touching her as if they might not see her again, they went back.

He followed her till they came to a muddied river. She moved as if an invisible force were trying to blow her away. Omovo saw capsized canoes and trailing, waterlogged clothes on the dark water. He saw floating items of sacrifice: loaves of bread in polythene[10] wrappings, gourds of food, Coca-Cola cans. When he looked at the canoes again they had changed into the shapes of swollen dead animals. He saw outdated currencies on the riverbank. He noticed the terrible smell in the air. Then he heard the sound of heavy breathing from behind him, then someone coughing and spitting. He recognized the voice of one of the soldiers urging the others to move faster. Omovo crouched in the shadow of a tree. The soldiers strode past. Not long afterward he heard a scream. The men had caught up with the woman. They crowded round her.

"Where are the others?" shouted one of them.

The woman was silent.

"You dis witch! You want to die, eh? Where are they?"

She stayed silent. Her head was bowed. One of the soldiers coughed and spat toward the river.

"Talk! Talk!" he said, slapping her.

The fat soldier tore off her veil and threw it to the ground. She bent down to pick it up and stopped in the attitude of kneeling, her head still bowed. Her head was bald, and disfigured with a deep **corrugation**. There was a **livid** gash along the side of her face. The bare-chested soldier pushed her. She fell on her face and lay still. The lights changed over the forest and for the first time Omovo saw that the dead animals on the river were in fact

> She moved as if an invisible force were trying to blow her away.

corrugation: wrinkle; furrow

livid: bruised; discolored

---

9 kwashiorkor: a disease of malnutrition that results from protein deficiency and causes children's stomachs to bloat

10 polythene: a synthetic substance like plastic wrap

the corpses of grown men. Their bodies were tangled with riverweed and their eyes were bloated. Before he could react, he heard another scream. The woman was getting up, with the veil in her hand. She turned to the fat soldier, drew herself to her fullest height, and spat in his face. Waving the veil in the air, she began to howl **dementedly**. The two other soldiers backed away. The fat soldier wiped his face and lifted the gun to the level of her stomach. A moment before Omovo heard the shot a violent beating of wings just above him scared him from his hiding place. He ran through the forest screaming. The soldiers tramped after him. He ran through a mist which seemed to have risen from the rocks. As he ran he saw an owl staring at him from a canopy of leaves. He tripped over the roots of a tree and blacked out when his head hit the ground.

When he woke up it was very dark. He waved his fingers in front of his face and saw nothing. Mistaking the darkness for blindness he screamed, thrashed around, and ran into a door. When he recovered from his shock he heard voices outside and the radio crackling on about the war. He found his way to the balcony, full of wonder that his sight had returned. But when he got there he was surprised to find his father sitting on the sunken cane chair, drinking palm wine with the three soldiers. Omovo rushed to his father and pointed frantically at the three men.

"You must thank them," his father said. "They brought you back from the forest."

Omovo, overcome with delirium, began to tell his father what he had seen. But his father, smiling apologetically at the soldiers, picked up his son and carried him off to bed.

dementedly:
hysterically;
madly

After You Read

Critical Reading

1. How do you interpret the references to shadows and the eclipse? Support your answer with examples from the text.

2. What part does the woman with the black veil play in this story?

3. In the story, several lies are told. What are these lies and what motivates the telling of them?

Literary Lens: Plot

In the story "In the Shadow of War," a young boy experiences a series of dramatic events over the course of a single afternoon and evening. Use the chart below to map out the plot of the story. Starting at the top, write a short phrase on each line to describe the story's significant events. Place a star by the climax of the story.

As the story opens	
When Omovo meets the soldiers	
When Omovo wakes up	
At the cave	
At the river	
In the woods	
Back home	

Focus on Research: Generate a Research Question

The Nigerian Civil War (1967–1970) forms the backdrop for this story. Conduct enough preliminary research on the war to develop a focused research question. The preliminary research should consist of a quick search through current periodicals, journals, and other sources to be aware of what has already been written about this topic. After skimming the information, develop and narrow your research question while considering your audience. Finally, revise your research question or questions as you delve more deeply into your research.

Loyalties

Adewale Maja-Pearce

Before You Read

Adewale Maja-Pearce (1953–) is a Nigerian journalist and author. He was born in London to British and Yoruba parents. His short stories focus on the Nigerian Civil War. He has also written essays on the British and Nigerian cultures.

World Context

Maja-Pearce has been severely critical of Western media, saying that they "stage-managed [suffering Africans] in the interests of careers." From 1967 to 1970, Ibo tribespeople in Nigeria fought to form a nation of their own, Biafra. The genocidal border conflict that ensued moved many Nigerian authors to make war one of their main subjects.

 LITERARY LENS Note the different types of **humor** employed in this first-person narrative.

I was twelve years old at the time. One afternoon my father came rushing home earlier than usual.

"Wife," he shouted to my mother who was out the back preparing food; "wife, have you not heard the news?" He was so excited he went rushing through the house. I followed him.

"Aren't you ashamed of yourself, a grown man like you rushing around like a small boy? What is it?" my mother said.

"Ojukwu has announced the new state of Biafra. We are no longer Nigerians, you hear? We are now Biafrans," he said and smiled.

"And what then?" my mother asked.

"Woman, don't you know what you are saying? Don't you realize this is an important day, an historic occasion?"

My mother stood up and put her hands on her hips. Her face was streaming from the heat of the fire.

"Whether we are in Nigeria or whether we are in Biafra we are almost out of firewood," she said.

My father raised his hands to the sky.

"Events of world importance are taking place and you are telling me about firewood. Trust a woman," he said and walked away.

"We are no longer Nigerians, you hear? We are now Biafrans . . ."

That evening the schoolmaster and the barber and the man who owned the Post Office came to our house.

"Boy, come here," the schoolmaster called.

"Come and hear what teacher has to say," my father ordered.

"Seven nines are?"

"Sixty-three," I answered.

"Good. Now, if twenty Nigerian soldiers march into our village and five Biafran women attack them with saucepans who will win?" he asked, and the barber collapsed on the floor. My mother took me by the arm and we left the room. But I crept back and stood by the door.

"What was I telling you the other day? That Ojukwu is a real man, just the sort of leader we need to get things moving. Those dirty Nigerians will taste pepper if they try to attack us, let me tell you," my father was saying.

"That's the way to talk," the schoolmaster said. "Just let them try. Biafra stands supreme."

"They were saying on the news that five countries have already recognized us," the postmaster said.

My mother called me. "Where were you? Must you always be sneaking about listening to what foolish men are saying? Biafra, Nigeria, what difference? Have we suddenly acquired two heads? Go and collect the goat and tie him up for the night," she said, and added: "After all, he is now a Biafran goat so we must take better care of him."

During the next few weeks everybody was talking about it. But as my mother kept saying, the only difference it made was the increased cost of food.

And then there was a rumour that Federal troops were marching towards us. Biafran soldiers appeared overnight. In their new uniforms and polished guns they looked smart. They drove up and down in their jeeps and raised dust everywhere. All my friends worshipped them.

One morning I woke up and heard gunfire in the distance. A plane flew overhead.

"Hurry, hurry, we are under attack," my father shouted.

"Where are we going?" my mother asked.

"Are you blind, woman, can't you see the others heading for the forest?" my father said.

"But what about our troops?" I asked.

"What troops? They ran away last night."

My mother rushed into the bedroom and started dragging clothes onto the bed.

"We have no time for that," my father said.

When we got outside I saw that it was true. The entire village was heading for the forest, the schoolmaster in the lead.

We spent two days and nights in the bush.

"So this is your great Biafra," my mother said. "Where is Ojukwu, I didn't see him?"

"Shut up, woman," my father said.

On the third day my father said to me: "Go and see if the soldiers are still there."

"You want to get the boy killed?" my mother said, reaching for me.

"Leave him, they won't harm a child," my father said; and to me: "I don't ask you to show yourself, you hear?"

I crept to the edge of the forest. The village was completely deserted, except for a few hens. And then I saw our goat. He was eating the food in front of the Post Office. I knew the owner would be angry. I forgot my father's warning and started running. Three armed Nigerian soldiers stepped out of the barber's shop, their rifles in their hands, and waited for me.

"Where are your people?" one of them asked. I pointed in the direction.

"Are they afraid of us?"

I nodded.

"Go and tell them we mean no harm."

As soon as I got back to the clearing everyone began talking at once. I told them what had happened. An argument began. Some wanted to stay and others wanted to go, but we were all hungry and there was no food left. Because of the mosquitoes no one had slept well. So we went.

The soldiers kept to their word. By the next day everything had returned to normal. At the end of the week the soldiers pulled out.

One evening the barber, the schoolmaster and the man who owned the Post Office came to our house. My father sent me out to buy bottles of beer. When I returned my father was saying:

"Those dirty Biafrans, what did I tell you? As usual it was all talk. When it comes to talk there is nothing they cannot do."

The schoolmaster called me. "Boy, if the Biafran soldiers cover twenty miles a day how long will it take them to reach the Cameroons?"

The barber held his sides and groaned.

"Don't mind them," my father said. My mother called me from the back.

"Go and collect our Nigerian goat," she said.

After You Read

Critical Reading

1. How does the mother's perspective differ from the other characters in the story? Why does the writer give the last word to the mother?

2. What elements in the story are repeated? What impact does this repetition have on the story?

3. The characters in this story do not respond to the border aggression as might be expected. Explain the reason for their lack of national loyalty. Use quotations from the text to support your ideas.

Literary Lens: Humor

The story "Loyalties" contains several layers of humor. The overall structure of the story is a comic parable, a humorous story told to illustrate a moral idea. Another element of its humor is the dialogue and the jokes told by the characters. Use the chart below to analyze the humor in Maja-Pearce's "Loyalties."

Element of humor	Find an example or quote from the story that illustrates this element of humor.	Why do you think the author chose to use humor in this way?
Story structure: comic parable		
Dialogue		
Jokes		

Focus on Research: Take Notes

Genocide is the deliberate destruction of an entire racial, political, or cultural group. Research the topic of genocide and take detailed notes from at least three of your sources, including important quotations, paraphrases, and citation information (title, author, and publication date). Then summarize your findings in a multimedia presentation.

The Literature of
Kenya

Background

Kenya has a diverse literary tradition. The region has been populated by humans longer than any other part of the planet—about 2 million years. Not surprisingly, such an ancient people have created a rich cultural heritage of storytelling.

Among the many languages used in Kenya, one of the most widespread is Swahili. This language was a by-product of the trade between the native Bantu speakers of the eastern coast of Africa and Arabs, Persians, and others. One of the oldest Kenyan works in Swahili is the epic *The Story of Tambuka*, written by a poet named Mwengo in 1728. It tells the story of warfare between Muslims and the Byzantine Empire between 628 and 1453.

Kenya also has a tradition of writers composing literature in English. This is a legacy of the period from 1890 to 1963, when Kenya was a British colony. Grace Ogot (1930–2015) was one of the most prominent Kenyan authors who wrote in English.

The United States and Kenya

The first novel by an East African writer to be published in English was *Weep Not, Child* by Kenyan author Ngugi wa Thiong'o in 1964. This story describes the violent rebellion against the British in the 1950s. Tragically, the rebellion thwarts the protagonist's hopes for an education. In Ngugi's view, colonialism corrupts even those who try to resist it.

The book reached the United States during the American civil rights movement, sparking interest in all things African as well as sympathy for people fighting oppression.

Research: Prepare Interview Questions

Although Ngugi wrote *Weep Not, Child* in English, he has since chosen to publish his books first in his native Gikuyu. Find out why, and write an imaginary interview with Ngugi in which you ask him five questions about this decision and suggest how you think he would respond.

A Meeting in the Dark

Ngugi wa Thiong'o

Before You Read

Ngugi wa Thiong'o (1938–) started writing in English and then switched to his native Gikuyu. Ngugi's work is highly political, often expressing his dislike of imperialism and capitalism. His popular Gikuyu play *I Will Marry When I Want* led to his arrest in Kenya. While in jail, he wrote the first modern novel in Gikuyu, *Devil on the Cross*, on prison-issued toilet paper. While in prison, he made the decision to write all of his works in Gikuyu. In his novel *Petals of Blood*, Ngugi points out that achieving a truly democratic society will require a struggle. In 1982, Ngugi left Kenya to live in London where he continues to write. He has been a professor at several universities in the United States.

World Context

One tradition mentioned in the story is the custom of female circumcision, a practice widespread in Nigeria as well as the rest of Africa. Those defending circumcision claim it is part of African culture and an important rite of passage for girls.

LITERARY LENS The **theme** of a work of fiction is the message or lesson of the work. A work's theme is rarely stated directly. Rather, is it advanced through character development, descriptions, events, and the climax of the plot. Watch for these specific details that advance the theme.

His mother used to tell him stories. "Once upon a time there was a young girl who lived with her father and mother in a lonely house that was hidden by a hill. The house was old but strong. When the rains came and the winds blew, the house remained firm. Her father and mother liked her, but they quarreled sometimes and she would cry. Otherwise, she was happy. Nobody knew of the house. So nobody came to see them. Then one day a stranger came. He was tall and handsome. He had milk-white teeth. Her mother gave him food. Then he told them of a beautiful country beyond the hill. The girl wanted to go there. Secretly, she followed the man. They had not gone very far when the stranger turned into an Irimu.[1] He became ugly and he had another mouth at the back which was hidden by his long hair. Occasionally, the hair was blown by the wind. Flies were taken in and the mouth would be shut. The girl ran back. The bad Irimu followed her. She ran hard, hard, and the Irimu could not catch her. But he was getting nearer to her all the time. When she came close to her home, she found the Irimu had stopped running. But the house was no longer there. She had no home to go to and she could not go forward to the beautiful land, to see all the good things, because the Irimu was in the way."

How did the story end? John wondered. He thought: "I wish I were young again in our old home, then I would ask my mother about it." But now he was not young; not young anymore. And he was not a man yet!

He stood at the door of the hut and saw his old, frail, but energetic father coming along the village street, with a rather dirty bag made out of strong calico swinging by his side. His father always carried this bag. John knew what it contained: a Bible, a hymn book, and probably a notebook and a pen. His father was a preacher. It must have been he who had stopped his mother from telling him stories. His mother had stopped telling him stories long ago. She would say, "Now, don't ask for any more stories. Your father may come." So he feared his father. John went in and warned his mother of his father's coming. Then his father came in. John stood aside, then walked toward the door. He lingered there doubtfully; then he went out.

"John, hei, John!"

"Baba!"

"Come back."

He stood doubtfully in front of his father. His heart beat faster and an agitated voice within him seemed to ask: Does he know?

"Sit down. Where are you going?"

"For a walk, Father," he answered evasively.

"To the village?"

"Well—yes—no. I mean, nowhere in particular." John saw his father look at him hard, seeming to read his face. John sighed a very slow sigh. He did not like the way his father eyed him. He always looked at him as though John was a sinner, one who had to be watched all the time. "I am," his heart told him. John guiltily refused to meet the old man's gaze and looked past

---

1 **Irimu:** a lion-demon of African myth

him and appealingly to his mother, who was quietly peeling potatoes. But she seemed to be **oblivious** of everything around her.

"Why do you look away? What have you done?"

John shrank within himself with fear. But his face remained expressionless. However, he could hear the loud beats of his heart. It was like an engine pumping water. He felt no doubt his father knew all about it. He thought: "Why does he torture me? Why does he not at once say he knows?" Then another voice told him: "No, he doesn't know, otherwise he would already have jumped at you." A **consolation**. He faced his thoughtful father with courage.

"When is the journey?"

Again John thought—why does he ask? I have told him many times.

Aloud, he said, "Next week, Tuesday."

"Right. Tomorrow we go to the shops, hear?"

"Yes, Father."

"Then be prepared."

"Yes, Father."

"You can go."

"Thank you, Father." He began to move.

"John!"

"Yes?" John's heart almost stopped beating. That second, before his father's next words, was an age.

"You seem to be in a hurry. I don't want to hear of you loitering in the village. I know you young men, going to show off just because you are going away! I don't want to hear of trouble in the village."

Much relieved, John went out. He could guess what his father meant by not wanting trouble in the village. How did the story end? Funny, but he could not remember how his mother had ended it. It had been so long ago. Her home was not there. Where did she go? What did she do?

"Why do you persecute the boy so much?" Susan spoke for the first time. Apparently she had carefully listened to the whole drama without a word. Now was her time to speak. She looked at her tough old preacher who had been a companion for life. She had married him a long time ago. She could not tell the number of years. They had been happy. Then the man became a convert. And everything in the home put on a religious tone. He even made her stop telling stories to the child. "Tell him of Jesus. Jesus died for you. Jesus died for the child. He must know the Lord." She too had been converted. But she was never blind to the moral torture he inflicted on the boy (that's what she always called John), so that the boy had grown up mortally afraid of him. She always wondered if it was love for the son. Or

oblivious: unaware; inattentive

consolation: comfort; relief

could it be a resentment because, well, they two had "sinned" before marriage? John had been the result of that sin. But that had not been John's fault. It was the boy who ought to complain. She often wondered if the boy had . . . but no. The boy had been very small when they left Fort Hall. She looked at her husband. He remained mute, though his left hand did, rather irritably, feel about his face.

"It is as if he was not your son. Or do you . . ."

"Hm, sister." The voice was pleading. She was seeking a quarrel but he did not feel equal to one. Really, women could never understand. Women were women, whether saved or not. Their son had to be protected against all evil influences. He must be made to grow in the footsteps of the Lord. He looked at her, frowning a little. She had made him sin but that had been a long time ago. And he had been saved. John must not follow the same road.

> Their son had to be protected against all evil influences.

"You ought to tell us to leave. You know I can go away. Go back to Fort Hall. And then everybody . . ."

"Look, sister." He hastily interrupted. He always called her sister. Sister-in-the-Lord, in full. But he sometimes wondered if she had been truly saved. In his heart, he prayed: Lord, be with our sister Susan. Aloud, he continued, "You know I want the boy to grow in the Lord."

"But you torture him so! You make him fear you!"

"Why! He should not fear me. I have really nothing against him."

"It is you. You. You have always been cruel to him . . ." She stood up. The peelings dropped from her dress and fell in a heap on the floor.

"Stanley!"

vehemence:
intensity; force

"Sister." He was startled by the **vehemence** in her voice. He had never seen her like this. Lord, take the devil out of her. Save her this minute. She did not say what she wanted to say. Stanley looked away from her. It was a surprise, but it seemed he feared his wife. If you had told people in the village about this, they would not have believed you. He took his Bible and began to read. On Sunday he would preach to a congregation of brethren and sisters.

Susan, a rather tall, thin woman who had once been beautiful, sat down again and went on with her work. She did not know what was troubling her son. Was it the coming journey?

Outside, John strolled aimlessly along the path that led from his home. He stood near the wattle tree which was a little way from his father's house, and surveyed the whole village. They lay before his eyes—crammed—rows and rows of mud and grass huts, ending in sharp sticks that pointed to heaven. Smoke was coming out of various huts, an indication that many women had already come from the *shambas*.[2] Night would soon fall. To the west, the sun was hurrying home behind the misty hills. Again, John looked at the crammed rows and rows of huts that formed Makeno Village, one of the new mushroom "towns" that grew up all over the country during the Mau Mau War.[3] It looked so ugly. A pang of pain rose in his heart and he felt like crying—I hate you, I hate you. You trapped me alive. Away from you, it would never have happened. He did not shout. He just watched.

A woman was coming toward where he stood. A path into the village was just near there. She was carrying a big load of *kuni*,[4] which bent her into an Akamba[5]-bow shape. She greeted him.

"Is it well with you, Njooni?"

"It is well with me, mother." There was no trace of bitterness in his voice. John was by nature polite. Everyone knew this. He was quite unlike the other proud, educated sons of the tribe—sons who came back from the other side of the waters with white or Negro wives who spoke English. And they behaved just like Europeans! John was a favorite, a model of humility and moral perfection. Everyone knew that, though a clergyman's son, John would never betray the tribe.

"When are you going to—to—"

"Makerere?"

"Makelele." She laughed. The way she pronounced the name was funny. And the way she laughed, too. She enjoyed it. But John felt hurt. So everyone knew of this.

"Next week."

"I wish you well."

"Thank you, mother."

She said quietly—as if trying to pronounce it better—"Makelele." She laughed at herself again but she was tired. The load was heavy.

"Stay well, son."

"Go well and in peace, mother."

And the woman, who all the time had stood, moved on, panting like a donkey, but obviously pleased with John's kindness.

---

2 *shambas*: residential gardens

3 **Mau Mau War**: (1952–1956), the conflict between natives and white Europeans for control of Kenya. The British forces prevailed, sending the revolutionaries back to the hills in 1956 and eventually relocating many of them.

4 *kuni*: Swahili for "wood"

5 **Akamba**: a group of Kenyan people known for their agricultural skills

John remained long looking at her. What made such a woman live on day to day, working hard, yet happy? Had she much faith in life? Or was her faith in the tribe? She and her kind, who had never been touched by the ways of the white man, looked as though they had something to cling to. As he watched her disappear, he felt proud that he had a place in their esteem. And then came the pang. *Father will know. They will know.* He did not know what he feared most: the action his father would take when he knew, or the loss of the little faith the simple villagers had placed in him, when they knew.

He went down to the small local tea shop. He met many people who wished him well at college. All of them knew that the Pastor's son had finished all the white man's learning in Kenya. He would now go to Uganda; they had read this in the *Baraza*, a Swahili[6] weekly paper. John did not stay long at the shop. The sun had already gone to rest and now

---

6 **Swahili:** the language of Swahili; the official language of Kenya and Tanzania and spoken throughout East Africa and parts of the Congo

darkness was coming. The evening meal was ready. His tough father was still at the table reading his Bible. He did not look up when John entered. Strange silence settled in the hut.

"You look unhappy." His mother broke the silence first. John laughed. It was a nervous little laugh.

"No, Mother," he hastily replied, nervously looking at his father. He secretly hoped that Wamuhu had not blabbed.

"Then I am glad."

She did not know. He ate his dinner and went out to his hut. A man's hut. Every young man had his own hut. John was never allowed to bring any girl visitor in there. He did not want trouble. Even to be seen standing with one was a crime. His father could easily thrash him. He wished he had rebelled earlier, like all the other young educated men. He lit the lantern. He took it in his hand. The yellow light flickered dangerously and then went out. He knew his hands were shaking. He lit it again and hurriedly took his big coat and a huge Kofia,[7] which were lying on the unmade bed. He left the lantern burning, so that his father would see it and think him in. John bit his lower lip spitefully. He hated himself for being so girlish. It was unnatural for a boy of his age.

Like a shadow, he stealthily crossed the courtyard and went on to the village street.

He met young men and women lining the streets. They were laughing, talking, whispering. They were obviously enjoying themselves. John thought, They are more free than I am. He envied their exuberance. They clearly stood outside or above the strict morality that the educated ones had to be judged by. Would he have gladly changed places with them? He wondered. At last, he came to the hut. It stood at the very heart of the village. How well he knew it—to his sorrow. He wondered what he would do! Wait for her outside? What if her mother came out instead? He decided to enter.

"Hodi!"[8]

"Enter. We are in."

John pulled down his hat before he entered. Indeed, they were all there—all except she whom he wanted. The fire in the hearth was dying. Only a small flame from a lighted lantern vaguely illuminated the whole hut. The flame and the giant shadow created on the wall seemed to be

---

7 **Kofia:** a brimless hat worn by Muslim men

8 **"Hodi!":** a customary Swahili greeting used when entering a home; the host will reply in kind, which means "Be welcome."

mocking him. He prayed that Wamuhu's parents would not recognize him. He tried to be "thin," and to disguise his voice as he greeted them. They recognized him and made themselves busy on his account. To be visited by such an educated one who knew all about the white man's world and knowledge, and who would now go to another land beyond, was not such a frequent occurrence that it could be taken lightly. Who knew but he might be interested in their daughter? Stranger things had happened. After all, learning was not the only thing. Though Wamuhu had no learning, yet charms she had and she could be trusted to captivate any young man's heart with her looks and smiles.

"You will sit down. Take that stool."

"No!" He noticed with bitterness that he did not call her "mother."

"Where is Wamuhu?" The mother threw a triumphant glance at her husband. They exchanged a knowing look. John bit his lip again and felt like bolting. He controlled himself with difficulty.

"She has gone out to get some tea leaves. Please sit down. She will cook you some tea when she comes."

"I am afraid . . ." He muttered some inaudible words and went out. He almost collided with Wamuhu.

In the hut:

"Didn't I tell you? Trust a woman's eye!"

"You don't know these young men."

"But you see, John is different. Everyone speaks well of him and he is a clergyman's son."

"Y-e-e-s! A clergyman's son? You forgot your daughter is circumcised."[9] The old man was remembering his own day. He had found for himself a good, virtuous woman, initiated in all the tribe's ways. And she had known no other man. He had married her. They were happy. Other men of his *Rika*[10] had done the same. All their girls had been virgins, it being a taboo to touch a girl in that way, even if you slept in the same bed, as indeed so many young men and girls did. Then the white men had come, preaching a strange religion, strange ways, which all men followed. The tribe's code of behavior was broken. The new faith could not keep the tribe together. How could it? The men who followed the new faith would not let the girls be circumcised. And they would not let their sons marry circumcised girls.

---

9 **circumcised:** had parts of the sexual organs removed; a cultural rite that can have initiation and/or purification significance

10 *Rika:* age group; members pass through initiation rituals at puberty together and remain like brothers and sisters for the rest of their lives

Puu! Look at what was happening. Their young men went away to the land of the white men. What did they bring? White women. Black women who spoke English. Aaa—bad. And the young men who were left just did not mind. They made unmarried girls their wives and then left them with fatherless children.

"What does it matter?" his wife was replying. "Is Wamuhu not as good as the best of them? Anyway, John is different."

"Different! different! Puu! They are all alike. Those coated with the white clay of the white man's ways are the worst. They have nothing inside. Nothing—nothing here." He took a piece of wood and nervously poked the dying fire. A strange numbness came over him. He trembled. And he feared; he feared for the tribe. For now he said it was not only the educated men who were coated with strange ways, but the whole tribe. The tribe had followed a false Irimu like the girl in the story. For the old man trembled and cried inside, mourning for a tribe that had crumbled. The tribe had nowhere to go to. And it could not be what it was before. He stopped poking and looked hard at the ground.

"I wonder why he came. I wonder." Then he looked at his wife and said, "Have you seen strange behavior with your daughter?"

His wife did not answer. She was preoccupied with her own great hopes . . .

John and Wamuhu walked on in silence. The intricate streets and turns were well known to them both. Wamuhu walked with quick light steps; John knew she was in a happy mood. His steps were heavy and he avoided people even though it was dark. But why should he feel ashamed? The girl was beautiful, probably the most beautiful girl in the whole of Limuru. Yet he feared being seen with her. It was all wrong. He knew that he could have loved her, even then he wondered if he did not love her. Perhaps it was hard to tell but had he been one of the young men he had met, he would not have hesitated in his answer.

Outside the village he stopped. She, too, stopped. Neither had spoken a word all through. Perhaps the silence spoke louder than words. Each was only too conscious of the other.

"Do they know?" Silence. Wamuhu was probably considering the question. "Don't keep me waiting. Please answer me," he implored. He felt weary, very weary, like an old man who had suddenly reached his journey's end.

"No. You told me to give you one more week. A week is over today."

"Yes. That's why I came!" John whispered hoarsely.

Wamuhu did not speak. John looked at her. Darkness was now between them. He was not really seeing her; before him was the image of his father—haughtily religious and dominating. Again he thought: I John, a priest's son, respected by all and going to college, will fall, fall to the ground. He did not want to contemplate the fall.

"It was your fault." He found himself accusing her. In his heart he knew he was lying.

"Why do you keep on telling me that? Don't you want to marry me?"

John sighed. He did not know what to do.

Once upon a time there was a young girl . . . She had no home to go to . . . She could not go forward to the beautiful land and see all the good things because the Irimu was in the way . . .

"When will you tell them?"

"Tonight." He felt desperate. Next week he would go to the college. If he could persuade her to wait, he might be able to get away and come back when the storm and consternation had **abated**. But then the government might withdraw his bursary.[11]

He was frightened and there was a sad note of appeal as he turned to her and said: "Look, Wamuhu, how long have you been pre—I mean like this?"

"I have told you over and over again. I have been pregnant for three months and Mother is being suspicious. Only yesterday she said I breathed like a woman with child."

"Do you think you could wait for three weeks more?" She laughed. Ah! the little witch! She knew his trick. Her laughter always aroused many emotions in him.

"All right. Give me just tomorrow. I'll think up something. Tomorrow I'll let you know all."

"I agree. Tomorrow. I cannot wait anymore unless you mean to marry me."

Why not marry her? She is beautiful! Why not marry her? And do I or don't I love her?

She left. John felt as if she was deliberately blackmailing him. His knees were weak and lost strength. He could not move but sank on the ground in a heap. Sweat poured profusely down his cheeks, as if he had been running hard under a strong sun. But this was cold sweat. He lay on the grass; he did not want to think. Oh! No! He could not possibly face his father. Or his mother. Or Reverend Thomas Carstone, who had had such faith in him.

---

11 **bursary:** a scholarship given for higher education

John realized that he was not more secure than anybody else, in spite of his education. He was no better than Wamuhu. *Then why don't you marry her?* He did not know. John had grown up under a Calvinistic[12] father and learned under a Calvinistic headmaster—a missionary! John tried to pray. But to whom was he praying? To Carstone's God? It sounded false. It was as if he was blaspheming.[13] Could he pray to the God of the tribe? His sense of guilt crushed him.

He woke up. Where was he? Then he understood. Wamuhu had left him. She had given him one day. He stood up; he felt good. Weakly, he began to walk back home. It was lucky that darkness blanketed the whole earth, and him in it. From the various huts, he could hear laughter, heated talks, or quarrels. Little fires could be seen flickering red through the open doors. Village stars, John thought. He raised up his eyes. The heavenly stars, cold and distant, looked down on him impersonally. Here and there, groups of boys and girls could be heard laughing and shouting. For them life seemed to go on as usual. John consoled himself by thinking that they, too, would come to face their day of trial.

John was shaky. Why! Why! Why could he not defy all expectations, all prospects of a future, and marry the girl? No. No. It was impossible. She was circumcised, and he knew that his father and the Church would never consent to such a marriage. She had no learning, or rather she had not gone beyond Standard 4. Marrying her would probably ruin his chances of ever going to a university . . .

He tried to move briskly. His strength had returned. His imagination and thought took flight. He was trying to explain his action before an accusing world—he had done so many times before, ever since he knew of this. He still wondered what he could have done. The girl had attracted him. She was graceful and her smile had been very bewitching. There was none who could equal her and no girl in the village had any pretense to any higher standard of education. Women's education was very low. Perhaps that was why so many Africans went "away" and came back married. He, too, wished he had gone with the others, especially in the last giant student airlift to America. If only Wamuhu had learning . . . and she was uncircumcised . . . then he might probably rebel . . .

The light still shone in his mother's hut. John wondered if he should go in for the night prayers. But he thought against it; he might not be strong

---

12 **Calvinistic:** like the Calvinists, a religious group regarded as being strict
13 **blaspheming:** using God's name disrespectfully

enough to face his parents. In his hut, the light had gone out. He hoped his father had not noticed it . . .

John woke up early. He was frightened. He was normally not superstitious but still he did not like the dreams of the night. He dreamed of circumcision; he had just been initiated in the tribal manner. Somebody—he could not tell his face—came and led him because he took pity on him. They went, went into a strange land. Somehow, he found himself alone. The somebody had vanished. A ghost came. He recognized it as the ghost of the home he had left. It pulled him back; then another ghost came. It was the ghost of the land he had come to. It pulled him from the front. The two contested. Then came other ghosts from all sides and pulled him from all sides so that his body began to fall into pieces. And the ghosts were unsubstantial. He could not cling to any. Only they were pulling him, and he was becoming nothing, nothing . . . he was now standing a distance away. It had not been him. But he was looking at the girl, the girl in the story. She had nowhere to go. He thought he would go to help her; he would show her the way. But as he went to her, he lost his way . . . He was all alone . . . Something destructive was coming toward him, coming, coming . . . He woke up. He was sweating all over—

Dreams about circumcision were no good. They **portended** death. He dismissed the dream with a laugh. He opened the window only to find the whole country clouded in mist. It was perfect July weather in Limuru. The hills, ridges, valleys, and plains that surrounded the village were lost in the mist. It looked such a strange place. But there was almost a magic fascination in it. Limuru was a land of contrasts and evoked differing emotions at different times. Once, John would be fascinated and would yearn to touch the land, embrace it or just be on the grass. At another time he would feel repelled by the dust, the strong sun, and the potholed roads. If only his struggle were just against the dust, the mist, the sun and the rain, he might feel content. Content to live here. At least he thought he would never like to die and be buried anywhere else but at Limuru. But there was the human element whose vices and betrayal of other men were embodied as the new ugly villages. The last night's incident rushed into his mind like a flood, making him weak again. He came out of his blankets and went out. Today he would go to the shops. He was uneasy. An odd feeling was coming to him, in fact had been coming, that his relationship with his father was perhaps unnatural. But he dismissed the thought. Tonight would be the "day of reckoning." He shuddered to think of it. It was unfortunate that this scar had come into his life at this time when he was going to Makerere and it would have brought him closer to his father.

They went to the shops. All day long, John remained quiet as they moved from shop to shop, buying things from the lanky but wistful Indian traders. And all day long, John wondered why he feared his father so much. He had grown up fearing him, trembling whenever he spoke or gave commands. John was not alone in this.

Stanley was feared by all.

He preached with great vigor, defying the very gates of hell. Even during the Emergency,[14] he had gone on preaching, scolding, judging, and condemning. All those who were not saved were destined for hell. Above all, Stanley was known for his great moral observances—a bit too strict, rather pharisaical[15] in nature. None noticed this; certainly not the sheep he shepherded. If an elder broke any of the rules, he was liable to be expelled, or excommunicated. Young men and women, seen standing together "in a manner prejudicial to church and God's morality" (they were one anyway), were liable to be excommunicated. And so, many young men tried to serve two masters, by seeing their girls at night and going to church by day. The alternative was to give up churchgoing altogether . . .

Stanley took a fatherly attitude toward all the people in the village. You must be strict with what is yours. And because of all this, he wanted his house to be a good example. That is why he wanted his son to grow up right. But motives behind many human actions may be mixed. He could never forget that he had also fallen before his marriage. Stanley was also a product of the disintegration of the tribe due to the new influences.

The shopping took a long time. His father strictly observed the silences between them and neither by word nor by hint did he refer to last night. They reached home and John was thinking that all was well when his father called him.

"John."

"Yes, Father."

"Why did you not come for prayers last night?"

"I forgot—"

"Where were you?"

Why do you ask me? What right have you to know where I was? One day I am going to revolt against you. But immediately, John knew that this act of rebellion was something beyond him—not unless something happened to push him into it. It needed someone with something he lacked.

"I—I—I mean, I was—"

---

14 **the Emergency:** the Mau Mau rebellion (1952–1956) against Britain
15 **pharisaical:** like the Pharisees, known for their rigid religious conduct

"You should not sleep so early before prayers. Remember to be there tonight."

"I will."

Something in the boy's voice made the father look up. John went away relieved. All was still well.

Evening came. John dressed like the night before and walked with faltering steps toward the fatal place. The night of reckoning had come. And he had not thought of anything. After this night, all would know. Even Reverend Thomas Carstone would hear of it. He remembered Mr. Carstone and the last words of blessing he had spoken to him. No! he did not want to remember. It was no good remembering these things; and yet the words came. They were clearly written in the air, or in the darkness of his mind.

> "The world is waiting even like a hungry lion, to swallow you, to devour you."

"You are going into the world. The world is waiting even like a hungry lion, to swallow you, to devour you. Therefore, beware of the world. Jesus said, Hold fast unto . . ." John felt a pain—a pain that wriggled through his flesh as he remembered these words. He contemplated the coming fall. Yes! He, John, would fall from the Gates of Heaven down through the open waiting gates of Hell. Ah! He could see it all, and what people would say. Everybody would shun his company, would give him oblique looks that told so much. The trouble with John was that his imagination magnified the fall from the heights of "goodness" out of proportion. And fear of people and consequences ranked high in the things that made him contemplate the fall with so much horror.

John devised all sorts of punishment for himself. And when it came to thinking of a way out, only fantastic and impossible ways of escape came into his head. He simply could not make up his mind. And because he could not and he feared father and people, and he did not know his true attitude toward the girl, he came to the agreed spot having nothing to tell the girl. Whatever he did looked fatal to him.

Then suddenly he said: "Look, Wamuhu. Let me give you money. You might then say that someone else was responsible. Lots of girls have done this. Then that man may marry you. For me, it is impossible. You know that."

"No. I cannot do that. How can you, you—"

"I will give you two hundred shillings."

"No!"

"Three hundred!"

"No!" She was almost crying. It pained her to see him so.

"Four hundred, five hundred, six hundred!" John had begun calmly but now his voice was running high. He was excited. He was becoming more desperate. Did he know what he was talking about? He spoke quickly, breathlessly, as if he was in a hurry. The figure was rapidly rising—nine thousand, ten thousand, twenty thousand . . . He is mad. He is foaming. He is quickly moving toward the girl in the dark. He has laid his hands on her shoulders and is madly imploring her in a hoarse voice. Deep inside him, something horrid that assumes the threatening anger of his father and the village seems to be pushing him. He is violently shaking Wamuhu, while his mind tells him that he is patting her gently. Yes. He is out of his mind. The figure has now reached fifty thousand shillings and is increasing. Wamuhu is afraid, extricates herself from him, the mad, educated son of a religious clergyman, and she runs. He runs after her and holds her, calling her by all sorts of endearing words. But he is shaking her, shake, shake, her, her—he tries to hug her by the neck, presses . . . She lets out one horrible scream and then falls on the ground. And so all of a sudden the struggle is over, the figures stop and John stands there trembling like the leaf of a tree on a windy day.

John, in the grip of fear, ran homeward. Soon everyone would know.

After You Read

Critical Reading

1. In the story John considers that his relationship with his father might be "unnatural." Use evidence from the story to support this idea.

2. What is the possible significance of the story John's mother tells him at the beginning of the passage?

3. Why does Wamuhu's father fear for the tribe?

4. Identify some of the attitudes toward females that are revealed in this story.

Literary Lens: Theme

The **theme** of a story is the main message or lesson of the tale. The author of the story develops and shapes the theme by providing specific details, including descriptions of settings, character development, and conflicts.

Re-create the graphic organizer below and use it to analyze the development of the theme through specific details in the story. In the center rows, record details that advance the theme. In the final row write an explanation of the story's theme.

What details advance the theme?
Detail 1:
Detail 2:
Detail 3:
Detail 4:
Theme:

Focus on Research: Consider Multiple Viewpoints

African colonialism is a complex topic with multiple viewpoints and perspectives. Britain and France were the predominant colonizing forces in the 1800s, with Portugal and Germany also claiming parts of Africa. The European powers often carried their domestic rivalries into their colonization efforts, which resulted in more territory and influence for them at the expense of African rulers. Use secondary sources to compile a short list of perspectives on the topic of African colonialism.

The Literature of
Uganda

Background

Formerly a British colony, Uganda achieved independence in 1962. It is a country of great ethnic diversity. No single ethnic group in the country accounts for more than 20 percent of the population. While English and Swahili are the official languages, many other languages are commonly spoken as well.

Much of Uganda's folklore heritage continues to thrive through storytelling. This oral tradition inspired the Ugandan writer Okot p'Bitek (1931–1982) to write poems in the voices of his country's common people. The most remarkable of these works is his epic poem *Song of Lawino*, composed in the Luo language and published in 1966. As with many works of African literature, the author grapples with the changes resulting from the clash between cultural traditions and Western attitudes and practices brought in through colonization.

Uganda and the United States

Uganda entered the awareness of many people in the United States for the first time in the 1970s. Much of the world looked on as Uganda's dictator Idi Amin unleashed a reign of terror upon his own people. A charismatic but dangerously unstable man, Amin was responsible for the deaths of more than 300,000 Ugandans before he was overthrown in 1979.

Amin's bloody reign provided the topic for an award-winning 1998 novel, *The Last King of Scotland,* by journalist Giles Foden. The book's title refers to one of the many titles Amin claimed for himself. Eight years later, the book was adapted into a highly successful English-language film. It starred the actor Forest Whitaker, who won the Academy Award for Best Actor for his powerful portrayal of Idi Amin.

Research: Explore an Online Magazine

Rajat Neogy (1938–1995), a Ugandan writer of Indian ancestry, founded the African literary periodical *Transition* in 1961. It originated as a creative and intellectual outlet for writers throughout East Africa and is now based in the United States. Visit the magazine's website. Write a paragraph summarizing the history of this journal and reflecting on the contents of a current issue.

The Pig

Barbara Kimenye

Before You Read

Barbara Kimenye (1940–2012) was originally from a small village in Uganda, and she set many of her stories in Kalasanda, a fictional village much like her own. She wrote humorously, and sometimes satirically, about ordinary people in everyday situations. Kimenye began writing short stories and a newspaper column when she was secretary to a Ugandan ruler. After a major political change in Uganda, she lived in England for several years.

World Context

Approximately 16 percent of Ugandans practice Islam and so are forbidden to eat pork. The Qur'an says, "Forbidden to you (for food) are: dead meat, blood, the flesh of swine, and that on which hath been invoked a name other than that of Allah."

LITERARY LENS As you read, look for where the **tone** is established and identify the words that help establish it.

Old Kibuka had long believed that retirement was no sort of life for a man like himself, who would, so he modestly believed, pass for not a day over forty-five. He had held a responsible post at the Ggombolola Headquarters,[1] until the Government had sent somebody from the Public Service Commission to nose around the offices and root out all employees over retirement age. Then the next thing Kibuka knew, despite his youthfully dyed hair, he had a pension, a Certificate of Service, but no longer a job.

He still worried about the state his filing system must be in today, for having once called in at the Headquarters, merely to see if the youngster who had replaced him needed any advice or help, he had been appalled at

---

1 **Ggombolola Headquarters:** central administrative offices

the lack of order. Papers were scattered everywhere, confidential folders were open for all the world to read, and his successor was flirting madly with some pin-brained girl at the other end of the newly installed telephone.

The visit had not been anything near a success, for not even his former colleagues showed anything but superficial interest in what Kibuka had to say.

So there he was, destined to waste the remainder of his life in the little cottage beside the Kalasanda stream, with plenty indeed to look back on, but not very much to look forward to, and his greatest friend, Yosefu Mukasa, was away in Budda County on business.

The self-pitying thought "I might as well be dead" kept recurring in his mind as he pumped his pressure stove to boil a kettle of tea. Then the noise of a car, grinding its way along the narrow, uneven track, heading in his direction, sent him eagerly to the door. It was his eldest grandson who climbed out of the battered Land Rover. A tall, loose-limbed young man in a khaki shirt and blue jeans. Old Kibuka practically choked with happiness as his frail fingers were squeezed in a **sinewy** grip, and the bones of his shoulders almost snapped under an affectionate hug.

sinewy: strong; muscular

"What a wonderful surprise! Come in, my boy. I was just making a cup of tea."

"Grandfather, this is a very short visit. I'm afraid I can't stay more than a few minutes." The boy's voice was musically deep, very much like his grandfather's once had been, before the tremor of age had changed it. "I just came to see how you are getting on, and I brought you a present."

"That's very kind of you, son!" The unexpected visit and now a present: in a matter of seconds Kibuka had completely reversed his opinion that life was no longer worth living. He was aglow with excitement.

"Yes. It's one of the piglets from the Farm School. The sow doesn't seem able to feed this new litter, so I thought you might like one for eating; it should make an excellent meal."

The boy strode back to the Land Rover and returned with a black, squealing bundle under his arm.

Kibuka was more delighted than ever. He had never seen so small a pig before, and he spent a good ten minutes marveling at its tiny twinkling eyes, its minute hoofs, and its wisp of a tail. When his grandson drove away, he waved happily from the doorstep, the piglet clutched tenderly to his chest.

He had told his grandson that he would take the creature up to the Mukasas and ask Miriamu to prepare it as a special "welcome home" supper for Yosefu, but he soon sensed a certain reluctance within himself to do this, because the piglet followed him about the house or squatted trustingly at his feet each time he sat down. Moreover, it obviously understood every word Kibuka said to it, for, whenever he spoke, it listened gravely with its dainty forefeet placed lightly upon his knee.

By nightfall Kibuka was enchanted with his new companion, and would have as much considered eating it as he would consider eating the beloved grandson who had given it to him. He fed the piglet little scraps of food from his own plate, besides providing it with a rich porridge mixture. Nevertheless, within a few days it was clear that the pig's appetite was increasing out of all proportion to its size, and Kibuka had to resort to collecting matoke peelings[2] in an old bucket from his friends and nearest neighbors.

The news that Kibuka was keeping a pig, the first ever actually reared in Kalasanda, caused something of a sensation. In no time at all there was little need for him to cart the bucket from house to house, because the women and children, on their way to draw water from the stream, made a practice of bringing the peelings and food scraps with them as part of the excuse for calling on him, and being allowed to fondle the animal and discuss its progress as if it were a dear relative with a delicate hold on life.

fastidiously: painstakingly; meticulously

No pig had ever had it so good. Fortunately, it proved to be a **fastidiously** clean creature, and for this reason Kibuka allowed it to spend its nights at the foot of his bed, although he was careful not to let his neighbors know of this. The pig, naturally enough, positively flourished in this cozy atmosphere of good will and personal attention. From a squealing bundle small enough to be held in one hand, it quickly developed into a handsome, hefty porker with eyes which held the faintest glint of malice even when it was at its most affectionate with Kibuka.

No pig had ever had it so good.

However, as the weeks went by, its rapid growth was accompanied by a variety of problems. For instance, it required more and more food, and, having been reared on the leavings of every kitchen in Kalasanda, was inclined to turn up its enormous snout at the idea of having to root in the shamba whenever it felt like something to eat. Every time it started to kick its empty dish about noisily, pausing now and then to glare balefully at old Kibuka and utter snorts of derision, the old man was driven to taking up his bucket and trudging forth to see if any scraps in the village had been overlooked.

---

2 **matoke peelings:** skins from the banana or plantain, common foods in Buganda

Also, while Kibuka had at first secretly enjoyed the warmth of a cuddly little piglet lying across his feet each night, he found himself at a distinct disadvantage when that same piglet acquired a bulk of some fifty or so pounds, and still insisted upon ponderously hoisting itself onto his bed as of right. Worse still, along with the weight, the piglet also produced a snore which regularly kept poor Kibuka awake until dawn. It was a grave decision he was finally called upon to make, yet one on which he simply dare not waver: in future, the pig would have to stay outside, tethered to a tree.

Who suffered most, Kibuka or his pig, would be hard to tell, for the animal's lamentations, continuing throughout the night, were equal in strength to the black remorse and wealth of recrimination churning in Kibuka's bosom. That pig never knew how often it was near to being brought indoors and pacified with a bowl of warm milk.

During the day it still was free to roam about until, that is, it adopted the irritating habit of falling into the stream. There it would be, **placidly** ambling after Kibuka as he pottered in his small shamba, or gently napping in the shade of a coffee tree, and then, for no apparent reason, off it would go to the water's edge, and either fall or plunge in before anybody could say "bacon."

placidly:
calmly; serenely

The Kalasanda stream had no real depth; many Kalasandans often bathed there or waded in; but sometimes, after a drop or two of rain, the current had more strength, and was quite capable of sweeping a child off its feet. The pig seemed always to choose such times for its immersion, and there wasn't anything anybody could really do as it spluttered and floundered with its hoofs flaying madly, and terror written plainly across its broad, black face.

At first, Kibuka would rush back and forth along the bank, calling frantically in the hope that it would struggle towards him, but what usually happened in the end was that a particularly strong eddy would sweep it round the bend into a thicket of weeds and rushes, and then the children playing there would have a good half-hour's fun driving it home.

This happened so often that Kibuka was forced to keep the pig tethered day and night. He visualized the time when no children would be playing in the reeds, and the pig would perhaps become entangled, dragged under and drowned.

By way of compensation he decided upon a regular evening walk for the animal, so by and by Kalasanda became accustomed to the sight of Kibuka, slight yet patriarchal in his kanzu and black waistcoat,[3] sedately traversing the countryside with a huge black pig at the end of a rope, and only strangers saw anything out of the ordinary in it. Without doubt, these walks were a source of great pleasure and exercise to the pig, who found them a wonderful change from the all too familiar view of Kibuka's shamba. Unfortunately, the same could not be said of their effect on old Kibuka. To be frank, Kibuka's corns[4] were killing him, and the excruciating pain of every step sometimes brought tears to his eyes. Still, he tried to bear his discomfort with **stoic fortitude,** for, as he said to Daudi Kulubya, who showed concern over his limp, it was always the same before the heavy rains: in fact, his corns were as good as a barometer when it came to forecasting the weather. But he was always glad to return home, where he could sit for an hour with his poor feet in a bowl of hot water and try to keep his mind off the small fortune he was spending on corn plasters[5] brought to Kalasanda by the peddlers in the market.

stoic:
composed;
unflappable

fortitude:
courage;
determination

How long this state of affairs would have continued is anybody's guess. There were occasions when Kibuka actually entertained the notion of parting with his pet at the first good offer from a reputable farmer or butcher. And yet, one trusting glance or gesture of affection from that waddling hunk of pork was enough for him to feel ashamed of what he regarded as his own treachery.

The end came at last in the most unlikely manner. One minute there was Kibuka contemplating the sunset, and, incidentally, giving his feet a rest by one of the obscure paths leading to the Sacred Tree,[6] while the pig scratched happily at the root of a clump of shrubs, its head hidden by foliage, while its carcass, broadside on, barricaded the path, and then, seconds later, there was the snarl of a motorcycle engine, the horrible grinding of brakes, followed by a whirling kaleidoscope of disaster. Kibuka, pig, bike and rider seemed to explode in all directions. Each had a momentary vision of the others sailing through the air.

When Kibuka eventually dared to open his eyes and cautiously move each limb, he was relieved to find he was still in one piece, although one shoulder felt painfully bruised and there was blood on both his hands. The rider, whom he now recognized as a certain Nathaniel Kiggundu, did not

---

3 **kanzu and black waistcoat:** the traditional clothing for Bugandan men, consisting of a long cotton outer garment and a black vest
4 **corns:** calluses on the toes and soles of the feet
5 **corn plasters:** bandages for one's calluses
6 **Sacred Tree:** a local spiritual landmark

appear to have fared very badly either. He was staggering out of a tangled mass of weeds, wiping mud off his face, and fingering a long tear in the knee of his trousers.

Somewhere from behind the hedge came the raucous cries of a pig in distress, and it was in this direction that both men headed, once they had regained their bearings. They were only just in time to see the injured animal give up the ghost and join its ancestors in that heavenly piggery which surely must exist somewhere above. There was scarcely a mark on it, but its head lay at a strange and awkward angle, so it can be safely assumed that it died of a broken neck.

Old Kibuka was terribly upset, and the accident had left him in a generally shaky condition. He sat down beside the dead animal and wondered what would happen next. Nathaniel Kiggundu, however, seeing Kibuka was comparatively unhurt, showed more concern over his motorcycle, which lay grotesquely twisted in a ditch. The inevitable crowd collected almost as soon as the pig expired, so there was much coming and going, first to stare at the fatal casualty, and then to stare at the motorbike. Nantondo kept up a running commentary, her version of how the accident happened, although nobody believed she had seen it, and by the time Musisi the Ggombolola Chief arrived on the scene, she had fully adopted the role of Mistress of Ceremonies.

After taking a statement from Kiggundu, Musisi approached Kibuka and insisted upon taking him home in the Land Rover. "You don't look at all well, Sir. Come. You can make your statement in the morning, when you have had a rest."

"But I can't leave my pig here." Kibuka refused to budge from the spot.

"Well, I can put it in the back of the Land Rover, if you like. Only it would be better to have the butcher cut it up, because I don't think pork will keep for long in this weather."

The idea of eating the pig had never entered Kibuka's mind. While sitting beside the body, he had been seriously considering just whereabouts in the shamba he could bury it. Now he opened his mouth to tell Musisi in no uncertain terms that eating one's good friends was a practice reserved for barbarians: and then, he suddenly had a clear picture of himself struggling to dig a grave. He was sure no Kalasandans would want to help him do it. Then came the realization of the effect a perpetual reminder of his porking friend in his shamba would have on him. He did not think he could stand it. Far better, indeed, to let the past bury itself and, besides, why deprive his fellow villagers of a tasty treat? They were, after all, the people who had nourished the creature on their leftovers.

"Very well. Get somebody to carve it up and share it out among the people who eat pork, and do be sure to send a whole back leg up to the Mukasas," he said at last, suddenly feeling far too weary to care.

"Musa the butcher won't do it," Nantondo piped. "He's a Muslim."

"Well, I'll take it along to the Ggombolola Headquarters and ask one of the askaris[7] to carve it up. Anybody who wants pork must go there at about seven o'clock tonight," declared Musisi, and ordered two of the onlookers to help him lift the carcass into the back of his vehicle.

Back at his cottage, Kibuka rubbed his injured shoulder with a concoction he used to cure most of his ailments, be they loose bowels or a sore throat, and then sat brooding over a cup of tea. He went to bed very early and awoke next day to find the sun well risen. He decided he had had the best night's sleep he had enjoyed for many a month. Musisi arrived as Kibuka was leaving home to see if the leg of pork had been safely delivered to Yosefu and Miriamu.

"No, I'm taking the meat there now, Sir," Musisi said. "Would you care to come with me?"

Kibuka gladly accepted the lift, although he declined the lump of pork Musisi had brought for him, personally. "You have it, son. I'm not a great lover of pork."

Miriamu went into raptures over the leg of pork, and Yosefu showed the keenest interest in the details of the accident. They pressed both Kibuka and Musisi to stay to lunch, but Musisi had to leave to attend a committee meeting in Mmengo, so only Kibuka remained. He and Yosefu, who lately had not seen as much of each other as usual, had plenty to discuss, and lunch was an exhilarating meal.

"I must say, you really are a wonderful cook!" Kibuka told Miriamu, helping himself to more food. Miriamu preened herself, shyly. "Well, that pork was as tender as a chicken, and very tasty, too!"

succulence: tastiness; richness

There was a moment of dismay when Kibuka realized he was eating and thoroughly enjoying the **succulence** of his late friend, but it quickly passed, and he continued piling his plate with meat, smiling to himself at the knowledge that there would be no need to take a walk in the late afternoon; he could have a good nap instead.

---

7 **askaris:** native officers of the peace

After You Read

Critical Reading

1. Identify the **conflicts** Kibuka faces in the story and how they are resolved.

2. List the things this Bugandan village has in common with an American town of a similar size. Explain your comparisons.

3. Identify the **irony** when Kibuka says, "You have it, son. I'm not a great lover of pork."

Literary Lens: Tone

The **tone** of a story is the author's attitude toward the subject. Identify details and words that establish the tone. Re-create the following table and identify the author's tone in the first row. Then list quotations from the passage that support your conclusion about the tone. In the right-hand column write a short explanation.

Tone:	
Quotation	**How it reveals the author's tone**

Focus on Research: Evaluate Multiple Sources

According to the Pew Research Center, the fastest growing religion over the next four decades will be Islam. Using a variety of resources, such as encyclopedias or journals, research the topic of Islam and its growth in the United States and other countries. If sources provide conflicting information, decide which source(s) is most reliable and synthesize the information in a short paragraph.

The Literature of
Zimbabwe

Background

Zimbabwe was once a British colony known as Southern Rhodesia. While whites comprised only 5 percent of the population, they ruled the country. When the blacks declared independence in 1965, Britain refused to accept their sovereignty until the black majority had more political power in the government. After years of violence, Rhodesia finally became the independent and democratic Republic of Zimbabwe in 1980. It was one of the last countries in Africa to win independence from a European colonial power.

Zimbabwean literature has often focused on the conflict between Africans and their colonial rulers. For example, the author and African nationalist Stanlake Samkange (1922–1988) wrote historical novels about European imperialism in Africa.

Samkange's best-known and most powerful book is his 1966 novel *On Trial for My Country*. In it he portrays the British colonialist Cecil Rhodes (1853–1902) and the Nbebele king Lobengula Kumalo (c. 1845–1894). In a style resembling traditional African storytelling, Samkange relates how both Rhodes and Lobengula are put on trial by their ancestors. Rhodes is judged for his exploitation of black Africans, and Lobengula for his failure to defend his people against oppression. Samkange's novel was banned in his own country.

Zimbabwe and the United States

In the United States, the best-known writer from Zimbabwe is Doris Lessing (1919–2013). Born to a British family (in Iran) who moved to Southern Rhodesia when she was five, Lessing lived much of her adult life there. In novels such as *The Grass Is Singing* and in story collections such as *This Was the Old Chief's Country* and *The Sun Between Their Feet*, she explored relations between whites and blacks in Africa. In 2007, Lessing won the Nobel Prize in Literature.

Research: Develop a Thesis Statement

Research Zimbabwe's history since its independence in 1980. Write a thesis statement for a paper exploring how a contemporary Zimbabwean writer, either white or black, might explore these troubled times in fiction or poetry.

No Witchcraft for Sale

Doris Lessing

Before You Read

Doris Lessing (1919–2013) was born in Iran, but her family later moved to a farm in Rhodesia (now Zimbabwe). Many of her stories are set in Rhodesia and depict the harsh treatment of black Africans by whites. Her most widely read work is *The Golden Notebook*, a novel about a woman writer's search for meaning. Lessing said, "If I don't write for any length of time, I get very irritable. If I had to stop, I would probably start wandering the streets, telling myself stories out loud."

World Context

The farm where Lessing grew up was typical for Africa: 3,000 acres of unfenced scrub bush—land covered with dense vegetation and undergrowth—and the open grassland known as the veld. Only a few hundred acres were cultivated, with the rest populated by many kinds of wild game.

LITERARY LENS As you read, consider how the development of the main **characters** advances the **plot**.

The Farquars had been childless for years when little Teddy was born; and they were touched by the pleasure of their servants, who brought presents of fowls and eggs and flowers to the homestead when they came to rejoice over the baby, exclaiming with delight over his downy golden head and his blue eyes. They congratulated Mrs. Farquar as if she had achieved a very great thing, and she felt that she had—her smile for the lingering, admiring natives was warm and grateful.

Later, when Teddy had his first haircut, Gideon the cook picked up the soft gold tufts from the ground and held them reverently in his hand. Then he smiled at the little boy and said: "Little Yellow Head." That became the native name for the child. Gideon and Teddy were great friends from the first. When Gideon had finished his work, he would lift Teddy on his shoulders to the shade of a big tree and play with him there, forming curious little toys from twigs and leaves and grass or shaping animals from wetted soil. When Teddy learned to walk it was often Gideon who crouched before him, clucking encouragement, finally catching him when he fell, tossing him up in the air till they both became breathless with laughter. Mrs. Farquar was fond of the old cook because of his love for her child.

There was no second baby; and one day Gideon said: "Ah, missus, missus, the Lord above sent this one; Little Yellow Head is the most good thing we have in our house." Because of the "we" Mrs. Farquar felt a warm impulse toward her cook, and at the end of the month she raised his wages. He had been with her now for several years; he was one of the few natives who had his wife and children in the compound and never wanted to go home to his kraal,[1] which was some hundreds of miles away. Sometimes a small piccanin,[2] who had been born the same time as Teddy, could be seen peering from the edge of the bush, staring in awe at the little white boy with his miraculous fair hair and Northern blue eyes. The two little children would gaze at each other with a wide, interested gaze, and once Teddy put out his hand curiously to touch the black child's cheeks and hair.

"Ah, missus, these are both children, and one will grow up to be a baas, and one will be a servant."

Gideon, who was watching, shook his head wonderingly, and said: "Ah, missus, these are both children, and one will grow up to be a baas,[3] and one will be a servant"; and Mrs. Farquar smiled and said sadly, "Yes, Gideon, I was thinking the same." She sighed. "It is God's will," said Gideon, who was a mission boy. The Farquars were very religious people, and this shared feeling about God bound servant and masters even closer together.

Teddy was about six years old when he was given a scooter and discovered the intoxications of speed. All day he would fly around the homestead, in and out of flowerbeds, scattering squawking chickens and irritated dogs, finishing with a wide, dizzying arc into the kitchen door. There he would cry: "Gideon, look at me!" And Gideon would laugh and

---

1 **kraal**: a local village
2 **piccanin**: a black child. This term is considered offensive.
3 **baas**: Afrikaans for "boss"

say: "Very clever, Little Yellow Head." Gideon's youngest son, who was now a herdsboy, came especially up from the compound to see the scooter. He was afraid to come near it, but Teddy showed off in front of him. "Piccanin," shouted Teddy, "get out of my way!" And he raced in circles around the black child until he was frightened and fled back to the bush.

"Why did you frighten him?" asked Gideon, gravely reproachful.

Teddy said defiantly: "He's only a black boy," and laughed. Then, when Gideon turned away from him without speaking, his face fell. Very soon he slipped into the house and found an orange and brought it to Gideon, saying: "This is for you." He could not bring himself to say he was sorry; but he could not bear to lose Gideon's affection either. Gideon took the orange unwillingly and sighed. "Soon you will be going away to school, Little Yellow Head," he said wonderingly, "and then you will be grown-up." He shook his head gently and said, "And that is how our lives go." He seemed to be putting a distance between himself and Teddy, not because of resentment, but in the way a person accepts something inevitable. The baby had lain in his arms and smiled up into his face; the tiny boy had swung from his shoulders and played with him by the hour. Now Gideon would not let his flesh touch the flesh of the white child. He was kind, but there was a grave formality in his voice that made Teddy pout and sulk away. Also, it made him into a man: With Gideon he was polite and carried himself formally, and if he came into the kitchen to ask for something, it was in the way a white man uses toward a servant, expecting to be obeyed.

But on the day that Teddy came staggering into the kitchen with his fists to his eyes, shrieking with pain, Gideon dropped the pot full of hot soup that he was holding, rushed to the child, and forced aside his fingers. "A snake!" he exclaimed. Teddy had been on his scooter and had come to a rest with his foot on the side of a big tub of plants. A tree snake, hanging by its tail from the roof, had spat full into his eyes. Mrs. Farquar came running when she heard the commotion. "He'll go blind," she sobbed, holding Teddy close against her. "Gideon, he'll go blind!" Already the eyes, with perhaps half an hour's sight left in them, were swollen up to the size of fists: Teddy's small white face was distorted by great purple oozing **protuberances**. Gideon said: "Wait a minute, missus, I'll get some medicine." He ran off into the bush.

Mrs. Farquar lifted the child into the house and bathed his eyes with permanganate. She had scarcely heard Gideon's words; but when she saw that her remedies had no effect at all, and remembered how she had seen natives with no sight in their eyes because of the spitting of a snake, she

protuberances: bulges; swellings

efficacy:
effectiveness;
power

began to look for the return of her cook, remembering what she heard of the **efficacy** of native herbs. She stood by the window, holding the terrified, sobbing little boy in her arms, and peered helplessly into the bush. It was not more than a few minutes before she saw Gideon come bounding back, and in his hand he held a plant.

"Do not be afraid, missus," said Gideon, "this will cure Little Yellow Head's eyes." He stripped the leaves from the plant, leaving a small white fleshy root. Without even washing it, he put the root in his mouth, chewed it vigorously, and then held the spittle there while he took the child forcibly from Mrs. Farquar. He gripped Teddy down between his knees and pressed the balls of his thumbs into the swollen eyes, so that the child screamed and Mrs. Farquar cried out in protest: "Gideon, Gideon!" But Gideon took no notice. He knelt over the writhing child, pushing back the puffy lids till chinks of eyeball showed, and then he spat hard, again and again, into first one eye and then the other. He finally lifted Teddy gently into his mother's arms and said: "His eyes will get better." But Mrs. Farquar was weeping with terror, and she could hardly thank him: It was impossible to believe that Teddy could keep his sight. In a couple of hours the swellings were gone. The eyes were inflamed and tender, but Teddy could see. Mr. and Mrs. Farquar went to Gideon in the kitchen and thanked him over and over again. They felt helpless because of the gratitude: It seemed they could do nothing to express it. They gave Gideon presents for his wife and children, and a big increase in wages, but these things could not pay for Teddy's now completely cured eyes. Mrs. Farquar said: "Gideon, God chose you as an instrument for His goodness," and Gideon said: "Yes, missus, God is very good."

Now, when such a thing happens on a farm, it cannot be long before everyone hears of it. Mr. and Mrs. Farquar told their neighbors, and the story was discussed from one end of the district to the other. The bush is full of secrets. No one can live in Africa, or at least on the veld, without learning very soon that there is an ancient wisdom of leaf and soil and season—and, too, perhaps most important of all, of the darker tracts of the human mind—which is the black man's heritage. Up and down the district people were telling anecdotes, reminding each other of things that had happened to them.

"But I saw it myself, I tell you. It was a puff adder[4] bite. The kaffir's[5] arm was swollen to the elbow, like a great shiny black bladder. He was groggy

---

4 **puff adder:** a poisonous snake
5 **kaffir:** a derogatory term for black South Africans

after a half a minute. He was dying. Then suddenly a kaffir walked out of the bush with his hands full of green stuff. He smeared something on the place, and the next day my boy was back at work, and all you could see was the two small punctures in the skin."

This was the kind of tale they told. And, as always, with a certain amount of exasperation, because while all of them knew that in the bush of Africa are waiting valuable drugs locked in bark, in simple-looking leaves, in roots, it was impossible to ever get the truth about them from the natives themselves.

The story eventually reached town; and perhaps it was at a sundowner party, or some such function, that a doctor who happened to be there challenged it. "Nonsense," he said, "These things get exaggerated in the telling. We are always checking up on this kind of story, and we draw a blank every time."

Anyway, one morning there arrived a strange car at the homestead, and out stepped one of the workers from the laboratory in town, with cases full of test tubes and chemicals.

Mr. and Mrs. Farquar were flustered and pleased and flattered. They asked the scientist to lunch, and they told the story all over again, for the hundredth time. Little Teddy was there too, his blue eyes sparking with health, to prove the truth of it. The scientist explained how humanity might benefit if this new drug could be offered for sale, and the Farquars were even more pleased: They were kind, simple people who liked to think of something good coming about because of them. But when the scientist began talking of the money that might result, their manner showed discomfort. Their feelings over the miracle (that was how they thought of it) were so strong and deep and religious that it was distasteful to them to think of money. The scientist, seeing their faces, went back to his first point, which was the advancement of humanity. He was perhaps a trifle **perfunctory:** It was not the first time he had come salting the tail[6] of a fabulous bush secret.

perfunctory: unenthusiastic; cursory

Eventually, when the meal was over, the Farquars called Gideon into their living room and explained to him that this baas here was a Big Doctor from the Big City, and he had come all the way to see Gideon. At this Gideon seemed afraid; he did not understand; and Mrs. Farquar explained quickly that it was because of the wonderful thing he had done with Teddy's eyes that the Big Baas had come.

---

6 **salting the tail:** investigating

Gideon looked from Mrs. Farquar to Mr. Farquar and then at the little boy, who was showing great importance because of the occasion. At last he said grudgingly: "The Big Baas want to know what medicine I used?" He spoke incredulously, as if he could not believe his old friends could so betray him. Mr. Farquar began explaining how a useful medicine could be made out of the root, and how it could be put on sale, and how thousands of people, black and white, up and down the continent of Africa, could be saved by the medicine when that spitting snake filled their eyes with poison. Gideon listened, his eyes bent on the ground, the skin of his forehead puckering in discomfort. When Mr. Farquar had finished he did not reply. The scientist, who all this time had been leaning back in a big chair, sipping his coffee and smiling with skeptical good humor, chipped in and explained all over again, in different words, about the making of drugs and the progress of science. Also, he offered Gideon a present.

There was a silence after this further explanation, and then Gideon remarked indifferently that he could not remember the root. His face was sullen and hostile, even when he looked at the Farquars, whom he usually treated like old friends. They were beginning to feel annoyed, and this feeling **annulled** the guilt that had been sprung into life by Gideon's accusing manner. They were beginning to feel that he was unreasonable. But it was at that moment that they all realized that he would never give in. The magical drug would remain where it was, unknown and useless except for the tiny scattering of Africans who had the knowledge, natives who might be digging a ditch for the municipality in a ragged shirt and a pair of patched shorts but who were still born to healing, hereditary healers, being the nephews or sons of the old witch doctors, whose ugly masks and bits of bone and all the uncouth properties of magic were the outward signs of real power and wisdom.

The Farquars might tread on that plant fifty times a day as they passed from house to garden, from cow kraal to mealie[7] field, but they would never know it.

But they went on persuading and arguing, with all the force of their exasperation; and Gideon continued to say that he could not remember, or that there was no such root, or that it was the wrong season of the year, or that it wasn't the root itself, but the spit from his mouth that had cured Teddy's eyes. He said all these things one after another and seemed not to care they were contradictory. He was rude and stubborn. The Farquars could

annulled: canceled; nullified

---

7 **mealie:** Indian corn

hardly recognize their gentle, lovable old servant in this ignorant, perversely obstinate African, standing there in front of them with lowered eyes, his hands twitching his cook's apron, repeating over and over whichever one of the stupid refusals first entered his head.

And suddenly he appeared to give in. He lifted his head; gave a long, blank, angry look at the circle of whites, who seemed to him like a circle of yelping dogs pressing around him; and said: "I will show you the root."

They walked single file away from the homestead down a kaffir path. It was a blazing December afternoon, with the sky full of hot rain clouds. Everything was hot: The sun was like a bronze tray whirling overhead, there was a heat shimmer over the fields, the soil was scorching underfoot, the dusty wind blew gritty and thick and warm in their faces. It was a terrible day, fit only for reclining on a veranda with iced drinks, which is where they would normally have been at that hour.

From time to time, remembering that on the day of the snake it had taken ten minutes to find the root, someone asked: "Is it much farther, Gideon?" And Gideon would answer over his shoulder, with angry politeness: "I'm looking for the root, baas." And indeed, he would frequently bend sideways and trail his hand among the grasses with a gesture that was insulting in its perfunctoriness. He walked them through the bush along unknown paths for two hours in that melting, destroying heat, so that the sweat trickled coldly down them and their heads ached. They were all quite silent; the Farquars because they were angry, the scientist because he was being proved right again; there was no such plant. His was a tactful silence.

At last, six miles from the house, Gideon suddenly decided they had had enough; or perhaps his anger evaporated at that moment. He picked up, without an attempt at looking anything but casual, a handful of blue flowers from the grass, flowers that had been growing plentifully all down the paths they had come. He handed them to the scientist without looking at him and marched off by himself on the way home, leaving them to follow him if they chose.

When they got back to the house, the scientist went to the kitchen to thank Gideon: he was being very polite, even though there was an amused look in his eyes. Gideon was not there. Throwing the flowers casually into the back of his car, the **eminent** visitor departed on his way back to his laboratory.

eminent: distinguished; high-ranking

Gideon was back in his kitchen in time to prepare dinner, but he was sulking. He spoke to Mr. Farquar like an unwilling servant. It was days before they liked each other again.

The Farquars made enquiries about the root from their laborers. Sometimes they were answered with distrustful stares. Sometimes the natives said: "We do not know. We have never heard of the root." One, the cattle boy, who had been with them a long time and had grown to trust them a little, said: "Ask your boy in the kitchen. Now, there's a doctor for you. He's the son of a famous medicine man who used to be in these parts, and there's nothing he cannot cure." Then he added politely: "Of course, he's not as good as the white man's doctor, we know that, but he's good for us."

After some time, when the soreness had gone from between the Farquars and Gideon, they began to joke: "When are you going to show us the snake root, Gideon?" And he would laugh and shake his head, saying, a little uncomfortably: "But I did show you, missus, have you forgotten?"

Much later, Teddy, as a schoolboy, would come into the kitchen and say: "You old rascal, Gideon! Do you remember that time you tricked us all by making us walk miles all over the veld for nothing? It was so far my father had to carry me!"

And Gideon would double up with polite laughter. After much laughing, he would suddenly straighten himself up, wipe his old eyes, and look sadly at Teddy, who was grinning mischievously at him across the kitchen: "Ah, Little Yellow Head, how you have grown! Soon you will be grown-up with a farm of your own . . . "

After You Read

Critical Reading

1. Gideon has worked for the Farquars for many years. What do he and the family have in common, and how does their asking him about the medicine alter their relationship?

2. Explain what Gideon has to fear from the scientist's and family's requests for his knowledge.

3. Use clues from the text to illustrate the implied relationship between the white and black populations of the story.

Literary Lens: Character and Plot

Plot and **character** development go hand in hand. Re-create the graphic organizer below to help map the relationship between character development and the plot. In each box, list a main event along with the impact, if any, the event has on the characters. Then identify the turning point in the plot.

Event	Impact on a character(s)
What is the turning point in the story?	

Focus on Research: Quote Sources Directly

Research the transition of power from the British colony Southern Rhodesia to the Republic of Zimbabwe. Summarize your findings in a brief paragraph in which you include at least two direct quotations from your sources. Be sure to use correct formatting and in-text citations when using quotations.

The Literature of
South Africa

Background

In the 1990s, decades of political pressure finally succeeded in unraveling South Africa's far-reaching system of racial segregation and discrimination called *apartheid*. Under apartheid, the white minority ruled the country, while the black majority was forced to live on the margins of society. By 1994, apartheid had completely ended, and black African leader Nelson Mandela became South Africa's first democratically elected president.

The world's attention was drawn to apartheid partially through the writings of two white South African writers, Alan Paton (1903–1988) and Nadine Gordimer (1923–2014). Paton's 1948 book *Cry, the Beloved Country* and his 1953 novel *Too Late the Phalarope* were vivid indictments of troubled racial relations in his country.

Gordimer's 1952 short story collection *The Soft Voice of the Serpent* and her 1953 novel *The Lying Days* were also bitter portrayals of the apartheid regime. She received the Nobel Prize in Literature in 1991.

South Africa and the United States

One man who helped stir American sentiment against apartheid was the South African political activist Steve Biko, founder of the anti-apartheid Black Consciousness Movement. Arrested several times for his political activities, Biko died in 1977 from beatings by South African police. His martyrdom shocked many people in the United States who had previously given little thought to the injustice of apartheid.

The anthology *I Write What I Like* is a selection of Steve Biko's writings. His life story is told in the book *Biko*, written by his friend Donald Woods. Biko became the inspiration for the 1987 movie *Cry Freedom*, starring Denzel Washington as Biko and Kevin Kline as Woods.

Research: Use Biographical Sources

Certain black South African writers have been deeply influenced by their native oral traditions. These include Thomas Mokopu Mofolo (1876–1948), Benedict Wallet Vilakazi (1906–1947), and Solomon Tshekiso Plaatje (1877–1932). Use a reliable biographical source to research one of these writers and write a paragraph describing how he drew on his particular ethnic oral tradition.

The Moment Before the Gun Went Off

Nadine Gordimer

Before You Read

Nadine Gordimer (1923–2014) was born in South Africa, and she always observed the moral and political complexities of her home country with a clear eye. Early on, she raised her voice against apartheid and injustice. When apartheid finally ended, she said it was "like a birth." In her works, she deals with the sometimes terrible choices made by people who find themselves in a changing world. Although Gordimer also wrote nonfiction, she remarked, "Nothing I say in essays and articles will be as true as my fiction."

World Context

Despite an unromantic and often critical view of her country, Gordimer sustained a deep vein of hopefulness throughout her career. South Africa still struggles with deep racial and economic divisions. Yet Gordimer's work continues to be a powerful voice for equality and national pride.

 LITERARY LENS A **complex character** has multiple or conflicting motivations. As you read, identify the motivations of the main character.

Marais Van der Vyver shot one of his farm labourers, dead. An accident, there are accidents with guns every day of the week—children playing a fatal game with a father's revolver in the cities where guns are domestic objects, nowadays, hunting mishaps like this one, in the country— but these won't be reported all over the world. Van der Vyver knows his will be. He knows that the story of the Afrikaner[1] farmer—regional Party leader and Commandant of the local security commando—shooting a black man

---

1 **Afrikaner:** a non-native African; a white settler, mainly of Dutch descent

who worked for him will fit exactly *their* version of South Africa, it's made for them. They'll be able to use it in their boycott and divestment campaigns,[2] it'll be another piece of evidence in their truth about the country. The papers at home will quote the story as it has appeared in the overseas press, and in the back-and-forth he and the black man will become those crudely-drawn figures on anti-apartheid[3] banners, units in statistics of white brutality against the blacks quoted at the United Nations—he, whom they will gleefully be able to call "a leading member" of the ruling Party.

People in the farming community understand how he must feel. Bad enough to have killed a man, without helping the Party's, the government's, the country's enemies, as well. They see the truth of that. They know, reading the Sunday papers, that when Van der Vyver is quoted saying he is "terribly shocked," he will "look after the wife and children," none of those Americans and English, and none of those people at home who want to destroy the white man's power will believe him. And how they will sneer when he even says of the farm boy (according to one paper, if you can trust any of those reporters), "He was my friend, I always took him hunting with me." Those city and overseas people don't know it's true: farmers usually have one particular black boy they like to take along with them in the lands; you could call it a kind of friend, yes, friends are not only your own white people, like yourself, you take into your house, pray with in church and work with on the Party committee. But how can those others know that? They don't want to know it. They think all blacks are like the big-mouth agitators in town. And Van der Vyver's face, in the photographs, strangely opened by distress—everyone in the district remembers Marais Van der Vyver as a little boy who would go away and hide himself if he caught you smiling at him, and everyone knows him now as a man who hides any change of expression round his mouth behind a thick, soft moustache, and in his eyes by always looking at some object in hand, leaf of a crop fingered, pen or stone picked up, while concentrating on what he is saying, or while listening to you. It just goes to show what shock can do; when you look at the newspaper photographs you feel like apologizing, as if you had stared in on some room where you should not be.

There will be an inquiry; there had better be, to stop the assumption of yet another case of brutality against farm workers, although there's nothing in doubt—an accident, and all the facts fully admitted by Van der Vyver. He

---

2 **boycott and divestment campaigns:** successful local and worldwide economic protests against the ruling whites of South Africa

3 **anti-apartheid:** against apartheid (Afrikaans for "apartness"), the system of segregated government in South Africa that was dismantled in 1994

comic knobbly knees. He also had a lot of fanciful ideas because he smiled at the clouds.

"Perhaps they want me to send a message to the children," he thought tenderly, noting that the clouds were drifting in the direction of his home some hundred miles away. But before he could frame the message, the warder[1] in charge of his work span[2] shouted:

"Hey, what you think you're doing, Brille?"

The prisoner swung round, blinking rapidly, yet at the same time sizing up the enemy. He was a new warder, named Jacobus Stephanus Hannetjie. His eyes were the color of the sky but they were frightening. A simple, primitive, brutal soul gazed out of them. The prisoner bent down quickly and a message was quietly passed down the line:

"We're in for trouble this time, comrades."

"Why?" rippled back up the line.

"Because he's not human," the reply rippled down, and yet only the crunching of the spades as they turned over the earth disturbed the stillness.

This particular work span was known as Span One. It was composed of ten men, and they were all political prisoners. They were grouped together for convenience, as it was one of the prison regulations that no black warder should be in charge of a political prisoner lest this prisoner convert him to his views. It never seemed to occur to the authorities that this very reasoning was the strength of Span One and a clue to the strange terror they aroused in the warders. As political prisoners they were unlike the other prisoners in the sense that they felt no guilt nor were they outcasts of society. All guilty men instinctively **cower**, which was why it was the kind of prison where men got knocked out cold with a blow at the back of the head from an iron bar. Up until the arrival of Warder Hannetjie, no warder had dared beat any member of Span One and no warder had lasted more than a week with them. The battle was entirely psychological. Span One was assertive and it was beyond the scope of white warders to handle assertive black men. Thus, Span One had got out of control. They were the best thieves and liars in the camp. They lived all day on raw cabbages. They chatted and smoked tobacco. And since they moved, thought and acted as one, they had perfected every technique of group concealment.

Trouble began that very day between Span One and Warder Hannetjie. It was because of the shortsightedness of Brille. That was the nickname he was given in prison and is the Afrikaans word for someone who wears

cower:
cringe; grovel

---

1 **warder:** the overseer
2 **work span:** a unit of prison workers

glasses. Brille could never judge the approach of the prison gates, and on several previous occasions he had munched on cabbages and dropped them almost at the feet of the warder, and all previous warders had overlooked this. Not so Warder Hannetjie.

"Who dropped that cabbage?" he thundered.

Brille stepped out of line.

"I did," he said meekly.

"All right," said Hannetjie. "The whole span goes three meals off."

"But I told you I did it," Brille protested.

The blood rushed to Warder Hennetjie's face.

"Look 'ere," he said. "I don't take orders from a kaffir. I don't know what kind of kaffir you think you are. Why don't you say Baas. I'm your Baas. Why don't you say Baas, hey?"

Brille blinked his eyes rapidly but by contrast his voice was strangely calm.

"I'm twenty years older than you," he said. It was the first thing that came to mind, but the comrades seemed to think it a huge joke. A titter swept up the line. The next thing Warder Hannetjie whipped out a knobkerrie[3] and gave Brille several blows about the head. What surprised his comrades was the speed with which Brille had removed his glasses or else they would have been smashed to pieces on the ground.

That evening in the cell Brille was very apologetic.

"I'm sorry, comrades," he said. "I've put you into a hell of a mess."

"Never mind, brother," they said. "What happens to one of us, happens to all."

"I'll try to make up for it, comrades," he said. "I'll steal something so that you don't go hungry."

Privately, Brille was very philosophical about his head wounds. It was the first time an act of violence had been perpetrated against him, but he had long been a witness of extreme, almost unbelievable human brutality. He had twelve children and his mind traveled back that evening through the sixteen years of bedlam in which he had lived. It had all happened in a small drab little three-bedroomed house in a small drab little street in the Eastern Cape, and the children kept coming year after year because neither he nor Martha managed the contraceptives the right way and a teacher's salary never allowed moving to a bigger house and he was always taking exams to improve this salary only to have it all eaten up by hungry mouths. Everything was pretty horrible, especially the way the children fought.

---

3 **knobkerrie:** a compact club

They'd get hold of each other's heads and give them a good bashing against the wall. Martha gave up somewhere along the line, so they worked out a thing between them. The bashings, biting and blood were to operate in full swing until he came home. He was to be the bogeyman,[4] and when it worked he never failed to have a sense of godhead[5] at the way in which his presence could change savages into fairly reasonable human beings.

Yet somehow it was this chaos and mismanagement at the center of his life that drove him into politics. It was really an ordered beautiful world with just a few basic slogans to learn along with the rights of mankind. At one stage, before things became very bad, there were conferences to attend, all very far away from home.

"Let's face it," he thought **ruefully**. "I'm only learning right now what it means to be a politician. All this while I've been running away from Martha and the kids."

ruefully: sadly; regretfully

And the pain in his head brought a hard lump to his throat. That was what the children did to each other daily and Martha wasn't managing, and if Warder Hannetjie had not interrupted him that morning, he would have sent the following message:

"Be good comrades, my children. Cooperate, then life will run smoothly."

The next day Warder Hannetjie caught this old man with twelve children stealing grapes from the farm shed. They were an enormous quantity of grapes in a ten-gallon tin, and for this misdeed the old man spent a week in the isolation cell. In fact, Span One as a whole was in constant trouble. Warder Hannetjie seemed to have eyes at the back of his head. He uncovered the trick about the cabbages; how they were split in two with the spade and immediately covered with earth and then unearthed again and eaten with split-second timing. He found out how tobacco smoke was beaten into the ground, and he found out how conversations were whispered down the wind.

For about two weeks Span One lived in **acute** misery. The cabbages, tobacco and conversations had been the **pivot** of jail life to them. Then one evening they noticed that their good old comrade who wore the glasses was looking rather pleased with himself. He pulled out a four-ounce packet of tobacco by way of explanation, and the comrades fell upon it with great greed. Brille merely smiled. After all, he was the father of many children. But when the last shred had disappeared, it occurred to the comrades that they ought to be puzzled. Someone said:

acute: sharp; intense

pivot: hub; center

---

4 **bogeyman:** the person who is scary or dreaded
5 **godhead:** being godlike

"I say, brother. We're watched like hawks these days. Where did you get the tobacco?"

"Hannetjie gave it to me," said Brille.

There was a long silence. Into it dropped a quiet bombshell.

"I saw Hannetjie in the shed today," and the failing eyesight blinked rapidly. "I caught him in the act of stealing five bags of fertilizer, and he bribed me to keep my mouth shut."

There was another long silence.

"Prison is an evil life," Brille continued, apparently discussing some irrelevant matter. "It makes a man contemplate all kinds of evil deeds."

He held out his hand and closed it.

"You know, comrades," he said. "I've got Hannetjie. I'll betray him tomorrow."

Everyone began talking at once.

"Forget it, brother. You'll get shot." Brille laughed.

"I won't," he said. "That is what I mean about evil. I am a father of children, and I saw today that Hannetjie is just a child and stupidly truthful. I'm going to punish him severely because we need a good warder."

The following day, with Brille as witness, Hannetjie confessed to the theft of the fertilizer and was fined a large sum of money. From then on Span One did very much as they pleased while Warder Hannetjie stood by and said nothing. But it was Brille who carried this to extremes. One day, at the close of work Warder Hannetjie said:

"Brille, pick up my jacket and carry it back to the camp."

"But nothing in the regulations says I'm your servant, Hannetjie," Brille replied coolly.

"I've told you not to call me Hannetjie. You must say Baas," but Warder Hannetjie's voice lacked conviction. In turn, Brille squinted up at him.

"I'll tell you something about this Baas business, Hannetjie," he said. "One of these days we are going to run the country. You are going to clean my car. Now, I have a fifteen-year-old son, and I'd die of shame if you had to tell him that I ever called you Baas."

Warder Hannetjie went red in the face and picked up his coat.

On another occasion Brille was seen to be walking about the prison yard, openly smoking tobacco. On being taken before the prison commander he claimed to have received the tobacco from Warder Hannetjie. All throughout the **tirade** from his chief, Warder Hannetjie failed to defend himself, but his nerve broke completely. He called Brille to one side.

tirade: tongue-lashing; long, scolding speech

"Brille," he said. "This thing between you and me must end. You may not know it, but I have a wife and children, and you're driving me to suicide."

"Why don't you like your own medicine, Hannetjie?" Brille asked quietly.

"I can give you anything you want," Warder Hannetjie said in desperation.

"It's not only me but the whole of Span One," said Brille cunningly. "The whole of Span One wants something from you."

Warder Hannetjie brightened with relief.

"I think I can manage if it's tobacco you want," he said.

Brille looked at him, for the first time struck with pity and guilt. He wondered if he had carried the whole business too far. The man was really a child.

"It's not tobacco we want, but you," he said. "We want you on our side. We want a good warder because without a good warder we won't be able to manage the long stretch ahead."

Warder Hannetjie interpreted this request in his own fashion, and his interpretation of what was good and human often left the prisoners of Span One speechless with surprise. He had a way of slipping off his revolver and picking up a spade and digging alongside Span One. He had a way of producing unheard-of-luxuries like boiled eggs from his farm nearby and things like cigarettes, and Span One responded nobly and got the reputation of being the best work span in the camp. And it wasn't only taken from their side. They were awfully good at stealing **commodities** like fertilizer which were needed on the farm of Warder Hannetjie.

commodities: goods; merchandise

After You Read

Critical Reading

1. In describing Span One, the **narrator** says, "As political prisoners they were unlike the other prisoners in the sense that they felt no guilt nor were they outcasts of society." Explain what the author means by this description.

2. While in prison, what does Brille come to understand about his family life?

3. In what ways does Warder Hannetjie remind Brille of a child?

Literary Lens: Character Interaction

Characters change because of the influences of the environment and interactions with other characters. "The Prisoner Who Wore Glasses" focuses on the conflict between Brille and Warder Hannetjie.

Re-create the chart below and use it to trace the relationship between Brille and Warder Hannetjie. Select three scenes from the story that contain both characters. Briefly describe the scene in the first column. Then describe the interaction between the two characters in the second column. In the third column, describe the outcome of the interaction.

Scene	Interaction	Outcome

Focus on Research: Revise for Content

Based on what you've read about South Africa in this and other books, write a few paragraphs explaining the history of apartheid. Revise your paragraphs for content. First, ask a partner to read them and point out places where more details are needed. Then conduct focused research to find information that can be added to your paragraphs to make the content more comprehensive.

Africa

Unit Review

Key Ideas and Details

1. In both "Marriage Is a Private Affair" and "A Meeting in the Dark," young men fret that their fathers will disapprove of their potential wives. Compare these two stories, looking at how the personalities and expectations of the young men and their fathers help to shape the eventual outcomes.

Craft and Structure

2. Select two stories from this unit and compare and contrast the narrative **point of view** of the two works.

3. The stories "In the Shadow of War" and "Loyalties" share the same setting, but they are strikingly different in **tone**. Compare and contrast the language and tone of the two works.

4. Pride is a **theme** that runs through the poems in this unit. What do you think is the connection between this theme and Africa's history of colonial rule?

5. In many of these selections, people are not given respect or allowed to thrive as human beings. Point out the stories in which lack of respect is a theme. Determine why this conflict is so powerful for both writer and reader alike.

Integration of Knowledge and Ideas

6. Look at how whites and blacks regard one another in "No Witchcraft for Sale," "The Moment Before the Gun Went Off," and "The Prisoner Who Wore Glasses." How do they help to teach and support one another and how do they fail? Think about what each group is trying to protect when it keeps something back from the other.

7. Many of the writers in this unit have suffered from imprisonment or exile, both voluntary and involuntary. Write a letter from prison or from abroad, giving yourself the fictitious identity of a writer who has suffered as a result of the strong expression of his or her beliefs. To add authenticity to the letter, make sure you have a specific audience in mind and add plenty of realistic details to your surroundings.

Research Projects

Speaking and Listening

Watch the Ted Talk "The Danger of a Single Story" given by Chimamanda Ngozi Adichie. It can be found at ted.com or on YouTube. Write down questions as you listen. With a small group of your classmates, narrow down your list of questions to two or three open-ended questions. With your classmates, conduct a Socratic seminar to discuss your questions. Begin with these questions: What does Ngozi Acichie mean by "a single story?" Why does she claim it is dangerous?

Multimedia Project

Research African masks using various sources, such as the library, Internet, and knowledgeable people in your area. Choose an image of a mask that resonates with you personally. Create a digital presentation in which you display your mask along with a brief summary of your research of African masks, their history, and use. Choose appropriate graphics, music, and artwork to create an interesting and informative presentation.

Research Follow-Up

News of Africa often focuses on natural disasters, civil wars, and poverty. However, the stories in this unit prove that Africa also has a thriving community of writers. Conduct research on a 21st-century artist, musician, writer, or filmmaker. Use primary sources, such as interviews, biographies, and their artwork, and also use secondary sources. Write a short research paper and include multimedia elements such as music or film clips. Provide a works cited list that demonstrates the use of credible sources through their timeliness, expertise, and reliability.

Synthesizing Through Research and Writing

Read works not in this book by two of the writers in this unit. Write a paper comparing the two writers. Note how they treat one of the common themes in African literature, such as the effects of colonialism or cultural conflicts. Include direct quotations and in-text citations in your paper.

Cultural Reflection

Write in your journal about the characters you encountered in this unit who opened your eyes to a new way of seeing the world. Explain that new perspective and how the characters helped you see it.

UNIT FOUR

The Literature of the Middle East & South Asia

Laura Winkiel
Professor of English, University of Colorado Boulder

For generations, the Middle East and South Asia have served as the intersection of many cultures and religions. The Middle East is home to both Arabic literature and Jewish literature. The spread of literature written in the Arabic language is linked to the rise of the Islamic religion in the 7th and 8th centuries. During this time, Islamic art, literature, culture, and trade flourished. The Islamic State extended throughout the Middle East, as far east as modern-day Afghanistan and as far west as Spain and Northern Africa. Arabic literature reflects the cultural influences of Africa, Europe, and Asia.

South Asia includes the gigantic subcontinent of India, a region with enormous cultural, religious, and linguistic diversity. The people of modern India speak more than twenty languages and many other regional dialects. They also practice all of the world's major religions, especially Hinduism, Buddhism, Jainism, and Islam. Throughout its long history, India has absorbed and transformed the cultures of the people who have conquered the region, including Greeks, Persians, Muslims, and Europeans. As a result, the Indian literary tradition is one of the world's oldest and richest.

With the exception of the European Crusades to Jerusalem in the 11th through 17th centuries, the most striking European influence in both the Middle East and South Asia occurred only recently, in the 18th and 19th centuries. As French and English colonists invaded these territories, the people of the Middle East and South Asia became aware of Western forms of technology and modernization. For example, Mohammed Ali, who ruled Egypt from 1805 to 1848, sent many of his best students to Europe and commissioned the translation of various French texts into Arabic. These texts spread widely in the Middle East, broadening the scope of the Arab world to include Western forms of thought. But because Middle Eastern and South Asian cultures already had an established written culture and history, the works from their own heritage circulated alongside the European materials. Modern writers from this region have combined traditions to create a world literature that reflects Islamic and South Asian cultures as well as European traditions.

The combination of Western and Eastern thought and ways of life often produced creative literature of great beauty and insight but sometimes resulted in conflict. The struggles have often been between peoples seeking to embrace modern ways, such as Western food, clothing, and equality between men and women, and those seeking to preserve their older cultural practices of religion, culture, trade, and traditional roles for the sexes.

For some people, the greatest symbol of Eastern resistance to Western ways of life is the veil. Muslim women who strictly practice their religion are instructed never to appear in public without having their hair and sometimes their face veiled and hidden from view. For many, the purpose of this practice is to preserve women's purity and devotion to their husbands, brothers, and fathers. Wearing the veil is also a sign of resistance to the Western world, including the United States.

In a region of the world that has a long history of conflict and that supports such a wide variety of religions, languages, cultures, and traditions, literature provides a window through which to view a rapidly changing world. In many of these stories and poems, children, parents, and grandparents see the world very differently from one another. These writers raise questions about globalization: Is it best that the East should adapt to the West's ways? What is lost when this occurs? How can the Middle East and South Asia adopt aspects of Western life without losing their heritage? These stories help us to understand the complex questions that Middle Easterners and South Asian people ask as they stand at a crossroads of cultural and religious change.

The Literature of the Middle East & South Asia 393

TURKEY

Muzaffer Izgü

SYRIA

Ulfat al-Idlibi

ALGERIA

Assia Djebar

EGYPT

Alifa Rifaat
Naguib Mahfouz

Literary Map of
The Middle East
& South Asia

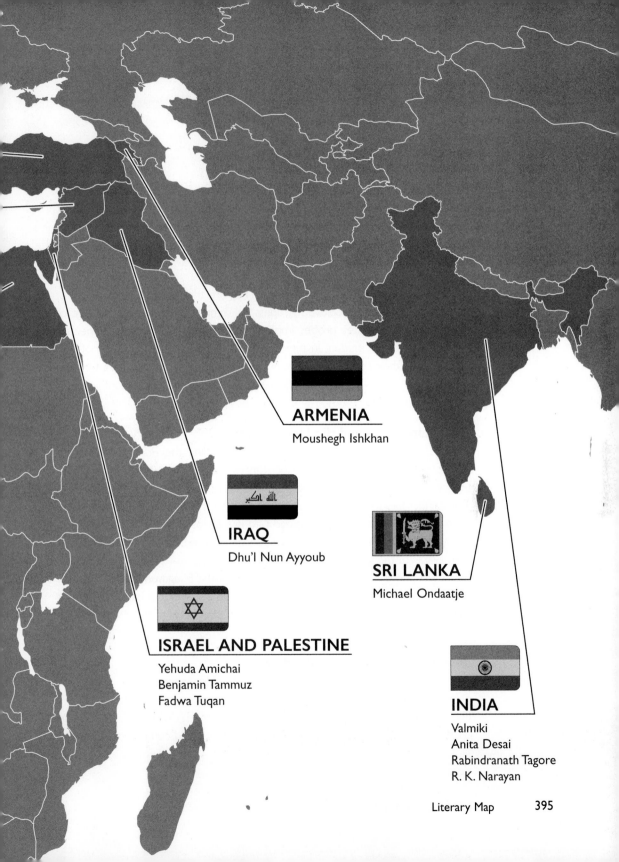

ARMENIA

Moushegh Ishkhan

IRAQ

Dhu'l Nun Ayyoub

SRI LANKA

Michael Ondaatje

ISRAEL AND PALESTINE

Yehuda Amichai
Benjamin Tammuz
Fadwa Tuqan

INDIA

Valmiki
Anita Desai
Rabindranath Tagore
R. K. Narayan

A South Asian Classic
The Ramayana

Background

Composed between 300 B.C.E. and C.E. 200, the Ramayana ranks with the Mahabharata as one of the two great epics of ancient India. It is the love story of Prince Rama and Princess Sita—their meeting, marriage, separation through treachery, and reunion. But the *Ramayana* is much more than a mere love story. Like other great literature, it provides wisdom on how to live. To many Hindus, it is a religious text.

Rama and Sita are no mere mortals. They are the avatars (incarnations) of the god Vishnu and his beloved goddess Lakshmi. The *Ramayana's* account of their earthly adventures probes important concepts of Hinduism—especially *dharma*, sacred law or duty. In their mortal forms, Rama and Sita are not fully conscious of their cosmic destinies. Even so, they fulfill their destinies by living moral, dutiful lives. The *Ramayana's* readers and listeners are meant to learn from their examples.

Hindu Literature and the United States

During the 19th century, Hindu literature, including the *Ramayana* and the *Mahabharata*, deeply influenced American writers. Ralph Waldo Emerson and Henry David Thoreau, leaders of the philosophical movement called Transcendentalism, were especially impressed by the *Bhagavad Gita*, a passage from the *Mahabharata*. The *Bhagavad Gita* is a philosophical dialogue between the warrior Arjuna and his charioteer Krishna—who, like Rama in the *Ramayana*, is an avatar of the god Vishnu.

"It was the first of books," wrote Emerson of the *Bhagavad Gita*. "It was as if an empire spoke to us." When Thoreau sought solitude in his hand-built hut at Walden Pond in Concord, Massachusetts, he took a copy of the *Bhagavad Gita* with him.

Research: Find Images and Videos

In Indonesia, parts of the *Ramayana* and the *Mahabharata* have long been performed in a traditional style of shadow puppet show called *wayang kulit*. Find photographs, paintings, and videos that show *wayang kulit* being presented. Then create a power presentation to display your findings. Add commentary for each slide.

from The Ramayana

Valmiki

Before You Read

Valmiki (400s B.C.E. or 300s B.C.E.) was an Indian poet who lived in what is now northern India. According to legend, he was a robber who once held up a Hindu holy man. The only wealth the holy man had was a mantra, a word used in meditation. Valmiki later became absorbed in meditation and composed the story of Rama. He used stories, legends, and myths derived from earlier oral traditions.

World Context

Like the Greek epics of Homer, the *Iliad* and the *Odyssey*, the *Ramayana* is set in ancient times and describes war and heroic feats. It centers on the exiled Prince Rama, who embodies part of the god Vishnu. Rama embarks on several adventures to regain control of his kingdom and save his wife Sita from the demon-king Ravana. Although Rama and Sita endure great hardships, they remain devoted to each other. Near the end of the tale, Rama becomes king.

Since the time of Valmiki, writers have continued to revise and reinterpret the story. The following excerpt is from a version by a modern Indian writer, R. K. Narayan. In it, Rama, his teacher Viswamithra, and his brother Lakshmana have just reached Mithila, where King Janaka and his daughter Sita live.

 LITERARY LENS What details did the author choose to reveal the nature of the main **characters** in this story?

Mithila, after all the forests, mountain paths, valleys, and places of solitude and silence through which we have traveled thus far, offers a pleasant change to a city of color and pleasure, with people enjoying the business of living. The very minute Rama steps into Mithila, he notices golden **turrets** and domes, and towers, and colorful flags fluttering in the wind as if to welcome a royal bridegroom-to-be. The streets glitter with odds and ends of jewelry cast off by the people (a necklace that had snapped during a dance or

turrets: small towers

a game; or had been flung off when found to be a nuisance during an embrace), with no one inclined to pick them up in a society of such affluence. There was no charity in [this] country since there was no one to receive it. Torn-off flower garlands lay in heaps on the roadside with honey-bees swarming over them. The *musth*[1] running down the haunches of mountainous elephants flowed in dark streams along the main thoroughfare, blending with the white froth dripping from the mouths of galloping horses, and churned with mud and dust by ever-turning chariot wheels.

On lofty terraces women were singing and dancing to the accompaniment of *veena*[2] and soft drums. Couples on swings suspended from tall *areca*[3] poles enjoyed the delight of swaying back and forth, their necklaces or garlands flying in the air. Rama and Lakshmana went on past shops displaying gems, gold, ivory, peacock feathers, beads, and wigs made of the hair of rare Himalayan deer. They observed arenas where strange elephant fights were in progress, cheered by crowds of young men; groups of women practicing ballads and love songs under wayside **canopies**; horses galloping without a break round and round bridle tracks, watched by elegant men and women; swimming pools with multicolored fish agitated by people sporting in the water.

They crossed the moat surrounding Janaka's palace, with its golden spires soaring above the other buildings of the city. Now Rama observed on a balcony Princess Sita playing with her companions. He stood arrested by her beauty, and she noticed him at the same moment. Their eyes met. They had been together not so long ago in Vaikunta, their original home in heaven, as Vishnu and his spouse Lakshmi, but in their present **incarnation**, suffering all the limitations of mortals, they looked at each other as strangers. Sita, decked in ornaments and flowers, in the midst of her attendants, flashed on his eyes like a streak of lightning. She paused to watch Rama slowly pass out of view, along with his sage-master and brother. The moment he vanished, her mind became uncontrollably agitated. The eye had admitted a slender shaft of love, which later expanded and spread into her whole being. She felt ill.

Observing the sudden change in her, and the sudden drooping and withering of her whole being, even the bangles on her wrist slipping down, her attendants took her away and spread a soft bed for her to lie on.

She lay tossing in her bed complaining, "You girls have forgotten how to make a soft bed. You are all out to tease me." Her maids in attendance

---

canopies:
a covering or structure similar to a roof

incarnation:
a bodily manifestation of a deity or spirit

---

1 *musth*: a type of liquid secreted by elephants
2 *veena*: a type of stringed musical instrument
3 *areca*: a type of palm tree

Sita Finds Rama

had never seen her in such a mood. They were bewildered and amused at first, but later became genuinely concerned, when they noticed tears streaming down her cheeks. They found her prattling involuntarily, "Shoulders of emerald, eyes like lotus petals, who is he? He invaded my heart and has deprived me of all shame! A robber who could ensnare my heart and snatch away my peace of mind! Broad-shouldered, but walked off so swiftly. Why could he not have halted his steps, so that I might have gained just one more glimpse and **quelled** this riotous heart of mine. He was here, he was there next second, and gone forever. He could not be a god—his eyelids flickered. . . . Or was he a sorcerer casting a spell on people?"

The sun set beyond the sea, so says the poet—and when a poet mentions a sea, we have to accept it. No harm in letting a poet describe his vision, no need to question his geography. The cry of birds settling down for the night and the sound of waves on the seashore became clearer as the evening advanced into dusk and night. A cool breeze blew from the sea, but none of it comforted Sita. Their hour sharpened the agony of love, and agitated her heart with hopeless longings. A rare bird, known as "Anril," somewhere called its mate. Normally at this hour, Sita would listen for its melodious warbling, but today its voice sounded harsh and odious. Sita implored, "Oh, bird, wherever you may be, please be quiet. You are bent upon mischief, annoying me with your cries and **lamentations**. The sins I committed in a previous birth have assumed your form and come to torture me now!" The full moon rose from the sea, flooding the earth with its soft light. At the sight of it, she covered her eyes with her palms. She felt that all the elements were alien to her mood and combining to aggravate her suffering. Her maids noticed her distress and feared that some deep-rooted ailment had suddenly seized her. They lit cool lamps whose wicks were fed with clarified butter, but found that even such a flame proved intolerable to her, and they extinguished the lamps and in their place kept luminous gems which emanated soft light. They made her a soft bed on a slab of **moonstone** with layers of soft petals, but the flowers wilted, Sita writhed and groaned and complained of everything—the night, stars, moonlight, and flowers: a whole universe of unsympathetic elements. The question went on drumming in her mind: "Who is he? Where is he gone? Flashing into view and gone again—or am I subject to a **hallucination**? It could not be so—a mere hallucination cannot weaken one so much."

At the guest house, Rama retired for the night. In the seclusion of his bedroom, he began to brood over the girl he had noticed on the palace

quelled:
reduced to
passivity

lamentations:
expressions of
sorrow

moonstone:
a transparent
or translucent
stone, often
used as a gem

hallucination:
a perception
of something
that is not
really there

balcony. For him, too, the moon seemed to emphasize his sense of loneliness. Although he had exhibited no sign of it, deeply within he felt a disturbance. His innate sense of discipline and propriety had made him conceal his feelings before other people. Now he kept thinking of the girl on the balcony and longed for another sight of her. Who could she be? Nothing to indicate that she was a princess—could be any one among the hundreds of girls in a palace. She could not be married: Rama realized that if she were married he would instinctively have recoiled from her. Now he caught himself contemplating her in every detail. He fancied that she was standing before him and longed to enclose [her] in his embrace. He said to himself, "Even if I cannot take her in my arms, shall I ever get another glimpse, however briefly, of that radiant face and those lips? Eyes, lips, those curly locks falling on the forehead—every item of those features seemingly poised to attack and quell me—me, on whose bow depended the destruction of demons, now at the mercy of one who wields only a bow of sugarcane and uses flowers for arrows . . ." He smiled at the irony of it.

The night spent itself. He had little sleep. The moon set and the dawn came. Rama found that it was time to arise and prepare himself to accompany his master to the ceremony at Janaka's palace.

At the assembly hall King Janaka noticed Rama and Lakshmana, and asked Viswamithra, "Who are those attractive-looking young men?" Viswamithra explained. When he heard of Rama's lineage and prowess, Janaka said with a sigh, "How I wish it were possible for me to propose my daughter for him." Viswamithra understood the cause of his despair. A seemingly insurmountable condition existed in any proposal concerning Sita's marriage.

King Janaka had in his possession an enormous bow which at one time belonged to Shiva, who had abandoned it and left it in the custody of an early ancestor of Janaka's, and it had remained an **heirloom**. Sita, as a baby girl, was a gift of Mother Earth to Janaka, being found in a **furrow** when a field was ploughed. Janaka adopted the child, tended her, and she grew up into a beauty, so much so that several princes who considered themselves eligible thronged Janaka's palace and contended for Sita's hand. Unable to favor anyone in particular, and in order to ward them off, King Janaka made it a condition that whoever could lift, bend, and string Shiva's bow would be considered fit to become Sita's husband. When her suitors took a look at the bow, they realized that it was a hopeless and unacceptable condition. They left in a rage, and later returned with their armies, prepared to win Sita by force. But Janaka resisted their aggression, and ultimately the suitors withdrew. As time passed Janaka became anxious whether he would ever see

heirloom:
an item of special value handed from one generation to the next

furrow:
a small trench in the ground made by a plow

his daughter married and settled—since the condition once made could not be withdrawn. No one on earth seemed worthy of approaching Shiva's bow. Janaka sighed. "I tremble when I think of Sita's future, and question my own judgment in linking her fate with this mighty, divine heirloom in our house."

"Do not despair," said Viswamithra soothingly. "How do you know it was not a divine inspiration that gave you the thought?"

"In all the worlds, is there anyone who can tackle this bow, the very sight of which in Shiva's hand made erring gods and **godlings** tremble and collapse—until Shiva put it away and renounced its use?"

"With your permission, may we see it?"

Janaka said, "I'll have it brought here. It has lain in its shed too long. . . . Who knows, moving it out may change all our fates." He called on his attendants to fetch the bow. . . . The attendants hesitated and he ordered, "Let the army be engaged for the task if necessary. After all, this spot is sanctified by the sacred rites recently performed . . . and the bow is fit to be brought in here."

The bow was placed in a carriage on eight pairs of wheels and arrived drawn by a vast number of men. During its passage from its shed through the streets, a crowd followed it. It was so huge that no one could comprehend it at one glance. "Is this a bow or that mountain called Meru, which churned the Ocean of Milk[4] in ancient times?" people marveled. "What target is there to receive the arrow shot out of this bow, even if someone lifts and strings it!" wondered some. "If Janaka meant seriously to find a son-in-law, he should have waived this condition. How unwise of him!"

Rama looked at his master. Viswamithra nodded as if to say, "Try it." As Rama approached the bow with slow dignity, the onlookers held their breath and watched. Some prayed silently for him. Some commented, "How cruel! This supposed sage is not ashamed to put the delicate, marvelous youth to this harsh trial!" "The King is perverse and cruel to place this godlike youth in this predicament. . . . If he was serious about it, he should have just placed Sita's hand in his instead of demanding all this acrobatic feat. . . . " "The King's aim is to keep Sita with him for ever—this is one way of never facing separation!" "If this man fails, we will all jump into fire," commented some young women who were lovestricken at the sight of Rama. "If he fails, Sita is sure to **immolate** herself and we will all follow her example."

While they were speculating thus, Rama approached the bow. Some of the onlookers, unable to bear the suspense, closed their eyes and prayed for

---

4 **Mount Meru, Ocean of Milk:** according to Hindu tradition, the gods used Mount Meru, the home of the main Hindu deity Brahma to stir a large body of water composed of milk

his success, saying, "If he fails to bring the ends of this bow together, what is to happen to the maiden?" What they missed, because they had shut their eyes, was to note how swiftly Rama picked up the bow, tugged the string taut, and brought the tips together. They were startled when they heard a deafening report, caused by the cracking of the bow at its arch, which could not stand the pressure of Rama's grip.

The atmosphere was suddenly relaxed. The gods showered down flowers and blessings, clouds parted and precipitated rains, the oceans tossed up in the air all the rare treasures from their depths. The sages cried, "Janaka's tribulations and trials are ended." Music filled the air. The citizens garlanded, embraced, and anointed each other with perfumes and sprinkled sandalwood powder in the air. People donned their best clothes, gathered at the palace gates and public squares, and danced and sang without any

Statues of Rama and Sita

restraint; flutes and pipes and drums created a din over the loud chants and songs from many throats. Gods and goddesses watching the happy scenes below assumed human form, mixed with the crowds, and shared their joy. "The beauty of our royal bridegroom can never be fully grasped unless one is blessed with a thousand eyes," commented the women. "See his brother! How very handsome! Blessed parents to have begotten such sons!"

Sita had secluded herself and was unaware of the latest development. She moved from bed to bed for lack of comfort, and lay beside a fountain on a slab of moonstone—the coolest bed they could find her. Even there she had no peace since the lotus blooms in the pool of the fountain teased her mind by reminding her of the shape of *his* eyes or *his* complexion. She grumbled, "No peace anywhere . . . I am deserted. My mind tortures me with reminders. What use are they if I can't even know where to look for him? What sort of a man can he be to cause all this torment and just pass on doing nothing to alleviate it? A regal appearance, but actually practicing sorcery!"

Her tortuous reflections were interrupted by the arrival of a maid. Instead of bowing and saluting her mistress, as was normal, she **pirouetted** around singing snatches of a love song. Sita sat up and commanded, "Be quiet! Are you intoxicated?" The maid answered, "The whole country is intoxicated. How would you know, my good mistress, if you lock yourself in and mope and moan!" She went on to explain in a rush of incoherence, "The king of Ayodhya's[5] . . . son, broad-shouldered and a god on earth. No one saw it happen, he was so quick and swift, but he pressed, so they say, one end with his feet, and seized the other end with his hand, and drew the string and oh! . . ."

"Oh, intoxicated beauty, what are you saying?" When Sita understood what had happened, she stood up . . . . She held herself erect as she said, "Do you know if this is the same man who struck me down with a look as he passed along the street? If it is someone else, I will end my life."

When the initial excitement subsided, King Janaka sought Viswamithra's advice. "What shall I do next? I suddenly find myself in an unexpected situation. Is it your desire that I should send for the priests and astrologer and fix the earliest date for the wedding, or send a message to Dasaratha[6] and wait for his convenience?"

Viswamithra replied, "Dispatch a messenger with the auspicious news immediately and invite Dasaratha formally." Janaka at once retired in order to compose a proper invitation to Dasaratha, with the help of his court poets and **epistle**-writers, and dispatched it.

pirouetted:
spun rapidly

epistle:
a letter

---

5 **Ayodhya:** Rama's home city
6 **Dasaratha:** Rama's father

In due course, Janaka's emissaries presented the epistle at Dasaratha's court. Dasaratha ordered his reader to receive the epistle and read it out: The message gave an account of all that had happened from the time Rama had left Ayodhya up to the snapping of Shiva's bow. Dasaratha heaped presents on the messengers, and commented light-heartedly, "Tell them in Mithila that we heard the sound of the bow snapping. . . . " He then passed orders: "Let the announcement in appropriate language be made widely that King Janaka has invited for Rama's wedding every man, woman, and child in our capital. Let those able to travel to Mithila start at once in advance of us." Professional announcers on elephants, accompanied with drums, carried the King's proclamation to every nook and corner of the capital.

Wall art of the wedding of Rama and Sita in the Jagannath Temple in India

After You Read

Critical Reading

1. The setting of a piece of literature involves both the time and place in which the action occurs. Analyze the setting described in the first two paragraphs of the Ramayana. What mood does the setting convey?

2. A **motif** is a recurring element in a story. The moon is a motif in this selection. **Imagery** and descriptions of the moon occur throughout this story. Analyze how this motif unifies or expresses a **theme** throughout the selection.

3. Identify two or more examples of **similes** in the selection and then describe how these similes convey a unique **voice**.

 ## Literary Lens: Characterization

Consider the details in the text that reveal the **characters** of Rama and Sita. Identify examples of these details from the text, and then consider what they reveal about each character.

	Examples from the text	What this reveals about the character
Rama		
Sita		

Focus on Research: Find Multimedia Sources

Multimedia sources can be text sources, video sources, images (including photos, drawings, and artwork), and more. Deepen your understanding of the text by conducting research using multimedia sources. In particular, find an animated film online or at the library called *Sita Sings the Blues* by Nina Paley. Watch the film, and then with a partner compare and contrast the film with the selection you read from the *Ramayana*.

The Literature of
Algeria

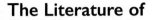

Background

Literature written by people in the region that is now known as Algeria dates back more than 1,500 years ago and has been written in several languages. Around the year 400 C.E., Christian theologian St. Augustine, writing in Latin, composed *Confessions*, one of the world's great spiritual autobiographies. Later, as the region converted to Islam, the native Berber population adopted Arabic as a common language. Then, between 1830 and 1962, Algeria was a French colony, and many writers wrote in French.

Two of the best-known Algerian writers of the 20th century are famous for their optimism. Mohammed Dib (1920–2003) offered a sweeping view of modern Algerian history in a set of three novels known as the *Algerian Trilogy*. A believer in the equality of all people, he once declared that "the things that make us different always remain secondary." Albert Camus (1913–1960), in novels such as *The Stranger*, explored the absurdity of human existence in an indifferent universe. Camus believed that humans could create their own meaning and treat one another justly.

Algeria and the United States

U.S.-Algerian relations have occasionally been tense over the past three centuries. In the 1790s, privateers (pirates licensed by a government) based in North Africa seized U.S. ships and sailors. These seizures resulted in a series of military battles. Over the past six decades, the two countries have clashed over the Israeli-Palestinian conflict in the Middle East. However, in recent years, record levels of trade have provided a closer link between the two countries. Today, almost 30 percent of Algeria's principal exports go to the United States. Most of these are natural gas or oil.

Research: Synthesize Multiple Sources

Dib and Camus belonged to a group of Algerian writers known as the Generation of 1952. Though friends, the two differed on the cause of Algerian independence from France. Dib supported it; Camus did not. With a partner, collaborate to find at least four sources and research the reasons for their positions. Write a one- to two-page imaginary conversation between these two men about the issue. Think carefully about how to divide the work and make a clear plan.

My Father Writes to My Mother

Assia Djebar

Before You Read

Fatima-Zohra Imalayan (1936–2015) was an Algerian novelist, poet, translator, and filmmaker. Her father, a teacher, sent her to school despite the fact that education was uncommon for Algerian girls. When she wrote her first novel, she began using the name Assia Djebar in case he didn't approve of her work. Djebar wrote in French, although she enriched that language with the sounds and rhythms of Arabic.

World Context

In Algeria, Muslim women are unable to do many things that Western women may take for granted. In the following story, Djebar explores the time when her father broke with tradition by writing to her mother.

 LITERARY LENS As you read, consider the importance of the story's **setting** (the time and place in which it takes place). Could it be set elsewhere and still make sense?

W henever my mother spoke of my father, she, in common with all the women in her town, simply used the personal pronoun in Arabic corresponding to "him." Thus, every time she used a verb in the third-person singular which didn't have a noun subject, she was naturally referring to her husband. This form of speech was characteristic of every married woman, from fifteen to sixty, with the **proviso** that in later years, if the husband had undertaken the pilgrimage to Mecca,[1] he could be given the title of "Hajj."

proviso: condition; stipulation

---

1 **pilgrimage to Mecca:** the visit made by Muslims to the birthplace of the prophet Muhammad at the Mecca in Saudi Arabia

Everybody, children and adults, especially girls and women, since all important conversations took place among the womenfolk, learnt very quickly to adapt to this rule whereby a husband and wife must never be referred to by name.

After she had been married a few years, my mother gradually learnt a little French. She was able to exchange a few halting words with the wives of my father's colleagues who had, for the most part, come from France and, like us, lived with their families in the little block of flats set aside for the village teachers.

I don't know exactly when my mother began to say, "*My husband* has come, *my husband* has gone out . . . I'll ask *my husband*," etc. Although my mother did make rapid progress in the language, in spite of taking it up fairly late in life, I can still hear the evident awkwardness in her voice betrayed by her labored phraseology,[2] her slow and deliberate enunciation at that time. Nevertheless, I can sense how much it cost her modesty to refer to my father directly in this way.

It was as if a floodgate had opened within her, perhaps in her relationship with her husband. Years later, during the summers we spent in her native town, when chatting in Arabic with her sisters or cousins, my mother would refer to him quite naturally by his first name, even with a touch of superiority. What a daring innovation! Yes, quite unhesitatingly—I was going to say, **unequivocally**—in any case, without any of the usual **euphemisms** and verbal **circumlocutions**. When her aunts and elderly female relations were present, she would once more use the traditional formalities, out of respect for them; such freedom of language would have appeared **insolent** and **incongruous** to the ears of the pious old ladies.

Years went by. As my mother's ability to speak French improved, while I was still a child of no more than twelve, I came to realize an **irrefutable** fact: namely that, in the face of all these womenfolk, my parents formed a couple. One thing was an even greater source of pride in me: when my mother referred to any of the day-to-day incidents of our village life—which in our city relatives' eyes was very backward—the tall figure of my father— my childhood hero—seemed to pop up in the midst of all these women engaged in idle chit-chat on the age-old patios to which they were confined.

My father, no one except my father; none of the other women ever saw fit to refer to their menfolk, their masters who spent the day outside the house and returned home in the evening, **taciturn**, with eyes on the ground. The nameless uncles, cousins, relatives by marriage, were for us an

unequivocally:
clearly;
unambiguously

euphemisms:
polite
expressions;
delicacies

circumlocutions:
roundabout
expressions

insolent:
disrespectful;
arrogant

incongruous:
improper;
inappropriate

irrefutable:
inarguable;
undeniable

taciturn:
not talkative;
quiet by nature

---

2 **phraseology:** a method of putting one's words together

unidentifiable collection of individuals to all of whom their spouses alluded impartially in the masculine gender.

With the exception of my father . . . My mother, with lowered eyes, would calmly pronounce his name "Tahar"—which, I learned very early, meant "The Pure"—and even when a suspicion of a smile flickered across the other women's faces or they looked half ill at ease, half indulgent, I thought that a rare distinction lit up my mother's face.

imperceptible:
unobservable;
unperceivable

These harem conversations ran their **imperceptible** course: my ears only caught those phrases which singled my mother out above the rest. Because she always made a point of bringing my father's name into these exchanges, he became for me still purer than his given name **betokened**.

betokened:
indicated;
showed

portent:
sign;
forewarning;
presage

One day something occurred which was a **portent** that their relationship would never be the same again—a commonplace enough event in any other society, but which was unusual to say the least with us: in the course of an exceptionally long journey away from home (to a neighboring province, I think), my father wrote to my mother—yes, to my mother!

He sent her a postcard, with a short greeting written diagonally across it in his large, legible handwriting, something like "Best wishes from this distant region" or possibly, "I am having a good journey and getting to know an unfamiliar region," etc. and he signed it simply with his first name. I am sure that, at the time, he himself would not have dared add any more intimate formula above his signature, such as "I am thinking of you," or even less, "Yours affectionately." But, on the half of the card reserved for the address of the recipient, he had written "Madame" followed by his own surname, with the possible addition—but here I'm not sure—"and children," that is to say we three, of whom I, then about ten years old, was the eldest . . .

The radical change in customs was apparent for all to see: my father had quite brazenly written his wife's name, in his own handwriting, on a postcard which was going to travel from one town to another, which was going to be exposed to so many masculine eyes, including eventually our village postman—a Muslim postman to boot—and, what is more, he had dared to refer to her in the western manner as "Madame So-and-So . . . ," whereas, no local man, poor or rich, ever referred to his wife and children in any other way than by the vague periphrasis: "the household."

So, my father had "written" to my mother. When she visited her family she mentioned this postcard, in the simplest possible words and tone of voice, to be sure. She was about to describe her husband's four or five days' absence from the village, explaining the practical problems this had posed:

my father having to order the provisions just before he left, so that the shopkeepers could deliver them every morning; she was going to explain how hard it was for a city woman to be isolated in a village with very young children and cut off in this way . . . . But the other women had interrupted, exclaiming, in the face of this new reality, this almost incredible detail:

"He wrote to you, *to you*?"

"He wrote his wife's name and the postman must have read it? Shame! . . . "

"He could at least have addressed the card to his son, for the principle of the thing, even if his son is only seven or eight!"

My mother did not reply. She was probably pleased, flattered even, but she said nothing. Perhaps she was suddenly ill at ease, or blushing from embarrassment; yes, her husband had written to her, in person! . . . The eldest child, the only one who might have been able to read the card, was her daughter: so, daughter or wife, where was the difference as far as the addressee was concerned?

"I must remind you that I've learned to read French now!"

This postcard was, in fact, a most daring manifestation of affection. Her modesty suffered at that very moment that she spoke of it. Yet, it came second to her pride as a wife, which was secretly flattered.

The murmured exchanges of these segregated women struck a faint chord with me, as a little girl with observing eyes. And so, for the first time, I seem to have some intuition of the possible happiness, the mystery in the union of a man and a woman.

My father had dared "to write" to my mother. Both of them referred to each other by name, which was **tantamount** to declaring openly their love for each other, my father by writing to her, my mother by quoting my father henceforward without false shame in all her conversations.

tantamount: equal; equivalent

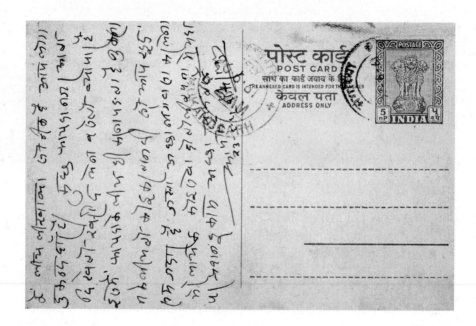

After You Read

Critical Reading

1. Consider the **character** of the narrator's mother. The story states that the mother had begun to learn "a little French" (page 409) and that her "French improved" as the "years went by" (page 409). Analyze the significance of the narrator's mother learning to speak French. Support your inference with details from the story.

2. The narrator notices how the mother's way of referring to the father changes. Identify the various ways the mother refers to the father, and then consider what this reveals about the character of the mother.

3. An **internal conflict** exists within a character, and an **external conflict** exists between a character and another character or an outer force. Identify an internal conflict and external conflict in the story. How do these conflicts advance the plot?

Literary Lens: Setting

The **setting** can be very significant to the meaning of the story. To an extent, the setting can even sometimes be considered akin to a **foil**, used to reveal the characters. Re-create the graphic organizer below and identify details about the setting of the story, the village in Algeria. Then describe how the setting reveals the characters, such as the narrator, the mother, the father, and/or the other women in the village.

Details about the setting	What this reveals about the narrator, her mother, her father, or women in the village

Focus on Research: Develop a Thesis Statement

Briefly research the topic of female heads of state from Muslim countries. Then develop a thesis statement that clearly presents a topic and a claim or point of view. Your thesis statement can be one to three sentences in length. In it, you should clearly state the topic (female heads of state in Muslim countries) and your point of view on the topic.

The Literature of
Egypt

Background

With a recorded history of more than 5,000 years, Egypt is one of the oldest countries on earth. It also has one of the world's longest literary traditions. Perhaps the greatest work of ancient Egyptian literature is The Tale of Sinuhe, a story set in the 20th century B.C.E. The title character flees Egypt after the assassination of his king, lives in exile in Syria where he gains political power, and finally returns to die in his home country.

The Tale of Sinuhe was retold by the Egyptian Nobel Prize-winning author Naguib Mahfouz (1911–2006) in his short story "The Return of Sinuhe." Mahfouz was one of many renowned Arabic-language writers that Egypt produced during the 20th century. Others include Tawfiq el-Hakim (1898–1987), who advanced Arabic drama with such plays as The People of the Cave; and Yahya Haqqi (1905–1992), who explored the impact of the West on Arabic life in his novella The Lamp of Umm Hashim.

Egypt and the United States

Beginning in December 2010, a series of anti-government protests rocked Tunisia, Morocco, Syria, Libya, Bahrain, and Egypt. Hundreds of protesters posted on social media, allowing Americans to watch the events unfold in real time. Authoritarian President Hosni Mubarak was ousted, and a new president was elected. However, according to Human Rights Watch, the new government continues to abuse human rights, arresting protesters and activists who criticize the current government.

The turbulent political situation has produced a new wave of dystopian and surrealistic fiction from writers dealing with the despair of the unending cycle of violence and repression. One Egyptian editor said, "These futuristic stories are all about lost utopia.... People really could imagine a better future, and now it's almost worse than it was before." Other writers, such as Ahdaf Soueif and Mona Prince, wrote firsthand nonfiction accounts of the 2011 protests.

Research: Summarize Findings

Until the discovery of the Rosetta Stone in 1799, scholars were unable to read the ancient Egyptian writing system known as hieroglyphics. Using print or online sources, research how the Rosetta Stone was used to understand Egyptian hieroglyphs. Write a paragraph summarizing what your research uncovered.

Another Evening at the Club

Alifa Rifaat

Before You Read

Alifa Rifaat (1930–1996) was born in rural Egypt. Instead of being allowed to go to a university, she was married off to her cousin. Nevertheless, Rifaat continued reading and educating herself. She began writing short stories criticizing the restrictions on women in her culture. When a few of her stories were published, they were very controversial, and her husband demanded that she stop writing. When she became a widow in 1974, Rifaat published 18 stories she had kept hidden. She became one of Egypt's most highly regarded authors.

World Context

Many of Rifaat's stories address the oppression of women. Rifaat believes that the oppression results from misinterpreting the Islamic holy book, the Koran.

LITERARY LENS Tone is the author's attitude toward the topic of a text. As you read, look for descriptions, imagery, and conflicts that reveal Rifaat's attitude toward the events in the story.

In a state of tension, she awaited the return of her husband. At a loss to predict what would happen between them, she moved herself back and forth in the rocking chair on the wide wooden verandah that ran along the bank and occupied part of the river itself, its supports being fixed in the river bed, while around it grew grasses and reeds. As though to banish her apprehension, she passed her fingers across her hair. The spectres of the eucalyptus trees ranged along the garden fence rocked before her gaze, with white egrets[1] slumbering on their high branches like huge white flowers among the thin leaves.

---

1 **egrets:** herons, water-loving birds with long necks and legs

The crescent moon rose from behind the eastern mountains and the peaks of the gently stirring waves glistened in its feeble rays, intermingled with threads of light leaking from the houses of Manfalout scattered along the opposite bank. The coloured bulbs fixed to the trees in the garden of the club at the far end of the town stood out against the surrounding darkness. Somewhere over there her husband now sat, most likely engrossed in a game of chess.

It was only a few years ago that she had first laid eyes on him at her father's house, meeting his gaze that weighed up her beauty and priced it before offering the dowry.[2] She had noted his eyes ranging over her as she presented him with the coffee in the Japanese cups that were kept safely locked away in the cupboard for important guests. Her mother had herself laid them out on the silver-plated tray with its elaborately embroidered spread. When the two men had taken their coffee, her father had looked up at her with a smile and had told her to sit down, and she had seated herself on the sofa facing them, drawing the end of her dress over her knees and looking through lowered lids at the man who might choose her as his wife. She had been glad to see that he was tall, well-built and clean-shaven except for a thin greying moustache. In particular she noticed the well-cut coat of English tweed and the silk shirt with gold links. She had felt herself blushing as she saw him returning her gaze. Then the man turned to her father and took out a gold case and offered him a cigarette.

"You really shouldn't, my dear sir," said her father, patting his chest with his left hand and extracting a cigarette with trembling fingers. Before he could bring out his box of matches Abboud Bey had produced his lighter.

"No, after you, my dear sir," said her father in embarrassment. Mingled with her sense of excitement at this man who gave out such an air of worldly self-confidence was guilty shame at her father's inadequacy.

After lighting her father's cigarette Abboud Bey sat back, crossing his legs, and took out a cigarette for himself. He tapped it against the case before putting it in the corner of his mouth and lighting it, then blew out circles of smoke that followed each other across the room.

"It's a great honour for us, my son," said her father, smiling first at Abboud Bey, then at his daughter, at which Abboud Bey looked across at her and asked:

"And the beautiful little girl's still at secondary school?"

She lowered her head modestly and her father had answered:

"As from today she'll be staying at home in readiness for your happy life together, Allah[3] permitting," and at a glance from her father she had hurried off to join her mother in the kitchen.

---

2 **dowry:** the gift or payment a man pays to his bride's family
3 **Allah:** the Muslim religion's Supreme Being

"You're a lucky girl," her mother had told her. "He's a real find. Any girl would be happy to have him. He's an Inspector of Irrigation though he's not yet forty. He earns a big salary and gets a fully furnished government house wherever he's posted, which will save us the expense of setting up a house—and I don't have to tell you what our situation is—and that's besides the house he owns in Alexandria where you'll be spending your holidays."

Samia had wondered to herself how such a splendid suitor had found his way to her door. Who had told him that Mr. Mahmoud Barakat, a mere clerk at the Court of Appeal, had a beautiful daughter of good reputation?

The days were then taken up with going the rounds of Cairo's shops and choosing clothes for the new grand life she would be living. This was made possible by her father borrowing on the security of his government pension.

Abboud Bey, on his part, never visited her without bringing a present. For her birthday, just before they were married, he bought her an emerald ring that came in a plush box bearing the name of a well-known jeweller in Kasr el-Nil Street. On her wedding night, as he put a diamond bracelet round her wrist, he had reminded her that she was marrying someone with a brilliant career in front of him and that one of the most important things in life was the opinion of others, particularly one's equals and seniors. Though she was still only a young girl she must try to act with suitable dignity.

. . . one of the most important things in life was the opinion of others, particularly one's equals and seniors.

"Tell people you're from the well-known Barakat family and that your father was a judge," and he went up to her and gently patted her cheeks in a fatherly, reassuring gesture that he was often to repeat during their times together.

Then, yesterday evening, she had returned from the club somewhat light-headed from the bottle of beer she had been required to drink on the occasion of someone's birthday. Her husband, noting the state she was in, hurriedly took her back home. She had undressed and put on her nightgown, leaving her jewellery on the dressing-table, and was fast asleep seconds after getting into bed. The following morning, fully recovered, she slept late, then rang the bell as usual and had breakfast brought to her. It was only as she was putting her jewellery away in the wooden and mother-of-pearl box that she realized her emerald ring was missing.

Could it have dropped from her finger at the club? In the car on the way back? No, she distinctly remembered it last thing at night, remembered the usual difficulty she had in getting it off her finger. She stripped the bed of its sheets, turned over the mattress, looked inside the pillow cases, crawled on hands and knees under the bed. The tray of breakfast lying on the small bedside table caught her eye and she remembered the young servant coming in that morning with it, remembered the noise of the tray being put down, the curtains being drawn, the tray then being lifted up again and placed on the bedside table. No one but the servant had entered the room. Should she call her and question her?

Eventually, having taken two aspirins, she decided to do nothing and await the return of her husband from work.

Directly after he arrived she told him what had happened and he took her by the arm and seated her down beside him:

"Let's just calm down and go over what happened."

She repeated, this time with further details, the whole story.

"And you've looked for it?"

"Everywhere. Every possible and impossible place in the bedroom and the bathroom. You see, I remember distinctly taking it off last night."

He grimaced at the thought of last night, then said:

"Anybody been in the room since Gazia when she brought in the breakfast?"

"Not a soul. I've even told Gazia not to do the room today."

"And you've not mentioned anything to her?"

"I thought I'd better leave it to you."

"Fine, go and tell her I want to speak to her. There's no point in your saying anything but I think it would be as well if you were present when I talk to her."

Five minutes later Gazia, the young servant girl they had recently employed, entered behind her mistress. Samia took herself to a far corner of the room while Gazia stood in front of Abboud Bey, her hands folded across her chest, her eyes lowered.

"Yes, sir?"

"Where's the ring?"

"What ring are you talking about, sir?"

"Now don't make out you don't know. The one with the green stone. It would be better for you if you hand it over and then nothing more need be said."

"May Allah blind me if I've set eyes on it."

He stood up and gave her a sudden slap on the face. The girl reeled back, put one hand to her cheek, then lowered it again to her chest and made no answer to any of Abboud's questions. Finally he said to her:

"You've got just fifteen seconds to say where you've hidden the ring or else, I swear to you, you're not going to have a good time of it."

As he lifted up his arm to look at his watch the girl flinched slightly but continued in her silence. When he went to the telephone Samia raised her head and saw that the girl's cheeks were wet with tears. Abboud Bey got through to the Superintendent of Police and told him briefly what had occurred.

"Of course I haven't got any actual proof but seeing that no one else entered the room, it's obvious she's pinched it. Anyway I'll leave the matter in your capable hands—I know your people have their ways and means."

He gave a short laugh, then listened for a while and said: "I'm really most grateful to you."

He put down the receiver and turned round to Samia:

"That's it, my dear. There's nothing more to worry about. The Superintendent has promised me we'll get it back. The patrol car's on the way."

• • • • •

The following day, in the late afternoon, she'd been sitting in front of her dressing-table rearranging her jewellery in its box when an earring slipped from her grasp and fell to the floor. As she bent to pick it up she saw the emerald ring stuck between the leg of the table and the wall. Since that moment she had sat in a state of panic awaiting her husband's return from the club. She even felt tempted to walk down to the water's edge and throw it into the river so as to be rid of the unpleasantness that lay ahead.

At the sound of the screech of tyres rounding the house to the garage, she slipped the ring onto her finger. As he entered she stood up and raised her hand to show him the ring. Quickly, trying to choose her words but knowing that she was expressing herself clumsily, she explained what an extraordinary thing it was that it should have lodged itself between the dressing-table and the wall, what an extraordinary coincidence she should have dropped the earring and so seen it, how she'd thought of ringing him at the club to tell him the good news but . . .

She stopped in mid-sentence when she saw his frown and added weakly: "I'm sorry. I can't think how it could have happened. What do we do now?"

He shrugged his shoulders as though in surprise.

"Are you asking me, my dear lady? Nothing of course."

"But they've been beating up the girl—you yourself said they'd not let her be till she confessed."

Unhurriedly, he sat himself down as though to consider this new aspect of the matter. Taking out his case, he tapped a cigarette against it in his accustomed manner, then moistened his lips, put the cigarette in place and lit it. The smoke rings hovered in the still air as he looked at his watch and said:

"In any case she's not got all that long before they let her go. They can't keep her for more than forty-eight hours without getting any evidence or a confession. It won't kill her to put up with things for a while longer. By now the whole town knows the servant stole the ring—or would you like me to tell everyone: 'Look, folks, the fact is that the wife got a bit tiddly on a couple of sips of beer and the ring took off on its own and hid itself behind the dressing-table'? What do you think?"

"I know the situation's a bit awkward . . . "

"Awkward? It's downright ludicrous. Listen, there's nothing to be done but to give it to me and the next time I go down to Cairo I'll sell it and get something else in its place. We'd be the laughingstock of the town."

He stretched out his hand and she found herself taking off the ring and placing it in the outstretched palm. She was careful that their eyes should not meet. For a moment she was on the point of protesting and in fact uttered a few words:

"I'd just like to say we could . . . "

Putting the ring away in his pocket, he bent over her and with both hands gently patted her on the cheeks. It was a gesture she had long become used to, a gesture that promised her continued security, that told her that this man who was her husband and the father of her child had also taken the place of her father who, as though assured that he had found her a suitable substitute, had followed up her marriage with his own funeral. The gesture told her more eloquently than any words that he was the man, she the woman, he the one who carried the responsibilities, made the decisions, she the one whose role it was to be beautiful, happy, carefree. Now, though, for the first time in their life together the gesture came like a slap in the face.

Directly he removed his hands her whole body was seized with an uncontrollable trembling. Frightened he would notice, she rose to her feet and walked with deliberate steps towards the large window. She leaned her forehead against the comforting cold surface and closed her eyes tightly for several seconds. When she opened them she noticed that the café lights strung between the trees on the opposite shore had been turned on and that there were men seated under them and a waiter moving among the tables. The dark shape of a boat momentarily blocked out the café scene; in the light from the hurricane lamp hanging from its bow she saw it cutting through several of those floating islands of Nile waterlilies that, rootless, are swept along with the current.

Suddenly she became aware of his presence alongside her.

"Why don't you go and change quickly while I take the car out? It's hot and it would be nice to have supper at the club."

"As you like. Why not?"

By the time she had turned round from the window she was smiling.

Translated by Denys Johnson-Davies

After You Read

Critical Reading

1. On page 421, Abboud's familiar gesture of patting Samia's cheek feels "like a slap in the face." What do you think caused this change for Samia?

2. Near the end of the story, Samia places the ring in "the outstretched palm" of Abboud. Analyze this scene. Of what other scene in the story does this remind you? What effect does this have on the reader?

3. Why do you think Samia is smiling in the last sentence of the story? What does this reveal about her **character**?

Literary Lens: Tone

This story provides many details about the treatment of women and people of different economic levels. Analyze the author's **word choice**, and consider how this word choice reveals the author's **tone**, or point of view, toward these topics.

Quotation	What this reveals about the author's point of view	Briefly describe the author's tone

Focus on Research: Use Book Reviews

When conducting research, you can use many different types of sources, including book reviews. Find several book reviews of Alifa Rifaat's short story collection, *Distant View of a Minaret*. Conduct research by reading these book reviews. As you read, look for details in the reviews to determine if the theme of the treatment of women is common in many of Alifa Rifaat's short stories and how her stories were received in Egypt and other countries.

The Happy Man

Naguib Mahfouz

Before You Read

Naguib Mahfouz (1911–2006) began writing at age 17. Although his earliest works were set in ancient Egypt, they often commented on modern society. His later and more mystical works often rely on allegory and symbolism to make political statements. His novel *Children of Gebelawi* was serialized in an Egyptian newspaper in 1959. This story about the search for spiritual values, with characters resembling Adam and Eve, Moses, Jesus, and Muhammad, caused such an uproar that its publication as a book was banned in Egypt. In 1988, Mahfouz won the Nobel Prize.

World Context

Mahfouz's fiction documents the vast changes in Egypt during the 1900s, focusing on social and philosophical concerns.

 LITERARY LENS Satire uses humor to expose human foibles. What aspects of society does this story expose?

He woke up in the morning and discovered that he was happy. "What's this?" he asked himself. He could not think of any word which described his state of mind more accurately and precisely than happy. This was distinctly peculiar when compared with the state he was usually in when he woke up. He would be half-asleep from staying so late at the newspaper office. He would face life with a sense of strain and contemplation. Then he would get up, whetting his determination to face up to all inconveniences and withstand all difficulties.

Today he felt happy, full of happiness, as a matter of fact. There was no arguing about it. The symptoms were quite clear, and their vigor and obviousness were such as to impose themselves on his senses and mind all at once. Yes, indeed; he was happy. If this was not happiness, then what was? He felt that his limbs were well proportioned and functioning perfectly. They were working in superb harmony with each other and with the world around him. Inside him, he felt a boundless power, an **imperishable** energy, an ability to achieve anything with confidence, precision, and obvious success. His heart was overflowing with love for people, animals, and things and with an all-engulfing sense of optimism and joy. It was as if he were no longer troubled or bothered by fear, anxiety, sickness, death, argument, or the question of earning a living. Even more important than that, and something he could not analyze, it was a feeling which penetrated to every cell of his body and soul; it played a tune full of delight, pleasure, serenity, and peace and hummed in its incredible melodies the whispering sound of the world which is denied to the unhappy.

imperishable: enduring; unending

He felt drunk with ecstasy and savored it slowly with a feeling of surprise. He asked himself where it had come from and how; the past provided no explanation, and the future could not justify it. Where did it come from, then, and how? How long would it last? Would it stay with him till breakfast? Would it give him enough time to get to the newspaper office? Just a minute though, he thought . . . it won't last because it can't. If it did, man would be turned into an angel or something even higher. So he told himself that he should devote his attention to savoring it, living with it, and storing up its nectar before it became a mere memory with no way of proving it or even being sure that it had ever existed.

> It was as if he were no longer troubled or bothered by fear, anxiety, sickness, death, argument, or the question of earning a living.

He ate his breakfast with relish, and this time nothing distracted his attention while he was eating. He gave "Uncle" Bashir, who was waiting on him, such a beaming smile that the poor man felt rather alarmed and taken aback. Usually he would only look in his direction to give orders or ask questions, although on most occasions he treated him fairly well.

"Tell me, Uncle Bashir," he asked the servant, "am I a happy man?"

The poor man was startled. He realized why his servant was confused; for the first time ever he was talking to him as a colleague or friend. He encouraged his servant to forget about his worries and asked him with unusual insistence to answer his question.

"Through God's grace and favor, you are happy," the servant replied.

"You mean, I should be happy. Anyone with my job, living in my house, and enjoying my health should be happy. That's what you want to say. But do you think I'm really happy?"

The servant replied, "You work too hard, Sir"; after yet more insistence, "It's more than any man can stand . . . ."

He hesitated, but his master gestured to him to continue with what he had to say.

"You get angry a lot," he said, "and have fierce arguments with your neighbors . . . ."

He interrupted him by laughing loudly. "What about you," he asked, "don't you have any worries?"

"Of course, no man can be free of worry."

"You mean that complete happiness is an impossible quest?"

"That applies to life in general . . . ."

How could he have dreamed up this incredible happiness? He or any other human being? It was a strange, unique happiness, as though it were a private secret he had been given. In the meeting hall of the newspaper building, he spotted his main rival in this world sitting down thumbing through a magazine. The man heard his footsteps but did not look up from the magazine. He had undoubtedly noticed him in some way and was therefore pretending to ignore him so as to keep his own peace of mind. At some circulation meetings, they would argue so violently with each other that sparks would begin to fly and they would exchange bitter words. One stage more, and they would come to blows. A week ago, his rival had won in the union elections and he had lost. He had felt pierced by a sharp, poisoned arrow, and the world had darkened before his eyes. Now here he was approaching his rival's seat; the sight of him sitting there did not make him excited, nor did the memories of their dispute spoil his composure. He approached him with a pure and carefree heart, feeling drunk with his incredible happiness; his face showed an expression full of tolerance and forgiveness. It was as though he were approaching some other man toward whom he had never had any feelings of **enmity**, or perhaps he might be renewing a friendship again. "Good morning!" he said without feeling any **compunction**.

The man looked up in amazement. He was silent for a few moments until he recovered, and then returned the greeting curtly. It was as though he did not believe his eyes and ears.

He sat down alongside the man. "Marvelous weather today . . . ," he said.

"Okay . . . ,"the other replied guardedly.

"Weather to fill your heart with happiness."

His rival looked at him closely and cautiously. "I'm glad that you're so happy . . . ," he muttered.

"**Inconceivably** happy . . . ," he replied with a laugh.

enmity:
hostility;
antagonism

compunction:
qualm;
misgiving

inconceivably:
unimaginably;
unbelievably

"I hope," the man continued in a rather hesitant tone of voice, "that I shan't spoil your happiness at the meeting of the administrative council . . . ."

"Not at all. My views are well known, but I don't mind if the members adopt your point of view. That won't spoil my happiness!"

"You've changed a great deal overnight," the man said with a smile.

"The fact is that I'm happy, inconceivably happy."

The man examined his face carefully. "I bet your dear son has changed his mind about staying in Canada?" he asked.

"Never, never, my friend," he replied, laughing loudly. "He is still sticking to his decision . . . ."

"But that was the principal reason for your being so sad . . . ."

"Quite true. I've often begged him to come back out of pity for me in my loneliness and to serve his country. But he told me that he's going to open an engineering office with a Canadian partner; in fact, he's invited me to join him in it. Let him live where he'll be happy. I'm quite happy here—as you can see, inconceivably happy . . . ."

The man still looked a little doubtful. "Quite extraordinarily brave!" he said.

"I don't know what it is, but I'm happy in the full meaning of the word."

Yes indeed, this was full happiness; full, firm, weighty, and vital. As deep as absolute power, widespread as the wind, fierce as fire, bewitching as scent, **transcending** nature. It could not possibly last.

The other man warmed to his display of affection. "The truth is," he said, "that I always picture you as someone with a fierce and violent temperament which causes him a good deal of trouble and leads him to trouble other people."

"Really?"

"You don't know how to make a truce, you've no concept of intermediate solutions. You work with your nerves, with the marrow in your bones. You fight bitterly, as though any problem is a matter of life and death!"

"Yes, that's true."

He accepted the criticism without any difficulty and with an open heart. His wave expanded into a boundless ocean of happiness. He struggled to control an innocent, happy laugh which the other man interpreted in a way far removed from its pure motives.

"So then," he asked, "you think it's necessary to be able to take a balanced view of events, do you?"

"Of course. I remember, by way of example, the argument we had the day before yesterday about racism. We both had the same views on the

transcending: surpassing; rising above

subject; it's something worth being zealous about, even to the point of anger. But what kind of anger? An intellectual anger, abstract to a certain extent; not the type which shatters your nerves, ruins your digestion, and gives you **palpitations**. Not so?"

"That's obvious; I quite understand . . . ." He struggled to control a second laugh and succeeded. His heart refused to renounce one drop of its joy. Racism, Vietnam, Palestine[1] . . . . no problem could assail that fortress of happiness which was encircling his heart. When he remembered a problem, his heart **guffawed**. He was happy. It was a **tyrannical** happiness, despising all misery and laughing at any hardship; it wanted to laugh, dance, sing, and distribute its spirit of laughter, dancing, and singing among the various problems of the world.

He could not bear to stay in his office at the newspaper; he felt no desire to work at all. He hated the very idea of thinking about his daily business and completely failed to bring his mind down from its stronghold in the kingdom of happiness. How could he possibly write about a trolley bus falling into the Nile when he was so intoxicated by this frightening happiness? Yes, it really was frightening. How could it be anything else, when there was no reason for it at all, when it was so strong that it made him exhausted and paralyzed his will—apart from the fact that it had been with him for half a day without letting up in the slightest degree?

He left the pages of paper blank and started walking backwards and forwards across the room, laughing and cracking his fingers . . . .

He felt slightly worried; it did not penetrate deep enough to spoil his happiness but paused on the surface of his mind like an abstract idea. It occurred to him that he might recall the tragedies of his life so that he could test their effect on his happiness. Perhaps they would be able to bring back some idea of balance or security, at least until his happiness began to flag a little. For example, he remembered his wife's death in all its various aspects and details. What had happened? The event appeared to him as a series of movements without any meaning or effect, as though it had happened to some other woman, the wife of another man, in some distant historical age. In fact, it had a contagious effect which prompted a smile and then even provoked laughter. He could not stop himself laughing, and there he was guffawing, ha . . . ha . . . ha!

The same thing happened when he remembered the first letter his son had sent him saying that he wanted to emigrate to Canada. The sound of his guffaws as he paraded the bloody tragedies of the world before him

palpitations: rapid heartbeats

guffawed: laughed; burst into laughter

tyrannical: controlling; dictatorial

---

1 **Racism, Vietnam, Palestine:** conflicts with long histories of violence and injustice

would have attracted the attention of the newspaper workers and passersby in the street had it not been for the thickness of the walls. He could do nothing to dislodge his happiness. Memories of unhappy times hit him like waves being thrown onto a sandy beach under the golden rays of the sun.

He excused himself from attending the administrative council and left the newspaper office without writing a word. After lunch, he lay down on his bed as usual but could not sleep. In fact, sleep seemed an impossibility to him. Nothing gave him any indication that it was coming, even slowly. He was in a place alight and gleaming, resounding with sleeplessness and joy. He had to calm down and relax, to quiet his senses and limbs, but how could he do it? He gave up trying to sleep and got up. He began to hum as he was walking around his house. If this keeps up, he told himself, I won't be able to sleep, just as I can't work or feel sad. It was almost time for him to go to the club, but he did not feel like meeting any friends. What was the point of exchanging views on public affairs and private worries? What would they think if they found him laughing at every major problem? What would they say? How would they picture things? How would they explain it? No, he did not need anyone, nor did he want to spend the evening talking. He should be by himself and go for a long walk to get rid of some of his excess vitality and think about his situation. What had happened to him? How was it that this incredible happiness had overwhelmed him? How long would he have to carry it on his shoulders? Would it keep depriving him of work, friends, sleep and peace of mind? Should he resign himself to it? Should he abandon himself to the flood to play with him as the whim took it? Or should he look for a way out for himself through thought, action, or advice?

· · · · ·

When he was called into the examination room in the clinic of his friend, the specialist in internal medicine, he felt a little alarmed. The doctor looked at him with a smile. "You don't look like someone who's complaining about being ill," he said.

"I haven't come to see you because I'm ill," he told the doctor in a hesitant tone of voice, "but because I'm happy!"

The doctor looked piercingly at him with a questioning air.

"Yes," he repeated to underline what he had said, "because I'm happy!"

There was a period of silence. On one side there was anxiety, and on the other, questioning and amazement.

"It's an incredible feeling which can't be defined in any other way, but it's very serious . . . ."

The doctor laughed. "I wish your illness was contagious," he said, prodding him jokingly.

"Don't treat it as a joke. It's very serious, as I told you. I'll describe it to you . . . ."

He told him all about his happiness from the time he had woken up in the morning till he had felt compelled to visit him.

"Haven't you been taking drugs, alcohol, or tranquilizers?"

"Absolutely nothing like that."

"Have you had some success in an important sphere of your life—work . . . love . . . money?"

"Nothing like that either. I've twice as much to worry about as I have to make me feel glad . . . ."

"Perhaps if you were patient for a while . . . ."

"I've been patient all day. I'm afraid I'll be spending the night wandering around . . . ."

The doctor gave him a precise, careful, and comprehensive examination and then shrugged his shoulders in despair. "You're a picture of health," he said.

"And so?"

"I could advise you to take a sleeping pill, but it would be better if you consulted a nerve specialist . . . ."

The examination was repeated in the nerve specialist's clinic with the selfsame precision, care, and comprehensiveness. "Your nerves are sound," the doctor told him. "They're in enviable condition!"

"Haven't you got a plausible explanation for my condition?" he asked hopefully.

"Consult a gland specialist!" the doctor replied, shaking his head.

The examination was conducted for a third time in the gland specialist's clinic with the same precision, care, and comprehensiveness. "I congratulate you!" the doctor told him. "Your glands are in good condition."

He laughed. He apologized for laughing, laughing as he did so. Laughter was his way of expressing his alarm and despair.

He left the clinic with the feeling that he was alone; alone in the hands of his tyrannical happiness with no helper, no guide, and no friend. Suddenly, he remembered the doctor's sign he sometimes saw from the window of his office in the newspaper building. It was true that he had no confidence in psychiatrists even though he had read about the significance

"The truth is, Doctor, that I've come to see you because I'm happy!"

tentacles:
feelers; long,
flexible
appendages

of psychoanalysis.[2] Apart from that, he knew that their **tentacles** were very long and they kept their patients tied in a sort of long association. He laughed as he remembered the method of cure through free association[3] and the problems which it eventually uncovers. He was laughing as his feet carried him toward the psychiatrist's clinic, and imagined the doctor listening to his incredible complaints about feeling happy, when he was used to hearing people complain about hysteria, schizophrenia,[4] anxiety, and so on.

"The truth is, Doctor, that I've come to see you because I'm happy!"

He looked at the doctor to see what effect his statement had had on him but noticed that he was keeping his composure. He felt ridiculous. "I'm inconceivably happy . . . ," he said in a tone of confidence.

debilitating:
weakening;
crippling

He began to tell the doctor his story, but the latter stopped him with a gesture of his hand. "An overwhelming, incredible, **debilitating** happiness?" he asked quietly.

He stared at him in amazement and was on the point of saying something, but the doctor spoke first. "A happiness which has made you stop working," he asked, "abandon your friends, and detest going to sleep? . . ."

"You're a miracle!" he shouted.

"Every time you get involved in some misfortune," the psychiatrist continued quietly, "you dissolve into laughter? . . ."

"Sir . . . are you familiar with the invisible?"

"No!" he said with a smile. "Nothing like that. But I get a similar case in my clinic at least once a week!"

"Is it an epidemic?" he asked.

"I didn't say that, and I wouldn't claim that it's been possible to analyze one case into its primary elements as yet."

"But is it a disease?"

"All the cases are still under treatment."

---

2 **psychoanalysis:** a kind of therapy in which a patient explores his or her unconscious psychological state

3 **free association:** the expression of one's thoughts without censorship in an attempt to reach one's unconscious

4 **schizophrenia:** a serious mental illness; a schizophrenic's sense of reality is severely distorted

"But are you satisfied without any doubt that they aren't natural cases? . . ."

"That's a necessary assumption for the job; there's only . . ."

"Have you noticed any of them to be deranged in . . . ," he asked anxiously, pointing to his head.

"Absolutely not," the doctor replied convincingly. "I assure you that they're all intelligent in every sense of the word . . . ."

The doctor thought for a moment. "We should have two sessions a week, I think," he said.

"Very well . . . ," he replied in resignation.

"There's no sense in getting alarmed or feeling sad . . . ."

Alarmed, sad? He smiled, and his smile kept on getting broader. A laugh slipped out, and before long, he was dissolving into laughter. He was determined to control himself, but his resistance collapsed completely. He started guffawing loudly . . . .

Translated by Akef Abadir and Roger Allen

After You Read

Critical Reading

1. Authors use the technique of **juxtaposition**, or placing two unusual or unexpected things side by side, as a way to express an idea, point of view, or worldview. Identify an example of juxtaposition in the story. What are the two unexpected things or events placed together? What do you think the author wanted to convey through this use of juxtaposition?

2. A **paradox** is a statement that might seem to be a contradiction but actually expresses a truth. On page 428, the man thinks about his happiness: "How long would he have to carry it on his shoulders?" Consider whether this statement is a paradox.

3. Summarize the **plot** of this story. Explain the impact the man's happiness has at each turn of the story's plot.

Literary Lens: Satire

The author uses **satire** in this short story to point out something true about the human experience. Consider two or more instances of satire. For each, describe what the satire is pointing out about the character of the happy man or about life in general. Re-create the chart below and fill it in to analyze the story's use of satire.

Example of satire	What this is pointing out about the happy man or the human experience in general

Focus on Research: Develop a Plan for Research

The ancient Egyptians held certain viewpoints about life and death. They viewed death not as an ending but as a beginning of a new life in an eternal paradise. Prepare to research the topic of ancient Egyptians' views on death by developing a research plan for writing a five-page research paper. Begin with the step of developing questions and end with the step of publishing your research paper. Write your plan and then compare it with a partner's plan. At which step(s) should you evaluate your plan and make adjustments?

The Literature of
Israel and Palestine

Background

Beginning in the mid-1800s, a movement grew among Jews in Europe called Zionism. The movement's goal was to create a Jewish state in the Mediterranean region of Palestine. This goal attracted increasing supporters after the Nazi Holocaust of World War II, during which six million Jews were murdered. As a result of Zionism and the Holocaust, the state of Israel was founded in 1948. Today, nearly three-fourths of the people in Israel are Jews, and almost one-fourth are Muslims. In addition, Israel controls several territories—East Jerusalem, the Golan Heights, the West Bank, and the Gaza Strip—that are predominantly Palestinian.

Since 1948, conflict between Jews and the Palestinians living in the region has dominated both the politics and the literature of this area. Two of the best-known writers who have focused on these difficult issues are Mahmoud Darwish (1941–2008) and David Grossman (1954–).

Israel, Palestine, and the United States

The United States has been intimately involved in the Israeli–Palestinian conflict since it began. The U.S. government has been a steady and strong supporter of Israel, but both Israeli and Palestinian writers have found large audiences in the United States. Writers, such as the late journalist and novelist Amos Oz (1939–2018), have achieved great success in both countries. Oz's attempts to balance his loyalty to the nation of Israel and his commitment to justice for the Palestinian Arabs who live in Palestinian regions controlled by Israel won him wide respect.

Research: Use a Primary Source

By the late 19th century, Hebrew had not been used as a spoken language for many centuries. The revival of spoken and literary Hebrew during the 20th century was unprecedented. Never before had a spoken language been resurrected after falling out of use for so long. Eliezer Ben-Yehuda (1858–1922) is generally credited as the driving force behind the revival of spoken Hebrew. Gather primary sources about Eliezer Ben-Yehuda. These primary sources could be excerpts from diaries or journals, autobiographies, photographs, audio recordings, and more.

An Arab Shepherd Is Searching for His Goat on Mount Zion

Yehuda Amichai

Before You Read

Yehuda Amichai (1924–2000) grew up in Palestine. During World War II, he fought with the Jewish Brigade of the British Army. He became a naturalized citizen of Israel when that nation was created in 1948, then fought again in the Arab-Israeli War the same year. Amichai has been called "the most widely translated Hebrew poet since King David." His books of poetry include *Songs of Jerusalem and Myself, Amen,* and *Even a Fist Was Once an Open Palm with Fingers.*

World Context

Having studied Hebrew literature and biblical texts at Hebrew University, Amichai is well placed to comment on conflicts between Arabs and Israelis. In the poem that follows, Amichai narrows the conflict to two men.

LITERARY LENS This poem contains multiple **allusions**, or references to artistic, literary, or historical events, words, or figures. How do these allusions add to readers' understanding of the poem?

An Arab shepherd is searching for his goat on Mount Zion[1]
and on the opposite mountain I am searching
for my little boy.

---

1   **Mount Zion:** a hill located in Jerusalem; in various religious texts, "Zion" is often used to mean the place where God dwells or a heavenly city; sometimes used as a reference to the city of Jerusalem, a city important to Judaism, Islam, and Christianity and claimed as the capital of both Israel and Palestine.

An Arab shepherd and a Jewish father
both in their temporary failure.   5
Our voices meet above the Sultan's Pool[2]
in the valley between us. Neither of us wants
the child or the goat to get caught in the wheels
of the terrible *Had Gadya*[3] machine.

Afterward we found them among the bushes   10
and our voices came back inside us, laughing and crying.
Searching for a goat or a son
has always been in the beginning
of a new religion in these mountains.

---

2 **Sultan's Pool:** a low-lying pool outside Jerusalem's famous walls

3 *Had Gadya*: Hebrew for "one kid;" a Passover poem that illustrates a chain of events in
   which a goat is bitten by a cat, which is bitten by a dog, and so forth. The poem is about the
   cycle of retribution.

An Arab Shepherd Is Searching for His Goat on Mount Zion

After You Read

Critical Reading

1. Consider the word "searching" in line 1. Compare and contrast the **connotation** and **denotation** of this word and how each reveals the meaning of the poem.

2. A **parable** is a story that is intended to express a principle, moral, or message. Do you think this poem could be considered a parable?

3. **Setting** is comprised of time and place. The poem offers several details about the place but few to no details about the time. Infer the author's motivation for doing this.

 Literary Lens: Allusion

There are three footnoted **allusions** in the poem. For each, cite the text, note what the allusion references, and then describe how this allusion develops the theme of the poem.

Allusion	What the allusion references	How the allusion develops the poem's theme

Focus on Research: Publish a Digital Presentation

The poem refers to a traditional Jewish poem or song called the *Had Gadya*. Gather three or more sources about the *Had Gadya*, including multimedia sources of the song's lyrics, video of performances of this song, and audio files. As a class or in small groups, review the multimedia sources about the *Had Gadya*. Discuss each source and describe how each added to your understanding of the *Had Gadya*. Create a digital presentation with links to the sources, share the presentation with your classmates, and publish it online.

The Swimming Contest

Benjamin Tammuz

Before You Read

In 1924, the family of young Benjamin Tammuz (1919–1989) moved from the Ukraine to Palestine. There, Tammuz eventually became a newspaper columnist and an author of novels and short stories. His fiction was often about the relationship between Arabs and Jews. In his earliest stories, Tammuz envisioned a utopian state where all could live in peace. Later, he wrote about the elusiveness of that dream. His novel *Orchard* is about half-brothers—one a Jew, the other an Arab. In his critically acclaimed novel *Minotau*, Tammuz contrasts the viewpoints of his characters to give a nuanced picture of the story's events.

World Context

Tammuz was involved in the Canaanite movement, which urged Israel to unite both Arabs and Jews in a nonreligious but Hebrew-speaking country. Critics charged that Tammuz's views were utopian.

 LITERARY LENS As you read, look for details that **foreshadow**, or give hints and clues about the ending of the story.

One hot summer's day many years ago I was sitting in the kitchen at home, staring out of the window. The chill of the red floor tiles seeped into my bare feet. With my elbows leaning on the oilcloth-covered table, I let my eyes stray outside. The rooms were pervaded by the afternoon stillness and I felt dreamily at peace.

Suddenly, galloping hoofbeats sounded down the road and a black Arab horse-cab—the kind that plied the roads before cars took over—came into view; it was like those cabs we used to hire to drive us to the Jaffa railway station when we travelled up to Jerusalem to spend Passover[1] with Grandmother.

The horses drew nearer and were reined in outside our house, and the Arab cabman alighted and knocked at our door. I jumped up to open it, and a musty smell filled the kitchen—a smell of horses and far-off places. The cabman's shoulders blocked out the light and prevented the **sultry** heat from forcing its way inside.

He handed me a letter. I glanced at it and saw it was in French, which I could not read. My mother entered and took the letter, and her face lit up. She asked the cabman in and placed a slice of cold watermelon and a fresh *pita*[2] on the table before him. Leaning his whip against the wall, the Arab thanked her for her kindness, sat down at the table, and began taking large bites out of the watermelon, filling the air with the smacking of his lips. My mother told me that the letter was from the old Arab woman who lived in the orange grove. She wrote that she was well again and her pains had left her, and that she had been cured by my mother's hands, which she kissed from afar. She also wrote that now that summer had come and she had heard our holidays would soon be coming round, she hoped my mother would be able to get away from her other patients and come with her son to stay at her house in the orange grove.

• • • • •

The sun was about to sink into the sea as we left the house and climbed into the cab. The cabman folded back the rounded leather hood, and as we sank into the deep, soft seat I was instantly overwhelmed by a sensation of travelling to distant parts. The Arab climbed onto his high perch, whistled to his horses, and flicked his whip in the air. The springs creaked, the seat sank and surged up again beneath us like an ocean swell, and a farewell whinny rose on the air. With a wrench of wheels the cab moved off, its rumble over the pitted road sounding like a joyful melody.

Before long we had left the Hassan-Beq Mosque behind and were plunging through the alleyways of the Manshieh quarter.[3] Smells of cooking assailed our nostrils: waves of *za'tr*,[4] of roast mutton, of fried aubergine[5]

---

1 **Passover:** the Jewish holiday in spring that commemorates the exodus of the Jews from Egypt, led by Moses

2 *pita:* Middle Eastern pocket bread

3 **quarter:** an urban district

4 *za'tr:* a spice combination of thyme, sesame seeds, and ground sumac

5 **aubergine:** eggplant

and mint-spiced salad washed over us in turn. The cabman's voice filled the air, sounding warnings right and left, coaxing street-hawkers to move out of our path, bawling at the **urchins** who squatted in the middle of the road. The horses trotted in a lively, unbroken rhythm, their brown shiny rumps swaying from side to side. The horse on the right, without breaking his stride, pricked up his tail and dropped his dung. Turning around on his lofty seat, the cabman threw us an apologetic smile and remarked that horses were shameless ill-bred creatures and we must excuse them.

We jogged along pleasurably and restfully in our seats till the city lay behind us and the horses were drawing the cab laboriously along a track of reddish sand lined with hedgerows of cactus and acacia. Waves of heat rose from the sand, settling beside us onto the cool seat. The sun must already have dipped into the sea, for beyond the orange groves the skies glowed crimson and a chilly dusk descended all around. Suddenly the horses stopped and made water on the sand in unison.

Again the cab lurched forward. A quiver rippled the horses' hides as their hooves struck a stretch of limestone-paved road, lined by cypresses on either side. Before us stood an archway of whitewashed stone, enclosing a large, closed wooden gate with a small wicket set in it. Near the wicket stood a girl of about my age, wearing a white frock and a pink ribbon in her hair. As the cab drew up at the gate she bolted inside, and the cabman said, "We're there!"

• • • • •

You don't see such courtyards any more. And if you should happen to come to a place where there once was such a courtyard, you will only find a scene of wartime destruction: heaps of rubble and rafters, with cobwebs trying to impart an air of antiquity to what only yesterday still breathed and laughed.

But in those days the courtyard was in good repair and throbbing with life. It was square-shaped and enclosed on three sides by a two-storey building, with stables and barns occupying the lower storey. Black and red hens roamed about the yard, their clucking mingling with the neighing of horses. On the second floor was a pump-house, and next to it a pool-like reservoir into which water splashed from a pipe leading from the pump. Goldfish gathered near the outlet, darting among the bubbles created by the jet of water. A wooden parapet[6] railed in a long veranda that always lay in the shade. A coloured glass door led from the veranda into a central reception room, from which numerous doors opened onto the living rooms, the kitchen and the pantries.

---

6 **parapet:** a low protective barrier

In the center of the room stood a long table surrounded by upholstered armchairs. In anticipation of our arrival that day, their white linen dust-covers had been removed and lay folded in neat piles in a corner. Earthenware vases painted red and gold were arranged about the room; they contained large paper roses and lilies, some of them fashioned into strange, unflowerlike shapes. One vase, its paint long faded, had been brought there on the wedding day of the elderly mistress of the house.

From gilt wooden frames on the walls stared the portraits of sword-bearing men in fezes. The old lady led my mother up to one of the pictures and said, "My husband, may he rest in peace! His father built this house. Now we live here during the summer and go back to Jaffa for the winter."

With a sigh my mother replied, "My husband's no longer alive, either. But his house and his father's house aren't here; everything remained over there, abroad, and I live in a rented apartment summer and winter."

"That's because you are newcomers, immigrants," the old lady said. "But with the help of God you'll thrive and build yourselves houses. You're hard-working people and your hands are blessed."

"We are out for peace, not war."

My mother caught the hint and threw her a grateful look, but I blurted out: "But it's not true that we're driving the Arabs out. We are out for peace, not war."

Placing her hand on my head, the old lady said, "It all depends on the individual; everyone who wants peace will live in peace."

At that moment the young girl appeared in the doorway.

•••••

"Come over here, Nahida," the old lady said, "and kiss the hand of the *hakima*[7] who cured your grandmother. And this is her son."

Nahida came hesitantly into the room and stood in front of my mother. My mother embraced her and kissed her on the cheek, and a flush suffused the girl's dark complexion. She hung her head and remained silent.

"Our Nahida is shy," the old lady said, "but her heart is kind."

Hitching up her white skirt, Nahida sat down in an armchair. The rest of us sat down, too, as though permitted to do so now that the most honoured person among us was seated.

The old lady made a remark in French and my mother laughed. Again Nahida blushed and I noticed her eyeing me to see whether I understood French.

---

7 *hakima*: female doctor

"I don't understand a word," I told her. "What are they saying?"

"My grandmother says you and I would make a fine couple."

"Rubbish!" I answered and stared at the floor.

"You can go and play," the old woman said. "We're not keeping you."

I got up and followed Nahida out onto the veranda. We went and sat down at the edge of the pool.

"Do you believe in God?" I asked her. "Because I don't, not at all."

"I do, and I have a place in the grove where I go and pray. If we become friends, I'll take you there and I'll show you there's a God."

"Then you fast in the month of Ramadan?"[8] I asked. "I eat even on Yom Kippur."[9]

"I don't fast because I'm still too young. Do you rest on the Sabbath?"

"That depends," I answered. "I rest if I've got nothing else to do. Not because there's a God, but just if I feel like it."

"But I love God," Nahida said.

"Then we certainly won't make a couple unless you stop believing."

Nahida was about to make some retort when we heard the gate open, and two men entered the yard. Nahida leapt up and rushed over to them, throwing her arms around the neck of the older man, who wore a fez and European clothes.

"Daddy, we have visitors!" she cried.

"I know," her father replied. "The *hakima* has come to see us."

I stood up and waited for them to mount the steps to the pool. The second man, who wore a *keffiyeh*[10] and *agal*[11] and looked about eighteen, was Nahida's uncle, her father's brother. He came up first and held out his hand to greet me. Nahida's father patted my cheek and ushered me into the house.

We had supper out on the veranda. We were served large dishes of fried potatoes, sliced aubergine in tomato sauce and diced salted cheese, and a bowl of pomegranates and watermelons. There was a heap of hot *pitas* in the centre of the table.

Nahida's uncle—his name was Abdul-Karim—asked me if I was in the Haganah.[12] When I told him that was a secret, he laughed and said it was an open secret which the whole country knew about.

---

8 **Ramadan:** the Muslim holy days, a month of fasting during daylight hours

9 **Yom Kippur:** the Day of Atonement, a Jewish holiday on which believers fast and pray for forgiveness of their sins

10 *keffiyeh:* (also *kaffiyah*), an Arabic head covering

11 *agal:* the cord that holds the *keffiyeh* in place

12 **Haganah:** an underground military organization in Israel from 1920 to 1948

"Abdul-Karim is studying at the College of the Mufti," Nahida's father told us. "And he's in constant fear of your Haganah."

Abdul-Karim's face darkened and he kept silent; but the old lady, his mother, laid her hand on his arm and said, "My Abdul-Karim is a fine, loyal man. Don't you tease him."

Abdul-Karim kissed his mother's hand and said nothing. Just then, a shaggy sheepdog appeared on the veranda and wriggled under the table, butting against the tangle of legs as it looked for a spot to lie down. Finally it came to rest with its head on Nahida's feet and its tail on mine; it kept licking Nahida's feet, and its wagging tail tickled mine. The tickling made me smile and I turned to explain to Nahida why I was smiling, but when I saw she was taking my smile as a mark of friendship, I kept quiet.

When supper was over, Nahida's father said to his brother:

"Abdul-Karim my brother, go and show the children what you've brought from town."

Motioning to Nahida and myself to follow him, Abdul-Karim went into a toolshed in the orange grove and came out with a brand-new shotgun.

"We'll go hunting rabbits tomorrow," he said. "Know how to fire a gun?"

"A little," I told him. "We can have a shooting match if you like."

"We had a swimming match here in the pool last week," Nahida said, "and my uncle beat them all."

"I'll take you on at swimming too, if you like," I said.

"*Ahlan usahlan!*"[13] Abdul-Karim agreed. "Tomorrow morning, then. Now let's get back to the house and listen to some songs. We have a gramophone."

Back in the house, Abdul-Karim put on a record, wound the handle and adjusted the soundbox. The sound of a *kamanji*[14] and drum and cymbals issued forth, immediately followed by an Arab song, sung in a sweet **plaintive** voice, with delicate, floating trills. Abdul-Karim sprawled back contentedly in his armchair, his face beaming. When the record ended he put on another, though to me it seemed as though the same song was being played over again. This went on again and again till I got bored and slipped out to another room where my mother was chatting with the old lady. But that bored me too, so I went out to the veranda and gazed at the pool and the orange grove beyond. A large moon hung just above the treetops and a chill rose from the water in the pool. Some night bird was calling nearby, but stopped whenever the gramophone fell silent. As a yawn escaped me, I thought regretfully of my pals at home who were probably roasting

plaintive:
melancholy;
mournful

---

13 "*Ahlan usahlan!*": a traditional welcoming phrase in Arabic
14 *kamanji*: a banjo-like stringed instrument

potatoes on a fire under the electricity pylon,[15] having pilfered the wood from the nearby sausage factory. What had made me come here, I asked myself.

Nahida found a queer way of waking me up next morning. They had a fat, lazy cat in the house, which Nahida dropped onto my face while I was asleep. I leapt out of bed and flung the cat back into her lap. That was how we started our second day in the house in the orange grove. I was still brushing my teeth when Abdul-Karim came into the kitchen and said, "What about our swimming race?"

"I'm ready," I told him.

We hurried through breakfast, got into bathing trunks and went outside. My mother, the old lady, and Nahida's father had already drawn up chairs at the side of the pool to watch the race.

"Ready, steady . . . go!" Nahida called out, and Abdul-Karim and I dived in. Either because I was over-excited or I wasn't used to fresh water, I sank to the bottom like a stone, and by the time I had recovered sufficiently to surface Abdul-Karim was already halfway across. I saw my mother bending over the parapet and heard her calling out to me, "Don't be afraid! Swim fast!" I started swimming, but it was no use. By the time I reached the pipe leading from the pump-house, Abdul-Karim was already sitting on the parapet on the far side, squeezing the water out of his hair.

"You beat me in the pool," I told him. "But I'll take you on at anything else, if you want."

"At what?" he asked.

"Let's say at arithmetic."

"Why not?" he answered, and told Nahida to fetch some paper and pencils. When Nahida came back with them, I tore a sheet of paper into two halves, and on each I wrote down seven million, nine hundred and eighty-four thousand, six hundred and ninety-eight multiplied by four million, nine hundred and eighty-six thousand, seven hundred and fifty-nine.

"Let's see who figures that out first," I said.

Taking a pencil, Abdul-Karim started jotting down figures, and so did I. I was through before he was and handed my sheet to Nahida's father to check. It turned out I had made a mistake. Then Abdul-Karim handed over his paper and it turned out that he had gone wrong, too.

"Then let's have a general knowledge competition," I challenged Abdul-Karim. "For instance: who discovered America?"

---

15 **pylon:** steel tower carrying the electric lines

"Columbus," Abdul-Karim answered.

"Wrong!" I said. "It was Amerigo Vespucci, and that's why it's called America!"

"He beat you!" Nahida called to her uncle. "You see, he beat you!"

"He beat me in America," Abdul-Karim said, "but I beat him *right here*, in the pool."

"You wait till I'm grown up and then I'll beat you right here in the pool," I told him.

Nahida seemed about to nod her agreement, but thought better of it and looked at her uncle to see what he was going to answer to that.

"If he ever manages to beat me here in the pool," Abdul-Karim said, "it will be very bad indeed. It will be bad for you too, Nahida. Bad for all of us."

We didn't get his meaning and I wanted to tell him to cut out his philosophizing; but I didn't know how to say that in Arabic, so I kept quiet.

Later we went hunting rabbits in the orange grove.

II

Many years had gone by and summer had come round once again. Tired out after that year's work, I was looking for some place where I could take a fortnight's[16] rest. Packing a small valise, I traveled up to Jerusalem, only to find all the boarding houses full. Finally, wearied by rushing about the city, I boarded a bus bound for the Arab village of Ein Karem. As I took my seat, I started wondering what I would do there and what had made me go there of all places.

At the end of the main street stood a domed building, with a fountain gushing out from under its floor. Opposite, on a hillside that sloped up to the Russian monastery on its summit, in the shade of a clump of sycamores, some men sat on low wooden stools, sipping coffee and puffing at their *narghiles*.[17] I walked over and sat down on one of the stools, and when the waiter came over to take my order, I asked him if he knew of a family that would be willing to put me up for a couple of weeks.

"I don't know of one," the lad answered. "But maybe the owner does."

The café proprietor came over to have a look at me. "A family to put you up?" he said. "What for?"

"To take a rest," I answered. "I'm tired and I'm looking for somewhere to rest."

---

16 **fortnight's:** two weeks'

17 *narghiles:* hookahs, or water-pipes for smoking tobacco

"And how much are you willing to pay?" he asked.

"As much as I have to," I replied.

The proprietor sent the lad to the house of a certain Abu-Nimr. Before long he came back and said:

"Go up that way. Abu-Nimr is willing."

Picking up my valise, I trudged up the hillside, wondering all the time what had made me come to this place. I entered a courtyard and knocked at the door of the house indicated. A tall, bald Arab of about forty-five came out and said, "Welcome! Come right in."

I let him precede me down a long, cool passage and into a small room, almost entirely taken up by a tall, wide bed.

"If you like it, you're very welcome," Abu-Nimr said.

"It's very nice," I said. "How much will it cost?"

"I don't know. My wife will tell you that," he said and left the room.

I unpacked my valise and sat down on the bed, instantly sinking into the soft bedding, which billowed up to my elbows. There was a deep stillness all around, pervaded by the familiar smells of frying oil, mint leaves, black coffee, rosewater and cardamom seeds. I felt my face break into a smile as my ears strained to catch a sound that was missing in order to complete a dim, distant memory.

Suddenly I heard a tap turned on in the kitchen and the sound of gushing water made me hold my breath: water gushing from a pipe into a pool!

I got up and went out to the yard. There was no pool, not even orange trees; but there was something about the apple and plum trees, some quality of strangeness peculiar to an Arab homestead. It was obvious that the courtyard had not evolved all at once, that each generation had added something of its own. One man had planted the apple tree by the water tap, another the mulberry tree near the dog kennel, and in time the garden had sprouted up to tell its masters' life stories. I stood listening, my fantasy peopling the courtyard with Nahida and her grandmother, with Abdul-Karim, with the horse-cab that would suddenly draw to a halt outside the gate and the horses that would stand and urinate.

$$\bullet\bullet\bullet\bullet\bullet$$

That evening I was invited to join the family at supper, and Abu-Nimr introduced me to the people who sat round the table: his round-faced, bustling wife, who smiled into space without resting her eyes on me; his two sons, aged thirteen and fifteen, who attended high school in the city; his plump, white-skinned daughter, married to a policeman who was away from home all week, and who came home loaded with a wicker basket containing a trussed pigeon, apples from Betar, and a dozen eggs commandeered from some villager who happened to call at the police station.

The food that was served was no more than a continuation of that faraway supper in the orange grove. At that moment I realized what I had come there for.

After supper the strains of an Arab song rose from the gramophone. Abu-Nimr asked me whether I would care to show his boys how to operate the English typewriter he had bought in the city the day before. I sat down to instruct the lads, who set about their task with tremendous awe while their parents looked on, their hearts overflowing with pride. After a while their mother brought me a glass of cocoa and urged me to take a little rest. The gramophone was still playing, and as I sipped my drink Nahida's voice came back to me and Abdul-Karim's features formed themselves before my eyes, and out of the gloom in the passage there rose the sounds of my mother chatting with the old lady. It was then that I knew that I had been waiting all these years for just this moment, that I would relive our stay at the house in the orange grove.

·····

Again the years went by. We were in the grip of war with the Arabs. I was serving in a company that was lined up to storm Tel Arish, an Arab stronghold in the Jaffa dunes, east of the city.

We had launched an abortive attack there several weeks before which had cost us twenty-six men. This time we felt sure of success and looked forward to the battle as a fierce retaliation.

We set out from Holon at midnight, and soon began crawling in the direction of the Tel Arish buildings. The sand dunes afforded excellent cover, and we slipped across them effortlessly and soundlessly. A west wind carried the Jaffa smells over to us, but later the wind veered round behind us, from the new estates going up in Holon, breathing the smell of new, white houses on our backs. The sand beneath us surrendered the sun's warmth it had absorbed during the day, telling of the days of light we had known among the white houses, and **auguring** the liberty and joy that would again be ours once victory had been gained.

auguring: signifying; foretelling

·····

When the Arabs spotted us it was too late for them to do anything about it. We were already within grenade-range of their position, and we stormed it from three sides. One of our first grenades burst inside their forward machine gun nest, putting all its crew out of action. We charged inside and raked the village with the German machine gun. The Arabs there panicked and rushed out of the houses, only to be cut down by our riflemen, who lay in ambush on our two flanks to the north and south. This left the Arabs only one escape route, westwards, and it appeared that some of them managed to slip through in that direction and escape into the cover of the nearby orange grove—the same grove where, about twenty years before, I had spent a few days with the old lady's family.

I had been expecting things to turn out like that, for that was how it had been planned. The house in the orange grove was our second objective that night. We didn't know whether there were any soldiers there, but we were quite sure that any we failed to destroy at the Tel Arish position would easily be able to reorganize and entrench themselves in the stone building and courtyard. It seemed that they had kept a reserve force in the house in the orange grove, for heavy fire was opened upon us from that direction, and there were other indications that fortified positions there were ready to go into action in the event that Tel Arish should fall.

Our luck didn't hold out there, however: the battle continued till dawn and we lost six men. This only heightened our desire for revenge, and besides, we still outnumbered them. Soon the defence of the house showed signs of weakening and the fire gradually slackened off. At dawn we rushed the courtyard, got through as far as the stables and laid a charge of high explosives, then withdrew. A few moments later there was a violent clap of thunder and the wing of the house next to the pool collapsed into a heap of rubble. This was immediately followed by the groans of the wounded and cries of surrender. We re-mustered[18] in the courtyard and shouted to the Arabs to come out and surrender.

•••••

I was not surprised to see Abdul-Karim. He seemed to have expected this, too, though that was something I had never dared to imagine. I recognized him straight away. I went up to him and called his name. When I explained who I was, he gave a weary smile of recollection.

"Nahida . . . is she here too?" I asked him.

"No," he said. "The family has left Jaffa."

Some of the boys listened to our conversation in surprise.

"D'you know him?" our officer asked me.

"I know him," I said.

"Can he give us any important information?"

"Maybe," I said. "But let me settle an old score with him first."

"Want to finish him off?" the officer asked me.

"No," I told him. "I just want to talk to him."

The boys burst out laughing at this. Abdul-Karim, who hadn't understood what we were saying, must have taken offence, for his hands trembled with suppressed fury.

I hastened to explain to him that I wanted to talk to him alone.

"You're the victors," he said. "We do as we're told."

"As long as I haven't beaten you in the pool," I told him, "there's no telling who is the victor."

Abdul-Karim smiled. He seemed to have got my meaning.

Our officer didn't seem to get it, however, for he ordered Abdul-Karim to be taken into the orange grove, where the prisoners were being rounded

---

18 **re-mustered:** came together again

up. I went up to the pool and sat down on the parapet. Our reinforcements from Bat-Yam and Holon began to appear and the orderlies set about attending to the wounded in the courtyard. I stripped and entered the water. It was warm and dirty: it must have been a long time since the pipe overhead had jetted water from the well pump.

"You beat me in America, but I beat you right here, in the pool."

Stretching out my arms, I swam across the pool, then back again. I closed my eyes and waited to hear my mother's voice, urging me on: "Don't be scared! Swim fast!" But instead, I heard Abdul-Karim say: "You beat me in America, but I beat you *right here*, in the pool."

Just then I heard a shot from the orange grove. My heart missed a beat. I knew Abdul-Karim had been killed. Leaping out of the water, I pulled on my trousers and rushed into the grove. There was some commotion and the officer was yelling:

"Who the hell fired that shot?"

"My gun went off," one of the boys said.

When he saw me coming up the officer said, "We've lost that information, damn it! They've killed that Arab of yours."

"We've lost it," I said.

I went over to Abdul-Karim's body and turned it over. He looked as though he had seen me swimming in the pool a few moments ago. His was not the expression of a man who had lost.

There, in the courtyard, it was I, all of us, who were the losers.

Translated by Joseph Schachter

After You Read

Critical Reading

1. After the gun goes off at the end of the story, the narrator describes Abdul-Karim's expression as "not the expression of a man who had lost" (page 449). What does this reveal about the narrator's **point of view** of the events of the story?

2. Why do you think the narrator wants to "relive" the stay at the house in the orange grove (page 446)? Support your response with details from the story.

3. Identify an **internal conflict** and an **external conflict** that the narrator faces in Part I of the story. Are these conflicts the same in Part II of the story, or have the conflicts the narrator faces changed?

4. How does the **narrator** change between Parts I and II of the story? Support your answer with details from the text.

Literary Lens: Foreshadowing

Throughout the story, Tammuz uses **foreshadowing** to build the mood of the story. Use the chart below to identify two or three examples of foreshadowing. In the second column, draw a conclusion about how the foreshadowing creates the mood.

Foreshadowing	What mood does this help to create?

Focus on Research: Search a Database

One way to gather sources for a research project is to search a database for different sources. A database is an organized collection of information. Some databases focus on a single topic; others are broader in scope. Search a database for sources of information about the history of Arab-Israeli relations. Find at least five sources. Keep a record of your sources and the database(s) you used to find them. Compare your list with two of your classmates.

Song of Becoming

Fadwa Tuqan

Before You Read

Born in Palestine, Fadwa Tuqan (1917–2003) was forced to leave school at age 13 because a boy sent her a flower. Her brother, the famous poet Ibrahim Tuqan, brought her to Jerusalem to live and introduced her to great literature. She learned to write traditional poetry and then expanded into free verse. She wrote about love and loss at both a personal and a national level.

World Context

Since 1948, Israel has been warring with its neighbors over land, especially the territories of the West Bank and Gaza, which the Palestinians claim as their own. Tuqan wrote "Song of Becoming" after the Arab defeat in the Arab-Israeli War of 1967.

 LITERARY LENS Figurative language includes metaphors, similes, personification, imagery, and more. While reading this poem, look for examples of figurative language.

They're only boys
who used to frolic and play
launching rainbowed kites
on the western wind,
their blue-red-green kites   5
whistling, leaping,
trading easy laughter and jokes
dueling with branches, pretending to be
great heroes in history.

Suddenly now they've grown, 10
grown more than the years of a normal life,
merged with secret and passionate words,
carried love's messages like the Bible or Quran,[1]
to be read in whispers.
They've grown to become trees 15
plunging deep roots into earth,
stretching high towards the sun.
Now their voices are ones that reject,
that knock down and build anew.
Anger smouldering on the fringes of a blocked horizon, 20
invading classrooms, streets, city quarters,
centering on squares,
facing sullen tanks with streams of stones.

Now they shake the gallows of dawn
assailing the night and its flood. 25
They've grown more than the years of a life
to become the worshipped and the worshippers.

When their torn limbs merged with the stuff of our earth,
they became legends,
they grew into vaulting bridges, 30
they grew and grew, becoming
larger than all poetry.

Translated by Naomi Shihab Nye

---

1 **Quran:** (also Koran), the Muslim holy book

After You Read

Critical Reading

1. What is the underlying **message,** or **theme,** of the poem? Support your answer with details from the poem.

2. In line 13, the poet writes that the boys "carried love's messages like the Bible or Quran." Why do you think the poet references both the Bible and the Quran?

3. Consider Tuqan's **word choice.** Identify three or more instances when the author chose to use gerunds (adjectives ending in *–ing*). Analyze the effect of this on the mood of the poem.

 ## Literary Lens: Figurative Language

Re-create the chart below to help you analyze the author's use of figurative language. In the first column, cite quotations from the poem that use **figurative language.** Then identify the type of figurative language. Lastly, consider what each example adds to the poem.

Quotation	Type of figurative language (metaphor, simile, personification, imagery, etc.)	What does this figurative language add to the poem's tone, mood, conflict, or theme?

Focus on Research: Use Transitions

When drafting a research report, use appropriate transition words to help readers understand your information and ideas. Here are some transition words:

at the beginning	first	in conclusion	nevertheless
because of this	following	in contrast to	on the other hand
besides	furthermore	in other words	particularly
despite	however	lastly	subsequently
finally	in addition	moreover	therefore

Pick several selections from this unit and write a paragraph about your experiences reading these selections. Work with a partner to read and evaluate each other's writing for transitions.

The Literature of
Syria

Background

For thousands of years, powerful empires have fought for control of what is today Syria. The area has been ruled by the Egyptians, Persians, Macedonians, Romans, Mongols, Turks, and French. Since 2011, Syria has been torn by civil war between several rebel sects and the Syrian government. Hundreds of thousands of Syrians have been killed, and more than 12 million (half the country's population) have been displaced.

Syrian writers have suffered considerable censorship. According to Mohja Kahf (1967–), a Syrian-born writer whose exiled parents brought her to live in the U.S. in 1971 at the age of three, her native country's authors often resort to "poetics of Syrian silence," indirectly expressing their dissent. Many Syrian writers, including the noted short story writer Zakaria Tamer (1931–), have chosen to live in exile in order to pursue freedom of expression.

Syria and the United States

Literary censorship in Syria began long before the country won independence. Under Ottoman rule during the late 19th and early 20th centuries, many Syrian writers were driven into exile. Some came to the United States. For example, the Syrian poet Nasib Arida (1887–1946) emigrated to New York in 1905. There he helped found the New York Pen League, also known as Al-Mahjar. Arabic writers in this movement influenced literature in their native countries by exercising free expression in the United States.

Research: Create an Annotated Bibliography

Mohja Kahf is noted for her short, witty poetry, such as the following:

Hijab Scene 2

"You people have such restrictive dress for women,"

she said, hobbling away in three-inch heels and panty hose

to finish out another pink-collar temp pool day.

Create a bibliography of at least five texts about Kahf and her poetry. You may include both online and print sources. Follow a standard format for the bibliography, and include a brief note for each title that evaluates the text and explains what it contributes to the knowledge of Kahf.

The Women's Baths

Ulfat al-Idlibi

Before You Read

Syrian author and literary critic Ulfat al-Idlibi (1912–2007) has been called "the grandmother of modern Syrian literature." She was born to a wealthy Damascus family who saw to it that she received a better education than most women of her time and culture. After her son died in 1947, Idlibi began writing realistic short stories. With her first book, *Al-Qarar Al-Akheer (The Final Decision)*, she began to win awards and recognition. Her other books include *Hikayet Jaddi (The Story of My Grandfather)*. Ulfat al-Idlibi's works have been translated and published in more than ten languages.

World Context

Public baths were popular for many reasons: they epitomized the Muslim concern for cleanliness and love of water, and they allowed customers to be pampered. They were also important meeting places, especially for women. Important rites of passage, such as births, puberty, and marriage, were often celebrated with a trip to the bathhouse. Today, despite modern plumbing, the baths continue to be a lavish experience.

 LITERARY LENS As you read, identify **sensory details** that help you picture the women's baths.

Our household was troubled by an unusual problem: my grandmother, who had passed the age of seventy, insisted on taking a bath at the beginning of every month at the public baths, or market baths as she used to call them.

In my grandmother's opinion the market baths had a delicious ambience about them which we, who had never experienced it, could not appreciate.

For our part we were afraid that the old lady might slip on the wet floor of the baths—this has often happened to people who go there—and break her leg, as her seventy years had made her bones dry and stiff; or she might

cogency:
force; validity

catch a severe chill coming outside from the warm air of the baths and contract a fatal illness as a result. But how could we convince this stubborn old lady of the **cogency** of these arguments?

It was quite out of the question that she should give up a custom to which she had adhered for seventy years, and she had done so without ever once having been stricken with the mishaps we feared. Grandmother had made up her mind that she would keep up this custom as long as she was able to walk on her own two feet, and her tenacity in clinging to her point of view only increased the more my mother tried to reason with her.

Yet Mother never tired of criticizing her mother-in-law, arguing with her and attempting to demonstrate the silliness of her views, even if only by implication. Whenever the subject of the public baths came up my mother proceeded to enumerate their shortcomings from the standpoints of health, of society, and even of economics.

The thing which really annoyed Mother was that my grandmother monopolized our only maid from the early morning onward on the day she went to the baths. She would summon her to her room to help her sweep it and change the sheets and do up the bundles to take to the baths. Then she would set out with her and would not bring her back until around sunset, when our maid would be exhausted and hardly able to perform her routine chores.

In our house I was the observer of a relentless, even though hidden, struggle between mother-in-law and daughter-in-law: between my grandmother, who clung to her position in the household and was resolved under no circumstances to relinquish it, and my mother, who strove to take her place.

Although girls usually side with their mother, I had a strong feeling of sympathy for my grandmother: old age had caught up with her since her husband had died some time before and left her a widow, and little by little her authority in the home shrank as my mother's authority gradually extended. It is the law of life: one takes, then one hands over to another in one's turn. But that does not mean we obey the law readily and willingly.

I used to feel a certain prick of pain when I saw Grandmother retire alone to her room for long hours after being defeated in an argument with Mother. I would sometimes hear her talking bitterly to herself, or I would see her monotonously shaking her head in silence, as though she were rehearsing the book of her long life, reviewing the days of her past, when she was the unchallenged mistress of the house, with the last word. I would often see her vent the force of her resentment on her thousand-bead rosary as her nervous fingers told its beads and she repeated the prayer to herself:

"Oh merciful God, remove this affliction!"

And who could this "affliction" be but my mother?

Then little by little she would calm down and forget the cause of her anger. There is nothing like the **invocation** of God for purifying the soul and enabling it to bear the hardships of life.

invocation: the act of petitioning or appealing to someone

One day when I saw my grandmother getting her things ready to go to the market baths I had the idea of accompanying her, thinking that perhaps I might uncover the secret which attracted her to them. When I expressed my wish to accompany her she was very pleased, but my mother did not like this sudden impulse at all, and said, in my grandmother's hearing, "Has the craze for going to the market baths affected you as well? Who knows—you may catch some infection, like scabies or something, and it will spread around the family."

Thereupon my father broke in with the final word: "What is the matter with you? Let her go with her grandmother. All of us went to the public baths when we were young and it never did any of us any harm."

My mother relapsed into a grudging silence, while my grandmother gave an exultant smile at this victory—my father rarely took her side against my mother.

Then Grandmother led me by the hand to the room where her massive trunk was kept. She produced the key from her pocket and opened the trunk in my presence—this was a great honor for me, for the venerable trunk had never before been opened in the presence of another person—and immediately there wafted out of it a strange yet familiar scent, a scent of age, a smell of the distant past, of years which have been folded up and stored away. Grandmother drew out of the depths of the trunk a bundle of red velvet, the corners of which were embroidered with pearls and sequins.

She opened it in front of me and handed me a wine-colored bathwrap decorated with golden stars. I had never set eyes on a more beautiful robe. She also gave me a number of white towels decorated around the edges with silver thread, saying "All these are brand new; no one has ever used them. I have saved them from the time I was married. Now I'm giving them to you as a present, since you are going to the baths with me. Alas . . . poor me. Nobody goes with me now except the servants."

She gave a deep, heart-felt sigh. Then she called the servant to carry the bundle containing our clothes and towels, and the large bag which held the bowl, the soap, the comb, the sponge-bag, and loofah,[1] the soil of Aleppo,[2] and the henna which would transform my grandmother's white hair to jet black. She put on her shawl, and we made our way toward the baths, which

---

1 **loofah:** a kind of sponge
2 **soil of Aleppo:** a type of perfumed clay used for hair-washing

were only a few paces from our house. Times without number I had read the words on the little plaque which crowned the low, unpretentious door as I passed by: "Whoever the Divine Blessing of health would achieve, should turn to the Lord and then to the baths of Afif."

We entered the baths.

The first thing I noticed was the female "intendant." She was a stout woman, sitting on the bench to the right of persons coming in. In front of her was a small box for collecting the day's revenue. Next to it was a *nargileh* decorated with flowers. It had a long mouthpiece which the intendant played with between her lips, while she looked at those around her with a proprietorial air. When she saw us she proceeded to welcome us without stirring from her place. Then she summoned Umm Abdu, the bath attendant. A woman hastened up and gave us a perfunctory welcome. She had penciled eyebrows, eyes painted with *kohl,*[3] and was dressed very neatly. She had adorned her hair with two roses and a sprig of jasmine. She was

voluble:
talkative; effusive

very **voluble**, and was like a spinning-top, never motionless, and her feet in her Shabrawi clogs made a rhythmic clatter on the floor of the baths. Her function was that of hostess to the bathers. She came up to my grandmother and led her to a special bench resembling a bed. Our maid hastened to undo one of our bundles, drawing out a small prayer rug which she spread out on the bench. My grandmother sat down on it to get undressed.

I was fascinated by what I saw around me. In particular my attention was drawn to the spacious hall called *al-barani.*[4] In the center of it was a gushing fountain. Around the hall were narrow benches on which were spread brightly-colored rugs where the bathers laid their things. The walls were decorated with mirrors, yellowed and spotted with age, and panels on which were inscribed various maxims. On one of them I read, "Cleanliness is part of Faith."

My grandmother urged me to undress. I took off my clothes and wrapped myself in the wine-colored bath-wrap, but as I was not doing it properly Umm Abdu came and helped me. She secured it around my body and then drew the free end over my left shoulder, making it appear like an Indian sari.

Then she helped my grandmother down from her bench, and conducted us toward a small door which led into a dark corridor, calling out at the top of her voice, "Marwah! Come and look after the Bey's mother!"

With a sigh a shape suddenly materialized in the gloom in front of me: it was a grey-haired, emaciated woman of middle age with a face in which

---

3 *kohl:* a dark powder used for eye makeup
4 *al-barani:* a public bath's outermost hall

suffering had engraved deep furrows. She was naked except for a faded cloth which hung from her waist to her knees. She welcomed us in a nasal tone, prattling on although I could not catch a single syllable of what she was saying, thanks to the babble of **discordant** voices which filled my ears and the hot thick steam which obstructed my sight; and there was a smell which nearly made me faint, the like of which I had never encountered in my life before. I felt nauseous, and was almost sick, leaning against the maid for support.

Nevertheless, in a few moments I grew accustomed to the odor and it no longer troubled me; my eyes, also, became accustomed to seeing through the steam.

We reached a small hall containing a large stone basin. A number of women circled around in it, chatting and washing at the same time. I asked my grandmother: "Why don't we join them?"

She replied: "This is the *wastani*;[5] I have hired a cubicle in the *juwani*.[6] I am not accustomed to bathing with the herd."

I followed her through a small door to the *juwani*, and found myself looking with confused curiosity at the scene that presented itself. There was

> discordant: inharmonious; conflicting

---

5 *wastani*: a public bath's interior hall
6 *juwani*: a public bath's innermost hall

a large rectangular hall, at each corner of which stood a large basin of white marble. Women sat around each one, busily engrossed in washing, scrubbing, and rubbing, as though they were in some kind of race. I raised my eyes to look at the ceiling, and saw a lofty dome with circular openings, glazed with crystal, through which enough light filtered to illuminate the hall. The uproar here was at its worst—there was a clashing of cans, the splashing of water, and the clamor of children.

My grandmother paused for a moment to greet a friend among the bathers, while I found myself following a violent quarrel which had arisen between two young women. I understood from the women around them that they were two wives of a **polygamous** marriage, who had met face to face for the first time at the baths. The furious quarrel led at length to an exchange of blows with metal bowls. Luckily a spirit of **chivalry** among some of the bathers induced them to separate the two warring wives before they could satisfy their thirst for revenge.

As we advanced a little way the howling of a small child drowned the hubbub of the hall. Its mother had put it on her lap, twisting one of its legs around her and proceeding to scrub its face with soap and pour hot water over it until its skin was scarlet red. I averted my gaze, fearing the child would expire before my eyes.

We reached the cubicle, and I felt a sense of oppression as we entered it. It consisted of nothing but a small chamber with a basin in the front. Its one advantage was that it screened those taking a bath inside from the other women.

We were received in the cubicle by a dark, stout woman with a pockmarked face and a harsh voice. She was Mistress Umm Mahmud. She took my grandmother from the attendant Marwah, who was being assailed by shouts from every direction:

"Cold water, Marwah, cold water, Marwah!"

The poor woman set about complying with the bathers' requests for cold water, dispensing it from two big buckets which she filled from the fountain in the outer hall. She was so weighed down with the buckets that she aroused pity in those who saw her struggle.

I turned back to Grandmother and found her sitting on the tiled floor in front of the basin. She had rested her head between the hands of Umm Mahmud, who sat behind her on a sort of wooden chair which was only slightly raised above the level of the floor. She proceeded to scour Grandmother's head with soap seven consecutive times—not more, not less.

I stood at the door of the cubicle, entertained by the scene presented by the bathers. I watched the younger women coming and going, from time to time going into the outer hall for the sake of diversion, their fresh youthfulness showing in their proud swaying gait. In their brightly colored wraps decorated with silver thread they resembled Hindu women in a temple filled with the fragrance of incense. Little circles of light fell from the dome onto their tender-skinned bodies, causing them to glisten.

I found the sight of the older women depressing: they sat close to the walls chatting with one another, while the cream of henna on their hair trickled in black rivulets along the wrinkles of their foreheads and cheeks, as they waited impatiently for their turn to bathe.

Suddenly I heard shrill exclamations of pleasure. I turned toward their source, and saw a group of women gathered around a pretty young girl, loudly expressing their delight at some matter.

Mistress Umm Mahmud said to me: "Our baths are doing well today: we have a bride here, we have a woman who has recently had a child, and we have the mother of the Bey—may God spare her for us!"

It was no wonder that my grandmother swelled with pride at being mentioned in the same breath with a bride and a young mother.

I enjoyed standing at the door of the cubicle watching the bride and her companions. Then I caught sight of a fair well-built woman enveloped in a dark blue wrap, giving vent to overflowing joy with little shrieks of delight. I realized from the words she was singing that she must be the bride's mother:

> "Seven bundles I packed for thee, and the eighth in the chest
>   is stored;
> To Thee, Whom all creatures need, praise be, oh Lord!"

A young woman, a relative or friend of the bride, replied:

> "Oh maiden coming from the *wastani*, with thy towel all
>   scented.
> He who at thy wedding shows no joy, shall die an infidel,[7]
>   from Paradise prevented!"

The bride's mother continued the song:

> "The little birds chirp and flutter among the trellis'd leaves;
> How sweet the bride! The bath upon her brow now pearly
>   crowns of moisture weaves.
> Thou canst touch the City Gate with thy little finger tip,
>   though it is so high;
> I have waited long, long years for this day's coming nigh!"

---

7 **infidel:** a nonbeliever

But the best verse was reserved for the bridegroom's mother:

"Oh my daughter-in-law! I take thee as my daughter!
The daughters of Syria are many, but my heart only desires
    and wishes for thee!
Pistachios, hazels and dates: the heart of the envious has
    been sore wounded;
Today we are merry, but the envious no merriment shall
    see!"

The singing finished as the bride and her companions formed a circle around a tray upon which had been placed cakes of Damascene[8] mincemeat, and a second one filled with various kinds of fruit. The bride's mother busied herself distributing the cakes right and left, and one of them fell to my share also!

> "The daughters of Syria are many, but my heart only desires and wishes for thee!"

In a far corner a woman was sitting with her four children around a large dish piled with *mujaddarah*[9] and pickled turnips, their preoccupation with their meal rendering them completely oblivious to what was going on around them in the baths. When the dish had been emptied of food the mother took from a basket by her side a large cabbage. Gripping its long green leaves, she raised it up and then brought it down hard on the tiled floor, until it split apart and scattered into fragments. The children tumbled over each other to snatch them up and greedily devoured them, savoring their fresh taste.

Then my attention was diverted by a pretty girl, about fifteen or sixteen years old, sitting on a bench along the wall of the boiler-house. She seemed impatient and restless, as though she found it hard to tolerate the pervasive heat. She was surrounded by three women, one of whom, apparently her mother, was feverishly fussing over her. She began to rub over her body a yellow ointment which exuded a scent of ginger (it was what was called "strengthening ointment"). My grandmother explained to me that it reinforced the blood vessels of a new mother, and restored her to the state of health she had enjoyed before having her child.

The attendant Umm Abdu came up to us and inquired after our comfort. She brought us both glasses of licorice sherbet as a present from the intendant. Then she lit a cigarette for my grandmother, who was obviously regarded as a patron of distinction.

---

8 **Damascene:** from Damascus, the Syrian capital
9 *mujaddarah:* a rice and lentil dish popular in Syria

It was now my turn. My grandmother moved aside, and I sat down in her place, entrusting my head to the attentions of Umm Mahmud for a thorough rubbing. After I had had my seven soapings I sat down before the door of the cubicle to relax a little. I was amused to watch the bath attendant Marwah scrubbing one of the bathers. Her right hand was covered with coarse sacking, which she rubbed over the body of the woman sitting in front of her. She began quite slowly, and then sped up, and as she did so little grey wicks began to appear under the sacking, which quickly became bigger and were shaken to the floor.

After we had finished being loofah-ed and rubbed, Umm Mahmud asked me to come back to her to have my head soaped an additional five times. I surrendered to her because I had promised myself that I would carry out the bathing rites through all their stages and degrees as protocol dictated, whatever rigors I had to endure in the process!

I was not finished until Umm Mahmud had poured the last basinful of water over my head, after anointing it with "soil of Aleppo," the scent of which clung to my hair for days afterwards.

Umm Mahmud rose, and standing at the door of the cubicle, called out in her harsh voice: "Marwah! Towels for the Bey's mother!"

With a light and agile bound Marwah was at the door of the *wastani*, calling out in a high-pitched tone, like a cockerel:[10] "Umm Abdu! Towels for the Bey's mother!" Her shout mingled with that of another "Mistress" who was standing in front of a cubicle opposite ours, likewise demanding towels for her client.

Umm Abdu appeared, clattering along in her Shabrawi clogs, with a pile of towels on her arm which she distributed among us, saying as she did: "Blessings upon you . . . Have an enjoyable bath, if God wills!"

Then she took my grandmother by the arm and led her to the *barani*, where she helped her to get up onto the high bench, and then to dry herself and get into her clothes.

Grandmother stood waiting her turn to pay her bill. There was a heated argument going on between the intendant and a middle-aged woman who had three girls with her. I gathered from what was being said that the usual custom was for the intendant to charge married women in full, but that widows and single women paid only half the normal fee. The lady was claiming that she was a widow, and her daughters were all single. The intendant listened to her skeptically, and obviously could not believe that the eldest of the girls was single, in that she was an adult and was very

---

10 **cockerel:** a young rooster

beautiful. But at last she was forced to accept what the woman said after the latter had sworn the most solemn oath that what she was saying was the truth.

My grandmother stepped forward and pressed something into the intendant's hand, telling her: "Here's what I owe you, with something extra for the cold water and the attendance."

The intendant peered down at her hand and then smiled; in fact she seemed very pleased, for I heard her say to my grandmother: "May God keep you, Madam, and we hope to see you every month."

Then my grandmother distributed tips to the attendant, the "Mistress," and Marwah, as they emerged from the *juwani* to bid her good-bye.

I have never known my grandmother to be so generous and open-handed as on the day which we spent at the market baths. She was pleased and proud as she listened to the blessings called down on her by those who had received her **largesse**.

Then she gave me an intentionally lofty look, as if to say: "Can you appreciate your grandmother's status now? How about telling your mother about *this*, now that she's begun to look down her nose at me?"

As she left the baths there was a certain air of haughtiness in her step, and she held herself proudly upright, although I had only known her walk resignedly, with a bent back, at home.

Now she was enjoying the esteem which was hers only when she visited the market baths. At last I understood their secret . . .

At last I understood their secret . . .

largesse:
generosity;
bounty

After You Read

Critical Reading

1. Compare the two sets of mother-in-law/daughter-in-law relationships in the story. What is the impact of the song the second pair sings?

2. Identify a **conflict** the narrator faces in the story, and then analyze whether this is an **internal** or **external** conflict.

3. What is the **epiphany** the narrator experiences in the story? When does this happen, and how does it change the narrator?

 ## Literary Lens: Sensory Details

Analyze the **sensory details** the narrator uses to describe the women's baths. Analyze how these sensory details influence the narrator's opinion of the baths. Re-create the table below to help you analyze the sensory details.

Sensory details	Quotation
Sight	
Sound	
Smell	
Touch	
Taste	
The narrator's opinion of the baths:	

Focus on Research: Paraphrase Sources

In the story, the narrator reads a message on one of the walls of the bath, which states "Cleanliness is part of Faith." Research to find out more about the connection between cleanliness and the Muslim faith. Then, paraphrase two or three details you found. To paraphrase, write the most important details in your own words. For example, a source might state: "Wudu is an Islamic tradition in which people use water to cleanse parts of the body, such as the hands, mouth, nose, head, and feet, before formal prayers, before reading the Qur'an, and before other specific religious activities." A paraphrase of this quotation is this: "Before they pray or read the Qur'an, Muslims practice Wudu, a ritual that involves cleansing their hands, mouth, nose, head, and feet."

The Literature of
Turkey

Background

Like many of the countries in Southwest Asia, Turkey is an overwhelmingly Muslim country. Beyond that, though, it is unlike many of its neighbors. Turkey is neither an Arabic-speaking country, such as Egypt, nor a Persian-speaking country, such as Iran. Turkey has its own distinctive ethnicity, language, and culture. While Turkey has professed to be a firmly secular government since its founding in 1923, the government's actions do not always support this claim.

Turkey's location has long made it a meeting ground for European and Islamic cultures. The literature of Turkey has been heavily influenced by Turkish culture as well as Islamic and European literary traditions. The Turkish novelist Orhan Pamuk (1952–) is known for his novels that encapsulate the clash of interwoven cultures in Turkey; Pamuk's work earned him the Nobel Prize in Literature in 2006. One of his most honored novels is *Benim Adım Kırmızı (My Name is Red)*, a highly experimental work set in 1591, when Turkey was the center of the powerful Ottoman Empire.

Turkey and the United States

Writers in Turkey are often censored by the authoritarian government. The Human Rights Watch website states, "Turkey remained the world leader in jailing journalists" in 2019. Yet many modern Turkish authors continue to write about terrorism, sexism, and political oppression. Elif Shafak writes about these issues in her novels *Three Daughters of Eve* and *10 Minutes and 38 Seconds in This Strange World*. In 2006, she was put on trial for "insulting Turkishness." Because of the lack of free speech in Turkey, Shafak now spends most of her time in the U.K. and the U.S. She says, "The novel . . . is one of our last remaining democratic spaces in today's extremely polarized world. . . . I believe it is a novelist's job to ask questions about difficult issues."

Research: Prepare Interview Questions

In 1996, the American-based Turkish scholar Kemal Silay published *An Anthology of Turkish Literature*, which includes writings from many periods translated into English. Explains Silay, "I believe that I have tried to do my part in contributing to the notion that Muslims and their fascinating cultural creations . . . have played an indispensable role in the formation of the world's civilization." Write five questions to ask Silay about the cultural importance of his anthology.

Wanted:
A Town Without a Crazy

Muzaffer Izgü

Before You Read

Muzaffer Izgü (1933–2017) is one of Turkey's best-known humorists. When Izgü was a child, his family was very poor and their small house was cold. At a friend's suggestion, he started going to the public library to do his homework. There, he also found books to read and decided to become a writer. Izgü wrote for both children and adults and won many awards.

World Context

Modern Turkey is poised between the developed and the developing worlds. It seeks to join the European Economic Union and partners with its European neighbors. Yet 99 percent of the population is Muslim. As in many Middle Eastern countries, Muslim fundamentalism has risen in recent years, creating problems for the government, schools, and civic life in some cases. Despite this revival, Turks are used to a tolerant form of Muslim worship. Turks are as fond of tradition as they are optimistic about their prospects in the modern world.

 LITERARY LENS As you read, consider how the story heightens moments of humor through the use of **irony**.

O n the table crouched someone my age with a messy beard and untidy hair. Using the broom in his hand sometimes as a guitar, sometimes as a microphone, his singing and dancing had the people in the coffeehouse dying with laughter. My brother-in-law explained, "That's our town crazy."

He did a little act between verses. Moving the broom handle forward and back and making a series of sounds, then holding the handle in his mouth, undulating his hips and dancing, the loony shouted, "Dem dérula, dem dérula!"[1] The crowd picked up the tempo, became exuberant and from time to time shouted, "Hurrah for Crazy Hilmi!"

For a moment, the name Hilmi stuck in my mind. Could this Hilmi be that *same* Hilmi? Even behind a tangled beard, the face resembled his. The squinty eyes, the forehead protruding like a fist, ears like the back of a shovel, even the arms, long like a bear's, were his.

"Look here!" I told my brother-in-law, "I probably know this crazy guy."

"You wouldn't know him," he replied. "This is your first visit to this town, so where could you have met him?"

"Is he from around here?"

"By God, I really don't know. I've lived here for three years and he was here when I came."

At this point the loony finished his concert, walked among the tables and after collecting fifty piastres from this one, a lira[2] from that and a "Get outa here!" from others, he left, **crestfallen**. I had to find out, so I arose quickly. I not only knew this man, but knew him well, having worked with him seven years previously in the same district office. After handing in my resignation and leaving, I had heard no news of Hilmi Bey again. But the Hilmi Bey I knew was a very serious-minded, sober man. I fell in behind him and just as he "lifted" a handful of chestnuts from a bag at the grocery store, saying, "Hilmi Bey!" I caught him.

He threw me a guilty glance then turned to the grocer. After the grocer pressed eight or ten more chestnuts into his hand, he said to me, "He brings good luck. Whatever store he takes something from does very good business that day."

Hilmi Bey moved off from there in a hurry; he was almost running. I started running too. I intended to learn whether this was my Hilmi or some other Hilmi. He was running toward the gardens. They say that a lunatic's strength is superior but I managed to keep close behind him. When he speeded up, I ran even faster to try and catch up with him. Finally, however, I lost him in a wooded area and started calling, "Hilmi Bey! Hilmi Bey!"

No answer. Who knew which tree he was hiding behind! After calling a few times, I heard his crazy laugh close by. There he was. He appeared from behind a bush and grinned.

"Hilmi Bey," I repeated.

"Huh!"

---

crestfallen:
downcast;
disappointed

1 **"Dem dérula, dem dérula!":** a nonsense phrase in Turkish
2 piastres . . . lira: former Turkish coins; the piastre is one hundredth of a lira.

Right, it was him . . . Yet inside I still had doubts. Approaching closer, I said, "See here, Hilmi Bey, what's the matter with you?"

"Hey," he replied, "I'm the town lunatic."

"Are you really crazy?"

He laughed again. "When you heard my laugh, you really thought at first that I was loony." He bounded over the bush to my side and placed before me things he took out of his pockets: candy, chestnuts, expensive cigarettes, nylon ribbons, a big chocolate bar, four large oranges, some first-class glasses, then he unwound from around his waist, three meters of greatcoat cloth . . . Hilmi's pockets could completely stock a sundries[3] shop.

"Tell me," I insisted, "when did you lose your mind?"

"Come on, lose what mind! Thank God there's nothing wrong with my head."

"Are you really all right?"

"Of course I'm all right. I understood when you resigned from the civil service, it was because there was nothing in it. If we paid the rent we couldn't eat or if we ate we couldn't pay the rent so I took a month's leave, rolled up my sleeves, and started searching for a town without a lunatic. Wearing a heavy overcoat, dark glasses, and carrying a large suitcase, I went from town to town. Every place I went, my first task was to find out if the place had a crazy. If they told me there was, I immediately moved on. In twenty-five days I went through nearly a hundred towns, but each one had a loony. Though I struggled and economized, I was down to my last piastre when finally I came to this town. I sat down in a coffeehouse and, after drinking a tea, called the waiter: 'Brother, I wonder if this town happens to have a lunatic.'"

•••••

"'Where, sir? Here? Eight years ago, we had a cuckoo but ever since he got run over by a truck, the whole town has missed him greatly. What a great guy he was, our cuckoo. He sang songs in the coffeehouses, wandered through the neighborhoods tying cloth on this door and that and played music when there was a wedding, using his nose for a pipe and his chest for a drum. It happened one Friday, Sefer the truckdriver ran him over. Believe me, we gave Crazy Davut a funeral that the town won't even give Mayor Riza Bey when he dies."

"The waiter heaved a great sigh, 'Ah, ah, after Davut left there was no joy in town. Where could you find another loony like him?'

---

3 sundries: miscellaneous items

"Well, after this conversation I left for home and my family. After packing a few things, I said to my wife, 'Well, tell me good-bye.'

"Surprised, she asked, 'Where are you going?'

"'I'm going crazy. I found a town without a lunatic.'

"'Sounds like you're already loony!'

"'Would you listen to her! Of course I've gone mad!'

"'Very well. So what will *we* do?'

"'You'll be the wife and children of a loony.'

"So to enter the town with the honor and glory befitting a loony, I had to start with my clothes. First, I went and had an extra long, bright red topcoat made. I smeared it with mud to make it look old and ripped holes in it left and right. Then I went to the flea market and bought piles of worthless old money and bizarre medals. These I pinned here and there on the coat. Around my waist I bound a thick belt and hung a frying pan to one end on a cord. The frying pan was to be my guitar. I hung things all around my belt: a ladle, wooden spoons, a potty, an old electric clock, a women's umbrella, a cast-iron stove-lid. Clanging and rattling all over, I boarded the bus. The people on the minibus broke into laughter, so I stood up, and using my frying pan as a guitar, sang all the songs I knew. Laughing and clapping, they were so light-hearted it was indescribable. Some threw oranges for me to eat, others gave me candy, and some money. Not only that, the bus driver not only failed to ask me for the fare but invited me to his home: 'Where have you been all this time? Come every day, the food and drinks are on me.'

• • • • •

"I got off the bus in town to the same laughter. As soon as I landed, eight or ten kids followed me. Their numbers grew to fifty, one hundred. You know kids! Everyone heard about me from them; that's how my fame spread through the town from the first day.

"'Did you hear, huh? A cuckoo came to town.'

"'Man, is he loony. Davut couldn't hold a candle to him!'

"God bless them! From that first day, I drank tea free, coffee too. I ate the best food in the restaurants free, and in addition, they gave me pocket money. It kills me to think that while these poor people were suffering all those years from the lack of a loony, I was putting numbers on documents, kowtowing when I entered the director's office, and wasting all that time for a mere thousand lira a month. If I'd known, wouldn't I have come to this town long before?

"The people are so happy at finding a loony that they don't even ask who or what he is or even where he comes from. Now when I enter the mayor's office, I don't say *selam* or hello and don't even bother to knock. I walk right in, lean against the mayor's arm then settle myself into an easy chair. After thrusting an expensive cigarette into my hand, he lights it with his own lighter and orders me a coffee. While I drink my coffee, he asks, 'You have any problems or anything, Hilmi?'

"I grin. So that means I have no difficulties. As I'm leaving the mayor puts his hand into his pocket and slips me a fiver. From there I go to the director of finance and from there to the doctor, then to the commissar.[4] God bless them, they stick fives and tens into my pockets. Then I go out among tradesmen. Grinning, I enter the shops and tug at the owners' sleeves; they quickly open the drawer, saying, 'May your fortune be bountiful, God willing, Hilmi.' They take out a ten or a five and hand it to me. If my hand happens to brush a bolt of cloth, they immediately tell an apprentice to cut off a couple of meters for me. I wind the two meters around my waist and enter a second store. Then the health services. It's as if they're at my beck and call. Recently, I developed a pain, so I lay down in the middle of the road. In an instant, God, what a commotion broke loose!"

•••••

"People rushed there crying, 'Our loony's fallen ill!' You won't believe it; not only the doctor but also the mayor came. People flocked around saying, 'Please, doctor, if you haven't made a diagnosis, let's get a taxi and take him to town. We have a pretty good loony and in return for our respect, God blesses our pocketbooks.'

"For a week I was treated like a king in the hospital. The mayor came to visit me three times, and the townspeople every day. What a departure I had from the hospital! It was as if one of the country's greats had had an important operation and was returning from the brink of death."

"Very well," I said, "what about your wife and children? How are they getting along?"

He grinned again: "I disappear for two or three days a month; the town is used to this. They say the poor fellow is having another fit of nervous agitation so he takes off in order not to bring any harm on the townspeople. As a matter of fact, I send some of the money and things I've collected by

---

4 **commissar:** a public official charged with maintaining citizen loyalty

mail and others I forward to a place agreed upon with my wife. Thus my family gets along very well. One of my sons is attending the university and a daughter has finished high school. We bought a flat in an apartment building and my wife has it furnished to suit her heart's desire."

"OK," I continued, "but when are you going to put an end to this lunacy?"

He grinned: "Are you nuts? There are lots of professional lunatics in this country. One of them would snatch my spot, so I can't leave town. What's more, I'm sort of used to this insanity."

As he leaped up and skipped away, he said, "Don't tell anyone. Even if you did, they wouldn't believe you!"

After You Read

Critical Reading

1. A **farce** is a form of comedy featuring exaggerated caricatures of people. Do you consider "Wanted: A Town Without a Crazy" to be a farce? Why or why not?

2. A **motif** is a recurring element in a story. Identify a motif in the story "Wanted: A Town Without a Crazy." Describe the effects of this motif on readers.

3. This story includes several instances of witty dialogue, also known as **repartee**. Cite a scene that involves repartee. Infer the author's purpose in using this motif.

4. Some writers tell a story along with a **subtext**, or a hidden meaning that can be inferred from the story. Is there a **subtext** in this story? If so, identify the subtext and describe why the author chose to include a subtext.

 ## Literary Lens: Irony

Consider the use of **irony** as a humorous device in this story. Analyze examples of irony and determine whether each example is a case of verbal irony, situational irony, or dramatic irony. Lastly, describe the effects of irony on the humor in the story.

Example of irony	Verbal, situational, or dramatic?
Effects of irony on the story's humor:	

Focus on Research: Use Quotations Effectively

Select a passage from this short story and a passage from another short story. Write a paragraph comparing the two passages. Include quotations from both stories. When using quotations, be sure to use commas and quotation marks appropriately. Provide context for the quotations by including who said it. Have a partner proofread your paragraph.

The Literature of
Armenia

Background

Armenia's history has been intertwined with Christianity for more than 1,700 years. Around the year 300 C.E., Armenia became the first country to adopt Christianity as its state religion. Armenian literature from that period was mostly religious. In later literature, Armenia's greatest epic hero is David of Sassoun, whose exploits reflect Christian themes. Today, Armenia remains one of the most religiously united countries in the world. About 95 percent of Armenians are Christians, and almost all of them belong to the Armenian Apostolic Church.

Since the late 1800s, Armenia has suffered wars, large-scale massacres, and cultural oppression, first under the Ottoman Empire of Turkey and then under the Soviet Union. Since Armenia's liberation from Soviet rule in 1991, Armenia has endured internal conflicts and war with its neighbor Azerbaijan.

Yet through all its troubles, Armenia has continued to produce a remarkable body of literature. An especially notable novelist and short story writer, Hrant Matevosian (1935–2002), wrote internationally renowned fiction even under Soviet censorship, including the book *The Orange Herd*.

Armenia and the United States

Several U.S. organizations are devoted to bringing Armenian culture to the attention of Americans. These include the Society for Armenian Studies, the National Association for Armenian Studies and Research, ArmenianHouse.org, and the Armenian Library and Museum of America (ALMA).

ALMA's mission statement is typical of all these institutions: "to locate, collect, preserve, and present the culture, history, art, and contributions of the Armenian people during the past 3,000 years."

Research: Find Online Newspapers

More than twice as many Armenians live outside the country as live within the country. Several newspapers and journals have been established with the goal of providing news about Armenia both to Armenians and English readers around the world. Search online for a newspaper that focuses on news from Armenia. Click on the website's "About" tab to discover the purpose and history of the news outlet. Find and read an article that interests you and create a works cited or bibliography entry that conforms to MLA, APA, or other style.

The Armenian Language Is the Home of the Armenian

Moushegh Ishkhan

Before You Read

Mousegh Ishkhan (1913–1990) wrote about the era of Armenian Dispersion, the period since the mid-1800s during which Armenians were victims of political persecution, forced exile, and genocide. His autobiographical work, *Farewell, Childhood,* tells of his family's relocation to Damascus after being chased out of Armenia by enemy armies. Ishkhan's writing encourages preserving Armenian identity and serving one's native land.

World Context

A small country caught between the Islamic and Christian worlds, Armenia has suffered constant invasions. In 1915, 1.5 million Armenians died in a Turkish massacre. Following that, a migration emptied Armenian villages and divided families. In 1988, 25,000 to 50,000 people died in an earthquake. Despite their traumas, Armenians are proud of their heritage and value books, education, and music.

 LITERARY LENS As you read, trace the central **metaphor** throughout the poem.

The Armenian language is the home
and haven where the wanderer can own
roof and wall and nourishment.
He can enter to find love and pride,
locking the hyena and the storm outside.   5
For centuries its architects have toiled
to give its ceilings height.

How many peasants working
day and night have kept
its cupboards full, lamps lit, ovens hot.   10
Always rejuvenated, always old, it lasts
century to century on the path
where every Armenian can find it when he's lost
in the wilderness of his future, or his past.

Translated by Diana der Hovanessian

The Refugees | Marc Chagall, 1976

After You Read

Critical Reading

1. Consider the **repetition** of the word *century*. How does this repetition add to the meaning and effect of the poem?

2. Analyze the use of **rhyme** in the poem. Identify two examples of end rhymes, and then explain how each example creates the **tone**.

3. Identify whether this poem uses a **third-person limited narrator** or a **third-person omniscient narrator**. Then support your answer with details from the poem.

Literary Lens: Metaphor

This poem presents a **metaphor**: the Armenian language is the home to Armenians. Identify details that develop this metaphor throughout the poem. For example, the poem describes the Armenian language as having a "roof and wall." This imagery suggests that a home is a place of solid protection from the elements and that the language is a place of emotional protection for Armenian people. Use a graphic organizer like the one below to identity more examples of how this metaphor is developed throughout the poem.

Quotation	What does this say about the "home"?	What does this say about the Armenian language?

Focus on Research: Create an Annotated Bibliography

When writing a research paper, it is best to use multiple sources and to list all of the sources at the end of the paper in a bibliography. Practice creating an annotated bibliography that includes a summary of the source. Find two sources about the Armenian Diaspora. Then write an annotated bibliography for each one. Refer to an online style guide for formatting.

The Literature of
Iraq

Background

The region that is today the country of Iraq has a distinguished literary heritage. Known in antiquity as Mesopotamia, it was the home of the world's first writing systems and some of the first literature ever written. Best-known of this early literature is *The Epic of Gilgamesh*, which was written over the course of about 1,500 years between 2100 and 1400 B.C.E.

Between the 8th and 13th centuries, the region formed the intellectual center of the Abbasid Empire. No empire in the world in this era—except China—rivaled this empire's accomplishments in science and literature. The rich tradition of poetry established under the Abbasids still shapes Iraqi literature.

The modern country of Iraq was created when the Ottoman Empire collapsed almost a century ago. Despite authoritarian governments, Iraq's writers, often in exile, have continued to create great literature. Among these is Saadi Youssef (1934–), whose 30 books of poetry include *Without an Alphabet, Without a Face*.

Iraq and the United States

Since Saddam Hussein's rise to power in 1979, the histories of the United States and Iraq have been intertwined. Although backed by the U.S. in his early years, Hussein was later deposed by the 2003 U.S.-led invasion. U.S. forces were instrumental in capturing Hussein and turning him over to be tried for his crimes. Even Iraqi authors who suffered persecution under Hussein's brutal regime expressed mixed feelings about the United States' involvement in their country. For example, Salah Al-Hamdani (1951–) began writing in Iraq while imprisoned for political dissent. Exiled to France, he continues to write deeply moving poetry about his experiences.

Research: Explore Online Magazines

At the end of his most famous poem, "Baghdad My Beloved," Salah Al-Hamdani expresses his longing to return to his native city: "Let me return to your flesh / So I might listen to the beating of your soul / and drink in the murmur of your breath." Search for poetry or other works of Salah Al-Hamdani that appear in online magazines. After finding and reading at least one poem, write an imaginary one-page interview with Al-Hamdani, exploring why he chose to live in exile despite his yearning for home.

from Behind the Veil

Dhu'l Nun Ayyoub

Before You Read

Dhu'l Nun Ayyoub (1908–1988) is a leading figure among modern Iraqi fiction writers. In his stories, individuals contend with the religious and political discord in the Arabic world as well as conflicts between tradition and modernity.

World Context

A veil is worn by many Muslim women, especially those in Middle Eastern cultures, to observe laws requiring them to cover their bodies while in public places. The rise of fundamentalism in recent years has returned the veil's popularity as a headdress and symbol of Muslim pride, religiosity, and feminine modesty.

 LITERARY LENS While you read, consider how the veil is a **foil**—for Siham, for Ihsan, and for traditional and modern Muslim cultures.

The street, although wide, was inconveniently full of strollers passing to and fro. The situation was not helped by the sleek swift cars, which sped by from time to time. They carried wealthy occupants, young women and ladies, who, protected from the curiosity of the outside world, displayed radiant faces. Their shining gaze roved across the street, smiling or frowning as they took in sights which pleased or displeased them.

Among the surging crowd was an amazing mixture of different clothes and contrasting shapes, which, if nothing else, serve to emphasize the varying tastes of these passers-by.

A European who had never been to the East before might be excused for thinking that its people were in the middle of a great festival. As time goes by, however, he is moved to say in amazement, "What long carnival celebrations you have in this country!" Our Western friend would think

that people wear these amazing clothes for a festival, just as they would do in his own country.

You can also see women in the crowd, both veiled and unveiled. A man can be surprised to find himself turning involuntarily towards those figures, wearing long silk gowns, which give them such an enticing and alluring shape, and make the observer yearn to uncover the magic and the secrets which lie beneath them.

His desire is only increased when his gaze falls on the filmy veil. Behind it he can catch a fleeting glimpse of fine features and penciled eyebrows, which serve to inflame the fires of his heart. It makes him want to devote the rest of his life to the exploration of this world full of shame-faced beauty.

Ihsan was one of those who would stroll along with the crowd displaying his smart and tasteful suit over his slim figure, patting his dark gleaming hair whenever he felt that the evening breezes had ruffled it, or spread a curl over his clear forehead.

This Ihsan was a young man of eighteen, good-looking with fine features which made him attractive to a number of women. Naturally he was aware of his appeal and attraction, and he had the youthful capacity to exploit it. That's why you can see him now, with his eyes wandering in search of a **quarry**.

quarry: target; hunted game

Ihsan was not interested in chasing unveiled girls. They exuded poise, which he found unattractive, and they were always looking anxiously to avoid criticism so they never looked the passers-by directly in the face. They would walk by without turning their heads, paying no attention to the expressions of flattery which came their way from the **gallants**, who, after getting as much out of them as a dog gets out of barking at clouds, would give them no further attention.

gallants: fashionable young men

This is the reason that makes Ihsan always sidle up to the girls with the long cloaks and the secret little movements which attract him: the burning sighs and the gentle laughter and the concealed glances.

Siham had gone out on the evening of that day as usual to take the air and stroll through the streets. This evening stroll had become a part of her life to such an extent that it was now indispensable. She couldn't remember exactly the date when she first set out to saunter through the

> Ihsan was not interested in chasing unveiled girls.

street, and did not really know the reason why she kept up her evening appointments. If she did, she did not admit it. Whatever the case, no sooner had Siham seen the bustle in the middle of the street than she headed for the pavement. She looked cautiously left and right until she saw Ihsan in the distance, and suddenly she felt the blood coursing through her veins.

She found herself unconsciously moving towards him until she was almost parallel with him, saw him staring at her from top to bottom, and felt a tremor throughout her body. When she saw his burning stare almost penetrating the cloak which covered her slender body her heart beat violently. She was used to seeing him every day at this time, and she used to stare at him freely each time until she had memorized his face. Of late, she had begun to feel her heart pounding whenever she saw him, and her face flushed with confusion. There was nothing to stop her from feasting her eyes on him, however, because she knew that the veil covered her face and concealed the overwhelming attraction she felt for him.

We cannot be certain what it was that made this youth know that the girl was interested in him, and whether his first overture to her came in the course of one of his habitual overtures, which he made to any girl. Whatever it was, he went up to the girl boldly on that first day, and sidled up to her, greeted her, and saw her turning round to look at him cautiously before hurrying on her way.

He knew immediately that she was not angry with him, and emboldened, he carried on behind her and saw her going into one of the public parks. She knew that he was following her, and hastened on her way, trembling with conflicting emotions of joy, fear, and caution.

He followed her into the park for a short distance, until he saw her sitting on her own, behind a big tree. He went up to her and spoke to her smilingly.

"Good evening."

"Good evening," she replied shyly.

Then she raised her veil from her brown face and her dark eyes, and Ihsan was captivated by the long dark eyelashes which cast a shadow over her features.

The features of her face were fine, and inspired the beholder with the strongest feelings of awe and worship. She was fearful and breathless, turning from side to side like a timid gazelle.[1] She knew that what she was doing amounted to an unpardonable crime, but drew comfort from one thing—the knowledge that this boy had not seen her before and did not know her. She was having an adventure, nothing more, and she was drawn into it by her youth and by the warm blood which coursed in her veins.

The boy's mind worked on some expressions of flattery and endearment. For his opening shot, he ventured: "I've seen you often, as you've passed by this street and then gone to walk among the trees. I wasn't able to talk to you because I respect you, and your whole appearance tells me that you are from a good family."

She replied, a little resentfully: "But I suppose you always try to talk with ordinary girls as well? Why don't you just chase the common girls, and satisfy your passions on them?"

"I'm sorry, really, I don't mean you any harm. But I'm alone, as you see, and I can't find a companion to share my walks with me. I saw that you were the only girl who found pleasure in these strolls, and so I felt that there was a link between us. Anyway, if you find my presence unpleasant in any way, I'll move off right now."

He made a move to get up, but she checked him and asked: "Do you know who I am?"

"I haven't the least idea, but this doesn't stop me from believing that I share your spirit," he replied softly.

---

1 **gazelle:** a small antelope noted for its graceful motion

"If you want to accompany me on these innocent walks, I don't see any objection," she mused. "There's no harm in strolling around with you for an hour or so, at intervals which we can agree on, the condition that you promise me that you won't try to follow me and try to find out who I am. I don't want you trying to contact me at any other times."

"I respect your wish and I shall honour it," he replied formally.

The two of them sat side by side on one of the stone benches, and a deep silence reigned over them, in which each felt the beating of their own hearts. This silence continued for a long time. Both of them had been overcome by the novelty of their strange and singular situation.

Ihsan, however, was a youth accustomed to flirtations, although he realized that this time he was faced with a girl who was pure and virtuous. There was something about her, a certain strength of purpose and character, which confused him, and stopped him from going too far. His mind worked to collect his thoughts and to rescue him from the situation into which he had unwittingly walked.

At length, he spoke, somewhat confused.

"What is your name, please?"

"Have you forgotten my condition that you should not try to identify me?"

"Of course. I'm sorry. But surely . . . in view of our future friendship . . . ?

"Have you forgotten? We live in a society in which this situation is unforgivable. If my people knew anything of this they'd kill me. While society is like this, we must learn to deceive. We must use the follies of our society in order to break its shackles!"

"What a penetrating mind you have!" said Ihsan admiringly.

"Thank you. Time's getting on and I must be getting back to the house. I will see you again in two days."

As she said goodbye he tried to put his arm around her waist, but she **rebuffed** him sharply. Then she relented slightly, saying: "I don't know who you are. You might be one of those mean boys who take delight in trapping girls for their own pleasure and sport."

rebuffed: snubbed; rejected

She went back to the house invigorated, but somewhat disturbed, for she had broken with the most binding and serious of traditions in one fell swoop. She didn't understand how it had begun and how it had ended, until it seemed to her that everything that had happened that day was a disturbing dream.

She threw her cloak on one side, and went to help her mother with the housework. She flattered her mother, made herself agreeable, and took delight in carrying out her orders and her arrangements. When her father returned home from work she welcomed him with a smiling face, then she went to her room to get on with her studies.

She set about her work mechanically, with nervous high spirits, and had disturbing dreams at night.

The meetings went on longer, and the subjects of their conversations diversified. The relationship between them developed, and things became deeply involved. She no longer felt that there was anything strange or unusual about the meetings, but she kept her head, using her lively mind to conceal her relationship with this boy, and to prevent him from trying to find out who she was and getting in touch with her.

· · · · ·

One day Siham was sitting with her father, talking to him after supper, while he was scanning the evening paper. His eye fell on a long article about women who had abandoned the veil, and, deciding to have his daughter's view, he read the article out loud. No sooner had he finished than Siham roundly abused the author for trying to break with convention and introduce modern **heresies**. Her father felt a greatly increased regard for his intelligent, well-brought-up daughter, who obviously knew the value of traditions and respected them. Such a difference between her and the rest of her irresponsible, scandalous friends, who, no sooner had they learned to read and write, went around throwing overboard society's conventions without shame or respect!

heresies: fallacies; dissenting beliefs

Impulsively, he moved towards his daughter and kissed her forehead.

"God preserve you as a treasure for your father."

When she reached her room Siham could barely stop herself from laughing out loud. She picked up her veil and danced with glee, then stopped in the middle of the room and began to whisper to the veil: "You black shroud, you know how I despise you and make use of you to keep him apart from me! I don't care about you, and I feel nothing for you. I defy you. But I love you too. These poor girls take refuge behind you in order to preserve their virginity, and their honour, and good morals. If they were more truthful they would say that they love you because you hide faults and scandals. I love you because you help me to enjoy my life in a way that only those who wear the veil can appreciate. I pity those wretched unveiled women. I scorn them."

Translated by S. Al-Bazzazz

After You Read

Critical Reading

1. Analyze the tensions in the story. Choose one **conflict** in the story and describe it in detail. Is it internal or external?

2. How does the **character** of Siham change or develop over the course of the story? Use evidence from the text to support your answer.

3. In this story, Siham says, "We must use the follies of our society in order to break its shackles" (page 483). Based on the details in the story, do you think that is what Siham is doing? Why or why not?

Literary Lens: Foil

The veil helps to reveal the character of Siham, and it also reveals the contrast between traditional and modern Muslim culture. Consider the issues in the chart below. Find a quotation about the veil that relates to each issue. Then analyze how the veil acts like a **foil** in the story and reveals Siham's character and the contrasting cultures.

Issue	Quotation about the veil	What this reveals about Siham	What this reveals about traditional vs. modern Muslim culture
How women should dress in public			
Role of women in society			
How women and men should interact			

Focus on Research: Organize Notes

Prepare to write a research paper in which you compare and contrast the courtship in this story with the courtship of Rama and Sita in the *Ramayana*. Take notes on both pieces and then organize the notes. You may choose to organize your notes by story—placing notes about one text together and notes about the other text together. Or you may choose to organize your notes by topic or main points. For example, you might organize your notes by grouping all the similarities together and all the differences together.

The Literature of
India and Sri Lanka

Background

Indian civilization dates back to about 2500 B.C.E. and has produced some of the world's greatest literature. India's earliest poems include the *Vedas*, sacred Hindu scriptures that were composed around 1500 to 1200 B.C.E. Several epics have come out of India, the greatest of which are the *Mahabharata* and the *Ramayana*. The dramatist Kālidāsa, who lived around the 5th century C.E., is famous for his plays such as *The Recognition of S'akuntalā* and *Mālavikā and Agnimitra*.

Modern Indian literature dates from the mid-19th century and a movement called the Hindu Renaissance. An important figure in this movement was Bankim Chandra Chatterjee (1838–1894), who produced such notable novels as *Mrinalini* and *Chandrasekhar*. Indian literature has flourished since the country won independence from Britain in 1947.

A year after India became independent from Great Britain, so did the island nation off its southern coast, Sri Lanka. The country has suffered a deadly ethnic conflict between its Sinhalese majority and its Tamil minority. Sri Lanka's most famous writer is Michael Ondaatje (1943–).

India and the United States

Because it is widely used in universities and businesses in India, English is the language favored by most Indian writers. As a result, Indian-born writers such as Bharati Mukherjee (1940–2017), Arundhati Roy (1961–), Anita Desai (1937–), and R. K. Narayan (1906–2001) are popular in the United States.

India's huge Hindi-language movie industry, known as Bollywood, has also helped familiarize people in the United States with Indian culture. Many classic and modern Indian movies can be streamed online.

Research: Take Notes and Represent Graphically

At least a dozen languages are spoken as the primary language of more than one billion people in India. Research the language diversity of India and make a table showing the leading languages of the country.

Five Hours to Simla

Anita Desai

T hen, miraculously, out of the pelt of yellow fur that was the dust growing across the great northern Indian plain, a wavering grey line emerged. It might have been a cloud bank looming, but it was not—the sun blazed, the earth shrivelled, the heat burnt away every trace of spring's **beneficence**. Yet the grey darkened, turned bluish, took on substance.

"Look—mountains!"

"Where?"

"I can't see any mountains."

"Are you blind? Look, look up—not down, fool!"

beneficence: kindness; generosity

A scuffle broke out between the boys on the sticky grime of the Rexine[1]-covered front seat. It was quieted by a tap on their heads from their mother in the back. "Yes, yes, mountains. The Himalayas.[2] We'll be there soon."

"Huh." A sceptical grunt from the driver of the tired, dust-buried grey Ambassador car. "At least five more hours to Simla." He ran his hand over the back of his neck where all the dirt of the road seemed to have found its way under the wilting cotton collar.

"Sim-la! Sim-la!" the boys set up a chant, their knees bouncing up and down in unison.

Smack, the driver's left hand landed on the closest pair, bringing out an instant stain of red and sudden, sullen silence.

"Be quiet!" the mother hissed from the back unnecessarily.

The Ambassador gave a sudden lurch, throwing everyone forwards. The baby, whose mouth had been glued to the teat of a bottle like a fly to syrup, came unstuck and wailed with indignation. Even their mother let out a small involuntary cry. Her daughter, who had been asleep on the back seat, her legs across her mother's lap, now stirred.

"Accident!" howled the small boy who had been smacked, triumphantly.

But it was not. His father had stopped just short of the bicycle rickshaw[3] ahead, which had just avoided running into the bullock[4] cart carrying farmers' families to market. A bus, loaded with baggage and spilling over with passengers, had also ground to a halt with a shrieking of brakes. Ahead of it was a truck, wrapped and folded in canvas sheets that blocked all else from sight. The mountains had disappeared and so had the road.

cacophony:
din; clamor

static:
steady;
unchanging

After the first **cacophony** of screeching brakes and grinding gears, there followed the comparatively **static** hum of engines, and drivers waited in exasperation for the next lurch forwards. For the moment there was a lull, curious on that highway. Then the waiting very quickly began to fray at the edges. The sun was beating on the metal of the vehicles, and the road lay flattened across the parched plain, with no trees to screen it from the sun. First one car horn began to honk, then a bicycle rickshaw began to clang its bell, then a truck blared its musical horn, and then the lesser ones began to

---

1 **Rexine:** artificial leather
2 **Himalayas:** an extensive mountain range in Asia, which includes Mount Everest, the highest mountain in the world
3 **rickshaw:** a passenger cart pulled by a human being
4 **bullock:** a young bull

go pom-pom, pom-pom almost in harmony, and suddenly, out of the centre of all that noise, a long, piercing wail emerged.

The two boys, the girl, the baby, all sat up, shocked. More so when they saw what their father was doing. Clenching the wheel with both hands, his head was lowered on to it, and the blare of the horn seemed to issue out of his fury.

The mother exclaimed.

The father raised his head and banged on the wheel, struck it. "How will we get to Simla before dark?" he howled.

The mother exclaimed again, shocked. "But we'll be moving again in a minute."

As if to contradict her, the driver of the truck stalled at the top of the line, swung himself out of the cabin into the road. He'd turned off his engine and stood in the deeply rutted dust, fumbling in his shirt pocket for cigarettes.

Other drivers got out of and down from their vehicles: the bullock-cart driver lowered himself from the creaking cart; the bicycle-rickshaw driver descended; the bus driver got out and stalked, in his sweat-drenched khakis, towards the truck driver standing at the head of the line; and they all demanded, "What's going on? Breakdown?"

The truck driver watched them approach but was lighting his cigarette and didn't answer. Then he waved an arm—his movements were leisurely, elegant, quite unlike what his driving had been—and said, "Stone throw. Somebody threw a stone. Hit windshield. Cracked it."

The father in the Ambassador had also joined them in the road. Hands on his hips, he demanded, "So?"

"So?" said the truck driver, narrowing his eyes. They were grey in a tanned face, heavily outlined and elongated with kohl, and his hair was tied up in a bandanna with a long loose end that dangled upon his shoulder. "So we won't be moving again till the person who did it is caught, and a *faisla* is made—a settlement."

Immediately a babble broke out. All the drivers flung out their hands and arms in angry, demanding gestures, their voices rose in questioning, in **cajoling**, in argument. The truck driver stood looking at them, watching them, his face **inscrutable**. Now and then he lifted the cigarette to his mouth and drew a deep puff. Then abruptly he swung around, clambered back into the cabin of his truck and started the engine with a roar at which the others fell back, their attitudes slackening in relief, but then he wheeled the truck around and parked it squarely across the highway so no traffic

cajoling: coaxing; wheedling

inscrutable: unknowable; indecipherable

could get past in either direction. The highway at that point had narrowed to a small culvert across a dry stream-bed full of stones. Now he clambered up the bank of the culvert and sat down, his legs wide apart in their loose and not too clean pyjamas,[5] regarding the traffic piling up in both directions as though he was watching sheep filing into a pen.

The knot of drivers in the road began to grow, joined by many of the passengers demanding to know the cause of this **impasse**.

impasse: deadlock; stalemate

"Dadd-ee! Dadd-ee!" the small boys yelled, hanging out of the door their father had left open and all but falling out into the dust. "What's happened, Dadd-ee?"

"Shut the door!" their mother ordered sharply but too late. A yellow pye-dog came crawling out of the shallow ditch that ran alongside the road and, spying an open door, came slinking up to it, thin, hairless tail between its legs, eyes showing their whites, hoping for bread but quite prepared for a blow instead.

The boys drew back on seeing its exploring snout, its teeth bared ready for a taste of bread. "Mad dog!" shouted one. "Mad dog!" bellowed the other.

"Shh!" hissed their mother.

Since no one in the car dared drive away a creature so dangerous, someone else did. A stone struck its ribs, and with a yelp it ducked under the car to hide, but already the next beggar was at the door, throwing himself in with much the same mixture of leering enquiry and cringing readiness to withdraw. "Bread," he whined, stretching out a bandaged hand. "*Paisa, paisa.* Mother, mother," he pleaded, seeing the mother cower in her seat with the baby. The children cowered too.

They knew that if they remained thus for long enough and made no move towards purse or coin, he would leave; he couldn't afford to waste too much time on them when there were so many potential donors lined up so conveniently along the highway. The mother stared glassily ahead through the windscreen at the heat beating off the metal bonnet.[6] The children could not tear their eyes away from the beggar—his sores, his bandages, his crippled leg, the flies gathering . . .

When he moved on, the mother raised a corner of her sari to her mouth and nose. From behind it she hissed: "Shut-the-door!"

Unsticking their damp legs from the moist, adhesive seat, the boys scrambled to do so. As they leaned out to grab the door however, and the good feel of the blazing sun and the open air struck at their faces and arms,

---

5 **pyjamas:** the loose top and pants favored by Indian men in tropical climates
6 **bonnet:** the Anglo-Indian term for a car hood

they turned around to plead, "Can we get out? Can we go and see what's happening?"

So **ardent** was their need that they were about to fall out of the open door when they saw their father detaching himself from the knot of passengers and drivers standing in the road and making his way back to them. The boys hastily edged back until he stood leaning in at the door. The family studied his face for signs; they were all adept at this, practising it daily over the breakfast table at home, and again when he came back from work. But this situation was a new one, a baffling one: they could not read it, or his position on it.

"What's happening?" the mother asked faintly at last.

"Damn truck driver," he swore through dark lips. "Some boy threw a rock—probably some goaterd in the field—and cracked his windscreen. He's parked the truck across the road, won't let anyone pass till there's a *faisla*. Says he won't move till the police come and get him compensation. Stupid damn fool—what compensation is a goatherd going to pay, even if they find him?"

The mother leaned her head back. What had reason to do with men's tempers? she might have asked. Instead, she sighed, "Is there a policeman?"

"What—here? In this forsaken desert?" her husband retorted, drawing in harsh breaths of overheated, dust-laden air as if he were breathing in all the stupidity around him. He could see passengers climbing down from the bus and the bullock cart, climbing across the ditch into the fields, and fanning out—some to lower their trousers, others to lift their saris behind the thorn bushes. If the glare was not playing tricks with his eyes, he thought he saw a puff of dust in the distance that might have been raised by goats' hooves.

"Take me to see, Dadd-ee, take me to see," the boys had begun to clamour, and to their astonishment he stood aside and let them climb out and even led them back to the truck that stood **imperviously** across the culvert.

imperviously: impassably; not allowing entrance or exit

The mother opened and shut her mouth silently. Her daughter stood up and hung over the front seat to watch the disappearing figures. In despair, she cried, "They're gone!"

"Sit down! Where can they go?"

"I want to go too, Mumm-ee, I want to go too-oo."

"Be quiet. There's nowhere to go."

The girl began to wail. It was usually a good strategy in a family with loud voices, but this time her grievance was genuine: her head ached from the long sleep in the car, from the heat beating on its metal top, from the lack of air, from the glare and from hunger. "I'm hung-gree," she wept.

"We were going to eat when we reached Solan," her mother reminded her. "There's such a nice-nice restaurant at the railway station in Solan. Such nice-nice omelettes they make there."

"I want an omelette!" wailed the child.

"Wait till we get to Solan."

"When will we reach it? *When?*"

"Oh, I don't know. Late. Sit down and open that basket at the back. You'll find something to eat there."

But now that omelettes at Solan had been mentioned the basket packed at home with Gluco biscuits and potato chips held no attraction for the girl. She stopped wailing but sulked instead, sucking her thumb, a habit she was supposed to have given up but which resurfaced for comfort when necessary.

She did not need to draw upon her thumb juices for long. The news of the traffic jam on the highway had spread. From somewhere—it seemed from nowhere for there was no village bazaar, market place or stall visible in that dusty **dereliction**—wooden barrows came trundling along towards

dereliction: area of neglect or abandonment

the waiting traffic, bearing freshly cut lengths of sugar cane; bananas already more black than yellow from the sun that baked them; peanuts in their shells roasting in pans set on embers. Men, women and children were climbing over the ditch like phantoms, materializing out of the dust, with baskets on their heads filled not only with food but with amusements as well—a trayload of paper toys painted **indigo** and violent pink, small bamboo pipes that released rude noises and a dyed feather on a spool. Kites, puppets, clay carts, wooden toys and tin whistles. The vendors milled around the buses, cars and rickshaws, and were soon standing at their car window, both vocally and manually proffering goods for sale.

The baby let drop its narcotic rubber teat, delighted. Its eyes grew big and shone at all it saw flowering about it. The little girl was perplexed, wondering what to choose from so much till the perfect choice presented itself in a rainbow of colour: green, pink and violet, her favourites. It was a barrow of soft drinks, and nothing on this day of gritty dust, yellow sun and frustrating delay could be more enticing than those bottles filled with syrups in those dazzling floral colours which provoked in her a scream of desire.

"Are you mad?" her mother said promptly. "You think I'll let you drink a bottle full of typhoid and cholera[7] germs?"

The girl gasped with disbelief at being denied. Her mouth opened wide to issue a protest, but her mother went on. "After you have your typhoid-and-cholera injection, you may. You want a nice, big typhoid-and-cholera injection first?"

The child's mouth was still open in contemplation of the impossible choice when her brothers came plodding back through the dust, each carrying a pith[8]-and-bamboo toy—a clown that jounced upon a stick and a bird that whirled upon a pin. Behind them the father slouched morosely. He had his hands deep in his pockets, and his face was lined with a frown deeply embedded with dust.

"We'll be here for hours," he informed his wife through the car window. "A rickshaw driver has gone off to the nearest *thana* to find a policeman who can put sense into that damn truck driver's thick head." Despondently he threw himself into the driver's seat and sprawled there. "Must be a hundred and twenty degrees," he sighed.

"Pinky, where is the water bottle? Pass the water bottle to Daddy," commanded the mother solicitously.

---

7 **typhoid and cholera:** infectious diseases affecting the intestines, often fatal
8 **pith:** the soft, inner part of a plant stem

He drank from the plastic bottle, tilting his head back and letting the water spill into his mouth. But it was so warm it was hardly refreshing, and he spat the last mouthful out of the car window into the dust. A scavenging chicken alongside the tyre skipped away with a squawk.

All along the road, in the stationary traffic, drivers and passengers were searching for shade, for news, for some sign of release. Every now and then someone brought information on how long the line of cars and trucks now was. Two miles in each direction was the latest estimate, at least two miles.

• • • • •

Up on the bank of the culvert the man who had caused it all sat sprawling, his legs wide apart. He had taken off his bandanna, revealing a twist of cotton wool dipped in fragrant oil that was tucked behind his ear. He had bought himself a length of sugar cane and sat chewing it, ripping off the tough outer fibre with strong flashing teeth, then drawing the sweet syrup out of its soft white inside and spitting out, with relish, the pale fibre sucked dry. He seemed deliberately to spit in the direction of those who stood watching in growing frustration.

"Get hold of that fellow! *Force* him to move his truck," somebody suddenly shouted out, driven to the limit of his endurance. "If he doesn't, he'll get the thrashing of his life."

"Calm down, Sirdarji," another placated him with a light laugh to help put things back in perspective. "Cool down. It's hot, but you'll get your cold beer when you get to Solan."

"When will that be? When my beard's gone grey?"

"Grey hair is nothing to be ashamed of," philosophized an elder who had a good deal of it to show. "Grey hair shows patience, forbearance, a long life. That is how to live long—patiently, with forbearance."

"And when one has work to do, what then?" the Sikh demanded, rolling up his hands into fists. The metal bangle on his wrist glinted.

"Work goes better after a little rest," the elder replied, and demonstrated by lowering himself on to his haunches and squatting there on the roadside like an old bird on its perch or a man waiting to be shaved by a roadside barber. And, like an answer to a call, a barber did miraculously appear, an itinerant barber who carried the tools of his trade in a tin box on his head. No one could imagine where he had emerged from, or how far he had travelled in search of custom. Now he squatted and began to unpack a mirror, scissors, soap, blades, even a small rusty cigarette tin full of water. An audience stood watching his expert moves and flourishes and the evident pleasure these gave the elder.

Suddenly the truck driver on the bank waved a hand and called, "Hey, come up here when you've finished. I could do with a shave too—and my ears need cleaning."

There was a gasp at his **insolence**, and then indignant protests.

insolence: boldness; disrespect

"Are you planning to get married over there? Are we not to move till your bride arrives and the wedding is over?" shouted someone.

This had the wrong effect: it made the crowd laugh. Even the truck driver laughed. He was somehow becoming a part of the conspiracy. How had this happened?

In the road, the men stood locked in bafflement. In the vehicles, the tired passengers waited. "Oo-oof," sighed the mother. The baby, asleep as if stunned by the heat, felt heavy as lead in her arms. "My head is paining, and it's time to have tea."

"Mama wants tea, mama wants tea!" chanted her daughter, kicking at the front seat.

"Stop it!" her father snapped. "Where is the kitchen? Where is the cook? Am I to get them out of the sky? Or is there a well filled with tea?"

The children all burst out laughing at the idea of drawing tea from a well, but while they giggled helplessly, a *chai wallah*[9] did appear, a tray with glasses on his head, a kettle dangling from his hand, searching for the passenger who had called for tea.

There was no mention of cholera or typhoid now. He was summoned, glasses were filled with milky, sweet tea and handed out, the parents slurped thirstily, and the children stared, demanding sips, then flinching from the scalding liquid.

Heartened, the father began to thrash around in the car, punch the horn, stamp ineffectually on the accelerator. "Damn fool," he swore. "How can this happen? How can this be allowed? Only in this bloody country. Where else can one man hold up four miles of traffic?"

Handing back an empty glass, the mother suggested, "Why don't you go and see if the policeman's arrived?"

"Am I to go up and down looking for a policeman? Should I walk to Solan to find one?" the man fumed. His tirade rolled like thunder out of the white blaze of the afternoon. The children listened, watched. Was it getting darker? Was a thundercloud approaching? Was it less bright? Perhaps it was evening. Perhaps it would be night soon.

---

9 *chai wallah:* a person employed to serve tea

"What will we do when it grows dark?" the girl whimpered. "Where will we sleep?"

"Here, on the road!" shouted the boys. "Here on the road!" Their toys were long since broken and discarded. They needed some distraction. Their sister could easily be moved to tears by mentioning night, jackals, ghosts that haunt highways, robbers who carry silk handkerchiefs to strangle their victims . . .

•••••

Suddenly, one of the drivers, hitching up his pyjamas and straightening his turban, came running back towards the stalled traffic, shouting, "They're moving! The policeman's come! They'll move now! There'll be a *faisla*!"

Instantly the picture changed from one of discouragement, despair and approaching darkness to animation, excitement, hope. All those loitering in the road leaped back into their vehicles, and in a moment the air was filled with the roar of revving engines as with applause.

The father too was pressing down on the accelerator, beating upon the steering wheel, and the children settling into position, all screaming, "Simla! Sim-la!" in unison.

But not a single vehicle moved an inch. None could. The obstructing truck had not been moved out of the way. The driver still sprawled on the bank, propped up on one elbow now, demanding of the policeman who had arrived, "So? Have you brought me compensation? NO? Why not? I told you I would not move till I received compensation. So where is it? Hah? What is the *faisla*? Hah?"

The roar of engines faltered, hiccuped, fell silent. After a while, car doors slammed as drivers and passengers climbed out again. Groups formed to discuss the latest development. What was to be done now? The elder's philosophical patience was no longer entertained. No one bandied jokes with the villain on the bank any more. Expressions turned grim.

Suddenly the mother wailed, "We'll be here all night," and the baby woke crying: it had had enough of being confined in the suffocating heat; it wanted air, it wanted escape. All the children began to whine. The mother drew herself up. "We'll have to get something to eat," she said and called over to her husband standing in the road, "Can't you get some food for the children?"

He threw her an irritated look over his shoulder. Together with the men in the road, he was going back to the culvert to see what could be done. There was an urgency about their talk now, their suggestions. Dusk had begun to creep across the fields like a thicker, greyer layer of dust. Some of the vendors lit kerosene lamps on their barrows, so small and faint that they did nothing but accentuate the darkness. Some of them were disappearing over the fields, along paths visible only to them, having sold their goods and possibly having a long way to travel. All that could be seen in the dark were the lighted pinpricks of their cigarettes.

What the small girl had most feared did now happen—the long, mournful howl of a jackal lifted itself out of the stones and thorn bushes and unfurled through the dark towards them. While she sat mute with fear, her brothers let out howls of delight and began to imitate the invisible creature's call.

The mother was shushing them fiercely when they heard the sound they had given up hope of hearing: the sound of a moving vehicle. It came roaring up the road from behind them—not at all where they had expected—overtaking them in a cloud of choking dust. Policemen in khaki, armed with steel-tipped canes, leaned out of it, their moustaches bristling, their teeth gleaming, eyes flashing and ferocious as tigers. And the huddled crowd stranded on the roadside fell aside like sheep; it might have been they who were at fault.

But the police truck overtook them all, sending them hurriedly into the ditch for safety, and drew up at the culvert. Here the police jumped out, landing with great thuds on the asphalt, and striking their canes hard upon it for good measure. The truck's headlights lit up the bank with its **pallid** wash.

> **pallid:** pale; colorless

Caught in that illumination, the truck driver rose calmly to his feet, dusted the seat of his pyjamas, wound up the bandanna round his head, all in one fluid movement, and without a word leaped lightly back into the driver's seat of his truck. He turned the key, started the engine, manoeuvred into an onward position and, while his audience held its disbelieving breath, set off towards the north.

After a moment they saw that he had switched on his lights. He had also turned on his radio, and a song could be heard.

> Father, I am leaving your roof,
> To my bridegroom's home I go . . .

His tail lights could be seen dwindling in the dark. The police swung around, flourishing their canes. "Get on! *Chalo!*" they bellowed. "*Chalo, chalo*, get on, all of you," and they did.

After You Read

Critical Reading

1. Identify the main **conflict** in this story and state whether it is **external**, meaning between the characters and outside forces, or **internal**, meaning within the character. Explain how the conflict develops the story's theme.

2. Reread the first paragraph of the story. Explain how this is an example of a story beginning **in media res**. Describe the effect this beginning has on readers.

3. What is the **tone**, or the narrator's perspective, in the story? Support your response with several details from the story.

Literary Lens: Mood

Desai builds the **mood** of the story through imagery, setting, characterization, and dialogue. Cite quotations for each of these techniques and then describe the mood they convey. Re-create the chart below to help you analyze the mood.

Technique	Quotation	Mood
Imagery		
Setting		
Characterization		
Dialogue		

Focus on Research: Evaluate Sources for Bias

Find two or more sources on Indian child-rearing practices. Read these sources and then evaluate them for bias. To do this, create a bias checklist similar to the one below and fill it out for each source. Work with a partner to add more qualities to the checklist. Then fill it out for each of your sources.

Source 1:		
	Yes	No
From a reliable publication		
Expresses only one person's experiences		
Supports points with multiple data or studies		

After evaluating your sources, write a few paragraphs in which you present multiple points of view about the topic—without showing bias in your writing.

The Cabuliwallah
(The Fruit Seller from Cabul)[1]

Rabindranath Tagore

Before You Read

The poet, essayist, playwright, fiction writer, and composer Rabindranath Tagore (1861–1941) is recognized as India's greatest artist of the 20th century. His poetry won him the Nobel Prize in 1913. He was also an innovative educator who founded an experimental school. In his 60s, he took up visual art and created modernistic sketches and paintings that revealed his nuanced inner life. Both India and Bangladesh adopted songs by Tagore as their national anthems.

World Context

Tagore considered his work "a confluence of three cultures: Hindu, Mohammedan, and British." Like his friend Mohandas Gandhi, Tagore spoke out against colonialism, even rejecting a knighthood. In his writing, Tagore interweaves strands of traditional Indian culture with Western influences.

 LITERARY LENS While reading the story, pay close attention to the way that the events unfold in the **plot**.

Mini, my five-year-old daughter, cannot live without chattering. I really believe that in all her life she has not wasted one minute in silence. Her mother is often vexed at this and would stop her prattle, but I do not. To see Mini quiet is unnatural and I cannot bear it for long. Because of this, our conversations are always lively.

One morning, for instance, when I was in the midst of the seventeenth chapter of my new novel, Mini stole into the room and putting her hand

---

1 **Cabul:** (also Kabul), the capital of Afghanistan

into mine, said: "Father! Ramdayal the door keeper calls a crow a krow! He doesn't know anything, does he?"

Before I could explain the language differences in this country, she was on the trace of another subject. "What do you think, Father? Shola says there is an elephant in the clouds, blowing water out of his trunk, and that is why it rains!"

The child had seated herself at my feet near the table and was playing softly, drumming on her knees. I was hard at work on my seventeenth chapter, where Pratap Singh, the hero, had just caught Kanchanlata, the heroine, in his arms and was about to escape with her by the third-story window of the castle, when all of a sudden Mini left her play and ran to the window, crying, "A Cabuliwallah! A Cabuliwallah!" Sure enough, in the street below was a Cabuliwallah passing slowly along. He wore the loose, soiled clothing of his people and a tall turban; there was a bag on his back, and he carried boxes of grapes in his hand.

I cannot tell what my daughter's feelings were at the sight of this man, but she began to call him loudly. Ah, I thought, he will come in and my seventeenth chapter will never be finished! At this exact moment the Cabuliwallah turned and looked up at the child. When she saw this she was overcome by terror, fled to her mother's protection, and disappeared. She had a blind belief that inside the bag which the big man carried were two or three children like herself. Meanwhile, the peddler entered my doorway and greeted me with a smiling face.

precarious:
insecure; risky

So **precarious** was the position of my hero and my heroine that my first impulse was to stop and buy something, especially since Mini had called to the man. I made some small purchases, and a conversation began about Abdurrahman, the Russians, the English, and the Frontier Policy.[2]

As he was about to leave, he asked: "And where is the little girl, sir?"

I, thinking that Mini must get rid of her false fear, had her brought out. She stood by my chair, watching the Cabuliwallah and his bag. He offered her nuts and raisins but she would not be tempted, and only clung closer to me, with all her doubts increased. This was their first meeting.

One morning, however, not many days later, as I was leaving the house I was startled to find Mini seated on a bench near the door, laughing and talking with the great Cabuliwallah at her feet. In all her life, it appeared, my small daughter had never found so patient a listener, except for her father. Already the corner of her little sari was stuffed with almonds and

---

2 **Abdurrahman . . . Policy:** Abdurrahman Khan, an Afghanistan ruler who came to power in 1880 after Great Britain relinquished its power over internal matters. Great Britain had been vying with Russia for control of the nation.

raisins, gifts from her visitor. "Why did you give her those?" I said, and taking out an eight-anna piece,[3] handed it to him. The man accepted the money without delay and slipped it into his pocket.

Alas, on my return an hour later, I found the unfortunate coin had made twice its own worth of trouble! The Cabuliwallah had given it to Mini, and her mother, seeing the bright, round object, had pounced on the child with: "Where did you get that eight-anna piece?"

"The Cabuliwallah gave it to me," said Mini cheerfully.

"The Cabuliwallah gave it to you!" cried her mother, much shocked. "Oh, Mini! How could you take it from him?"

Entering at this moment, I saved her from **impending** disaster and proceeded to make my own inquiries. I found that it was not the first or the second time the two had met. The Cabuliwallah had overcome the child's first terror by a **judicious** bribery of nuts and almonds, and the two were now great friends.

They had many quaint jokes which afforded them a great deal of amusement. Seated in front of him, and looking with all her tiny dignity on his gigantic frame, Mini would ripple her face with laughter and begin, "O Cabuliwallah! Cabuliwallah! what have you got in your bag?"

He would reply in the nasal accents of a mountaineer: "An elephant!" Not much cause for merriment, perhaps, but how they both enjoyed their joke! And for me, this child's talk with a grown-up man always had in it something strangely fascinating.

Then the Cabuliwallah, not to be caught behind, would take his turn with: "Well, little one, and when are you going to the father-in-law's house?"

"Well, little one, and when are you going to the father-in-law's house?"

Now most small Bengali maidens have heard long ago about the father-in-law's house, but we, being a little modern, had kept these things from our child, and at this question Mini must have been a trifle bewildered. But she would not show it, and with instant composure replied: "Are you going there?"

Among men of the Cabuliwallah's class, however, it is well known that the words "father-in-law's house" have a double meaning. It is a euphemism for jail, the place where we are well cared for at no expense. The sturdy peddler would take my daughter's question in this sense. "Ah," he would say, shaking his fist at an invisible policeman, "I will thrash my father-in-law!" Hearing this, and picturing the poor, uncomfortable relative, Mini would go into peals of laughter, joined by her formidable friend.

---

3 **eight-anna piece:** a former Indian coin

These were autumn mornings, the time of year when kings of old went forth to conquest; and I, never stirring from my little corner in Calcutta, would let my mind wander over the whole world. At the very name of another country, my heart would go out to it, and at the sight of a foreigner in the streets, I would fall to weaving a network of dreams: the mountains, the glens, the forests of his distant homeland with a cottage in its setting, and the free and independent life of faraway wilds. Perhaps these scenes of travel pass in my imagination all the more vividly because I lead a vegetable existence such that a call to travel would fall upon me like a thunderbolt. In the presence of this Cabuliwallah I was immediately transported to the foot of mountains, with narrow defiles twisting in and out amongst their towering, arid peaks. I could see the string of camels bearing merchandise, and the company of turbaned merchants carrying queer old firearms and some of their spears down toward the plains. I could see—but at this point Mini's mother would intervene, **imploring** me to "beware of that man."

imploring: beseeching; entreating

Unfortunately Mini's mother is a very timid lady. Whenever she hears a noise in the street or sees people coming toward the house, she always jumps to the conclusion that they are either thieves, drunkards, snakes, tigers, malaria, cockroaches, caterpillars, or an English sailor. Even after all these years of experience, she is not able to overcome her terror. Thus she was full of doubts about the Cabuliwallah and used to beg me to keep a watchful eye on him.

I tried to gently laugh her fear away, but then she would turn on me seriously and ask solemn questions.

Were children never kidnapped?

Was it, then, not true that there was slavery in Cabul?

Was it so very absurd that this big man should be able to carry off a tiny child?

I told her that, though not impossible, it was highly improbable. But this was not enough, and her dread persisted. As her suspicion was unfounded, however, it did not seem right to forbid the man to come to the house, and his familiarity went unchecked.

Once a year, in the middle of January, Rahmun the Cabuliwallah was in the habit of returning to his country, and as the time approached he would be very busy going from house to house collecting his debts. This year, however, he always found time to come and see Mini. It would have seemed to an outsider that there was some conspiracy between them, for when he could not come in the morning, he would appear in the evening.

Even to me it was a little startling now and then, to suddenly surprise this tall, loose-garmented man of bags in the corner of a dark room; but when Mini would run in, smiling, with her "O Cabuliwallah! Cabuliwallah!" and the two friends so far apart in age would subside into their old laughter and their old jokes, I felt reassured.

One morning, a few days before he had made up his mind to go, I was correcting my proof sheets[4] in my study. It was chilly weather. Through the window the rays of the sun touched my feet, and the slight warmth was very welcome. It was almost eight o'clock, and the early pedestrians were returning home with their heads covered. All at once I heard an uproar in the street and, looking out, saw Rahmun bound and being led away between two policemen, followed by a crowd of curious boys. There were bloodstains on the clothes of the Cabuliwallah, and one of the policemen carried a knife. Hurrying out, I stopped them and inquired what it all meant. Partly from one, partly from another, I gathered that a certain neighbor had owed the peddler something for a Rampuri shawl but had falsely denied having bought it, and that in the course of the quarrel Rahmun had struck him. Now, in the heat of his excitement, the prisoner began calling his enemy all sorts of names. Suddenly, from a verandah of my house my little Mini appeared, with her usual exclamation: "O Cabuliwallah! Cabuliwallah!" Rahmun's face lighted up as he turned to her. He had no bag under his arm today, so she could not discuss the elephant with him. She at once therefore proceeded to the next question: "Are you going to the father-in-law's house?" Rahmun laughed and said: "Just where I am going, little one!" Then seeing that the reply did not amuse the child, he held up his **fettered** hands. "Ah," he said, "I would have thrashed that old father-in-law, but my hands are bound!"

fettered: bound; shackled

On a charge of murderous assault, Rahmun was sentenced to many years of imprisonment.

• • • • •

Time passed and he was forgotten. The accustomed work in the accustomed place was ours, and the thought of the once-free mountaineer spending his years in prison seldom occurred to us. Even my lighthearted Mini, I am ashamed to say, forgot her old friend. New companions filled her life. As she grew older she spent more of her time with girls, so much in fact that she came no more to her father's room. I was scarcely on speaking terms with her.

---

4   **proof sheets:** texts requiring editing or corrections

Many years passed. It was autumn once again and we had made arrangements for Mini's marriage; it was to take place during the Puja[5] holidays. With the goddess Durga returning to her seasonal home in Mount Kailas, the light of our home was also to depart, leaving our house in shadows.

The morning was bright. After the rains, there was a sense of cleanness in the air, and the rays of the sun looked like pure gold, so bright that they radiated even to the sordid brick walls of our Calcutta lanes. Since early dawn, the wedding pipes had been sounding, and at each beat my own heart throbbed. The wailing tune, Bhairavi, seemed to intensify my pain at the approaching separation. My Mini was to be married tonight.

From early morning, noise and bustle pervaded the house. In the courtyard the canopy had to be slung on its bamboo poles; the tinkling chandeliers should be hung in each room and verandah; there was great hurry and excitement. I was sitting in my study, looking through the accounts, when someone entered, saluting respectfully, and stood before me. It was Rahmun the Cabuliwallah, and at first I did not recognize him. He had no bag, nor the long hair, nor the same vigor that he used to have. But he smiled, and I knew him again.

"When did you come, Rahmun?" I asked him.

"Last evening," he said, "I was released from jail."

The words struck harsh upon my ears. I had never talked with anyone who had wounded his fellow man, and my heart shrank when I realized this, for I felt that the day would have been better omened if he had not turned up.

"There are ceremonies going on," I said, "and I am busy. Could you perhaps come another day?"

At once he turned to go, but as he reached the door he hesitated and said: "May I not see the little one, sir, for a moment?" It was his belief that Mini was still the same. He had pictured her running to him as she used to do, calling, "O Cabuliwallah! Cabuliwallah!" He had imagined that they would laugh and talk together, just as in the past. In fact, in memory of those former days he had brought, carefully wrapped up in paper, a few almonds and raisins and grapes, somehow obtained from a countryman—his own little fund was gone.

I said again: "There is a ceremony in the house, and you will not be able to see anyone today."

The man's face fell. He looked wistfully at me for a moment, said "Good morning," and went out.

---

5 **Puja:** a Hindu observance of certain deities or gods

I felt a little sorry and would have called him back but saw that he was returning of his own accord. He came close up to me, holding out his offerings, and said: "I brought these few things, sir, for the little one. Will you give them to her?"

I took them and was going to pay him, but he caught my hand and said: "You are very kind, sir! Keep me in your recollection; do not offer me money! You have a little girl; I too have one like her in my own home. I thought of my own and brought fruits to your child, not to make a profit for myself."

Saying this, he put his hand inside his big loose robe and brought out a small dirty piece of paper. With great care he unfolded this and smoothed it out with both hands on my table. It bore the impression of a little hand, not a photograph, not a drawing. The impression of an ink-smeared hand laid flat on the paper. This touch of his own little daughter had been always on his heart, as he had come year after year to Calcutta to sell his wares in the streets.

Tears came to my eyes. I forgot that he was a poor Cabuli fruitseller, while I was—but no, was I more than he? He was also a father.

That impression of the hand of his little Parbati in her distant mountain home reminded me of my own little Mini, and I immediately sent for her from the inner apartment. Many excuses were raised, but I would not listen. Clad in the red silk of her wedding day, with the sandal paste on her forehead, and adorned as a young bride, Mini came and stood bashfully before me.

The Cabuliwallah was staggered at the sight of her. There was no hope of reviving their old friendship. At last he smiled and said: "Little one, are you going to your father-in-law's house?"

But Mini now understood the meaning of the word "father-in-law," and she could not reply to him as in the past. She flushed at the question and stood before him with her bride's face looking down.

I remembered the day when the Cabuliwallah and my Mini first met, and I felt sad. When she had gone, Rahmun heaved a deep sigh and sat down on the floor. The idea had suddenly come to him that his daughter also must have grown up during this long time, and that he would have to make friends with her all over again. Surely he would not find her as he used to know her; besides, what might have happened to her in these eight years?

The marriage pipes sounded, and the mild autumn sun streamed around us. But Rahmun sat in the little Calcutta lane and saw before him the barren mountains of Afghanistan.

I took out a bank note and gave it to him, saying: "Go back to your own daughter, Rahmun, in your own country, and may the happiness of your meeting bring good fortune to my child!"

After giving this gift, I had to eliminate some of the festivities. I could not have the electric lights, nor the military band, and the ladies of the house were saddened. But to me the wedding feast was brighter because of the thought that in a distant land a long-lost father met again with his only child.

After You Read

Critical Reading

1. Think about the colloquial phrase mentioned several times in the story: "going to your father-in-law's house." What are the two meanings for this phrase described in the story? Would you consider this phrase to be a **pun,** or a play on words?

2. Analyze the **character** of Mini's father. When does he experience an **epiphany** in the story? Identify the scene, and identify how he changes.

3. How does Mini's relationship with both the Cabuliwallah and her father change by the time she is ready for marriage? Describe the changes in the character of Mini.

4. Analyze the **subtext** of the story. What is the story's hidden meaning regarding poor, working people like the Cabuliwallah?

Literary Lens: Plot

Consider the way the events in the **plot** unfold. Identify a major event from each stage of the plot, and describe how each stage helped to trigger the next stage of the plot.

Stage	Major event	How did this trigger the next stage of the plot?
Exposition		
Rising action		
Climax		
Falling action		
Resolution		

Focus on Research: Conduct a Survey

There are many ways to gather information. One way is by conducting a survey. Use a digital survey program, such as Google Forms or Survey Monkey, to survey your class. In this story, the character called Cabuliwallah is sent to prison. Ask each person questions about whether class and bias had an effect on Cabuliwallah's imprisonment. Possible questions include the following: Do you think the Cabuliwallah committed a crime? Do you think Cabuliwallah's imprisonment was fair and just?

Like the Sun

R. K. Narayan

Before You Read

Rasipuram Krishnaswami Narayanswami (1906–2001) shortened his name to R. K. Narayan at the suggestion of his English publisher. He wrote his often-humorous stories, novels, and essays in English. In Narayan's most highly praised novel, *The Guide*, a former convict is mistaken for a holy man. His *Gods, Demons and Others* is a retelling of ancient tales from the *Ramayana* and other Hindu epics.

World Context

Many of Narayan's works are set in the fictitious South Indian town of Malgudi. In his graceful style, marked by simplicity and touches of humor, Narayan captures human relationships and the conflict between ancient Indian traditions and the realities of living in a modern world.

 LITERARY LENS As you read, consider the **theme**, or the underlying message, Narayan communicates in "Like the Sun."

Truth, Sekhar reflected, is like the sun. I suppose no human being can ever look it straight in the face without blinking or being dazed. He realized that, morning till night, the essence of human relationships consisted in tempering truth so that it might not shock. This day he set apart as a unique day—at least one day in the year we must give and take absolute Truth whatever may happen. Otherwise life is not worth living. The day ahead seemed to him full of possibilities. He told no one of his experiment. It was a quiet resolve, a secret pact between him and eternity.

The very first test came while his wife served him his morning meal. He showed hesitation over a tidbit, which she had thought was her **culinary** masterpiece. She asked, "Why, isn't it good?" At other times he would have said, considering her feelings in the matter, "I feel full-up, that's all." But

culinary: related to the kitchen or cooking

today he said, "It isn't good. I'm unable to swallow it." He saw her wince and said to himself, Can't be helped. Truth is like the sun.

His next trial was in the common room when one of his colleagues came up and said, "Did you hear of the death of so and so? Don't you think it a pity?" "No," Sekhar answered. "He was such a fine man—" the other began. But Sekhar cut him short with: "Far from it. He always struck me as a mean and selfish brute."

During the last period when he was teaching geography for Third Form A,[1] Sekhar received a note from the headmaster: "Please see me before you go home." Sekhar said to himself: It must be about these horrible test papers. A hundred papers in the boys' scrawls; he had shirked this work for weeks, feeling all the time as if a sword were hanging over his head.

The bell rang and the boys burst out of the class.

Sekhar paused for a moment outside the headmaster's room to button up his coat; that was another subject the headmaster always sermonized about.

He stepped in with a very polite "Good evening, sir."

The headmaster looked up at him in a very friendly manner and asked, "Are you free this evening?"

Sekhar replied, "Just some outing which I have promised the children at home—"

"Well, you can take them out another day. Come home with me now."

"Oh . . . yes, sir, certainly . . . " And then he added timidly, "Anything special, sir?"

"Yes," replied the headmaster, smiling to himself . . . "You didn't know my weakness for music?"

"Oh, yes, sir . . . "

"I've been learning and practicing secretly, and now I want you to hear me this evening. I've engaged a drummer and a violinist to accompany me—this is the first time I'm doing it full-dress and I want your opinion. I know it will be valuable."

Sekhar's taste in music was well known. He was one of the most dreaded music critics in the town. But he never anticipated his musical inclinations would lead him to this trial . . . "Rather a surprise for you, isn't it?" asked the headmaster. "I've spent a fortune on it behind closed doors . . . " They started for the headmaster's house. "God hasn't given me a child, but at least let him not deny me the consolation of music," the headmaster said, pathetically, as they walked. He incessantly chattered about music: how he

---

1 **Third Form A:** a class or grade level in an Anglo-Indian secondary school

began one day out of sheer boredom; how his teacher at first laughed at him, and then gave him hope; how his ambition in life was to forget himself in music.

At home the headmaster proved very **ingratiating**. He sat Sekhar on a red silk carpet, set before him several dishes of delicacies, and fussed over him as if he were a son-in-law of the house. He even said, "Well, you must listen with a free mind. Don't worry about these test papers." He added half humorously, "I will give you a week's time."

"Make it ten days, sir," Sekhar pleaded.

"All right, granted," the headmaster said generously. Sekhar felt really relieved now—he would attack them at the rate of ten a day and get rid of the nuisance.

The headmaster lighted incense sticks. "Just to create the right atmosphere," he explained. A drummer and a violinist, already seated on a Rangoon[2] mat, were waiting for him. The headmaster sat down between them like a professional at a concert, cleared his throat, and began an alapana,[3] and paused to ask, "Isn't it good Kalyani?" Sekhar pretended not to have heard the question. The headmaster went on to sing a full song composed by Thyagaraja and followed it with two more. All the time the headmaster was singing, Sekhar went on commenting within himself, He croaks like a dozen frogs. He is bellowing like a buffalo. Now he sounds like loose window shutters in a storm.

The incense sticks burnt low. Sekhar's head throbbed with the medley of sounds that had assailed his ear-drums for a couple of hours now. He felt half stupefied. The headmaster had gone nearly hoarse, when he paused to ask, "Shall I go on?" Sekhar replied, "Please don't, sir, I think this will do. . . ." The headmaster looked stunned. His face was beaded with perspiration. Sekhar felt the greatest pity for him. But he felt he could not help it. No judge delivering a sentence felt more pained and helpless. Sekhar noticed that the headmaster's wife peeped in from the kitchen, with eager curiosity. The drummer and the violinist put away their burdens with an air of relief. The headmaster removed his spectacles, mopped his brow, and asked, "Now, come out with your opinion."

"Can't I give it tomorrow, sir?" Sekhar asked tentatively.

"No. I want it immediately—your frank opinion. Was it good?"

"No, sir . . . " Sekhar replied.

---

2 **Rangoon:** made in Rangoon, the capital of Burma
3 **alapana:** the beginning of a song in southern India

"Oh! . . . Is there any use continuing my lessons?"

"Absolutely none, sir . . . " Sekhar said with his voice trembling. He felt very unhappy that he could not speak more soothingly. Truth, he reflected, required as much strength to give as to receive.

Truth, he reflected, required as much strength to give as to receive.

All the way home he felt worried. He felt that his official life was not going to be smooth sailing hereafter. There were questions of **increment** and confirmation and so on, all depending upon the headmaster's goodwill. All kinds of worries seemed to be in store for him. . . . Did not Harischandra[4] lose his throne, wife, child, because he would speak nothing less than the absolute Truth whatever happened?

increment: increase; step up (as on a salary scale)

At home his wife served him with a sullen face. He knew she was still angry with him for his remark of the morning. Two casualties for today, Sekhar said to himself. If I practice it for a week, I don't think I shall have a single friend left.

He received a call from the headmaster in his classroom the next day. He went up apprehensively.

"Your suggestion was useful. I have paid off the music master. No one would tell me the truth about my music all these days. Why such antics at my age! Thank you. By the way, what about those test papers?"

"You gave me ten days, sir, for correcting them."

"Oh, I've reconsidered it. I must positively have them here tomorrow. . . . " A hundred papers in a day! That meant all night's sitting up! "Give me a couple of days, sir . . . "

"No. I must have them tomorrow morning. And remember, every paper must be thoroughly **scrutinized**."

scrutinized: examined; inspected

"Yes, sir," Sekhar said, feeling that sitting up all night with a hundred test papers was a small price to pay for the luxury of practicing Truth.

---

4 **Harischandra:** (1850–1885), an Indian famous for his poetry, criticism, and reportage

After You Read

Critical Reading

1. A **parable** is a type of literary text intended to reveal a religious principle, moral lesson, or general truth. How is this story like a parable?

2. A **hero** is a main character whose actions are considered honorable, noble, and brave. An **antihero** is a character who generally possesses both positive and negative qualities. He or she is self-conscious, uncertain, or has questionable motives. Consider the character of Sekhar. Would you consider Sekhar to be a **hero** or an **anti-hero**? Support your answer with details from the story.

3. Based on **word choice**, how would you describe the tone of the story? Cite examples to support your position.

Literary Lens: Theme

Authors can communicate a **theme** in many ways, such as through **sensory details, setting, conflict**, and **characterization**. Consider the details in the story and then describe the theme in your own words.

Techniques	Details from the story
Sensory details	
Setting	
Conflict	
Theme:	

Focus on Research: Evaluate Sources for Credibility

R. K. Narayan once said, "Only the story matters. That is all." Conduct research to discover when and in what context Narayan made this comment. Identify the rest of the quotation. Compare multiple sources to make sure you have the most accurate information. Then write a short explanation of Narayan's words. What is he saying about his writing?

Sweet Like a Crow

(for Helli Cvorea, 8 years old)

Michael Ondaatje

Before You Read

Poet, memoirist, novelist, and filmmaker Michael Ondaatje (1943–) was born in Ceylon (now Sri Lanka). He moved to England in 1954 and grew up in London; he settled permanently in Canada in 1962. He has written several books of poetry, including *The Cinnamon Peeler* and *Handwriting*. His novels include *In the Skin of the Lion* and *The English Patient*. The latter was made into an Academy Award-winning movie.

World Context

In Sri Lanka, Ondaatje grew to know the Sinhalese, the nation's main ethnic group. The poem below is a response to a comment by the American writer Paul Bowles.

 LITERARY LENS A **simile** is a comparison that uses the word *like* or *as*. What is the effect of the similes in the poem that follows?

"The Sinhalese are beyond a doubt one of the least musical people in the world. It would be quite impossible to have less sense of pitch, line or rhythm."
—Paul Bowles[1]

Your voice sounds like a scorpion being pushed
through a glass tube
like someone has just trod on a peacock

---

1 **Paul Bowles:** (1910–1999), an American writer and composer who lived much of his life in Morocco

like wind howling in a coconut
like a rusty bible, like someone pulling barbed wire   5
across a stone courtyard, like a pig drowning,
a vattacka[2] being fried
a bone shaking hands
a frog singing at Carnegie Hall.
Like a crow swimming in milk,   10
like a nose being hit by a mango
like the crowd at the Royal-Thomian match,
a womb full of twins, a pariah[3] dog
with a magpie in its mouth
like the midnight jet from Casablanca[4]   15
like Air Pakistan curry,
a typewriter on fire, like a hundred
pappadams[5] being crunched, like someone
trying to light matches in a dark room,
the clicking sound of a reef when you put your head into   20
     the sea,
a dolphin reciting epic poetry to a sleepy audience,
the sound of a fan when someone throws brinjals[6] at it,
like pineapples being sliced in the Pettah[7] market
like betel[8] juice hitting a butterfly in mid-air   25
like a whole village running naked onto the street
and tearing their sarongs, like an angry family
pushing a jeep out of the mud, like dirt on the needle,
like 8 sharks being carried on the back of a bicycle
like 3 old ladies locked in the lavatory   30
like the sound I heard when having an afternoon sleep
and someone walked through my room in ankle bracelets.

---

2 **vattacka:** a kind of pumpkin
3 **pariah:** an outcast
4 **Casablanca:** the largest city in Morocco
5 **pappadams:** deep-fried crackers
6 **brinjals:** eggplants
7 **Pettah:** an Anglo-Indian term for a public market located outside of a fortress
   city or town
8 **betel:** a popular leaf chewed in many Asian countries

After You Read

Critical Reading

1. Do you think that the narrator of the poem agrees with the message of the opening quotation? Why or why not?

2. This poem uses **humor**. Identify two to three images or lines from the poem that are humorous. Then describe how the humor reveals the narrator's tone.

3. Analyze the form of this poem in terms of **repetition**, lines, and lists. Does this form create a **rhythm**?

4. Explain how this poem illustrates the dangers in making generalizations about a culture that is not one's own.

Literary Lens: Simile

A **simile** compares one thing to another through the use of the words *like* or *as*. This poem uses several similes to compare the voice of an eight-year-old to many different aspects of Sinhalese and Sri Lankan culture. Identify several similes used in the poem. Then for each, in your own words, describe what you think Ondaatje was trying to express through the simile.

Simile	Meaning

Focus on Research: Use a Variety of Methods to Take Notes

The Sri Lankan Civil War lasted from 1983 until 2009. Conduct research to find out more about this civil war. As you conduct this research, use a variety of methods to take notes. When taking notes, consider what method you will use for recording your notes and what information to include in each of your notes. In terms of method, there are many ways to take notes. For example, you can take notes on note cards, in a computer file, or in a notebook. In terms of information to include, you can note the most important details, the author, and the source.

The Middle East & South Asia

Unit Review

Key Ideas and Details

1. What do you learn about the role of women in the societies described in the selections by Djebar, Rifaat, al-Idlibi, and Ayyoub? Discuss how the women cope with the **conflicts** they encounter. Use evidence from the text to support your ideas.
2. Are cultures different only in their **details**? Discuss the assumptions about men and women, class status, religion, race, and the body that you encounter in one of the selections in this unit.
3. Characters in the selections by Indian writers Desai and Tagore experience both **conflict** and satisfaction from interacting with people who are unlike themselves. Discuss why such a **theme** might be common for a writer from this part of the world and why it might be less common for writers from the Arabic-speaking Muslim worlds.
4. Western readers have not been as exposed to Arabic-speaking Muslim societies as they have to other cultures. What do you learn about Arabic cultures in the selections here, and what more would you like to know?

Craft and Structure

5. **Setting** (the time and place in which a literary work takes place) and **mood** (atmosphere) are important elements in many of these selections. Choose one selection and describe some aspects of its setting: where it takes place; what mood is created by the details of weather, place, and time; and how this setting helps to convey the theme of the selections.
6. Many of the poets in this unit communicate their thoughts about their cultures by using words rich in **connotations**. Choose a poem from this unit and analyze the connotations of its key words. Then write a poem about something you appreciate. Express your point of view by using words with rich connotations.

Integration of Knowledge and Ideas

7. Which selection in this unit best helped you understand the day-to-day effects the conflict between Israel and Palestine has on people living in this region? Explain.
8. In terms of **themes**, do the works in this unit bear more resemblance to the works from the Americas, Europe, or Africa? Give abundant examples to back up your view.

Research Projects

Conduct an Interview

Interview one of your parents, grandparents, or other older family members or friends to find out what knowledge they would like to pass down to you and your siblings. What values, insights, and experiences can they share with you? What life principles worked (or didn't work) for them? Prepare your interview questions beforehand, and use your cell phone to record the interview. Afterwards, write a transcript and summary of the interview.

Multimedia Project

Music from the Middle East and South Asia is often quite different from Western music in terms of its tone, rhythm, structure, instrumentation, and uses. Choose any country from this region and research a style or type of music. Find video, audio, and written sources on your topic. Then organize your research in a multimedia presentation. Possible options include bringing in musical instruments, playing a recording of musical works, or having an artist perform live.

Research Follow-Up

Choose an author from this unit whose literary work explores the differences between traditional culture and modern culture. Research the life of this author. Draft a one- or two-page biography, emphasizing the author's experiences of cultural identity and motivations for writing.

Mapmaking and Revising for Content

Research the religions practiced in the Middle East and South Asia. Make a map of this region. Label the countries and identify where each religion is widely practiced. Then review the map to check for errors and revise the graphic as needed. Check the spelling of the countries' names and their shape and location, the location of the religions, and the details in the map key.

Cultural Reflections

Write about any new insights you gained about the cultures of the Middle East and South Asia from reading the selections in this unit. What did you learn about yourself and your own cultural identify?

The Literature of East Asia and the Pacific Rim

Michael Harris
Retired Professor of English, Central College, Pella, Iowa

"**O**h, East is East, and West is West, and never the twain shall meet." With this famous line, British writer Rudyard Kipling has captured the idea that the East and West are so radically different that their people can't possibly understand one another. Indeed, one of the main themes of the literature of East Asia and the Pacific Rim is the region's relationship to the West. A primary reason for this focus is that most countries in these regions have experienced an aggressive, sometimes imperial, presence by Western European countries and the United States.

Japan itself was an imperial power at different points in its history. In the early 20th century, Japan invaded China and Korea. Its shattering defeat in World War II—symbolized by the atomic bombs on Hiroshima and Nagasaki—led Japanese writers to reassess the country's culture and tradition. Countries formerly under Japan's control also began to redefine, with the help of writers, their culture and national identity.

Modern Japanese literature retains traditional elements while also reflecting a Western influence. The traditional Japanese verse form, the *haiku*, remains popular in Japan and throughout the world. Japan's ancient tradition of fiction writing has been revived in the modern era. Influential writers address such social issues as the role of gender and the gap between rich and poor created by Japan's postwar adoption of Western capitalism.

Following World War II, the central events reflected in Chinese writing have been the Chinese Civil War between Communists and Nationalists (1927–1936) and the Cultural Revolution (1966–1976). As with other countries in this region, such as Korea and Vietnam, Chinese resistance to the West resulted in a divided state. After Mao Tse-tung established Communist rule on the mainland, the Nationalists fled to Taiwan. During the Cultural Revolution, the works of many Chinese writers and intellectuals were discredited and destroyed by the government in a period marked by violent suppression.

Other East Asian and Pacific nations that are divided as a result of Japanese, Western, or U.S. involvement are Korea and Vietnam. At the end of World War II, Korea was divided in two at the 38th parallel: the Communist North and the democratic South. The division in Korea deepened during the Korean War (1950–1953). This arbitrary boundary left families divided and relatives almost permanently cut off from one another.

Vietnam also suffered from a partition between the Communist North and the U.S.-supported South, a division that lasted throughout the bloody Vietnam War (1955–1975) until the Communist victory in 1975.

Literature from the Pacific Rim countries also bears the mark of encounters with Western powers. Australia, for example, experienced a profound change when it went from being a British colony to a separate Commonwealth country in 1901. The British settlers living in this strange, sometimes hostile, environment produced literature about people making adjustments, sacrifices, and searching for an identity to fit their new land. In some Australian literature, the land itself becomes a significant character. Later Australian writing often looks with irony and skepticism upon the effects of colonizing and "Westernizing" this continent that was previously occupied by generations of Aboriginals. In recent years, Aboriginal writers from Australia and Maori writers from New Zealand have written about their people's cultural experiences, challenges experienced in a post-colonial world, and efforts to hold on to traditional ways of life.

Although seemingly a world away from the United States, writers from East Asia and the Pacific Rim have much to tell us. Due to the rapid advances in communication and transportation, the East is not so far away anymore. We owe it to ourselves to find out about our neighbors in this vitally important part of the world.

The Literature of East Asia and the Pacific Rim

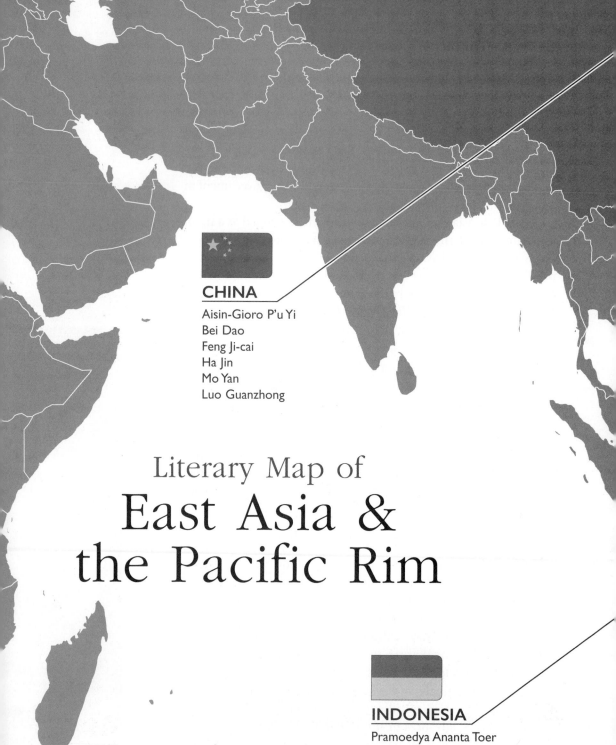

CHINA

Aisin-Gioro P'u Yi
Bei Dao
Feng Ji-cai
Ha Jin
Mo Yan
Luo Guanzhong

Literary Map of
East Asia &
the Pacific Rim

INDONESIA

Pramoedya Ananta Toer

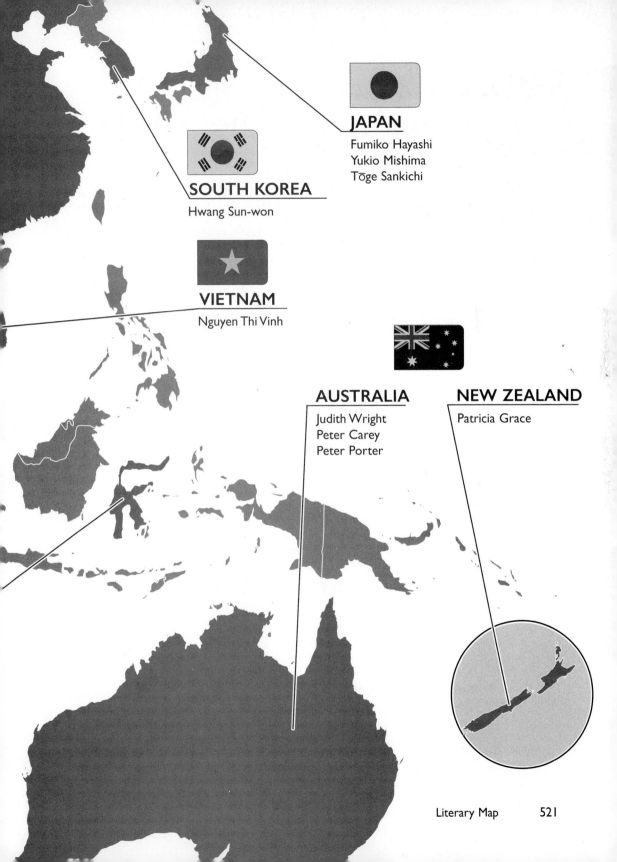

JAPAN
Fumiko Hayashi
Yukio Mishima
Tōge Sankichi

SOUTH KOREA
Hwang Sun-won

VIETNAM
Nguyen Thi Vinh

AUSTRALIA
Judith Wright
Peter Carey
Peter Porter

NEW ZEALAND
Patricia Grace

An East Asian Classic

Romance of the Three Kingdoms

Background

Romance of the Three Kingdoms was probably written by the Chinese author Luo Guanzhong in the 14th century. Like other great epics of world literature, it is a rambling tale filled with sharply drawn characters, fiercely fought battles, and compelling political intrigues. *Romance of the Three Kingdoms* extols the traditional values of the Chinese philosopher Confucius. The heroes demonstrate the loyalty to family, friends, and leaders that the well-known Chinese philosopher Confucius (551–479 B.C.E.) praised in his writings. The evil characters are treacherous and self-serving.

Romance of the Three Kingdoms has become one of the most influential novels in world literature. Its popularity has extended beyond China throughout East Asia. Literature written in Korea, Japan, and Vietnam all reflect the influence of the book. Today, the story remains well known. In one of the famous scenes from the story, the three heroes share an oath of loyalty in a peach orchard. Today, many Chinese business leaders hang a painting of this scene in their offices as a sign of their trustworthiness. In a more sinister vein, the peach orchard oath is the basis of the vows taken by members of a far-reaching Chinese criminal society called the Triad.

Romance of the Three Kingdoms and the United States

Over time, as economic and political ties between China and the United States have become more important, more and more people in the United States will no doubt become familiar with *Romance of the Three Kingdoms*. Many people in the United States already know the novel through video games based on it, including *Romance of the Three Kingdoms* franchise, the *Dynasty Warriors* series, and *Total War: Three Kingdoms*.

Research: Use the Internet

Like many historical novels, *The Romance of the Three Kingdoms* is rooted in real events. Use the Internet to find out what historical sources were used in writing this novel. What liberties did the author take with historical facts in retelling this story? For example, is there any evidence that the oath of the peach orchard actually occurred? Write a one-page summary of your research.

from Romance of the Three Kingdoms

Luo Guanzhong

Before You Read

Luo Guanzhong (c. 1318–c. 1400) was probably from the city of Taiyuan in north central China. He based *Romance of the Three Kingdoms* on stories in the oral tradition. At first, his compilation of stories was circulated in handwritten manuscript copies. Not until after the author's death was it printed. Guanzhong wrote numerous other novels and plays, only a few of which still exist. Almost all were fictionalized accounts of historical events. In addition to *Romance of the Three Kingdoms,* he may have been the author, co-author, or editor of another Chinese classic, *Water Margin.*

World Context

Romance of the Three Kingdoms is the oldest of four classic novels that have shaped modern Chinese literature. The other three classic novels were written between the late 14th and 18th centuries. They are *Dream of the Red Chamber, Water Margin,* and *Journey to the West.*

The plot of *Romance of the Three Kingdoms* is complex. It draws upon stories set in the Han Dynasty of eastern China (2nd and 3rd centuries C.E.). The Han rulers had grown weak, and courtiers had assumed control of the government. In the words of the story, "Court administration became so corrupt that across the land men's thoughts turned to rebellion, and outlaws swarmed like hornets." The novel honors those who remain loyal to the government and uphold tradition.

The following excerpt introduces three heroes from the first part of the story: Xuande, Lord Guan, and Zhang Fei. The oath of loyalty they give to one another in a peach orchard is one of the best-known scenes from Chinese literature.

 LITERARY LENS Watch for details that provide evidence of the **author's purpose** for writing.

One rebel group, the Yellow Scarves, was organized by three brothers from the Julu district—Zhang Jue, Zhang Bao, and Zhang Liang. Zhang Jue had failed the official provincial-level examination and repaired to the hills where he gathered medicinal herbs. One day he met an ancient mystic, emerald-eyed and with a youthful face, gripping a staff of **goosefoot** wood. The old man summoned Zhang Jue into a cave where he placed in his hands a sacred book in three volumes. "Here is the *Essential Arts for the Millennium*," he said. "Now that you have it, spread its teachings far and wide as Heaven's messenger for the salvation of our age. But think no **seditious** thoughts, or retribution will follow." Zhang Jue asked the old man's name, and he replied, "The Old Hermit From Mount Hua Summit—Zhuangzi, the **Taoist** sage." Then he changed into a puff of pure breeze and was gone.

Zhang Jue applied himself to the text day and night. By acquiring such arts as summoning the wind and invoking the rain, he became known as the Master of the Millennium. During the first month of the first year of the reign Central Stability,[1] a pestilence spread through the land. Styling himself Great and Worthy Teacher, Zhang Jue distributed charms and potions to the afflicted. He had more than five hundred followers, each of whom could write the charms and recite the spells. They traveled widely, and wherever they passed, new recruits joined until Zhang Jue had established thirty-six commands—ranging in size from six or seven thousand to over ten thousand—under thirty-six chieftains titled general or commander.

A seditious song began to circulate at this time:

> The pale sky is on the wane,
> Next, a yellow one shall reign;
> The calendar's rotation
> Spells fortune for the nation.

Jue ordered the words "new cycle" chalked on the front gate of every house, and soon the name Zhang Jue, Great and Worthy Teacher, was hailed throughout the eight provinces of the realm—Qingzhou, Youzhou, Xuzhou, Jizhou, Jingzhou, Yangzhou, Yanzhou, and Yuzhou. At this point Zhang Jue had his trusted follower Ma Yuanyi bribe the [courtier] Feng Xu to work inside the court on behalf of the rebels. Then Zhang Jue made a proposal to his two brothers: "Popular support is the hardest thing to win. Today the people favor us. Why waste this chance to seize the realm for ourselves?"

goosefoot:
a type of plant with leaves that look like the feet of geese

seditious:
actions or words that encourage rebellion

Taoist:
a follower of Taoism, a belief system that emphasizes humility and harmony with nature

---

1   **Central Stability:** C.E. 184

Zhang Jue had yellow banners made ready, fixed the date for the uprising, and sent one of his followers, Tang Zhou, to inform the agent at court, the eunuch Feng Xu. Instead, Tang Zhou reported the imminent insurrection to the palace. The Emperor summoned Regent He Jin to arrest and behead Ma Yuanyi. This done, Feng Xu and his group were seized and jailed.

His plot exposed, Zhang Jue mustered his forces in great haste. Titling himself General of Heaven, his first brother General of the Earth, and his second brother General of Men, he addressed his massed followers: "Han's fated end is near. A new sage is due to appear. Let one and all obey Heaven and follow the true cause so that we may rejoice in the millennium."

From the four corners of the realm the common folk, nearly half a million strong, bound their heads with yellow scarves and followed Zhang Jue in rebellion, gathering such force that the government troops scattered on the rumor of their approach. Regent-Marshal He Jin appealed to the Emperor to order every district to defend itself and every warrior to render distinguished service in putting down the uprising. Meanwhile, the regent also gave three Imperial Corps commanders—Lu Zhi, Huangfu Song, and Zhu Jun—command of three elite field armies with orders to bring the rebels to justice.

As for Zhang Jue's army, it began advancing on Youzhou district. The governor, Liu Yan, was a native of Jingling county in Jiangxia and a descendant of Prince Gong of Lu of the imperial clan. Threatened by the approaching rebels, Liu Yan summoned Commandant Zou Jing for his estimate of the situation. "They are many," said Jing, "and we are few. The best course, Your Lordship, is to recruit an army quickly to deal with the enemy." The governor agreed and issued a call for volunteers loyal to the throne.

The call was posted in Zhuo county, where it drew the attention of a man of heroic **mettle**. This man, though no scholar, was gentle and generous by nature, taciturn and reserved. His one ambition was to cultivate the friendship of the boldest spirits of the empire. He stood seven and a half **spans** tall, with arms that reached below his knees. His ear lobes were elongated, his eyes widely set and able to see his own ears. His face was flawless as jade, and his lips like dabs of rouge.

This man was a descendant of Liu Sheng, Prince Jing of Zhongshan, a great-great-grandson of the fourth Han emperor, Jing. His name was Liu Bei; his style, Xuande. Generations before, during the reign of Emperor Wu, Liu Sheng's son, Zhen, was made lord of Zhuolu precinct, but the fief and title were later forfeited when Zhen was accused of making an unsatisfactory offering at the eighth-month **libation** in the Emperor's ancestral temple. Thus a branch of the Liu family came to settle in Zhuo county.

mettle:
a person's character or courage

spans:
a span is about nine inches

libation:
the pouring of a drink as an act of respect

filial:
of or due from
a child

Xuande's grandfather was Liu Xiong; his father, Liu Hong. Local authorities had recommended Hong to the court for his **filial** devotion and personal integrity. He received appointment and actually held a minor office; but he died young. Orphaned, Xuande served his widowed mother with unstinting affection. However, they had been left so poor that he had to sell sandals and weave mats to live.

Old Stone Statue Liu Bei Three Kingdoms |
Wuhou Memorial, Temple, Chengdu, Sichuan, China. This temple was built in the 1700s.

The family resided in a county hamlet called Two-Story Mulberry after a tree of some fifty spans just southeast of their home. Seen from afar, the mulberry rose tall and spread broadly like a carriage canopy. "An eminent man will come from this house," a fortuneteller once predicted. While playing beneath the tree with the boys in the hamlet, young Xuande often boasted, "When I'm the Son of Heaven, my chariot will have a canopy like this." Impressed by these words, his uncle Liu Yuanqi remarked, "This is no ordinary child." Yuanqi sympathized with the impoverished family and often helped out his nephew. At fifteen Xuande was sent away by his mother to study, and Zheng Xuan and Lu Zhi were among his teachers. He also formed a close friendship with Gongsun Zan.

Xuande was twenty-eight when Governor Liu issued his call for volunteers. Reading the notice in Zhuo that day, Xuande sighed heavily. "Why such long sighs?" someone behind him asked **brusquely**. "A real man should be serving his emperor in the hour of peril." Xuande turned and faced a man eight spans

brusquely:
abruptly

tall, with a blunt head like a panther's, huge round eyes, a swallow's heavy jowls, a tiger's whiskers, a thunderous voice, and a stance like a dashing horse. Half in fear, half in admiration, Xuande asked his name.

"The surname," the man replied, "is Zhang; given name, Fei; Style, Yide. We've lived in this county for generations, farming our piece of land, selling wine, and slaughtering pigs. I seek to befriend men of bold spirit; when I saw you sighing and studying the recruitment call, I took the occasion to address you."

"As a mater of fact," Xuande answered, "I am related to the imperial family. My surname is Liu; given name, Bei. Reading of the trouble the Yellow

Scarves are stirring up, I had decided to help destroy the bandits and protect the people and was sighing for my inability to do so when you came by."

"I have resources," said Zhang Fei, "that could be used to recruit in this area. Let's work together for the cause. What about it?"

Xuande was elated, and the two went to a tavern. As they drank, they watched a strapping fellow pushing a wheelbarrow stop to rest at the tavern entrance. "Some wine, and quickly—I'm off to the city to volunteer," the stranger said as he entered and took a seat. Xuande observed him; a man of enormous height, nine spans tall, with a two-foot-long beard flowing from his rich, ruddy cheeks. He had glistening lips, eyes sweeping sharply back like those of the crimson-faced **phoenix**, and brows like nestling silkworms. His stature was imposing, his bearing awesome. Xuande invited him to share their table and asked who he was.

phoenix: a mythical bird

"My surname is Guan," the man replied. "My given name is Yu; my style, Changsheng, was later changed to Yunchang. I am from Jieliang in Hedong, but I had to leave there after killing a local bully who was persecuting his neighbors and have been on the move these five or six years. As soon as I heard about the recruitment, I came to sign up."

Xuande then told of his own ambitions, to Lord Guan's great satisfaction. Together the three left the tavern and went to Zhang Fei's farm to continue their discussion. "There's a peach garden behind my farm," said Zhang Fei. "The flowers are in full bloom. Tomorrow let us offer sacrifice there to Heaven and earth, and pledge to combine our strength and purpose as sworn brothers. Then we'll plan our course of action." Xuande and Lord Guan agreed with one voice: "So be it."

The next day the three men had a black bull, a white horse, and other offerings brought to the peach garden. Amid the smoke of incense they performed their ritual prostration and took their oath:

> We three, though of separate ancestry, join in brotherhood here, combining strength and purpose, to relieve the present crisis. We will perform our duty to the Emperor and protect the common folk of the land. We dare not hope to be together always but hereby vow to die the selfsame day. Let shining Heaven above and the fruitful land below bear witness to our resolve. May Heaven and man scourge whosoever fails this vow.

So swearing, Xuande became the eldest brother; Lord Guan, the second; and Zhang Fei, the youngest. After the ceremonies they butchered the bull and spread forth a feast in the peach garden for the three hundred local youths they had recruited; and all drank to their heart's content.

from Romance of the Three Kingdoms   527

After You Read

Critical Reading

1. **Summarize** the events in the story. Write a three- to five-sentence paragraph in which you note the most important characters and events in your summary.

2. Xuande becomes the "eldest brother." Make an inference about why this role is given to him. Support your inference with details from the story.

3. Describe the author's **tone**, or point of view, toward the events in the story. Based on this, what can you infer about the author's attitude toward the government? Cite details from the story.

Literary Lens: Author's Purpose

An author's purpose is his or her reason for writing. General purposes for writing include to inform, to entertain, or to persuade. Authors may have one primary purpose or several purposes for writing. Analyze the author's purpose for writing *Romance of the Three Kingdoms*. Re-create the chart below and fill it in to analyze the author's purpose. Provide supporting details as evidence for your conclusion about the author's purpose.

Author's Purpose	Yes/No	Supporting Details
To explain		
To entertain		
To persuade		

Focus on Research: Gather Sources

Begin a research project to find out more about *Romance of the Three Kingdoms*. Find thee or more sources that provide information about the story—this information might be about the history of the book, the ways in which the text has become part of Chinese or American culture, or about the author Luo Guanzhong. Create a works cited list of eight to ten sources from a variety of formats, including print, digital, and multimedia formats.

The Literature of
China

Background

With more than 1.3 billion people, China is the most populous country in the world. Its culture dates back more than 6,000 years. The Chinese language is one of the oldest "surviving" languages in the world. During China's long history, Chinese writers have produced some of the world's greatest works of literature. Among these are the philosophical and religious writings of Confucius (551–479 B.C.E.), Lao Tzu (c. 6th century B.C.E.), and Mencius (c. 372–c. 289 B.C.E.), as well as some of the first novels ever written.

During the 20th century, China suffered from civil war, a brutal invasion and occupation by Japan, and then several decades of Communist dictatorship. Today, the Chinese government, through the General Administration of Press and Publication (GAPP), controls all licenses for publication, exercising considerable powers of censorship. This has led to a huge underground publication industry. Some experts think that up to 40 percent of the books for sale in China are produced illegally.

China and the United States

Today, China and the United States have closely interconnected economies. The United States is one of the most important customers for China's exports, and China is one of the most important investors in the U.S. government's debt.

In literature, the two countries are also connected. Many writers of Chinese heritage are popular in the United States. Among them are Amy Tan (1952–), Maxine Hong Kingston (1940–), Ha Jin (1956–), and Bette Bao Lord (1938–). In return, U.S. literature has been influential in China since at least since the early 1900s, when Harriet Beecher Stowe's 1852 classic *Uncle Tom's Cabin* was translated into Chinese.

Research: Synthesize Information

In recent years, the Internet has helped writers in totalitarian countries exercise free expression. Chinese authorities, however, have managed to enforce censorship even on the Internet. Conduct focused research of print and online sources on the topic of the Chinese government's censorship of the Internet. Then write a brief synopsis of your findings.

from # From Emperor to Citizen

Aisin-Gioro P'u Yi

Before You Read

Aisin-Gioro P'u Yi (1906–1967) was the last emperor of China. In 1908, at age three, P'u Yi assumed his title, but the Republican Revolution four years later forced him to relinquish his throne. The young man was allowed to retain his title, money, and home in the Forbidden City, an area inside the Imperial Palace reserved for the emperor and his employees. The following excerpt from his autobiography covers this time period.

The rest of his life was not so pampered. In 1924, he and his family were forced at gunpoint to flee China. After World War II he was charged with war crimes and imprisoned in Communist China. His eventual release and "rehabilitation" led to a new career as a mechanic in a public garden, a position he held until his death.

World Context

P'u Yi's autobiography, *From Emperor to Citizen,* was written under the strict supervision of the Communist government. A movie about his life, *The Last Emperor,* won the 1987 Oscar for best picture.

 LITERARY LENS Watch for specific passages that reveal P'u Yi's **tone**—his attitude toward the subject he is writing about.

T he "Articles for Favorable Treatment" stipulated that I could live temporarily in the Imperial Palace without fixing any definite time limit. Apart from three large halls that were handed over to the Republic, the rest of the Forbidden City continued to belong to the Imperial Palace. It was in this tiny world that I was to spend the most absurd childhood possible until I was driven out by the soldiers of the National Army in 1924. I call it absurd because at a time when China was called a republic and mankind had advanced into the twentieth century, I was still living the life of an emperor, breathing the dust of the nineteenth century.

Whenever I think of my childhood, my head fills with a yellow mist. The glazed tiles were yellow, my sedan chair was yellow, my chair cushions were yellow, the linings of my hats and clothes were yellow, the girdle round my waist was yellow, the dishes and bowls from which I ate and drank, the padded cover of the rice-gruel saucepan, the material in which my books were wrapped, the window curtains, the bridle of my horse . . . everything was yellow. This color, the so-called "brilliant yellow," was used exclusively by the imperial household and made me feel from my earliest years that I was unique and had a "heavenly" nature different from that of everybody else.

When I was ten, my grandmother and mother started to come and visit me on the orders of the High Consorts,[1] and they brought my brother Pu Chieh and my first sister to play with me for a few days. Their first visit started off very drearily: I and my grandmother sat on the *kang*,[2] and she watched me playing dominoes while my brother and sister stood below us very properly, gazing at me with a fixed stare like attendants on duty in a *yamen*.[3] Later it occurred to me to take them along to the part of the palace in which I lived, where I asked Pu Chieh, "What games do you play at home?"

"Pu Chieh can play hide-and-seek," said my brother, who was a year younger than I, in a very respectful way.

"So you play hide-and-seek too? It's a jolly good game." I was very excited. I had played it with the eunuchs[4] but never with children younger than myself. So we started to play hide-and-seek, and in the excitement of the game, my brother and sister forgot their inhibitions. We deliberately let down the blinds to make the room very dark. My sister, who was two years younger than I, was at the same time enraptured and terrified, and as my brother and I kept giving her frights, we got so carried away that we were laughing and shouting. When we were exhausted, we climbed up onto the *kang* to get our breath back, and I told them to think of some new game. Pu Chieh was thoughtful for a while, then started to gaze at me wordlessly, a silly smile on his face.

"What are you grinning at?"

He went on grinning.

---

1 **High Consorts:** widows of previous emperors
2 *kang*: a brick platform used for sleeping
3 *yamen*: office of a Chinese public official
4 **eunuchs:** castrated men, sometimes in charge of a harem or other duties in a palace

"Tell me! Tell me!" I urged him impatiently, thinking that he must certainly have thought out some new game. To my surprise he came out with, "I thought, oh, Pu Chieh thought that Your Majesty would be different from ordinary people. The emperors on the stage have long beards. . . ." As he spoke, he pretended to be stroking his beard.

This gesture was his undoing. As he raised his hand, I noticed that the lining of his sleeve was a very familiar color. My face blackened.

"Pu Chieh, are you allowed to wear that color?"

"But . . . bu . . . but isn't it apricot?"

"Nonsense! It's imperial brilliant yellow."

"Yes, sire, yes, sire. . . ." Pu Chieh stood away from me, his arms hanging respectfully by his sides. My sister slipped over to stand with him, frightened to the point of tears.

"It's brilliant yellow. You have no business to be wearing it."

"Yes, sire."

With his "yes, sire" my brother reverted to being my subject. The sound "yes, sire" died out long ago, and it seems very funny when one thinks of it today. But I got used to it from early childhood, and if people did not use the words when replying to me, I would not stand for it. It was the same with kneeling and kowtowing.

From my infancy I was accustomed to having people kowtow to me, particularly people over ten times my own age. They included old officials of the Ching Dynasty[5] and the elders of my own clan, men in the court robes of the Ching Dynasty and officials of the Republic in Western dress.

Another strange thing which seemed quite normal at the time was the daily **pomp**.

pomp:
splendor; show
of magnificence

Every time I went to my schoolroom to study, or visited the High Consorts to pay my respects, or went for a stroll in the garden, I was always followed by a large **retinue**. Every trip I made to the Summer Palace must have cost thousands of Mexican dollars: the Republic's police had to be asked to line the roads to protect me, and I was accompanied by a motorcade consisting of dozens of vehicles.

retinue:
following;
entourage

Whenever I went for a stroll in the garden, a procession had to be organized. In front went a eunuch from the Administrative Bureau whose function was roughly that of a motor horn: he walked twenty or thirty yards ahead of the rest of the party intoning the sound "chir . . . chir . . . " as a warning to anyone who might be in the vicinity to go away at once. Next

---

5 **Ching Dynasty:** (1644–1912) the most recent dynasty in China's history

came two chief eunuchs, advancing crabwise on either side of the path; ten paces behind them came the center of the procession—the Empress Dowager[6] or myself. If I was being carried in a chair, there would be two junior eunuchs walking beside me to attend to my wants at any moment; if I was walking, they would be supporting me. Next came a eunuch with a large silk canopy followed by a large group of eunuchs of whom some were empty-handed and others were holding all sorts of things: a seat in case I wanted to rest, change of clothing, umbrellas and parasols. After these eunuchs of the imperial presence came eunuchs of the imperial tea bureau with boxes of various kinds of cakes and delicacies and, of course, jugs of hot water and a tea service; they were followed by eunuchs of the imperial **dispensary** bearing cases of medicine and first-aid equipment suspended from carrying poles. The medicines carried always included potions prepared from lampwick sedge, chrysanthemums, the roots of reeds, bamboo leaves, and bamboo skins; in summer there were always Essence of Betony Pills for Rectifying the Vapor, Six Harmony Pills for Stabilizing the Center, Gold coated, Heat-dispersing Cinnabar, Fragrant Herb Pills, Omnipurpose Bars, colic medicine and anti-plague powder; and throughout all four seasons there would be the Three Immortals Beverage to aid the digestion, as well as many other medicaments. At the end of the procession came the eunuchs who carried commodes and chamber pots. If I was walking, a sedan chair, open or covered according to the season, would bring up the rear. This **motley** procession of several dozen people would proceed in perfect silence and order.

> **dispensary:** medicine store; place where medicines are stored and distributed

> **motley:** varied; miscellaneous

But I would often throw it into confusion. When I was young, I liked to run around when I was in high spirits as just any child does. At first they would all scuttle along after me puffing and panting with their procession reduced to chaos. When I grew a little older and knew how to give orders, I would tell them to stand and wait for me; then, apart from the junior eunuchs of the imperial presence who came with me, they would all stand there waiting in silence with their loads. After I had finished running around, they would form up again behind me. When I learned to ride a bicycle and ordered the removal of all the upright wooden thresholds in the palace so that I could ride around without obstruction, the procession was no longer able to follow me, and so it had to be temporarily abolished. But when I went to pay my respects to the High Consorts or to my schoolroom, I still had to have something of a retinue, and without it I would have felt rather odd.

---

6 **Empress Dowager:** the widow of the deceased emperor

When I heard people telling the story of the last emperor of the Ming Dynasty who had only one eunuch left with him at the end, I felt very uncomfortable.

The type of extravagant display that wasted the most effort, money and material was meals. There were special terms to refer to the emperor's eating, and it was absolutely forbidden to fail to use them correctly. Food was called not "food" but "viands"; eating was called "consuming viands"; serving the meal was "transmitting the viands"; and the kitchen was the "imperial viands room." When it was time to eat (and the times of the meals were not set but were whenever the emperor felt like eating), I would give the command "Transmit the viands!" The junior eunuchs of the presence would then repeat "Transmit the viands" to the eunuchs standing in the main hall of the palace in which I lived, and they would pass it on to the eunuchs standing on duty outside the hall; these would in turn call it out to the eunuchs of the "imperial viands room" waiting in the Western Avenue of the Forbidden City. Thus my order went straight to the kitchens, and before its echoes had died away a procession rather of the sort that used to take a bride's trousseau[7] to her groom's house had already issued from the "viands room." It was made up of an imposing column of several dozen neatly dressed eunuchs hurrying to the Mind Nurture Palace with seven tables of various sizes and scores of red-lacquered boxes painted with golden dragons. When they reached the main hall, they handed their burdens over to young eunuchs wearing white sleeves, who laid out the meal in an eastern room of the palace.

Usually there were two tables of main dishes with another one of chafing dishes added in winter; there were three tables with cakes, rice and porridge, respectively; and there was another small table of salted vegetables. All the crockery was imperial yellow porcelain with dragon designs and the words "Ten thousand long lives without limit" painted on it. In winter I ate from silver dishes placed on top of porcelain bowls of hot water. Every dish or bowl had a strip of silver on it as a precaution against poison, and for the same reason all the food was tasted by a eunuch before it was brought in. This was called "appraising the viands." When everything had been tasted and laid out, and before I took my place, a young eunuch would call out "Remove the covers." This was the signal for four or five other junior eunuchs to take the silver lids off all the food dishes, put them in a large box and carry them out. I then began to "use the viands."

And what was the food laid out "ten cubits square"?[8] The empress dowager Lung Yu would have about a hundred main dishes on six tables, an extravagance

---

7   trousseau: a bride's belongings, including clothing, accessories, and household items
8   ten cubits square: each side measuring sixteen to eighteen feet

inherited from the empress dowager Tzu Hsi. I had about thirty. But these dishes, which were brought in with such ceremony, were only for show. The reason why the food could be served almost as soon as I gave the word was that it had been prepared several hours or even a whole day in advance and was being kept warm over the kitchen stoves. The cooks knew that at least since the time of Kuang Hsu, the emperor had not eaten this food. The food I ate was sent over by the Empress Dowager, and after her death, by the High Consorts.

> The empress dowager Lung Yu would have about a hundred main dishes on six tables . . .

She and each of the High Consorts had kitchens of their own staffed by highly skilled chefs who produced twenty or more really delicious dishes for every meal. This was the food that was put in front of me, while that prepared by the imperial kitchens was set some distance away as it was only there for the sake of appearances.

To show how they loved and cared for me, the High Consorts also sent a responsible eunuch to report on how I had "consumed viands." This too was a pure formality. No matter what I had really eaten, the eunuch would go to the quarters of the High Consorts, kneel before them and say:

"Your slave reports to his masters: the Lord of Ten Thousand Years consumed one bowl of old rice viands (or white rice viands), one steamed breadroll (or a griddle cake) and a bowl of congee. He consumed it with relish."

At Chinese New Year and other festivals and on the birthdays of the High Consorts, my kitchen sent a spread of food to the Consorts as a mark of my filial[9] piety. This food could be described as expensive and showy without being good, and was neither nutritious nor tasty.

According to the record of one month of the second year of my reign, the empress dowager Lung Yu, the four High Consorts and myself used up 3,960 catties of meat (over two tons) and 388 chickens and ducks every month, of which 810 catties and 240 chickens and ducks were for me, a four-year-old child. In addition there was a monthly allocation for the numerous people in the palace who served us: members of the grand council, imperial bodyguards, tutors, Hanlin academicians, painters, men who drew the outlines of characters for others to fill in, important eunuchs, shaman[10] magicians who came every day to sacrifice to the spirits, and many others. Including the Dowager, the Consorts and myself, the monthly consumption

---

9 **filial:** befitting a son or daughter

10 *shaman:* a high priest

of pork was 14,642 catties at a cost of 2,342.72 taels[11] of silver. On top of this there were the extra dishes we had every day, which often cost several times as much again. In the month in question there were 31,844 catties of extra meat, 814 catties of extra pork fat and 4,786 extra chickens and ducks, to say nothing of the fish, shrimps and eggs. All these extras cost 11,641.07 taels, and with miscellaneous items added, the total expenditure came to 14,794.19 taels. It is obvious that all this money (except what was embezzled) was wasted in order to display the grandeur of the emperor. This figure, moreover, does not include the cost of the cakes, fruit, sweets and drinks that were constantly being devoured.

Just as food was cooked in huge quantities but not eaten, so was a vast amount of clothing made which was never worn. I cannot now remember much about this, but I do know that while the Dowager and the High Consorts had fixed yearly allocations, there were no limits for the emperor, for whom clothes were constantly made throughout the year. I do not know what exactly was made, but everything I wore was always new. I have before me an account from an unspecified year headed "List of materials actually used in making clothes for His Majesty's use from the sixth day of the eleventh month." According to this list the following garments were made for me that month: eleven fur jackets, six fur inner and outer gowns, two fur waistcoats, and thirty padded waistcoats and pairs of trousers. Leaving aside the cost of the main materials and of the labor, the bill for such minor items as the edgings, pockets, buttons and thread came to 2,137.6335 silver dollars.

My changes of clothing were all laid down in regulations and were the responsibility of the

---

11 **taels:** Chinese units of money

**Manchu Emperor Hsuan Tung
as a young boy, 1917**

eunuchs of the clothing storerooms. Even my everyday gowns came in twenty-eight different styles, from the one in black and white inlaid fur that I started wearing on the nineteenth of the first lunar month to the sable one I changed into on the first day of the eleventh month. Needless to say, my clothes were far more complicated on festivals and ceremonial occasions.

To manage all this extravagant pomp there was, of course, a suitable proliferation of offices and personnel. The Household Department, which administered the domestic affairs of the emperor, had under its control seven bureaus and forty-eight offices. The seven bureaus—the storage bureau, the guard bureau, the protocol, the counting house, the stock-raising bureau, the disciplinary bureau and the construction bureau—all had storerooms, workshops and so on under them. The storage bureau, for example, was for stores for silver, fur, porcelain, satin, clothes and tea. According to a list of officials dating from 1909, the personnel of the Household Department numbered 1,023 (excluding the Palace Guard, the eunuchs and the servants known as "sulas"); in the early years of the Republic, this number was reduced to something over 600, and at the time I left the Imperial Palace there were still more than 300. It is not hard to imagine an organization as large as this with so many people in it, but the triviality of some of its functions was almost unthinkable. One of the forty-eight offices, for example, was the As You Wish Lodge (Ju Yi Kuan). Its only purpose was to paint pictures and do calligraphy for the Empress Dowager and the High Consorts; if the Dowager wanted to paint something, the As You Wish Lodge would outline a design for her so that all she had to do was to fill in the colors and write a title on it. The calligraphy for large tablets was sketched out by the experts of the Great Diligence Hall or else done by the Hanlin academicians. Nearly all late Ching inscriptions that purport to be the brushwork of a dowager or an emperor were produced in this way.

The buildings all around me and the furniture of the palace were all a part of my indoctrination. Apart from the golden-glazed tiles that were exclusively for the use of the emperor, the very height of the buildings was an imperial **prerogative** that served to teach me from an early age that not only was everything under heaven the emperor's land but even the sky above my head belonged to nobody else. Every piece of furniture was "direct method" teaching material for me. It was said that the emperor Chien Lung once laid it down that nothing in the palace, not even a blade of grass, must be lost. To put this principle into practice, he put some blades of grass on a table in the palace and gave orders that they were to be counted every day to see that not a single one of them was missing. This

prerogative: right; special privilege

was called "taking the grass as a standard." Even in my time these thirty-six withered blades of grass were still preserved in a cloisonné[12] canister in the Mind Nurture Palace. This grass filled me with unbounded admiration for my ancestor and unbridled hatred for the Revolution of 1911.

There is no longer any way of calculating exactly the enormous cost of the daily life of an emperor, but a record called "A comparison between the expenditure of the seventh year of Hsuan Tung (1915) and the past three years" compiled by the Household Department shows that expenditure in 1915 topped 2,790,000 taels and that, while it dropped in each of the following three years, it was always over 1,890,000 taels. Thus it was that with the **connivance** of the Republican authorities we continued our **prodigious** waste of the sweat and blood of the people in order to maintain our former pomp and continue our parasitic way of life.

Some of the rules in the palace were originally not simply for the sake of show. The system by which all the food dishes had strips of silver on them and the food was tasted before the emperor ate it and the large-scale security precautions [were taken] whenever he went out was basically to protect him against any attempt on his life. It was said that the reason why emperors had no outside privies was that one emperor had been set upon by an assassin when going out to relieve himself. These stories and all the display had the same effect on me: they made me believe that I was a very important and august[13] person, a man apart who ruled and owned the universe.

connivance: complicity; secret cooperation

prodigious: tremendous; monstrous

---

12 **cloisonné:** decorative enamel
13 **august:** majestically dignified

After You Read

Critical Reading

1. A **euphemism** is a neutral word or phrase used to conceal an embarrassing or painful truth. For example, people often say a loved one "passed on" instead of saying they "died." Identify two examples of euphemistic language in the passage. Explain the truths the euphemisms are concealing.

2. P'u Yi describes scenes of incredible extravagance and waste. Cite one such scene. What purpose do you think P'u Yi had for including such descriptions of extravagance?

 ## Literary Lens: Tone

P'u Yi's autobiography, from which this excerpt is taken, was published in 1960 with the "help" of a Chinese government editor. Some historians believe the former emperor was forced by Communist leaders to criticize the dynastic system. Cite one passage that you feel has an authentic tone. Then cite one passage that has an artificial tone. For each passage, explain why the author uses that tone and support your decision with details from the passage.

Selected passages	Why did the author use this tone?	Details that support your selection
With authentic tone		
With artificial tone		

Focus on Research: Search a Database

One way to gather sources for a research project is to search a database for different sources. A database is an organized collection of information. Some databases contain a variety of information on infinite topics, such as your Academic Search Complete or JSTOR. Subject-specific databases focus on a single academic disciple or a group of related disciplines. Examples include PsycINFO (psychology) and Business Source Complete (business). Find two databases (one general and one specific) that would be useful for finding sources about the last years of the Ch'ing Dynasty. Then find two possible sources using each database. Which type of database did you find more helpful for this topic?

An Ancient Temple

Bei Dao

Before You Read

Bei Dao (1949–) is the pen name of Zhao Zhenkai, who was born in Beijing, China. He joined the Red Guard in 1960 to take part in Chairman Mao Tse-tung's Cultural Revolution. He grew disillusioned with Maoism and became involved in China's democracy movement. He also helped create an intensely personal verse genre called "cloud/mist poetry." He was away from China in 1989 during the pro-democracy demonstration at Tiananmen Square, which ended in the massacre of hundreds of protesters. Nevertheless, the government accused him of helping to incite the protest, and he has remained in exile ever since. Despite his hardships, he warns poets not to underestimate their own importance, because poetry "came into the world when humans did. It's what makes human beings human." His works in English translation include *City of the Sun*, *The August Sleepwalker*, and *Forms of Distance*.

World Context

"An Ancient Temple" was included in the 1982 anthology, *Meng Long Shi (Misty Poems)*. The Misty Poets, as they were called, rejected social realism, the officially sanctioned artistic ideology of the Communist Party. They sought, instead, to evoke subjective experience through ambiguous (misty) images and metaphors.

LITERARY LENS A **motif** is a reoccurring idea or image. As you read this poem, identify the repeated motif that is related to things missing, silent, or gone.

The long ago songs of a bell
weaved this spider web; in the column's crevices,
grown outward, one sees annual rings there for the counting.
No memories are here; stones
that merely scattered the echoes in this mountain valley,   5
have no memories.

That little path, even, by-passed it;
its dragons and strange birds are gone.
They took with them the silent bells that hung from the eaves.
They took the unrecorded legends of the place, too.   10
The words on the walls are all worn clean and torn.
Maybe if it caught on fire
one could read the words on the inside.
See the annual growths of the wild grasses,
so indifferent.   15
They don't care if they submit to any master,
to the shoes of the old monks,
or to the winds, either.
Out front the sky is held up by a broken stone tablet.
Still, led by the gaze of some living person,   20
the tortoise may revive and
come out carrying his heavy secret,
crawl right out there on the temple's threshold.

Translated by Gordon T. Osing and De-An Wu Swihart

After You Read

Critical Reading

1. Select a line or phrase from the poem that you feel could stand as a thematic statement of the entire poem. Explain your choice and support your response with details from the poem.

2. Consider the use of **personification** in this poem. Identify and explain several examples of personification. What does this personification accomplish in the poem?

3. This poem involves the use of many **sensory details**. Identify two sensory details from the poem. What **mood** do these details evoke?

Literary Lens: Motif

A motif in the poem is things missing, silent, or absent. Use a chart like the one below to identify quotations that are examples of this motif. In the final row, write an explanation of how the motif reveals the theme of the poem.

Motif = Missing, Silent, Absent	Quotation
bells	
legends	
words	
Theme:	

Focus on Research: Develop Inquiry Questions

The setting of "An Ancient Temple" appears to be an abandoned Buddhist temple. Write at least five questions you have about Buddhism or Buddhist temples in China. Make sure you could use these questions to guide research on the topic.

The Tall Woman and Her Short Husband

Feng Ji-cai

Before You Read

Feng Ji-cai (1942–) was a professional basketball player until an injury put an end to that career. After his first novel, *The Boxer*, was published, Feng began to focus on writing novels, short stories, scripts, and nonfiction. He is a student of Chinese history and culture. Ji-cai says that writing can be just reporting, but an intellectual considers wider matters—such as the culture, the past, and the future.

World Context

When the Cultural Revolution took place in the mid-1960s, the Communist Party forced strict conformity in lifestyle and beliefs. Anyone skirting party dictates or social conventions was subject to ridicule, slander, and even imprisonment.

 LITERARY LENS While reading the story, look for cases when two unexpected things have been placed side by side. This literary technique is called **juxtaposition** and is used to highlight the difference between two things.

1

Say you have a small tree in your yard and are used to its smooth trunk. If one day it turns twisted and gnarled it strikes you as awkward. As time goes by, however, you grow to like it, as if that was how this tree should always have been. Were it suddenly to straighten out again you would feel indescribably put out. A trunk as dull and boring as a stick! In fact it would simply have reverted to its original form, so why should you worry?

Is this force of habit? Well, don't underestimate "habit." It runs through everything done under the sun. It is not a law to be strictly observed, yet flouting it is simply asking for trouble. Don't complain though if it proves so binding that sometimes, unconsciously, you conform to it. For instance, do you presume to throw your weight about before your superiors? Do you air your views recklessly in front of your seniors? When a group photograph is taken, can you shove celebrities aside to stand swaggering and chortling in the middle? You can't, of course you can't. Or again, would you choose a wife ten years older than you, heftier than you or a head taller than you? Don't be in a rush to answer. Here's an instance of such a couple.

2

She was seventeen centimetres taller than he.

One point seven five metres in height, she towered above most of her sex like a crane over chickens. Her husband, a bare 1.58 metres, had been nicknamed Shorty at college. He came up to her earlobes but actually looked two heads shorter.

And take their appearances. She seemed dried up and scrawny with a face like an unvarnished ping-pong bat. Her features would pass, but they were small and insignificant as if carved in shallow relief. She was flat-chested, had a ramrod back and buttocks as scraggy as a scrubbing board. Her husband on the other hand seemed a rubber rolypoly: well-fleshed, solid and radiant. Everything about him—his calves, insteps, lips, nose and fingers—were like pudgy little meatballs. He had soft skin and a fine complexion shining with excess fat and ruddy because of all the red blood in his veins. His eyes were like two high-voltage little light bulbs, while his wife's were like glazed marbles. The two of them just did not match, and formed a marked contrast. But they were inseparable.

One day some of their neighbours were having a family reunion. After drinking his fill the grandfather put a tall, thin empty wine bottle on the table next to a squat tin of pork.

"Who do these remind you of?" he asked. Before anyone could guess he gave the answer. "That tall woman downstairs and that short husband of hers."

Everyone burst out laughing and went on laughing through the meal.

What had brought such a pair together?

This was a mystery to the dozens of households living in Unity Mansions. Ever since this couple moved in, the old residents had eyed them curiously. Some registered a question mark in their minds, while others put their curiosity into words. Tongues started wagging, especially in wet weather when the two of them went out and it was always Mrs. Tall who held the umbrella. If anything dropped to the ground, though, it was

simpler for Mr. Short to pick it up. Some old ladies at a loose end would
gesticulate, finding this comic, and splutter with laughter. This set a bad
example for the children who would burst out laughing at sight of the pair
and hoot, "Long carrying-pole; big, low stool!" The husband and wife
pretended not to hear and kept their tempers, paying no attention. Maybe
for this reason their relations with their neighbours remained rather cool.

officious:
intrusive; meddlesome

The few less **officious** ones simply nodded a greeting when they met. This made it hard for those really intrigued by them to find out more about them. For instance, how did they hit it off? Why had they married? Which gave way to the other? They could only speculate.

This was an old-fashioned block of flats with large sunny rooms and wide, dark corridors. It stood in a big courtyard with a small gatehouse. The man who lived there was a tailor, a decent fellow. His wife, who brimmed over with energy, liked to call on her neighbours and gossip. Most of all she liked to **ferret** out their secrets. She knew exactly how husbands and wives got on, why sisters-in-law quarrelled, who was lazy, who hard-working, and how much everyone earned. If she was unclear about anything she would leave no stone unturned to get at the truth. The thirst for knowledge makes even the ignorant wise. In this respect she was outstanding. She analyzed conversations, watched expressions, and could even tell what people were secretly thinking. Simply by using her nose, she knew which household was eating meat or fish, and from that could deduce their income. For some reason or other, ever since the sixties each housing estate had chosen someone like this as a "neighbourhood activist," giving legal status to these nosey-parkers so that their officiousness could have full play. It seems the Creator will never waste any talent.

ferret:
seek; pry

Though the tailor's wife was **indefatigable** she failed to discover how this **incongruous** couple who passed daily before her eyes had come to marry. She found this most frustrating; it posed a formidable challenge. On the basis of her experience, however, and by racking her brains she finally came up with a **plausible** explanation: either husband or wife must have some physiological deficiency. Otherwise no one would marry someone a whole head taller or shorter. Her grounds for this reasoning were that after three years of marriage they still had no children. The residents of Unity Mansions were all convinced by this brilliant hypothesis.

indefatigable:
tireless; inexhaustible

incongruous:
incompatible; odd

plausible:
believable; likely

But facts are merciless. The tailor's wife was **debunked** and lost face when Mrs. Tall appeared in the family way. Her womb could be seen swelling from day to day, for being relatively far from the ground it was all too evident. Regardless of their amazement, misgivings or embarrassment, she gave birth to a fine baby. When the sun was hot or it rained and the couple went out, Mrs. Tall would carry the baby while Mr. Short held the umbrella. He plodded along comically on his plump legs, the umbrella held high, keeping just behind his wife. And the neighbours remained as intrigued as at the start of this ill-assorted, inseparable couple. They went on making plausible **conjectures**, but could find no confirmation for any of them.

debunked:
disproved; deflated

conjectures:
guesses; suppositions

The tailor's wife said, "They must have something to hide, those two. Why else should they keep to themselves? Well, it's bound to come to light some day, just wait and see."

One evening, sure enough, she heard the sound of breaking glass in their flat. On the pretext of collecting money for sweeping the yard she rushed to knock on their door, sure that their long hidden feud had come to a head and avid to watch the confrontation between them. The door opened. Mrs. Tall asked her in with a smile. Mr. Short was smiling too at a smashed plate on the floor—that was all the tailor's wife saw. She hastily collected the money and left to puzzle over what had happened. A plate had been smashed, yet instead of quarrelling they had treated it as a joke. How very strange!

Later the tailor's wife became the residents' representative for Unity Mansions. When she helped the police check up on living permits, she at last found the answer to this puzzle. A reliable and irrefutable answer. The tall woman and her short husband both worked in the Research Institute of the Ministry of Chemical Industry. He was chief engineer, with a salary of over 180 yuan! She was an ordinary laboratory technician earning less than sixty yuan, and her father was a hard-working low-paid postman. So that explained why she had married a man so much shorter. For status, money and an easy life. Right! The tailor's wife lost no time in passing on this priceless information to all the bored old ladies in Unity Mansions. Judging others by themselves, they believed her. At last this riddle was solved. They saw the light. Rich Mr. Short was congenitally deficient while poor Mrs. Tall was a money-grabber on the make. When they discussed the good luck of this tall woman who looked like a horse, they often voiced resentment—especially the tailor's wife.

3

Sometimes good luck turns into bad.

In 1966, disaster struck China.[1] Great changes came into the lives of all the residents in Unity Mansions, which was like a **microcosm** of the whole country. Mr. Short as chief engineer was the first to suffer. His flat was raided, his furniture moved out, he was struggled against and confined in his institute. And worse was to come. He was accused of smuggling out the results of his research to write up at home in the evenings, with a view to fleeing the country to join a wealthy relative abroad. This preposterous charge of passing on scientific secrets to foreign capitalists was widely

microcosm: little world; miniature representation

---

1 In . . . China: 1966 was the beginning of the Cultural Revolution led by Communist leader Mao Tse-tung

believed. In that period of lunacy people took leave of their senses and cruelly made up groundless accusations in order to find some Hitler in their midst. The institute kept a stranglehold on its chief engineer. He was threatened, beaten up, put under all kinds of pressure; his wife was ordered to hand over that manuscript which no one had ever seen. But all was to no effect. Someone proposed holding a struggle meeting against them both in the courtyard of Unity Mansions. As everyone dreads losing face in front of relatives and friends, this would put more pressure on them. Since all else had failed, it was at least worth trying. Never before had Unity Mansions been the scene of such excitement.

In the afternoon the institute sent people to fix up ropes between two trees in the yard, on which to hang a poster with the name of Mr. Short on it—crossed out. Inside and outside the yard they pasted up threatening slogans, and on the wall put eighteen more posters listing the engineer's "crimes." As the meeting was to be held after supper, an electrician was sent to fix up four big 500-watt bulbs. By now the tailor's wife, promoted to be the chairman of the neighbourhood's Public Security Committee, was a powerful person, full of self-importance, and much fatter than before. She had been busy all day bossing the other women about, helping to put up slogans and make tea for the revolutionaries from the institute. The wiring for the lights had been fixed up from her gatehouse as if she were celebrating a wedding!

After supper, the tailor's wife assembled all the residents in the yard, lit up as brilliantly as a sportsground at night. Their shadows, magnified ten-fold, were thrown on the wall of the building. These shadows stayed stock-still, not even the children daring to play about. The tailor's wife led a group also wearing red armbands, in those days most awe-inspiring, to guard the gate and keep outsiders out. Presently a crowd from the institute, wearing armbands and shouting slogans, marched in the tall woman and her short husband. He had a placard hung round his neck, she had none. The two of them were marched in front of the platform, and stood there side by side with lowered heads.

The tailor's wife darted forward. "This wretch is too short for the revolutionary masses at the back to see," she cried. "I'll soon fix that." She dashed into the gatehouse, her fat shoulders heaving, to fetch a soapbox which she turned upside down. Mr. Short standing on this was the same height as his wife. But at this point little attention was paid to the relative heights of this couple facing disaster.

The meeting followed the customary procedure. After slogans had been shouted, passionate accusations were made, punctuated by more slogans. The pressure built up. First Mrs. Tall was ordered to come clean, to produce that "manuscript." Questions and denunciations were fired at her, hysterical screams, angry shouts and threatening growls. But she simply shook her head gravely and sincerely. What use was sincerity? To believe in her would have made the whole business a farce.

No matter what bullies sprang forward to shake their fists at her, or what tricky questions were asked to try to trap her, she simply shook her head. The members of the institute were at a loss, afraid that if this went on the struggle meeting would fizzle out and end up a fiasco.

The tailor's wife had listened with mounting exasperation. Being illiterate she took no interest in the "manuscript" they wanted, and felt these research workers were too soft-spoken. All of a sudden she ran to the platform. Raising her right arm with its red armband she pointed accusingly at Mrs. Tall.

"Say!" she screeched. "Why did you marry him?"

The members of the institute were staggered by this unexpected question. What connection had it with their investigation?

Mrs. Tall was staggered too. This wasn't the sort of question asked these days. She looked up with surprise on her thin face which showed the ravages of the last few months.

"So you don't dare answer, eh?" The tailor's wife raised her voice. "I'll answer for you! You married this scoundrel, didn't you, for his money? If he hadn't had money who'd want such a short fellow!" She sounded rather smug, as if she alone had seen through Mrs. Tall.

Mrs. Tall neither nodded nor shook her head. She had seen through the tailor's wife too. Her eyes glinted with derision and contempt.

"All right, you won't admit it. This wretch is done for now, he's a broken reed. Oh, I know what you're thinking." The tailor's wife slapped her chest and brandished one hand gloatingly. Some other women chimed in.

The members of the institute were **flummoxed**. A question like this was best ignored. But though these women had strayed far from the subject, they had also livened up the meeting. So the institute members let them take the field. The women yelled:

> flummoxed: confounded; confused

"How much has he paid you? What has he bought you? What has he bought you? Own up!"

"Two hundred a month isn't enough for you, is it? You have to go abroad!"

> "Say!" she screeched. "Why did you marry him?"

"Is Deng Tuo[2] behind you?"

"That day you made a long-distance call to Beijing, were you ringing up the Three Family Village?"[3]

The success of a meeting depends on the enthusiasm worked up. The institute members who had convened this meeting saw that the time was ripe now to shout a few more slogans and conclude it. They then searched Mrs. Tall's flat, **prizing** up floorboards and stripping off wallpaper. When they discovered nothing, they marched her husband away, leaving her behind.

prizing: prying; forcing open

Mrs. Tall stayed in all the next day but went out alone after dark, unaware that though the light in the gatehouse was out the tailor's wife was watching her from the window. She trailed her out of the gate and past two crossroads till Mrs. Tall stopped to knock softly on a gate. The tailor's wife ducked behind a telegraph pole and waited, holding her breath, as if to pounce on a rabbit when it popped out of its burrow.

The gate creaked open. An old woman led out a child.

"All over, is it?" she asked.

Mrs. Tall's answer was inaudible.

"He's had his supper and a sleep," the old woman said. "Take him home quickly now."

The tailor's wife realized that this was the woman who minded their little boy. Her excitement died down as Mrs. Tall turned back to lead her son home. All was silence apart from the sound of their footsteps. The tailor's wife stood motionless behind the telegraph pole till they had gone, then scurried home herself.

The next morning when Mrs. Tall led her son out, her eyes were red. No one would speak to her, but they all saw her red, swollen eyes. Those who had denounced her the previous day had a strange feeling of guilt. They turned away so as not to meet her eyes.

4

After the struggle meeting Mr. Short was not allowed home again. The tailor's wife, who was in the know, said he had been imprisoned as an active counter-revolutionary. That made Mrs. Tall the lowest of the low, naturally unfit to live in a roomy flat. She was forced to change places with the tailor's

---

2 **Deng Tuo:** historian and author who criticized Mao for his policies during the Cultural Revolution

3 **Three Family Village:** three writers of a newspaper column deemed subversive during the Cultural Revolution

wife and moved into the little gatehouse. This didn't worry her, as it meant she could avoid the other residents who snubbed her. But they could look through her window and see her all alone there. Where she had sent her son, they didn't know, for he only came home for a few days at a time. Ostracized by all, she looked older than a woman in her thirties.

"Mark my words," the tailor's wife said, "she can only keep this up for at most a year. Then if Shorty doesn't get out she'll have to remarry. If I were her I'd get a divorce and remarry. Even if he's let out his name will be mud, and he won't have any money."

A year went by. Mr. Short still didn't come back and Mrs. Tall kept to herself. In silence she went to work, came back, lit her stove and went out with a big shabby shopping basket. Day after day she did this, the whole year round . . . But one day in autumn Mr. Short reappeared—thinly clad, his head shaved, and his whole appearance changed. He seemed to have shrunk and his skin no longer gleamed with health. He went straight to his old flat. Its new master, the honest tailor, directed him to the gatehouse. Mrs. Tall was squatting in the doorway chopping firewood. At the sound of his voice she sprang up to stare at him. After two years' separation both were appalled by the change in the other. One was wrinkled, the other haggard; one looked taller than before, the other shorter. After gazing at each other they hastily turned away, and Mrs. Tall ran inside. When finally she came out again he had picked up the axe and squatted down to chop firewood, until two big boxes of wood had been chopped into kindling, as if he feared some new disaster might befall them at any moment. After that they were inseparable again, going to work together and coming back together just as before. The neighbours, finding them unchanged, gradually lost interest in them and ignored them.

One morning Mrs. Tall had an accident. Her husband rushed frantically out and came back with an ambulance to fetch her. For days the gatehouse was empty and dark at night. After three weeks Mr. Short returned with a stranger. They were carrying her on a stretcher. She was confined to her room. He went to work as usual, hurrying back at dusk to light the stove and go out with the shopping basket. This was the same basket she had used every day. In his hand it looked even bigger and nearly reached the ground.

When the weather turned warmer Mrs. Tall came out. After so long in bed her face was deathly white, and she swayed from side to side. She held a cane in her right hand and kept her elbow bent in front of her. Her half-paralysed left leg made walking difficult. She had obviously had a stroke. Every morning and every evening Mr. Short helped her twice round the yard, painfully and slowly. By hunching up his shoulders he was able to grip her crooked arm in both hands. It was hard for him, but he smiled to encourage her. As she couldn't raise her left foot, he tied a rope round it and pulled this up when she wanted to take a step forward. This was a pathetic yet impressive sight, and the neighbours were touched by it. Now when they met the couple they nodded cordially to them.

5

Mrs. Tall's luck had run out: she was not to linger long by the side of the short husband who had loved her so dearly. Death and life were equally cruel to her. Life had struck her down and now death carried her off. Mr. Short was left all alone.

But after her death fortune smiled on him again. He was rehabilitated, his confiscated possessions were returned, and he received all his back pay. Only his flat, occupied by the tailor's wife, was not given back to him. The neighbours watched to see what he would do. It was said that some of his colleagues had proposed finding him another wife, but he had declined their offers.

"I know the kind of woman he wants," said the tailor's wife. "Just leave it to me!"

zenith: peak; high point

Having passed her **zenith** she had become more subdued. Stripped of her power she had to wear a smile. With a photograph of a pretty girl in her pocket she went to the gatehouse to find Mr. Short. The girl in the picture was her niece.

She sat in the gatehouse sizing up its furnishing as she proposed this match to rich Mr. Short. Smiling all over her face she held forth with gusto until suddenly she realized that he had not said a word, his face was black, and behind him hung a picture of him and Mrs. Tall on their wedding day. Then she beat a retreat without venturing to produce the photograph of her niece.

Since then several years have passed. Mr. Short is still a widower, but on Sundays he fetches his son home to keep him company. At the sight of his squat, lonely figure, his neighbours recall all that he has been through and have come to understand why he goes on living alone. When it rains and he takes an umbrella to go to work, out of force of habit perhaps he still holds it high. Then they have the strange sensation that there is a big empty space under that umbrella, a vacuum that nothing on earth can fill.

Translated by Gladys Yang

After You Read

Critical Reading

1. Consider the **point of view** in the story. Does the author use a **third-person limited point of view** or a **third-person omniscient point of view**? Support your answer with details from the story. Explain why the author uses this point of view.

2. Readers learn about **characters** by the way they interact with other characters or with the environment. Trace the interaction of two of the characters in "The Tall Woman and Her Short Husband." Use quotations from the story to show how your selected characters change (or don't change) over the course of the text.

3. Conformity to the norm is a major concern of some of the characters in this story. In a short paragraph, discuss your sense of the author's **tone**, or attitude, toward conformity.

Literary Lens: Juxtaposition

Juxtaposition is the intentional side-by-side placement of two ideas, images, characters, or actions in a story. An author uses juxtaposition to highlight similarities and differences between the two items. Use a chart similar to the one below to identify two or more examples of juxtaposition in the story. For each, describe what unexpected things were placed in combination. Then infer what the author hoped to reveal through the use of this juxtaposition.

Examples of juxtaposition or the unexpected things placed in combination	What the author hopes to reveal?

Focus on Research: Organize Information

Find three sources on the Cultural Revolution in China and take notes. Based on your notes, decide how to best organize the information for a one-page report. Options include cause and effect, chronological, or main idea and supporting details. Share your report with a partner and ask them to evaluate the organization of the information.

Saboteur[1]

Ha Jin

Before You Read

Ha Jin (1956–) is the pen name of Xuefei Jin. Born and raised in China, Jin struggled to get an education in the anti-intellectual climate of the Cultural Revolution. In 1985, he came to the United States to study. After the 1989 massacre of student protesters at Tiananmen Square, Jin chose not return to China, embarking instead on a writing career in the United States. He has won many prizes, including the National Book Award for his novel *Waiting*.

World Context

The climate in China just after the Cultural Revolution (1966–1969) was repressive. Ha Jin focuses his attention on this period in his story "Saboteur."

 LITERARY LENS As you read, identify examples of **foreshadowing,** or hints or clues about what will happen later in the story.

Mr. Chiu and his bride were having lunch in the square before Muji Train Station. On the table between them were two bottles of soda spewing out brown foam and two paper boxes of rice and sautéed cucumber and pork. "Let's eat," he said to her, and broke the connected ends of the chopsticks. He picked up a slice of streaky pork and put it into his mouth. As he was chewing, a few crinkles appeared on his thin jaw.

To his right, at another table, two railroad policemen were drinking tea and laughing; it seemed that the stout, middle-aged man was telling a joke to his young comrade, who was tall and of athletic build. Now and again they would steal a glance at Mr. Chiu's table.

The air smelled of rotten melon. A few flies kept buzzing above the couple's lunch. Hundreds of people were rushing around to get on the

---

1 **saboteur:** one who practices sabotage, or the deliberate destruction of another's property or plans

platform or to catch buses to downtown. Food and fruit vendors were crying for customers in lazy voices. About a dozen young women, representing the local hotels, held up placards which displayed the daily prices and words as large as a palm, like FREE MEALS, AIR-CONDITIONING, and ON THE RIVER. In the center of the square stood a concrete statue of Chairman Mao,[2] at whose feet peasants were napping, their backs on the warm granite and their faces toward the sunny sky. A flock of pigeons perched on the Chairman's raised hand and forearm.

The rice and cucumber tasted good, and Mr. Chiu was eating unhurriedly. His **sallow** face showed exhaustion. He was glad that the honeymoon was finally over and that he and his bride were heading back for Harbin. During the two weeks' vacation, he had been worried about his liver, because three months ago he had suffered from acute hepatitis; he was afraid he might have a relapse. But he had had no severe symptoms, despite his liver being still big and tender. On the whole he was pleased with his health, which could endure even the strain of a honeymoon; indeed, he was on the course of recovery. He looked at his bride, who took off her wire glasses, kneading the root of her nose with her fingertips. Beads of sweat coated her pale cheeks.

sallow: yellowish; sickly

"Are you all right, sweetheart?" he asked.

"I have a headache. I didn't sleep well last night."

"Take an aspirin, will you?"

"It's not that serious. Tomorrow is Sunday and I can sleep in. Don't worry."

As they were talking, the stout policeman at the next table stood up and threw a bowl of tea in their direction. Both Mr. Chiu's and his bride's sandals were wet instantly.

"Hooligan!" she said in a low voice.

Mr. Chiu got to his feet and said out loud, "Comrade Policeman, why did you do this?" He stretched out his right foot to show the wet sandal.

"Do what?" the stout man asked huskily, glaring at Mr. Chiu while the young fellow was whistling.

"See, you dumped tea on our feet."

"You're lying. You wet your shoes yourself."

"Comrade Policeman, your duty is to keep order, but you purposely tortured us common citizens. Why violate the law you are supposed to enforce?" As Mr. Chiu was speaking, dozens of people began gathering around.

With a wave of his hand, the man said to the young fellow, "Let's get hold of him!"

---

2 **Chairman Mao:** Mao Tse-tung, Communist Party leader responsible for the Cultural Revolution (1966–1969)

They grabbed Mr. Chiu and clamped handcuffs around his wrists. He cried, "You can't do this to me. This is utterly unreasonable."

"Shut up!" The man pulled out his pistol. "You can use your tongue at our headquarters."

The young fellow added, "You're a saboteur, you know that? You're disrupting public order."

The bride was too petrified to say anything coherent. She was a recent college graduate, had majored in fine arts, and had never seen the police make an arrest. All she could say was, "Oh, please, please!"

The policemen were pulling Mr. Chiu, but he refused to go with them, holding the corner of the table and shouting, "We have a train to catch. We already bought the tickets."

The stout man punched him in the chest. "Shut up. Let your ticket expire." With the pistol butt he chopped Mr. Chiu's hands, which at once released the table. Together the two men were dragging him away to the police station.

Realizing he had to go with them, Mr. Chiu turned his head and shouted to his bride, "Don't wait for me here. Take the train. If I'm not back by tomorrow morning, send someone over to get me out."

She nodded, covering her sobbing mouth with her palm.

• • • • •

After removing his belt, they locked Mr. Chiu into a cell in the back of the Railroad Police Station. The single window in the room was blocked by six steel bars; it faced a spacious yard, in which stood a few pines. Beyond the trees, two swings hung from an iron frame, swaying gently in the breeze. Somewhere in the building a cleaver[3] was chopping rhythmically. There must be a kitchen upstairs, Mr. Chiu thought.

He was too exhausted to worry about what they would do to him, so he lay down on the narrow bed and shut his eyes. He wasn't afraid. The Cultural Revolution was over already, and recently the Party had been **propagating** the idea that all citizens were equal before the law. The police ought to be a law-abiding model for common people. As long as he remained coolheaded and reasoned with them, they probably wouldn't harm him.

Late in the afternoon he was taken to the Interrogation Bureau on the second floor. On his way there, in the stairwell, he ran into the middle-aged policeman who had manhandled him. The man grinned, rolling his bulgy

propagating: spreading; broadcasting

---

3 **cleaver:** a sharp knife used to butcher animal carcasses

eyes and pointing his fingers at him as if firing a pistol. Egg of a tortoise! Mr. Chiu cursed mentally.

The moment he sat down in the office, he burped, his palm shielding his mouth. In front of him, across a long desk, sat the chief of the bureau and a donkey-faced man. On the glass desktop was a folder containing information on his case. He felt it bizarre that in just a matter of hours they had accumulated a small pile of writing about him. On second thought he began to wonder whether they had kept a file on him all the time. How could this have happened? He lived and worked in Harbin, more than three hundred miles away, and this was his first time in Muji City.

The chief of the bureau was a thin, bald man who looked serene and intelligent. His slim hands handled the written pages in the folder in the manner of a lecturing scholar. To Mr. Chiu's left sat a young scribe, with a clipboard on his knee and a black fountain pen in his hand.

"Your name?" the chief asked, apparently reading out the question from a form.

"Chiu Maguang."

"Age?"

"Thirty-four."

"Profession?"

"Lecturer."

"Work unit?"

"Harbin University."

"Political status?"

"Communist Party member."

The chief put down the paper and began to speak. "Your crime is sabotage, although it hasn't induced serious consequences yet. Because you are a Party member, you should be punished more. You have failed to be a model for the masses and you—"

"Excuse me, sir," Mr. Chiu cut him off.

"What?"

"I didn't do anything. Your men are the saboteurs of our social order. They threw hot tea on my feet and on my wife's feet. Logically speaking, you should criticize them, if not punish them."

"That statement is groundless. You have no witness. Why should I believe you?" the chief said matter-of-factly.

"This is my evidence." He raised his right hand. "Your man hit my fingers with a pistol."

"That doesn't prove how your feet got wet. Besides, you could have hurt your fingers yourself."

"But I am telling the truth!" Anger flared up in Mr. Chiu. "Your police station owes me an apology. My train ticket has expired, my new leather sandals are ruined, and I am late for a conference in the provincial capital. You must compensate me for the damage and losses. Don't mistake me for a common citizen who would tremble when you sneeze. I'm a scholar, a philosopher, and an expert in dialectical materialism.[4] If necessary, we will argue about this in *The Northeastern Daily*, or we will go to the highest People's Court in Beijing. Tell me, what's your name?" He got carried away with his **harangue**, which was by no means trivial and had worked to his advantage on numerous occasions.

harangue: lecture; tirade

"Stop bluffing us," the donkey-faced man broke in. "We have seen a lot of your kind. We can easily prove you are guilty. Here are some of the statements given by eyewitnesses." He pushed a few sheets of paper toward Mr. Chiu.

Mr. Chiu was dazed to see the different handwritings, which all stated that he had shouted in the square to attract attention and refused to obey the police. One of the witnesses had identified herself as a purchasing agent from a shipyard in Shanghai. Something stirred in Mr. Chiu's stomach, a pain rising to his rib. He gave out a faint moan.

"Now you have to admit you are guilty," the chief said. "Although it's a serious crime, we won't punish you severely, provided you write out a self-criticism and promise that you won't disrupt the public order again. In other words, your release will depend on your attitude toward this crime."

"You're daydreaming," Mr. Chiu cried. "I won't write a word, because I'm innocent. I demand that you provide me with a letter of apology so I can explain to my university why I'm late."

Both the interrogators smiled contemptuously. "Well, we've never done that," said the chief, taking a puff at his cigarette.

"Then make this a precedent."

"That's unnecessary. We are pretty certain that you will comply with our wishes." The chief blew a column of smoke toward Mr. Chiu's face.

At the tilt of the chief's head, two guards stepped forward and grabbed the criminal by the arms. Mr. Chiu meanwhile went on saying, "I shall report you to the Provincial Administration. You'll have to pay for this! You are worse than the Japanese military police."

They dragged him out of the room.

• • • • •

---

4 **dialectical materialism:** A Marxian theory emphasizing that reality is dynamic rather than static and that economic systems greatly affect political and cultural developments.

After dinner, which consisted of a bowl of millet porridge, a corn bun, and a piece of pickled turnip, Mr. Chiu began to have a fever, shaking with a chill and sweating profusely. He knew that the fire of anger had gotten into his liver and that he was probably having a relapse. No medicine was available, because his briefcase had been left with his bride. At home it would have been time for him to sit in front of their color TV, drinking jasmine tea and watching the evening news. It was so lonesome in here. The orange bulb above the single bed was the only source of light, which enabled the guards to keep him under surveillance at night. A moment ago he had asked them for a newspaper or a magazine to read, but they turned him down.

Through the small opening on the door noises came in. It seemed that the police on duty were playing cards or chess in a nearby office; shouts and laughter could be heard now and then. Meanwhile, an accordion kept coughing from a remote corner in the building. Looking at the ballpoint and the letter paper left for him by the guards when they took him back from the Interrogation Bureau, Mr. Chiu remembered the old saying, "When a scholar runs into soldiers, the more he argues, the muddier his point becomes." How ridiculous this whole thing was. He ruffled his thick hair with his fingers.

He felt miserable, massaging his stomach continually. To tell the truth, he was more upset than frightened, because he would have to catch up with his work once he was back home—a paper that was due at the printers next week, and two dozen books he ought to read for the course he was going to teach in the fall.

A human shadow flitted across the opening. Mr. Chiu rushed to the door and shouted through the hole, "Comrade Guard, Comrade Guard!"

"What do you want?" a voice rasped.

"I want you to inform your leaders that I'm very sick. I have heart disease and hepatitis. I may die here if you keep me like this without medication."

"No leader is on duty on the weekend. You have to wait till Monday."

"What? You mean I'll stay in here tomorrow?"

"Yes."

"Your station will be held responsible if anything happens to me."

"We know that. Take it easy, you won't die."

It seemed illogical that Mr. Chiu slept quite well that night, though the light above his head had been on all the time and the straw mattress was hard and infested with fleas. He was afraid of ticks, mosquitoes, cockroaches—any kind of insect but fleas and bedbugs. Once, in the countryside, where his school's faculty and staff had helped the peasants harvest crops for a week, his colleagues had joked about his flesh, which they said must have tasted nonhuman to fleas. Except for him, they were all afflicted with hundreds of bites.

More amazing now, he didn't miss his bride a lot. He even enjoyed sleeping alone, perhaps because the honeymoon had tired him out and he needed more rest.

The backyard was quiet on Sunday morning. Pale sunlight streamed through the pine branches. A few sparrows were jumping on the ground, catching caterpillars and ladybugs. Holding the steel bars, Mr. Chiu inhaled the morning air, which smelled meaty. There must have been an eatery or a cooked-meat stand nearby. He reminded himself that he should take this detention with ease. A sentence that Chairman Mao had written to a hospitalized friend rose in his mind: "Since you are already in here, you may as well stay and make the best of it."

His desire for peace of mind originated in his fear that his hepatitis might get worse. He tried to remain unperturbed. However, he was sure that his liver was swelling up, since the fever still persisted. For a whole day he lay in bed, thinking about his paper on the nature of contradictions. Time and again he was overwhelmed by anger, cursing aloud, "A bunch of thugs!" He swore that once he was out, he would write an article about this experience. He had better find out some of the policemen's names.

It turned out to be a restful day for the most part; he was certain that his university would send somebody to his rescue. All he should do now was remain calm and wait patiently. Sooner or later the police would have to release him, although they had no idea that he might refuse to leave unless they wrote him an apology. Damn those hoodlums, they had ordered more than they could eat!

When he woke up on Monday morning, it was already light. Somewhere a man was moaning; the sound came from the backyard. After a long yawn, and kicking off the tattered blanket, Mr. Chiu climbed out of bed and went to the window. In the middle of the yard, a young man was fastened to a pine, his wrists handcuffed around the trunk from behind. He was wriggling and swearing loudly, but there was no sight of anyone else in the yard. He looked familiar to Mr. Chiu.

Mr. Chiu squinted his eyes to see who it was. To his astonishment, he recognized the man, who was Fenjin, a recent graduate from the Law Department at Harbin University. Two years ago Mr. Chiu had taught a course in Marxist materialism, in which Fenjin had enrolled. Now, how on earth had this young devil landed here?

Then it dawned on him that Fenjin must have been sent over by his bride. What a stupid woman! A bookworm, who only knew how to read foreign novels! He had expected that she would contact the school's Security Section, which would for sure send a cadre[5] here. Fenjin held no official position; he merely worked in a private law firm that had just two lawyers; in fact, they had little business except for some detective work for men and women who suspected their spouses of having extramarital affairs. Mr. Chiu was overcome with a wave of nausea.

Should he call out to let his student know he was nearby? He decided not to, because he didn't know what had happened. Fenjin must have quarreled with the police to incur such a punishment. Yet this could never have occurred if Fenjin hadn't come to his rescue. So no matter what, Mr. Chiu had to do something. But what could he do?

It was going to be a scorcher. He could see purple steam shimmering and rising from the ground among the pines. Poor devil, he thought, as he raised a bowl of corn glue to his mouth, sipped, and took a bite of a piece of salted celery.

When a guard came to collect the bowl and the chopsticks, Mr. Chiu asked him what had happened to the man in the backyard. "He called our boss 'bandit,'" the guard said. "He claimed he was a lawyer or something. An arrogant son of a rabbit."

Now it was obvious to Mr. Chiu that he had to do something to help his rescuer. Before he could figure out a way, a scream broke out in the backyard. He rushed to the window and saw a tall policeman standing before Fenjin, an iron bucket on the ground. It was the same young fellow who had arrested Mr. Chiu in the square two days before. The man pinched Fenjin's nose, then raised his hand, which stayed in the air for a few seconds, then slapped the lawyer across the face. As Fenjin was groaning, the man lifted up the bucket and poured water on his head.

"This will keep you from getting sunstroke, boy. I'll give you some more every hour," the man said loudly.

Fenjin kept his eyes shut, yet his wry face showed that he was struggling to hold back from cursing the policeman, or, more likely, that he was sobbing in silence. He sneezed, then raised his face and shouted, "Let me go take a piss."

"Oh yeah?" the man bawled. "Pee in your pants."

Still Mr. Chiu didn't make any noise, gripping the steel bars with both hands, his fingers white. The policeman turned and glanced at the cell's

---

5 **cadre:** a group of revolutionary leaders

window; his pistol, partly holstered, glittered in the sun. With a snort he spat his cigarette butt to the ground and stamped it into the dust.

Then the door opened and the guards motioned Mr. Chiu to come out. Again they took him upstairs to the Interrogation Bureau.

The same men were in the office, though this time the scribe was sitting there empty-handed. At the sight of Mr. Chiu the chief said, "Ah, here you are. Please be seated."

After Mr. Chiu sat down, the chief waved a white silk fan and said to him, "You may have seen your lawyer. He's a young man without manners, so our director had him taught a crash course in the back yard."

"It's illegal to do that. Aren't you afraid to appear in a newspaper?"

"No, we are not, not even on TV. What else can you do? We are not afraid of any story you make up. We call it fiction. What we do care about is that you cooperate with us. That is to say, you must admit your crime."

"What if I refuse to cooperate?"

"Then your lawyer will continue his education in the sunshine."

A swoon swayed Mr. Chiu, and he held the arms of the chair to steady himself. A numb pain stung him in the upper stomach and nauseated him, and his head was throbbing. He was sure that the hepatitis was finally attacking him. Anger was flaming up in his chest; his throat was tight and clogged.

The chief resumed, "As a matter of fact, you don't even have to write out your self-criticism. We have your crime described clearly here. All we need is your signature."

Holding back his rage, Mr. Chiu said, "Let me look at that."

With a smirk the donkey-faced man handed him a sheet, which carried these words:

> I hereby admit that on July 13 I disrupted public order at Muji Train Station, and that I refused to listen to reason when the railroad police issued their warning. Thus I myself am responsible for my arrest. After two days' detention, I have realized the **reactionary** nature of my crime. From now on, I shall continue to educate myself with all my effort and shall never commit this kind of crime again.

reactionary: not progressive; opposed to change

A voice started screaming in Mr. Chiu's ears, "Lie, lie!" But he shook his head and forced the voice away. He asked the chief, "If I sign this, will you release both my lawyer and me?"

"Of course, we'll do that." The chief was drumming his fingers on the blue folder—their file on him.

Mr. Chiu signed his name and put his thumbprint under his signature.

"Now you are free to go," the chief said with a smile, and handed him a piece of paper to wipe his thumb with.

Mr. Chiu was so sick that he couldn't stand up from the chair at first try. Then he doubled his effort and rose to his feet. He staggered out of the building to meet his lawyer in the backyard, having forgotten to ask for his belt back. In his chest he felt as though there were a bomb. If he were able to, he would have razed the entire police station and eliminated all their families. Though he knew he could do nothing like that, he made up his mind to do something.

● ● ● ● ●

"I'm sorry about this torture, Fenjin," Mr. Chiu said when they met.

"It doesn't matter. They are savages." The lawyer brushed a patch of dirt off his jacket with trembling fingers. Water was still dribbling from the bottoms of his trouser legs.

"Let's go now," the teacher said.

The moment they came out of the police station, Mr. Chiu caught sight of a tea stand. He grabbed Fenjin's arm and walked over to the old woman at the table. "Two bowls of black tea," he said and handed her a one-yuan note.

After the first bowl, they each had another one. Then they set out for the train station. But before they walked fifty yards, Mr. Chiu insisted on eating a bowl of tree-ear soup at a food stand. Fenjin agreed. He told his teacher, "You mustn't treat me like a guest."

"No, I want to eat something myself."

As if dying of hunger, Mr. Chiu dragged his lawyer from restaurant to restaurant near the police station, but at each place he ordered no more than two bowls of food. Fenjin wondered why his teacher wouldn't stay at one place and eat his fill.

Mr. Chiu bought noodles, wonton, eight-grain porridge, and chicken soup, respectively, at four restaurants. While eating, he kept saying through his teeth, "If only I could kill all the bastards!" At the last place he merely took a few sips of the soup without tasting the chicken cubes and mushrooms.

Fenjin was baffled by his teacher, who looked ferocious and muttered to himself mysteriously, and whose jaundiced[6] face was covered with dark puckers. For the first time Fenjin thought of Mr. Chiu as an ugly man.

•••••

Within a month over eight hundred people contracted acute hepatitis in Muji. Six died of the disease, including two children. Nobody knew how the epidemic had started.

---

6 **jaundiced:** affected with jaundice, a disease that makes skin look yellow

After You Read

Critical Reading

1. Consider the character of Mr. Chiu. Would you consider Mr. Chiu to be a **hero** or an **anti-hero**? Support your answer with details from the story.

2. Mr. Chiu's attitude toward the police changes throughout the course of the story. Describe his attitude at the beginning, in the middle, and at the end of the story. Why did his attitude change? Support your answer with details from the story.

3. Do you think the mistreatment Mr. Chiu experiences in the story justifies his action at the end? Explain your answer.

Literary Lens: Foreshadowing

Foreshadowing is a literary device in which a writer drops hints of what will come later in the story. A writer may incorporate foreshadowing into the description of the characters' actions, into dialogue between characters, or even in the title of the story. Foreshadowing creates an atmosphere of suspense and anticipation in the reader. Use a graphic organizer like the one below to identify hints and clues in the story that foreshadow the event in the final paragraph of the story.

Hints and clues	Why is this an example of foreshadowing? How did this hint at the final event in the story?

Focus on Research: Quote Sources Directly

Good research reports use quotations effectively and sparingly. Use quotations to show authority, precision, and vividness. For example, a statement from an expert that is especially well-stated should be quoted directly instead of simply paraphrased. Conduct research to find out more information about "the Party" referred to in this story (page 538). Then write a brief analysis of your findings. In your analysis use two direct quotations. Be sure to use quotation marks to correctly punctuate the quotation. In addition, provide an in-text citation using MLA or APA style.

from The Garlic Ballads

Mo Yan

Before You Read

Mo Yan (1955–) is one of the most famous Chinese authors of his generation, having produced multiple novels, novellas, collections of short stories, essays, and speeches. Frequently in his work, Yan tackles issues like political ideology, corruption, and the effects of greed on individuals and communities. In 2012, Mo Yan received a Nobel Prize in Literature, the first Chinese resident to have ever received the award.

World Context

After being awarded the Nobel Prize, Yan's work came under intense scrutiny. Some Chinese writers and literary critics accused Yan's work of, at times, creating a sympathetic portrayal of the Communist Party in China. Others praised his work for portraying in fiction some of the serious tragedies that occurred in Chinese history. His book *The Garlic Ballads* was banned in China when it was first published. "At first I thought I was the target of the disputes," Yan explains, "but over time I've come to realize that the real target was a person who had nothing to do with me . . . No writer has yet appeared, anywhere in the world, who is liked by all his readers; that is especially true during times like these."

LITERARY LENS As you read, observe the use of **repetition** in the chapter and consider how this repetition influences character development and mood.

"Gao[1] Yang!"

The noonday sun beat down fiercely; dusty air carried the stink of rotting garlic after a prolonged dry spell. A flock of indigo crows flew wearily across the sky, casting a shadowy wedge. There had been no time to braid the garlic, which lay in heaps,

---

1 **Gao:** a common and widely used surname in China

reeking as it baked in the sun. Gao Yang, whose eyebrows sloped downward at the end, was squatting alongside a table, holding a bowl of garlic broth and fighting back the waves of nausea rising from his stomach. The urgent shout had come in through his unlatched gate as he was about to take a sip of the broth. He recognized the voice as belonging to the village boss, Gao Jinjiao. Hastily laying down his bowl, he shouted a reply and walked to the door. "Is that you, Uncle[2] Jinijiao? Come on in."

This time the voice was gentler. "Gao Yang, come out here for a minute. I have to talk to you about something."

Knowing the consequences of slighting the village boss, Gao Yang turned to his blind eight-year-old daughter, who sat frozen at the table like a dark statue, her black, beautiful, sightless eyes opened wide. "Don't touch anything, Xinghua, or you might **scald** yourself."

scald:
to burn

Baked earth burned the soles of his feet; the intense heat made his eyes water. With the sun beating down on his bare back, he scraped caked-on dirt from his chest. He heard the cry of this newborn baby on the kang, a brick platform that served as the family's bed, and thought he heard his wife mumble something. Finally, he had a son. It was a comforting thought. The fragrance of new **millet** drifted up on a southwestern breeze, reminding him that harvest was approaching. Suddenly his heart sank, and a chill worked its way up his spine. He wanted desperately to stop walking, but his legs kept propelling him forward, as the pungent odor of garlic stalks and bulbs made his eyes water. He raised his bare arm to wipe them, confident that he wasn't crying.

millet:
a grain grown
for food

He opened the gate. "What is it, Uncle?" he asked. "Ow! . . . Mother—!" Emerald bits streaked past him, like millions of green garlic stalks swirling in the air; something struck his right ankle, a dull, heavy, gut-wrenching blow. Momentarily stunned, he closed his eyes and assumed that the sound he heard was his own scream as he slumped to one side. Another dull thud behind his left knee. He screamed in pain—there was no denying it this time—and pitched forward, winding up on his knees on the stone steps. Dazed, he tried to open his eyes, but the lids were too heavy, and the pungent, garlicky air drew tears. Still, he knew he wasn't crying. He raised his hand to rub his eyes, only to discover that his wrists were snared painfully by something cold and hard; two faint metallic clicks knifed into his brain.

---

2   **Uncle:** in parts of China, words like "auntie" and "uncle" are sometimes used to refer to middle-aged people who hold a moderate level of authority

tunics:
a type of
clothing,
frequently
a belted coat
worn by the
military

Finally he opened his eyes. Through the film of tears—I'm not crying, he thought—he saw two policemen in white **tunics** and green pants with red stripes down the legs; they towered over him, pale smudges on their pants and dark stains on their tunics. But what caught his attention were the pistols and the dark nightsticks that hung from wide, cordovan-colored, artificial-leather belts cinching up their tunics. The buckles glinted in the sun. He looked up into the men's expressionless faces, but before he could utter a sound, the man on the left waved a sheet of paper with an official red seal in front of him and said with a slight stammer, "Y-you're under arrest."

That was when he noticed the shiny steel bracelets on his sunburned wrists. They were linked by a slack, heavy, silvery chain that swayed lazily when he raised his hands. A powerful shudder wracked him . . .

The policeman on the left took Gao Yang's arm in his ice-cold hand to help him up. Another slight stammer. "G-get up."

Still dazed, Gao Yang reached for the policeman's arm, but the handcuffs, clanking softly, dug into his flesh and forced him to let go. Fearfully, he held his arms stiffly out in front, as if cupping a precious, fragile object.

"G-get up!" The policeman's order rang out. He struggled to his feet, but was no sooner standing than a searing pain tore through his ankle. He lurched sideways and fell to his hands and knees on the stone steps.

The policemen grabbed him under the arms and picked him up. But his legs were so rubbery that his **gangly** frame dangled in their grasp like a **pendulum**. The policeman on his right drove his knee into Gao Yang's tailbone. "Stand up!" he growled. "What happened to the hero who demolished the county offices?"

gangly:
lanky;
awkward

pendulum:
a device that
swings from
a fixed point

The comment was lost on Gao Yang, but the rock-hard knee against his tailbone helped him forget the pain in this ankle. With a shudder he planted his feet and stood up. The policemen loosened their grip, and the one with the stammer said softly, "G-get moving, and h-hurry."

His head was swimming, but he remained confident that he wasn't crying, even as hot tears welled up and spilled over to cloud his vision. The handcuffs dug deeply into his wrists each time he was shoved forward, and he suddenly—finally—realized what was happening. He knew he had to find the will to force his stiffened tongue to move: not daring to address his tormentors, he gazed pitifully at Gao Jinjiao, who was cowering beneath an acacia tree, and said, "Uncle, why are they arresting me? I haven't done anything wrong."

Wails and sobs followed. This time he knew he was crying, even though no tears flowed from his now dry, burning eyes. He must plead his case to the village boss, who had tricked him into coming outside in the first place. But Gao Jinjiao was rocking back and forth, bumping against the tree like a **penitent** little boy. A muscle on Gao Yang's face twitched. "I haven't done anything, Uncle, why did you trick me like that?" He was shouting. A large bead of sweat on the village boss's forehead refused to roll down. With his yellow teeth bared, he looked like a cornered man about to break and run.

The policeman again drove his knee into Gao Yang's tailbone to get him moving. "Comrade[3] Officer," he protested, taming to look into the man's face, "you've got the wrong man. My name's Gao Yang. I'm not—"

"W-we've got the right man," the stammerer insisted.

"My name's Gao Yang."

"Gao Yang is who we want!"

"What did I do?"

"At noon on May twenty-eight you were one of the leaders of a mob that demolished the county offices."

The lights went out as Gao Yang crumpled to the ground. When they picked him up again, he rolled his eyes and said timidly, "You call that a *crime*?"

"That's right—now get moving!"

"But I wasn't alone. Lots of people were involved."

"And we'll catch every last one of them."

He hung his head, wishing he could butt it into the wall and end everything. But he was being held too firmly to squirm free, and he could hear the faint strains of Shang Kous moving yet dreary ballad:

> In the tenth year of the Republic
> A hot-blooded young man came out of nowhere
> To hoist the red flag in Paradise County[4]
> And lead the peasants in a protest against unfair taxes.
> Village elders dispatched soldiers to surround them,
> Arrested Gao Dayi and sent him to the executioner's block.
> He went to his death proudly, defiantly,
> For the Communists, like scallions, could not all be felled.

He felt a warmth in his belly as the strength returned to his legs. His lips trembled, and he felt strangely compelled to shout a defiant slogan. But then he turned and stared at the bright red insignia on the policeman's

penitent: regretful; remorseful

---

3 **Comrade:** a term used to mean "ally" or "friend," which has commonly come to be associated with communism

4 **Paradise County:** the country in China in which farmers revolted in 1987 due to a glut in garlic

wide-brimmed cap, and lowered his head again, overcome with shame and remorse; letting his arms fall slack in front of him, he followed obediently.

Then he heard a tapping sound behind him and strained to see what it was: his daughter, Xinghua, was walking toward him, tapping the ground with a scarred and scorched bamboo staff that banged crisply against the stone steps and resonated painfully in his heart. He grimaced, as hot tears gushed from his eyes. He was truly crying; there was no denying it now. A scalding liquid stopped up his throat when he tried to speak. . . .

She took high, arching steps—he noticed for the first time what long legs she had—as she crossed the threshold and stood on the stone steps where he had knelt a moment earlier. Her staff was a foot or so taller than she, and he was suddenly and surprisingly aware of how tall she had grown. He tried again to force down the gooey lump in his throat as he gazed at the two shiny black dots in her cinder-streaked face. Her eyes were a dense, demonic black, seemingly with no white at all, and as she cocked her head, a strange expression of mature worldliness settled over her face. She called out to him softly, tentatively, before a scream tore from her throat: "Daddy!"

Moisture gathered in the corners of her mouth. One of the policemen prodded him hesitantly. "C-come on," he said gently, "get moving. They may let you out in a day or two."

Spasms wracked Gao Yang's throat and guts as he stared at the stammering policeman, with his smug, ingratiating look; Gao Yang's teeth parted, and out gushed a stream of white froth streaked with pale-blue threads. He wasted no time, now that his throat was clear: "Xinghua! Go tell Mommy—" His throat closed up again before he could get the rest out.

Gao Jinjiao slinked up to the gate and said, "Go home and tell your mommy that your daddy's been taken away by the police."

Gao Yang watched his daughter drop down on the threshold and rock backward, barely catching herself with a hand on the ground. With the help of her bamboo staff, she stood up again; her mouth was open, as if screaming, though Gao Yang heard nothing but a rumbling noise that might have been far off or could have been right next to him. Another wave of nausea hit him. His daughter looked like a chained monkey being whipped and dragged roughly along, leaping silently but wildly from side to side. Her staff tapped the stone threshold, tapped the rotting wood around it, tapped the hard, dry earth, leaving a track of pale scars in the ground.

His wife's tormented screams from the yard pounded in his years. "Village Chief Gao," the policeman said, "you lead the way. Let's get out of here." They lifted Gao Yang by the arms, as they would a stubborn, spindly little boy, and dragged him toward the village as fast as their legs would carry them.

After You Read

Critical Reading

1. Consider the use of the word "Uncle." What are the **connotations** of this word as it is used in the story?

2. Identify examples of **foreshadowing** in the text. Explain what the foreshadowing contributes to the tone of the story.

3. The text begins by describing the stink of rotten garlic. How is the garlic a **symbol** in this story? What does it symbolize? Support your answer with details from the text.

Literary Lens: Repetition

Throughout the story, Gao Yang comments about whether he was or wasn't crying. Identify two or more instances in which crying is mentioned. Analyze whether Gao Yang was or was not crying in those instances and make an inference about what this reveals about the character. Lastly, how would you describe the effect of this repetition on the mood of the story?

Example of Repetition	Was Gao Yang crying in this instance? Yes/No	What does this reveal about Gao Yang?
Effect of repetition on mood:		

Focus on Research: Summarize Information

Research parts of Chinese history, such as the Great Leap Forward (1950s–1960s), the Cultural Revolution (1960s–1970s), and the Chinese farmers' revolt in Paradise County in 1987 (also called the 1987 Garlic Glut). For each source you find, write a note in which you summarize the most important information you found from that source. Include key source information with each note so that someone else can find the source and check your information.

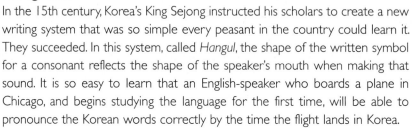

The Literature of
Korea

Background

In the 15th century, Korea's King Sejong instructed his scholars to create a new writing system that was so simple every peasant in the country could learn it. They succeeded. In this system, called *Hangul*, the shape of the written symbol for a consonant reflects the shape of the speaker's mouth when making that sound. It is so easy to learn that an English-speaker who boards a plane in Chicago, and begins studying the language for the first time, will be able to pronounce the Korean words correctly by the time the flight lands in Korea.

The creation of Hangul reflected Korea's strong national pride. The first great literary achievement in Hangul was *Yongbieocheonga (Songs of the Dragons Flying to Heaven)*, a compilation of poems celebrating Korean identity.

Korea and the United States

At the end of World War II, the Soviet Union occupied northern Korea and the United States occupied southern Korea. These occupations were supposed to be temporary until a postwar government could be organized. However, the two parts of Korea quickly fell into conflict. In 1950, full-scale war broke out. The United States and its allies supported South Korea. The Soviet Union and China backed North Korea. Three years of fighting resulted in 3 to 4 million casualties. More than 50,000 Americans died.

Today, Korea remains divided, and the United States still stations about 25,000 troops in South Korea. Many Koreans still hope for reunification, although the totalitarian rule of Kim Jong-un in North Korea makes this hope less likely to be fulfilled in the near future. Reunification is the theme of *Changma (The Rainy Spell and Other Korean Stories)*, a collection of short stories by South Korean writer Yun Heung-gil (1942–), and of "Falling Persimmons," a poem by North Korean writer Byungu Chon.

Research: Prepare a Bibliography

Most Americans know very little about North Korea. Research the country, focusing on one aspect of its literature, government, geography, history, or culture. Prepare a bibliography you could use for a report on your focused topic.

Cranes

Hwang Sun-won

Before You Read

Hwang Sun-won (1915–2000) lived through hard times in his native Korea. When the Japanese occupied the country, they banned writing in Korean, his native language. After World War II and the outbreak of the Korean War, Hwang and his family fled to the American-occupied South. In spite of these displacements, Sun-won continued to write. His stories include a wide range of characters: outcasts from society, soldiers, country dwellers, and city people. His work appears in English in *The Book of Masks* and *Shadows of a Sound*.

World Context

The setting of "Cranes" is the 38th parallel, the dividing line between North and South Korea. This political division is a symbol for the divisions that have disrupted families, friends, and communities since the creation of the two Koreas.

 LITERARY LENS A **flashback** is an interruption of the normal chronological order of the plot to narrate events that happened earlier. Watch for flashbacks as you read.

The northern village at the border of the Thirty-eighth Parallel was snugly settled under the high, bright autumn sky.

One white gourd lay against another on the dirt floor of an empty farmhouse. The occasional village elders first put out their bamboo pipes before passing by, and the children, too, turned aside some distance off. Their faces were ridden with fear.

The village as a whole showed few traces of destruction from the war, but it did not seem like the same village Song-sam had known as a boy.

At the foot of a chestnut grove on the hill behind the village he stopped and climbed a chestnut tree. Somewhere far back in his mind he heard the old man with a wen[1] shout, "You bad boy, you're climbing up my chestnut tree again!"

The old man must have passed away, for among the few village elders Song-sam had met, the old man was not to be found. Holding the trunk of the tree, Song-sam gazed at the blue sky for a while. Some chestnuts fell to the ground as the dry clusters opened of their own accord.

•••••

In front of the farmhouse that had been turned into a public peace-police office, a young man stood, tied up. He seemed to be a stranger, so Song-sam approached him to have a close look. He was taken aback; it was none other than his boyhood playmate, Tok-chae.

Song-sam asked the police officer who had come with him from Chontae what it was all about. The prisoner was vice-chairman of the Farmers' Communist League and had just been flushed out of his hideout in his own house, Song-sam learned.

Song-sam sat down on the dirt floor and lit a cigarette.

Tok-chae was to be escorted to Chongdan by one of the peace policemen.

After a time, Song-sam lit a new cigarette from the first and stood up.

"I'll take the fellow with me."

Tok-chae, his face averted, refused to look at Song-sam. They left the village.

Song-sam kept on smoking, but the tobacco had no taste. He just kept drawing in the smoke and blowing it out. Then suddenly he thought that Tok-chae, too, must want a puff. He thought of the days when they used to share dried gourd leaves behind walls, hidden from the adults. But today, how could he offer a cigarette to a fellow like this?

Once, when they were small, he went with Tok-chae to steal some chestnuts from the grandpa[2] with the wen. It was Song-sam's turn to go up the tree. Suddenly there came shouts from the old man. He slipped and fell to the ground. Song-sam got chestnut needles all over his bottom, but he kept on running. It was only when they reached a safe place where the old man could not overtake them that he turned his bottom to Tok-chae. Plucking out those needles hurt so much that he could not keep tears from welling up in his eyes. Tok-chae produced a fistful of chestnuts from his pocket and thrust them into Song-sam's . . . Song-sam threw away the

---

1   **wen:** a harmless tumor, often on the head

2   **grandpa:** elderly man

cigarette he had just lit. Then he made up his mind not to light another while he was escorting Tok-chae.

• • • • •

They reached the hill pass, the hill where he and Tok-chae used to cut fodder for the cows until Song-sam had had to move near Chontae, south of the Thirty-eighth Parallel, two years before the liberation.[3]

Song-sam felt a sudden surge of anger in spite of himself and shouted, "So how many have you killed?"

For the first time, Tok-chae cast a quick glance at him and then turned away.

---

3 **liberation:** In 1945, Japan surrendered to Allied forces, ending World War II and Japan's control of Korea.

"How many did you kill, you?" he asked again.

Tok-chae turned toward him once again and glared. The glare grew intense and his mouth twitched.

"So you managed to kill many, eh?" Song-sam felt his heart becoming clear from within, as if an obstruction had been removed. "If you were vice-chairman of the Communist League, why didn't you run? You must have been lying low with a secret mission."

Tok-chae did not answer.

"Speak up, what was your mission?"

Tok-chae kept walking. Tok-chae is hiding something, Song-sam thought. He wanted to take a good look at him, but Tok-chae would not turn his averted face.

Fingering the revolver at his side, Song-sam went on: "No excuse is necessary. You are sure to be shot anyway. Why don't you tell the truth, here and now?"

"I'm not going to make any excuses. They made me vice-chairman of the league because I was one of the poorest and I was a hard-working farmer. If that constitutes a crime worthy of death, so be it. I am still what I used to be—the only thing I'm good at is digging in the soil." After a short pause, he added, "My old man is bedridden at home. He's been ill almost half a year." Tok-chae's father was a widower, a hard-working poor farmer who lived only for his son. Seven years ago his back had given out and his skin had become diseased.

"You married?"

"Yes," replied Tok-chae after a while.

"To whom?"

"Shorty."

"To Shorty?" How interesting! A woman so small and plump that she knew the earth's vastness but not the sky's altitude. Such a cold fish! He and Tok-chae used to tease her and make her cry. And Tok-chae had married that girl.

"How many kids?"

"The first is arriving this fall, she says."

Song-sam had difficulty swallowing a laugh about to explode in spite of himself. Although he had asked how many kids Tok-chae had, he could not help wanting to burst into laughter at the image of her sitting down, with a large stomach, one span around. But he realized this was no time to laugh or joke over such matters.

"Anyway, it's strange you did not run away."

"I tried to escape. They said that once the South invaded, no man would be spared. So men between seventeen and forty were forcibly taken to the

North. I thought of evacuating, even if I had to carry my father on my back. But father said no. How could the farmers leave the land behind when the crops were ready for harvest? He grew old on that farm depending on me as the prop and mainstay of the family. I wanted to be with him in his last moments so that I could close his eyes with my own hand. Besides, where can farmers like us go, who know only living on the land?"

•••••

Last June Song-sam had had to take refuge. At night he had broken the news privately to his father. But his father had said the same thing! Where can a farmer go, leaving all the chores behind? So Song-sam left alone. Roaming about the strange streets and villages in the South, Song-sam had been haunted by thoughts of his old parents and the young children, left with all the chores. Fortunately, his family was safe then, as now.

They crossed the ridge of a hill. This time Song-sam walked with his face averted. The autumn sun was hot on his forehead. This was an ideal day for the harvest, he thought.

•••••

When they reached the foot of the hill, Song-sam hesitatingly stopped. In the middle of a field he spied a group of cranes that looked like men in white clothes bending over. This used to be the neutralized zone[4] along the Thirty-eighth Parallel. The cranes were still living here, as before, while the people were all gone.

Once, when Song-sam and Tok-chae were about twelve, they had set a trap here, without the knowledge of the adults, and had caught a crane, a Tanjong crane.[5] They had roped the crane, even its wings, and had paid daily visits, patting its neck and riding on its back. Then one day they overheard the neighbors whispering. Someone had come from Seoul with a permit from the governor-general's office[6] to catch cranes as specimens or something. Then and there the two boys dashed off to the field. That they

> . . . all they worried about was the fate of their crane.

---

4   neutralized zone: an area between North and South Korea that is not controlled by anyone militarily

5   Tanjong crane: a large, long-legged North Korean bird

6   governor-general's office: office of Korea's chief executive, appointed when Japan was in control of Korea

would be found out and punished was no longer a weighty concern; all they worried about was the fate of their crane. Without a moment's delay, still out of breath from running, they untied the crane's feet and wings. But the bird could hardly walk. It must have been worn out from being bound.

The two held it up in the air. Then, all of a sudden, a shot was fired. The crane fluttered its wings a couple of times and came down again.

It was shot, they thought. But the next moment, as another crane from a nearby bush fluttered its wings, the boys' crane stretched its long neck with a whoop and disappeared into the sky. For a long time the two boys could not take their eyes away from the blue sky into which their crane had soared.

"Hey, why don't we stop here for a crane hunt?" Song-sam spoke up suddenly.

Tok-chae was puzzled, struck dumb.

"I'll make a trap with this rope; you flush a crane over here."

Having untied Tok-chae's hands, Song-sam had already started crawling among the weeds.

Tok-chae's face turned white. "You are sure to be shot anyway"—these words flashed through his mind. Pretty soon a bullet would fly from where Song-sam has gone, he thought.

Some paces away, Song-sam quickly turned toward him.

"Hey, how come you're standing there like you're dumb? Go flush the crane!"

Only then did Tok-chae catch on. He started crawling among the weeds.

A couple of Tanjong cranes soared high into the clear blue autumn sky, fluttering their huge wings.

Translated by Peter H. Lee

After You Read

Critical Reading

1. In a paragraph, summarize both the **explicit**, or **literal**, meaning of the ending as well as the **implicit**, or **implied**, meaning.

2. Write a statement that expresses the **theme** of the story. Then identify two details from the story that support the theme.

3. Song-sam is dealing with several **conflicts**, both **internal** and **external**. Identify an internal conflict and an external conflict that Song-sam faces. Then describe how he resolves these conflicts. Support your response with details from the story.

Literary Lens: Flashback

A **flashback** is an interruption in the normal sequence of events in a story in order to describe events that occurred earlier. Identify and briefly describe two or more of the flashback scenes. Cite details from the scene. Then infer why the author included flashbacks in the story.

Flashback	Quotation
Why did the author use flashbacks in the story? What effect do you think the author wanted to achieve?	

Focus on Research: Create an Annotated Bibliography

Practice creating an annotated bibliography. Find three sources about the history of the Korean War. Use a variety of sources including books, scholarly articles, and videos. Use an online style guide to help you create an annotated bibliography for each source.

The Literature of

Vietnam

Background

Vietnam's culture has been greatly influenced by its powerful neighbor to the north, China. In its early history, Vietnamese authors wrote using a traditional form of classical Chinese. Today, the Vietnamese use an alphabet based on Latin letters introduced by French colonists in the early 1800s.

Modern Vietnam has been shaped by many forces, including the Vietnam War that ravaged the country between 1955 and 1975. The basic conflict was between a Communist government in the North and an anti-Communist government in the South. However, fighting spread to Vietnam's neighbors, the countries of Laos and Cambodia. Many historians estimate that over 4 million people died before the North won and the war ended.

Under the new Communist government, writers faced censorship, and many went into exile. Writer Duong Thu Huong (1947–) supported the Communists during the war, but after criticizing corruption in the Communist Party, she was expelled from the party. The government even banned several of her novels, restricted her travel, and imprisoned her for short periods. Duong finally moved to France in 2006.

Vietnam and the United States

The United States government supported the South in the Vietnam War. Close to 3 million U.S. troops served in Vietnam; more than 58,000 died. The United States' participation in the war bitterly divided U. S. citizens. After the war ended, writers began to reflect on it in novels, short stories, and poems. One of the most celebrated novels about the war is American author Denis Johnson's *Tree of Smoke*, which won the National Book Award in 2007.

Research: Compare Sources

Starting in the 1990s, many U.S. war veterans began visiting Vietnam. Some have had friendly meetings with soldiers against whom they once fought. "I contend that when a war veteran can shake hands with his former enemy, there's a cleansing that happens," remarked former U.S. Marine Tom Wiseman. Compare sources from both sides of the conflict that discuss relations between soldiers after the war. Explain your findings in a paragraph.

Thoughts of Hanoi

Nguyen Thi Vinh

Before You Read

In the 1950s, Nguyen Thi Vinh (1924–) relocated from her hometown in North Vietnam to Saigon in the South to escape Communist rule. She remained in Saigon even after the Communists gained control of the whole country in 1975. In the late 1980s, Vinh left her homeland and traveled by boat to Norway, where she has resettled with her husband and children.

World Context

During the Vietnam War (1954–1975), Hanoi, then the capital of North Vietnam, was heavily bombed. Communist forces eventually prevailed over the South, and Hanoi became the capital of the united territories.

 LITERARY LENS As you read, consider the **tone** used to describe the setting of the poem.

The night is deep and chill
as in early autumn. Pitchblack,
it thickens after each lightning flash.
I dream of Hanoi:
Co-ngu Road   5
ten years of separation
the way back sliced by a frontier of hatred.
I want to bury the past
to burn the future
still I yearn   10
still I fear
those endless nights
waiting for dawn.

Brother,
how is Hang Dao now?   15
How is Ngoc Son temple?
Do the trains still run
each day from Hanoi
to the neighboring towns?
To Bac-ninh, Cam-giang, Yen-bai,   20
the small villages, islands
of brown thatch in a lush green sea?

The girls
    bright eyes
        ruddy cheeks   25
    four-piece dresses
        raven-bill scarves[1]
    sowing harvesting
        spinning weaving
    all year round,   30
the boys
    ploughing
        transplanting
    in the fields
        in their shops   35
    running across
        the meadow at evening
    to fly kites
        and sing alternating songs.

Stainless blue sky,   40
    jubilant voices of children
stumbling through the alphabet,
    village graybeards strolling to the temple,
grandmothers basking in twilight sun,
    chewing betel leaves   45
while the children run—

---

1   **raven-bill scarves:** head scarves folded into triangles, like the bill of a bird

Brother,
how is all that now?
Or is it obsolete?
Are you like me,   50
reliving the past,
imagining the future?
Do you count me as a friend
or am I the enemy in your eyes?
Brother, I am afraid   55
that one day I'll be with the March-North Army[2]
meeting you on your way to the South.
I might be the one to shoot you then
or you me
but please
not with hatred.   60

For don't you remember how it was,
you and I in school together,
plotting our lives together?
Those roots go deep!

Brother, we are men,   65
conscious of more
than material needs.
How can this happen to us
my friend
my foe?   70

Translated by Nguyen Ngoc Bich

---

2 **March-North Army:** the South Vietnamese army marching into North Vietnam

After You Read

Critical Reading

1. Who is the speaker addressing? Describe the relationship between the speaker and the person being addressed. Cite specific lines from the poem to support your response.

2. Identify at least two examples of **enjambment** in the poem. What effect does this have on the reader's experience of the poem? How does this support the ideas communicated through the poetry?

3. This poem includes many questions. How does this **syntax** affect the mood of the poem? Support your answer with multiple examples of questions and other details from the poem.

 ## Literary Lens: Setting and Tone

In this poem, the speaker frequently describes the **setting**, or the time and the place in which the poem occurs. Cite two or more examples of descriptions of the setting. Then describe the **tone**, or the author's attitude toward the setting, revealed in these descriptions. Refer to specific words and phrases as you discuss the author's tone.

Description of setting	Author's tone

Focus on Research: Evaluate Arguments and Evidence

Conduct research to find out more information about varying viewpoints on the Vietnam War. Find two sources that disagree on an aspect of the war or its aftermath and evaluate the arguments presented. Consider if the sources are biased and why. For example, a veteran's organization might have a different viewpoint than a nonprofit that works with Vietnamese refugees.

The Literature of
Japan

Background

For the past 1,400 years, Japanese authors have steadily produced fine literature. Many of its greatest writers have been poets. Perhaps the most important of all Japanese authors, though, was a novelist, the noblewoman Murasaki Shikibu (c. 978–c. 1014). Her masterpiece about life at the imperial court, *The Tale of Genji*, is considered one of the first Japanese novels ever written and is possibly one of the first novels written in the world.

During World War II, censorship limited Japanese writers, but literary expression flowered after the war ended in 1945. Among Japan's important novelists is Kenzaburō Ōe (1935–). His first novel, *Memushiri Kouchi (Nip the Buds, Shoot the Kids)*, deals with a group of adolescent boys living in devastated postwar Japan. Ōe received the Nobel Prize in Literature in 1994.

Japan and the United States

In the 17th century, Japan watched as Europeans invaded and colonized lands around the world. Hoping to protect themselves, the Japanese established strict regulations to limit contact with foreigners. But in 1854, U.S. gunships under Commodore Matthew Perry entered a Japanese harbor and forced the Japanese to open their markets to foreign trade. Following the introduction of Western ideas, Japan quickly developed into an industrial power.

In the past 150 years, Japan has become a major trading partner with the United States, both in physical goods and in culture. Japanese poetry has shaped the work of many American poets, including Ezra Pound (1885–1972). Inspired by the terse Japanese verse form of haiku, Pound and others have composed poems that focus on concrete details rather than feelings or ideas.

However, sometimes this influence shows up in more surprising ways. For example, the *Star Wars* movies were originally inspired by *The Hidden Fortress*, a film by the legendary Japanese director Akira Kurosawa (1910–1998). In recent years, Japanese manga and anime have surged in popularity in the U.S.

Research: Do Informal Research

A haiku is a poem usually consisting of seventeen syllables in three lines of five, seven, and five syllables. Due to their shortness, haikus may sound simple to write. They're not. Read some Japanese haikus in translation, and then try writing one of your own.

Tokyo

Fumiko Hayashi

Before You Read

Fumiko Hayashi (1904–1951) is one of Japan's most popular and critically acclaimed female writers. Her first novel, *Journal of a Vagabond,* was published in 1927. Over her lifetime, Hayashi published more than 270 books, including fiction, nonfiction, and poetry.

World Context

Hayashi became familiar with life on the Tokyo streets from holding a variety of menial jobs that often left her homeless. Drawing on her own experience, Hayashi began writing stories about poor yet hardworking people on the fringe of society.

 LITERARY LENS As you read, identify details that help you infer the **theme** of the story.

It was a bitter, windy afternoon. As Ryo hurried down the street with her rucksack, she kept to the side where the pale sun shone down over the roofs of the office buildings. Every now and then she looked about curiously—at a building, at a parked car—at one of those innumerable bomb sites[1] scattered through downtown Tokyo.

Glancing over a boarding, Ryo saw a huge pile of rusty iron, and next to it a cabin with a glass door. A fire was burning within, and the warm sound of the crackling wood reached where she was standing. In front of the cabin stood a man in overalls with a red kerchief about his head. There was something pleasant about this tall fellow, and Ryo screwed up her courage to call out, "Tea for sale! Would you like some tea, please?"

"Tea?" said the man.

---

1 **bomb sites:** places where bombs were dropped during World War II

"Tea," said Ryo with a nervous smile. "It's Shizuoka tea."[2]

She stepped in through an opening in the boarding and, unfastening the straps of her rucksack, put it down by the cabin. Inside she could see a fire burning in an iron stove; from a bar above hung a brass kettle with a wisp of steam rising from the spout.

"Excuse me," said Ryo, "but would you mind if I came in and warmed myself by your stove a few minutes? It's freezing out, and I've been walking for miles."

"Of course you can come in," said the man. "Close the door and get warm."

He pointed towards the stool, which was his only article of furniture, and sat down on a packing case in the corner. Ryo hesitated a moment. Then she dragged her rucksack into the cabin and, crouching by the stove, held up her hands to the fire.

"You'll be more comfortable on that stool," said the man, glancing at her attractive face, flushed in the sudden warmth, and at her shabby attire.

"Surely this isn't what you usually do—hawk tea from door to door?"

"Oh yes, it's how I make my living," Ryo said. "I was told that this was a good neighborhood, but I've been walking around here since early morning and have only managed to sell one packet of tea. I'm about ready to go home now, but I thought I'd have my lunch somewhere on the way."

"Well, you're perfectly welcome to stay here and eat your lunch," said the man. "And don't worry about not having sold your tea," he added, smiling. "It's all a matter of luck, you know! You'll probably have a good day tomorrow."

The kettle came to a boil with a whistling sound. As he unhooked it from the bar, Ryo had a chance to look about her. She took in the boarded ceiling black with soot, the blackboard by the window, the shelf for family gods on which stood a potted sakaki tree. The man took a limp-looking packet from the table, and unwrapping it, disclosed a piece of cod. A few minutes later the smell of baking fish permeated the cabin.

"Come on," said the man. "Sit down and have your meal."

Ryo took her lunch box out of the rucksack and seated herself on the stool.

"Selling things is never much fun, is it?" remarked the man, turning the cod over on the grill. "Tell me, how much do you get for a hundred grams of that tea?"

"I should get thirty-five yen to make any sort of profit. The people who send me the stuff often mix in bad tea, so I'm lucky if I can get thirty yen."

In Ryo's lunch box were two small fish covered with some boiled barley and a few bean-paste pickles. She began eating.

---

2 **Shizuoka tea:** tea from the Honshu region of Japan

"Where do you live?" the man asked her.

"In the Shitaya district. Actually, I don't know one part of Tokyo from another! I've only been here a few weeks and a friend's putting me up until I find something better."

The cod was ready now. He cut it in two and gave Ryo half, adding potatoes and rice from a platter. Ryo smiled and bowed slightly in thanks, then took out a bag of tea from her rucksack and poured some into a paper handkerchief.

"Do put this into the kettle," she said, holding it out to him.

He shook his head and smiled, showing his white teeth.

"Good Lord, no! It's far too expensive."

Quickly Ryo removed the lid and poured the tea in before he could stop her. Laughing, the man went to fetch a teacup and a mug from the shelf.

"What about your husband?" he asked, while ranging them on the packing case. "You're married, aren't you?"

"Oh yes, I am. My husband's still in Siberia.[3] That's why I have to work like this."

Ryo's thoughts flew to her husband, from whom she had not heard for six years; by now he had come to seem so remote that it required an effort to remember his looks, or the once-familiar sound of his voice. She woke up each morning with a feeling of emptiness and desolation. At times it seemed to Ryo that her husband had frozen into a ghost in that subarctic Siberia—a ghost, or a thin white pillar, or just a breath of frosty air. Nowadays no one any longer mentioned the war and she was almost embarrassed to let people know that her husband was still a prisoner.

"It's funny," the man said. "The fact is, I was in Siberia myself! I spent three years chopping wood near the Amur River—I only managed to get sent home last year. Well, it's all in a matter of luck! It's tough on your husband. But it's just as tough on you."

repatriated:
sent back;
returned to
one's home
country

"So you've really been **repatriated** from Siberia! You don't seem any the worse for it," Ryo said.

"Well, I don't know about that!" the man shrugged his shoulders. "Anyway, as you see, I'm still alive."

Ryo closed her lunch box, and as she did so, she studied him. There was a simplicity and directness about this man that made her want to talk openly in a way that she found difficult with more educated people.

"Got any kids?" he said.

---

3 **Siberia:** region of the former Soviet Union where prisoners of war were held

"Yes, a boy of six. He should be at school, but I've had difficulty getting him registered here in Tokyo. These officials certainly know how to make life complicated for people!"

The man untied his kerchief, wiped the cup and the mug with it, and poured out the steaming tea.

"It's good stuff this!" he said, sipping noisily.

"Do you like it? It's not the best quality, you know: only two hundred and ten yen a kilo wholesale. But you're right—it's quite good."

The wind had grown stronger while they were talking; it whistled over the tin roof of the cabin. Ryo glanced out of the window, steeling herself for her long walk home.

"I'll have some of your tea—seven hundred and fifty grams," the man told her, extracting two crumbled hundred-yen notes from the pocket of his overalls.

"Don't be silly," said Ryo. "You can have it for nothing."

"Oh no, that won't do. Business is business!" He forced the money into her hand. "Well, if you're ever in this part of the world again, come in and have another chat."

"I should like to," said Ryo, glancing around the tiny cabin. "But you don't live here, do you?"

"Oh, but I do! I look after that iron out there and help load the trucks. I'm here most of the day."

He opened a door under the shelf, disclosing a sort of cubbyhole containing a bed neatly made up. Ryo noticed a colored postcard of the Fifty Bells of Yamada tacked to the back of the door.

"My, you've fixed it up nicely," she said smiling. "You're really quite snug here, aren't you?"

She wondered how old he could be.

2

From that day on, Ryo came regularly to the Yotsugi district to sell tea; each time she visited the cabin on the bomb site. She learned that the man's name was Tsuruishi Yoshio. Almost invariably he had some small delicacy waiting for her to put in her lunch box—a pickled plum, a piece of beef, a sardine. Her business began to improve and she acquired a few regular customers in the neighborhood.

A week after their first meeting, she brought along her boy, Ryukichi. Tsuruishi chatted with the child for a while and then took him out for a walk. When they returned, Ryukichi was carrying a large caramel cake.

"He's got a good appetite, this youngster of yours," said Tsuruishi, patting the boy's close-cropped head.

Ryo wondered vaguely whether her new friend was married; in fact she found herself wondering about various aspects of his life. She was now twenty-nine, and she realized with a start that this was the first time she had been seriously interested in any man but her husband. Tsuruishi's easy, carefree temperament somehow appealed to her, though she took great care not to let him guess that.

A little later Tsuruishi suggested taking Ryo and Ryukichi to see Asakusa[4] on his next free day. They met in front of the information booth in Ueno Station, Tsuruishi wearing an ancient gray suit that looked far too tight, Ryo clad in a blue dress of kimono material and a light-brown coat. In spite of her cheap clothes, she had about her something youthful and elegant as she stood there in the crowded station. Beside the tall, heavy Tsuruishi, she looked like a schoolgirl off on a holiday. In her shopping bag lay their lunch: bread, oranges, and seaweed stuffed with rice.

"Well, let's hope it doesn't rain," said Tsuruishi, putting his arm lightly round Ryo's waist as he steered her through the crowd.

They took the subway to Asakusa Station, then walked from the Matsuya Department Store to the Niten Shinto Gate past hundreds of tiny stalls. The Asakusa district was quite different from what Ryo had imagined. She was amazed when Tsuruishi pointed to a small red-lacquered temple and told her that this was the home of the famous Asakusa Goddess of Mercy. In the distance she could hear the plaintive wail of a trumpet and a saxophone emerging from some loud-speaker; it mingled strangely with the sound of the wind whistling through the branches of the ancient sakaki trees.

They made their way through the old-clothes market, and came to a row of food-stalls squeezed tightly against each other beside the Asakusa Pond; here the air was **redolent** with the smell of burning oil. Tsuruishi went to one of the stalls and bought Ryukichi a stick of yellow candy-floss. The boy nibbled at it, as the three of them walked down a narrow street plastered with American-style billboards advertising restaurants, movies, revues. It was less than a month since Ryo had first noticed Tsuruishi by his cabin, yet she felt as much at ease with him as if she had known him all her life.

"Well, it's started raining after all," he said, holding out his hand. Ryo looked up to see scattered drops of rain falling from the gray sky. So their precious excursion would be ruined, she thought.

redolent: smelling; scented

---

4 **Asakusa:** a shopping district in Tokyo

"We'd better go in there," said Tsuruishi, pointing to one of the shops, outside which hung a garish lantern with characters announcing the "Merry Teahouse." They took seats at a table underneath a ceiling decorated with artificial cherry blossoms. The place had a strangely unhomelike atmosphere, but they were determined to make the best of it and ordered a pot of tea; Ryo distributed her stuffed seaweed, bread, and oranges. It was not long before the meal was finished and by then it had started raining in earnest.

"We'd better wait till it lets up a bit," suggested Tsuruishi. "Then I'll take you home."

Ryo wondered if he was referring to her place or his. She was staying in the cramped apartment of a friend from her home town and did not even have a room to call her own; rather than go there, she would have preferred returning to Tsuruishi's cabin, but that too was scarcely large enough to hold three people. Taking out her purse, she counted her money under the table. The seven hundred yen should be enough to get shelter for a few hours at an inn.

"D'you know what I'd really like?" she said. "I'd like us to go to a movie and then find some inn and have a dish of food before saying good-bye to each other. But I suppose that's all rather expensive!"

"Yes, I suppose it is," said Tsuruishi, laughing. "Come on! We'll do it all the same."

Taking his overcoat off the peg, he threw it over Ryukichi's head, and ran through the downpour to a movie theatre. Of course there were no seats! Standing watching the film, the little boy went sound asleep, leaning against Tsuruishi. The air in the theatre seemed to get thicker and hotter every moment; on the roof they could hear the rain beating down.

It was getting dark as they left the theatre and hurried through the rain, which pelted down with the swishing sound of banana leaves in a high wind. At last they found a small inn where the landlord led them to a carpeted room at the end of a drafty passage. Ryo took off her wet socks. The boy sat down in a corner and promptly went back to sleep

"Here, he can use this as a pillow," said Tsuruishi, picking up an old cushion from a chair and putting it under Ryukichi's head.

From an overflowing gutter above the window the water poured in a steady stream onto the courtyard. It sounded like a waterfall in some faraway mountain village.

Tsuruishi took out a handkerchief and began wiping Ryo's wet hair. A feeling of happiness coursed through her as she looked up at him. It was as if the rain had begun to wash away all the loneliness which had been gathering within her year after year.

She went to see if they could get some food and in the corridor met a maid in Western clothes carrying a tea tray. After Ryo had ordered two bowls of spaghetti, she and Tsuruishi sat down to drink their tea, facing each other across an empty brazier. Later Tsuruishi came and sat on the floor beside Ryo. Leaning their backs against the wall they gazed out at the darkening, rainy sky.

"How old are you, Ryo?" Tsuruishi asked her. "I should guess twenty-five."

Ryo laughed. "I'm afraid not, Tsuru, I'm already an old woman! I'm twenty-nine."

"Oh, so you're a year older than me."

"My goodness, you're young!" said Ryo. "I thought you must be at least thirty."

She looked straight at him, into his dark, gentle eyes with their bushy brows. He seemed to be blushing slightly. Then he bent forward and took off his wet socks.

The rain continued unabated. Presently the maid came with some cold spaghetti and soup. Ryo woke the boy and gave him a plate of soup; he was half asleep as he sipped it.

"Look, Ryo," Tsuruishi said, "we might as well all stay the night at this inn. You can't go home in this rain, can you?"

"No," said Ryo. "No, I suppose not."

Tsuruishi left the room and returned with a load of quilted bedrolls which he spread on the floor. At once the whole room seemed to be full of bedding. Ryo tucked up her son in one of the rolls, the boy sleeping soundly as she did so. Then she turned out the light, undressed, and lay down. She could hear Tsuruishi settling down at the other end of the room.

"I suppose the people in this inn think we're married," said Tsuruishi after a while.

"Yes, I suppose so. It's not very nice of us to fool them!"

She spoke in jest, but now that she lay undressed in her bedroll, she felt for the first time vaguely disturbed and guilty. Her husband for some reason seemed much closer than he had for years. But of course she was only here because of the rain, she reminded herself . . . And gradually her thoughts began to wander pleasantly afield, and she dozed off.

When she awoke it was still dark. She could hear Tsuruishi whispering her name from his corner, and she sat up with a start.

"Ryo, Ryo, can I come and talk to you for a while?"

"No, Tsuru," she said, "I don't think you should."

On the roof the rain was still pattering down, but the force of the storm was over; only a trickle was dropping from the gutter into the yard. Under the sound of the rain she thought she could hear Tsuruishi sigh softly.

"Look Tsuru," she said after a pause. "I've never asked you before, but are you married?"

"No. Not now," Tsuruishi said.

"You used to be?"

"Yes. I used to be. When I got back from the army, I found that my wife was living with another man."

"Were you—angry?"

"Angry? Yes, I suppose I was. Still, there wasn't much I could do about it. She'd left me, and that was that."

They were silent again.

"What shall we talk about?" Ryo asked.

Tsuruishi laughed. "Well, there really doesn't seem to be anything special to talk about. That spaghetti wasn't very good, was it?"

"No, one certainly couldn't call it good. And they charged us a hundred yen each for it!"

"It would be nice if you and Ryukichi had your own room to live in, wouldn't it?" Tsuruishi remarked.

"Oh yes, it would be marvelous! You don't think we might find a room near you? I'd really like to live near you, Tsuru, you know."

"It's pretty hard to find rooms these days, especially downtown. But I'll keep a lookout and let you know . . . You're such a wonderful person, Ryo!"

"Me?" said Ryo laughing. "Don't be silly!"

"Yes, yes, you're wonderful! . . . really wonderful!"

Ryo lay back on the floor. Suddenly she wanted to throw her arms around Tsuruishi, to feel his body close to hers. She did not dare speak for fear that her voice might betray her; her breath came almost painfully; her whole body tingled. Outside the window an early morning truck clattered past.

"Where are your parents, Tsuru?" she asked after a while.

"In the country near Fukuoka."

"But you have a sister in Tokyo?"

"Yes. She's all alone, like you, with two kids to take care of. She's got a sewing machine and makes Western-style clothes. Her husband was killed several years ago in the war in China. War, always war!"

Outside the window Ryo could make out the first glimmer of dawn. So their night together was almost over, she thought unhappily. In a way she wished that Tsuruishi hadn't given up so easily, and yet she was convinced that it was best like this. If he had been a man she hardly knew, or for whom she felt nothing, she might have given herself to him with no afterthought. With Tsuruishi it would have been different—quite different.

"Ryo, I can't get to sleep." His voice reached her again. "I'm wide awake, you know. I suppose I'm not used to this sort of thing."

"What sort of thing?"

"Why—sleeping in the same room with a girl."

"Oh Tsuru, don't tell me that you don't have girl friends occasionally!"

"Only professional girl friends."

Ryo laughed. "Men have it easy! In some ways, at least. . . ."

She heard Tsuruishi moving about. Suddenly he was beside her, bending over her. Ryo did not move, not even when she felt his arms around her, his face against hers. In the dark her eyes were wide open, and before them bright lights seemed to be flashing. His hot lips were pressed to her cheek.

"Ryo . . . Ryo."

"It's wrong you know," she murmured. "Wrong to my husband. . . ."

But almost at once she regretted the words. As Tsuruishi bent over her, she could make out the silhouette of his face against the lightening sky. Bowed forward like that, he seemed to be offering **obeisance** to some god. Ryo hesitated for a moment. Then she threw her warm arms about his neck.

obeisance: homage; gesture of respect

3

Two days later Ryo set out happily with her boy to visit Tsuruishi. When she reached the bomb site, she was surprised not to see him before his cabin, his red kerchief tied about his head. Ryukichi ran ahead to find out if he were home and came back in a moment.

"There are strangers there, Mamma!"

Seized with panic, Ryo hurried over to the cabin and peered in. Two workmen were busy piling up Tsuruishi's effects in a corner.

"What is it, ma'am?" one of them said, turning his head.

"I'm looking for Tsuruishi."

"Oh, don't you know? Tsuruishi died yesterday."

"Died," she said. She wanted to say something more but no words would come.

She had noticed a small candle burning on the shelf for family gods, and now she was aware of its somber meaning.

"Yes," went on the man, "he was killed about eight o'clock last night. He went in a truck with one of the men to deliver some iron bars in Omiya, and on their way back the truck overturned on a narrow bridge. He and the driver were both killed. His sister went to Omiya today with one of the company officials to see about the cremation."

Ryo stared vacantly before her. Vacantly she watched the two men piling up Tsuruishi's belongings. Beside the candle on the shelf she caught sight of the two bags of tea he had bought from her that first day—could it be only two weeks ago? One of them was folded over halfway down; the other was still unopened.

"You were a friend of his, ma'am, I imagine? He was a fine fellow, Tsuru! Funny to think that he needn't have gone to Omiya at all. The driver wasn't feeling well and Tsuru said he'd go along to Omiya to help him unload. Crazy, isn't it—after getting through the war and Siberia and all the rest of it, to be killed like that!"

One of the men took down the postcard of the Fifty Bells of Yamada and blew the dust off it. Ryo stood looking at Tsuruishi's belongings piled on the floor—the kettle, the frying pan, the rubber boots. When her eyes reached the blackboard, she noticed for the first time a message scratched awkwardly in red chalk: 'Ryo—I waited for you till two o'clock. Back this evening.'

Automatically she bowed to the two men and swung the rucksack on her back. She felt numb as she left the cabin, holding Ryukichi by the hand, but as they passed the bomb site, the burning tears welled into her eyes.

"Did that man die, Mamma?"

"Yes, he died," Ryo said.

"Why did he die?"

"He fell into a river."

The tears were running down her cheeks now; they poured out uncontrollably as she hurried through the downtown streets. They came to an arched bridge over the Sumida River, crossed it, and walked along the bank in the direction of Hakuho.

"Don't worry if you get pregnant," Tsuruishi had told her that morning in Asakusa, "I'll look after you whatever happens, Ryo!" And later on, just before they parted, he had said, "I haven't got much money, but you must let me help you a bit. I can give you two thousand yen a month out of my salary." He had taken Ryukichi to a shop that specialized in foreign goods and bought him a baseball cap with his name written on it. Then the three of them had walked gaily along the streetcar lines, skirting the

"I'll look after you whatever happens, Ryo!"

enormous puddles left by the rain. When they came to a milk bar, Tsuruishi had taken them in and ordered them each a big glass of milk . . . .

Now an icy wind seemed to have blown up from the dark river. A flock of waterfowl stood on the opposite bank, looking frozen and miserable. Barges moved slowly up and down the river.

"Mamma, I want a sketchbook. You said I could have a sketchbook."

"Later," answered Ryo, "I'll get you one later."

"But Mamma, we just passed a stall with hundreds of sketchbooks. I'm hungry, Mamma. Can't we have something to eat?"

"Later. A little later!"

They were passing a long row of barrack-like buildings. They must be private houses, she thought. The people who lived there probably all had rooms of their own. From one of the windows a bedroll had been hung out to air and inside a woman could be seen tidying the room.

"Tea for sale!" called out Ryo softly. "Best quality Shizuoka tea!"

There was no reply and Ryo repeated her call a little louder.

"I don't want any," said the woman. She pulled in the bedroll and shut the window with a bang.

Ryo went from house to house down the row calling her ware, but nobody wanted any tea. Ryukichi followed behind, muttering that he was hungry and tired. Ryo's rucksack cut painfully into her shoulders, and occasionally she had to stop to adjust the straps. Yet in a way she almost welcomed the physical pain.

4

The next day she went downtown by herself, leaving Ryukichi at home. When she came to the bomb site she noticed that a fire was burning inside the cabin. She ran to the door and walked in. By Tsuruishi's stove sat an old man in a short workman's overcoat, feeding the flames with firewood. The room was full of smoke and it was billowing out of the window.

"What do you want?" said the old man, looking round.

"I've come to sell some Shizuoka tea."

"Shizuoka tea? I've got plenty of good tea right here."

Ryo turned without a word and hurried off. She had thought of asking for the address of Tsuruishi's sister and of going to burn a stick of incense in his memory, but suddenly this seemed quite pointless. She walked back to the river, which reflected the late afternoon sun, and sat down by a pile of broken concrete. The body of a dead kitten was lying upside down a few yards away. As her thoughts went to Tsuruishi, she wondered vaguely whether it would have been better never to have met him. No, no, certainly not that! She could never regret knowing him, nor anything that had happened with him. Nor did she regret having come to Tokyo. When she had arrived, a month or so before, she had planned to return to the country if her business was unsuccessful, but now she knew that she would be staying on here in Tokyo—yes, probably right here in downtown Tokyo where Tsuruishi had lived.

She got up, swung the rucksack on her back, and walked away from the river. As she strolled along a side street, she noticed a hut which seemed to consist of old boards nailed haphazardly together. Going to the door, she called out, "Tea for sale! Would anyone like some tea?" The door opened and in the entrance appeared a woman dressed far more poorly than Ryo herself.

"How much does it cost?" asked the woman. And, then, seeing the rucksack, she added, "Come in and rest a while, if you like. I'll see how much money we've got left. We may have enough for some tea."

Ryo went in and put down her rucksack. In the small room four sewing women were sitting on the floor around an oil stove, working on a mass of shirts and socks. They were women like herself, thought Ryo, as she watched their busy needles moving in and out of the material. A feeling of warmth came over her.

Translated by Ivan Morris

After You Read

Critical Reading

1. Describe the **setting** (the time and place) of the story. Then identify specific passages in the story that evoke this setting.

2. Describe the **character** of Ryo. Then explain why she has a "feeling of warmth" at the end of the story. Support your answers with details from the text.

3. The author uses **foreshadowing** to hint that Yoshio will die. Identify details or scenes that were clues to this upcoming event and explain how they are examples of foreshadowing.

Literary Lens: Theme

Consider the **theme**, or message, of each section of the story. Then write a two- to three-sentence statement detailing the overall theme of the story.

Section	Theme
1	
2	
3	
4	
Story's overall theme:	

Focus on Research: Evaluate Sources for Credibility

In the story, Ryo is selling Shizuoka tea. She says, "it's not the best quality" but that it is "quite good." Find three or more sources that provide information about Shizuoka tea, or tea grown in Shizuoka, Japan. Use the sample below to create checklist; use your checklist to evaluate each of your sources.

Source 1: Title of Source _____	Yes	No
From a reliable publication		
Recent publication date; offers up-to-date information		
Written by an author who is known to be an expert or informed on the topic		
Supports points with multiple data or studies		
Uses a professional writing style; contains few punctuation or spelling errors		

Swaddling Clothes

Yukio Mishima

Before You Read

Yukio Mishima (1925–1970) was born Kimitake Hiraoka in an aristocratic Japanese family. He adopted the pseudonym Yukio Mishima to keep his father from learning that he was a writer. In his novel, *Confessions of a Mask*, Mishima wrote autobiographically about his experiences as a gay man in modern China. His most famous novels include *The Sound of Waves* and *The Sailor Who Fell from Grace with the Sea*.

World Context

Mishima became fanatically devoted to Japan's authoritarian past. He created a tiny private army to promote Samurai values. The day he delivered his last novel to his publisher, Mishima publicly committed *seppuku*, ritual disembowelment.

 LITERARY LENS As you read, watch for the way **character** interactions advance the **plot**.

H e was always busy, Toshiko's husband. Even tonight he had to dash off to an appointment, leaving her to go home alone by taxi. But what else could a woman expect when she married an actor—an attractive one? No doubt she had been foolish to hope that he would spend the evening with her. And yet he must have known how she dreaded going back to their house, unhomely with its Western-style furniture and with the bloodstains still showing on the floor.

Toshiko had been oversensitive since girlhood: that was her nature. As the result of constant worrying she never put on weight, and now, an adult woman, she looked more like a transparent picture than a creature of flesh and blood. Her delicacy of spirit was evident to her most casual acquaintance.

Earlier that evening, when she had joined her husband at a night club, she had been shocked to find him entertaining friends with an account of "the incident." Sitting there in his American-style suit, puffing at a cigarette, he had seemed to her almost a stranger.

"It's a fantastic story," he was saying, gesturing **flamboyantly** as if in an attempt to outweigh the attractions of the dance band. "Here this new nurse for our baby arrives from the employment agency, and the very first thing I notice about her is her stomach. It's enormous—as if she had a pillow stuck under her kimono![1] No wonder, I thought, for I soon saw that she could eat more than the rest of us put together. She polished off the contents of our rice bin like that . . . ." He snapped his fingers. "'Gastric dilation'—that's how she explained her girth and her appetite. Well, the day before yesterday we heard groans and moans coming from the nursery. We rushed in and found her squatting on the floor, holding her stomach in her two hands, and moaning like a cow. Next to her our baby lay in his cot, scared out of his wits and crying at the top of his lungs. A pretty scene, I can tell you!"

"So the cat was out of the bag?" suggested one of their friends, a film actor like Toshiko's husband.

"Indeed it was! And it gave me the shock of my life. You see, I'd completely swallowed that story about 'gastric dilation.' Well, I didn't waste any time. I rescued our good rug from the floor and spread a blanket for her to lie on. The whole time the girl was yelling like a stuck pig. By the time the doctor from the maternity clinic arrived, the baby had already been born. But our sitting room was a pretty shambles!"

"Oh, that I'm sure of!" said another of their friends, and the whole company burst into laughter.

Toshiko was dumbfounded to hear her husband discussing the horrifying happening as though it were no more than an amusing incident which they chanced to have witnessed. She shut her eyes for a moment and all at once she saw the newborn baby lying before her: on the parquet[2] floor the infant lay, and his frail body was wrapped in bloodstained newspapers.

Toshiko was sure that the doctor had done the whole thing out of spite. As if to emphasize his scorn for this mother who had given birth to a bastard under such sordid conditions, he had told his assistant to wrap the baby in some loose newspapers, rather than proper swaddling. This callous treatment of the newborn child had offended Toshiko. Overcoming her disgust at the entire scene, she had fetched a brand-new piece of flannel

---

1   **kimono:** a traditional Japanese robe
2   **parquet:** a patterned wood surface

from her cupboard and, having swaddled the baby in it, had lain him carefully in an armchair.

This all had taken place in the evening after her husband had left the house. Toshiko had told him nothing of it, fearing that he would think her oversoft, oversentimental; yet the scene had engraved itself deeply in her mind. Tonight she sat silently thinking back on it, while the jazz orchestra **brayed** and her husband chatted cheerfully with his friends. She knew that she would never forget the sight of the baby, wrapped in stained newspapers and lying on the floor—it was a scene fit for a butchershop. Toshiko, whose own life had been spent in solid comfort, **poignantly** felt the wretchedness of the illegitimate baby.

I am the only person to have witnessed its shame, the thought occurred to her. The mother never saw her child lying there in its newspaper wrappings, and the baby itself of course didn't know. I alone shall have to preserve that terrible scene in my memory. When the baby grows up and wants to find out about his birth, there will be no one to tell him, so long as I preserve the silence. How strange that I should have this feeling of guilt! After all, it was I who took him up from the floor, swathed him properly in flannel, and laid him down to sleep in the armchair.

brayed: played loudly or harshly

poignantly: painfully; touchingly

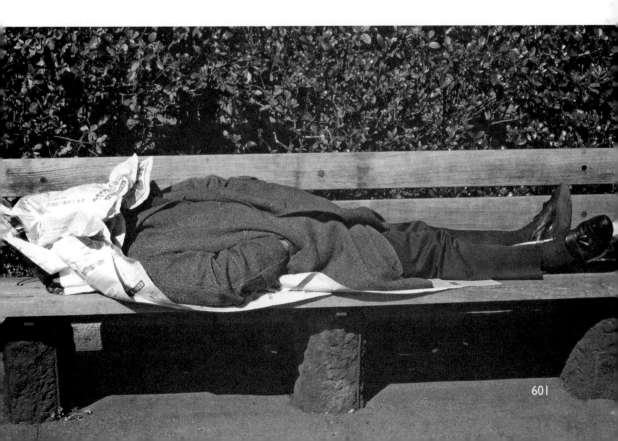

They left the night club and Toshiko stepped into the taxi that her husband had called for her. "Take this lady to Ushigomé," he told the driver and shut the door from the outside. Toshiko gazed through the window at her husband's smiling face and noticed his strong, white teeth. Then she leaned back in the seat, oppressed by the knowledge that their life together was in some way too easy, too painless. It would have been difficult for her to put her thoughts into words. Through the rear window of the taxi she took a last look at her husband. He was striding along the street toward his Nash car, and soon the back of his rather garish tweed coat had blended with the figures of the passers-by.

The taxi drove off, passed down a street dotted with bars and then by a theatre, in front of which the throngs of people jostled each other on the pavement. Although the performance had only just ended, the lights had already been turned out and in the half dark outside it was depressingly obvious that the cherry blossoms decorating the front of the theatre were merely scraps of white paper.

Even if that baby should grow up in ignorance of the secret of his birth, he can never become a respectable citizen, reflected Toshiko, pursuing the same train of thoughts. Those soiled newspaper swaddling clothes will be the symbol of his entire life. But why should I keep worrying about him so much? Is it because I feel uneasy about the future of my own child? Say twenty years from now, when our boy will have grown up into a fine, carefully educated young man, one day by a quirk of fate he meets the other boy, who then will also have turned twenty. And say that the other boy, who has been sinned against, savagely stabs him with a knife . . . .

It was a warm, overcast April night, but thoughts of the future made Toshiko feel cold and miserable. She shivered on the back seat of the car.

No, when the time comes I shall take my son's place, she told herself suddenly. Twenty years from now I shall be forty-three. I shall go to that young man and tell him straight out about everything—about his newspaper swaddling clothes, and about how I went and wrapped him in flannel.

The taxi ran along the dark wide road that was bordered by the park and by the Imperial Palace moat. In the distance Toshiko noticed the pinpricks of light which came from the blocks of tall office buildings.

desolate:
bleak; cheerless

Twenty years from now that wretched child will be in utter misery. He will be living a **desolate**, hopeless, poverty-stricken existence—a lonely rat. What else could happen to a baby who has had such a birth? He'll be wandering through the streets by himself, cursing his father, loathing his mother.

No doubt Toshiko derived a certain satisfaction from her somber thoughts: she tortured herself with them without cease. The taxi approached Hanzomon and drove past the compound of the British Embassy. At that point the famous rows of cherry trees were spread out before Toshiko in all their purity. On the spur of the moment she decided to go and view the blossoms by herself in the dark night. It was a strange decision for a timid and unadventurous young woman, but then she was in a strange state of mind and she dreaded the return home. That evening all sorts of unsettling fancies had burst open in her mind.

She crossed the wide street—a slim, solitary figure in the darkness. As a rule when she walked in the traffic Toshiko used to cling fearfully to her companion, but tonight she darted alone between the cars and a moment later had reached the long narrow park that borders the Palace moat. Chidorigafuchi, it is called—the Abyss of the Thousand Birds.

Tonight the whole park had become a grove of blossoming cherry trees. Under the calm cloudy sky the blossoms formed a mass of solid whiteness. The paper lanterns that hung from wires between the trees had been put out; in their place electric light bulbs, red, yellow, and green, shone dully beneath the blossoms. It was well past ten o'clock and most of the flower-viewers had gone home. As the occasional passers-by strolled through the park, they would automatically kick aside the empty bottles or crush the waste paper beneath their feet.

Newspapers, thought Toshiko, her mind going back once again to those happenings. Bloodstained newspapers. If a man were ever to hear of that piteous birth and know that it was he who had lain there, it would ruin his entire life. To think that I, a perfect stranger, should from now on have to keep such a secret—the secret of a man's whole existence . . . .

Lost in these thoughts, Toshiko walked on through the park. Most of the people still remaining there were quiet couples; no one paid her any attention. She noticed two people sitting on a stone bench beside the moat, not looking at the blossoms, but gazing silently at the water. Pitch black it was, and swathed in heavy shadows. Beyond the moat the somber forest of the Imperial Palace blocked her view. The trees reached up, to form a solid dark mass against the night sky. Toshiko walked slowly along the path beneath the blossoms hanging heavily overhead.

On a stone bench, slightly apart from the others, she noticed a pale object—not, as she had at first imagined, a pile of cherry blossoms, nor a garment forgotten by one of the visitors to the park. Only when she came closer did she see that it was a human form lying on the bench. Was it, she wondered, one of those miserable drunks often to be seen sleeping in public places? Obviously not, for the body had been systematically covered with newspapers, and it was the whiteness of those papers that had attracted Toshiko's attention. Standing by the bench, she gazed down at the sleeping figure.

It was a man in a brown jersey who lay there, curled up on layers of newspapers, other newspapers covering him. No doubt this had become his normal night residence now that spring had arrived. Toshiko gazed down at the man's dirty, unkempt hair, which in places had become hopelessly matted. As she observed the sleeping figure wrapped in its newspapers, she was inevitably reminded of the baby who had lain on the floor in its wretched swaddling clothes. The shoulder of the man's jersey rose and fell in the darkness in time with his heavy breathing.

It seemed to Toshiko that all her fears and premonitions had suddenly taken concrete form. In the darkness the man's pale forehead stood out, and it was a young forehead, though carved with the wrinkles of long poverty and hardship. His khaki trousers had been slightly pulled up; on his sockless feet he wore a pair of battered gym shoes. She could not see his face and suddenly had an overmastering desire to get one glimpse of it.

She walked to the head of the bench and looked down. The man's head was half buried in his arms, but Toshiko could see that he was surprisingly young. She noticed the thick eyebrows and the fine bridge of his nose. His slightly open mouth was alive with youth.

But Toshiko had approached too close. In the silent night the newspaper bedding rustled, and abruptly the man opened his eyes. Seeing the young woman standing directly beside him, he raised himself with a jerk, and his eyes lit up. A second later a powerful hand reached out and seized Toshiko by her slender wrist.

She did not feel in the least afraid and made no effort to free herself. In a flash the thought had struck her. Ah, so the twenty years have already gone by! The forest of the Imperial Palace was pitch dark and utterly silent.

Translated by Ivan Morris

After You Read

Critical Reading

1. Identify the **internal** and **external conflicts** Toshiko faces in this story. Explain how the conflicts are resolved.

2. This story uses both **flashbacks** and **foreshadowing**. Consider the scene in which Toshiko is in the taxi. Identify an example of a flashback during this scene and an example of foreshadowing in this scene. How are these used to reveal the character of Toshiko?

3. **Interior monologue** is a character's unspoken interior thoughts or feelings described in a literary work. The author chose to reveal the character of Toshiko through her interior monologue instead of through spoken dialogue. Identify two or more examples of interior monologue from the story. Then infer why the author may have chosen to use this technique.

Literary Lens: Character and Plot

Using only information from the first four paragraphs of the story, compare and contrast Toshiko and her husband. Then write a three- to five-sentence paragraph explaining how their differences advance the plot.

Character	Toshiko	Her husband
Dialogue		
Interior monologue		
Actions		
Conflicts		
Other		

Focus on Research: Identify Gaps in Research

In the story, the character of Toshiko thinks that "[E]ven if that baby should grow up in ignorance of the secret of his birth, he can never become a respectable citizen" (page 584). Based on this story and your own knowledge, write questions you have about cultural attitudes in Japan toward class and social hierarchies. Conduct research to answer these questions. As you research, identify any gaps in your research and any questions for which you haven't found answers.

The Shadow

Tōge Sankichi

Before You Read

Tōge Sankichi (1921–1953) was a student in Hiroshima when the atomic bomb was dropped on that city. He survived the initial explosion but later suffered from leukemia—an effect of radiation from the bomb. Sankichi died from leukemia when he was 36. "The Shadow" can be found with other poems about the atomic bomb in *Hiroshima: Three Witnesses*.

World Context

Of his attempt to capture the bomb blast and its aftereffect, Sankichi said he "couldn't strike the reality." He felt, though, that his poetry is a gift for those who seek to "consider the feelings we in Hiroshima have about the bomb."

LITERARY LENS Consider how the poet's **word choice** sets the **tone** in the following poem. Identify words that are especially powerful.

Cheap movie theaters, saloons, fly-by-night markets,
burned, rebuilt, standing, crumbling, spreading like the itch—
the new Hiroshima,
head shiny with hair oil,
barefaced in its resurgence;   5
already visible all over the place,
in growing numbers, billboards in English;
one of these: "Historic A-Bomb Site."

Enclosed by a painted fence
on a corner of the bank steps,   10
stained onto the grain of the dark red stone:
a quiet pattern.

That morning
a flash tens of thousands of degrees hot
burned it all of a sudden onto the thick slab of granite: 15
someone's trunk.

Burned onto the step, cracked and watery red,
the mark of the blood that flowed as intestines melted to mush:
a shadow.

Ah! If you are from Hiroshima   20
and on that morning,
amid indescribable flash and heat and smoke,
were buffeted in the whirlpool of the glare of the flames, the
    shadow of the cloud,
crawled about dragging skin that was peeling off,   25
so transformed that even your wife and children
would not have known you,
this shadow
is etched in tragic memory
and will never fade.   30

**A human shadow etched into the steps of the Sumitomo Bank of Hiroshima,
November 20, 1945**

Right beside the street where the people of the city come and go,
well-meaning but utterly indifferent,
assaulted by the sun, attacked by the rain, covered over by dust,
growing fainter year by year: this shadow.

The bank with the "Historic Site" sign at the foot of its steps   35
dumped out into the street pieces of stone and glass, burned gritty,
completed a major reconstruction,
and set the whole enormous building sparkling in the evening sun.
In the vacant lot diagonally across,
drawing a crowd: a quack in the garb of a mountain ascetic.   40

Indifferent, the authorities say: "If we don't protect it with glass
    or something,
it will fade away," but do nothing.
Today, too,
foreign sailors amble up in their white leggings,   45
come to a stop with a click of their heels,
and, each having taken a snapshot, go off;
the shoeshine boy who followed them here
peers over the fence, wonders why all the fuss,
and goes on his way.   50

Translated by Richard H. Minear

After You Read

Critical Reading

1. Consider the title of the poem: "The Shadow." What is the **literal meaning** of this title within the context of the poem? What is the **connotative meaning**? Support your answer with details from the poem.

2. This poem is an example of **free verse poetry**. Consider the characteristics of free verse poetry, such as absence of rhyme and varying line and stanza lengths. Describe how these characteristics help to express the **theme** of the poem.

3. What is the main **conflict**, or problem, the speaker of the poem is facing? Support your answer with details from the poem.

Literary Lens: Word Choice and Tone

Consider the **tone** of the poem. What is the speaker's attitude toward the places, people, and things described in the poem. Identify examples of words and phrases that reveal the narrator's tone. Then describe the tone of the poem in a brief statement.

People, places, and things	Word choices and phrases that reveal tone
The narrator's tone:	

Focus on Research: Use a Variety of Primary Sources

Find three or four primary source documents about the 1945 bombing of Hiroshima. These primary sources could be excerpts from diaries or journals, autobiographies, photographs, audio recordings, and more. Your sources should include a variety of formats. Gather pictures or screenshots of your sources and compile them into a computer document or digital presentation. Write a short explanation of each source and include a works cited entry.

The Literature of
Indonesia

Background

Indonesia is the fourth most populous country in the world, behind China, India, and the United States. It is made up of more than 17,000 islands located between Southeast Asia and Australia. Before the 14th century, most people on these islands were Hindus or Buddhists. Today, about 87 percent of Indonesians are Muslims, which gives it the largest Muslim population in the world.

Long a colony of the Netherlands, Indonesia gained its independence in 1949. Years of bloody political turmoil and dictatorship followed. Since 1998, however, Indonesia has made progress toward democracy.

Much of Indonesia's storytelling, poetry, and song have been passed on orally and through performance. Censorship under the Dutch and political dictators, however, slowed the development of a national literature. Among the Indonesian writers who protested the repressive government was the poet Chairil Anwar (1922–1949). His most famous poem, "Aku," is a testament to an independent spirit. The poem is often read at protest rallies.

Indonesia and the United States

In 2005, news reporter Sahil K. Mahtani observed, "Currently, there are only three universities in America that teach Indonesian literature.... Of over 3,500 American universities, there are fewer than 20 that teach the Indonesian language." Mahtani protested this cultural neglect of the world's largest Muslim nation—particularly in post–9/11 America.

However, some aspects of Indonesian culture have found attention in the United States. Several notable American poets have written pantoums, intricate poems based on the traditional Indonesian pantun verse form. And in the performance arts, Indonesia's wayang kulit, a traditional form of shadow puppet theater, has greatly influenced the art of puppetry in the United States.

Research: Develop a Thesis

In his poem "Aku," Chairil Anwar wrote, "Though bullets should pierce my skin / I shall still strike and march forth." Using such quotations from Chairil Anwar's poetry and focused research, develop a working thesis you could use for a research paper on the poet.

Inem

Pramoedya Ananta Toer

Before You Read

Pramoedya Ananta Toer (1925–2006) was born in Indonesia (then the Dutch West Indies). Toer began writing while in prison for opposing Dutch colonial rule. He was released after Indonesia achieved independence in 1949. But in 1965, he was arrested again for his Marxist sympathies and beaten so badly that he lost most of his hearing. He remained in prison until 1979, during which time he wrote a group of novels called *The Buru Quartet*. Much of the time Toer was in prison, he was not allowed to write. His prison mates secretly gave him paper and helped him to recall the stories he had composed in his head.

World Context

Toer once observed, "It is impossible to separate politics from literature or any other part of human life, because everyone is touched by political power."

 LITERARY LENS Pay close attention to the **point of view** from which this story is told.

Inem was one of the girls I knew. She was eight years old—two years older than me. She was no different from the others. And if there was a difference, it was that she was one of the prettier little girls in our neighborhood. People liked to look at her. She was polite, unspoiled, deft, and hard-working—qualities which quickly spread her fame even into other neighborhoods as a girl who would make a good daughter-in-law.

And once when she was heating water in the kitchen, she said to me, "Gus[1] Muk, I'm going to be married."

"You're fooling!" I said.

---

1 **Gus:** a title of respect used by servants for their employers

"No, the proposal came a week ago. Mama and Papa and all the relatives have accepted the proposal."

"What fun to be a bride!" I exclaimed happily.

"Yes, it'll be fun, I know it will! They'll buy me all sorts of nice clothes. I'll be dressed up in a bride's outfit, with flowers in my hair, and they'll make me up with powder and mascara. Oh, I'll like that!"

• • • • •

And it was true. One afternoon her mother called on mine. At that time Inem was living with us as a servant. Her daily tasks were to help with the cooking and to watch over me and my younger brothers and sisters as we played.

Inem's mother made a living by doing batik[2] work. That was what the women in our neighborhood did when they were not working in the rice fields. Some put batik designs on sarongs,[3] while others worked on head cloths. The poorer ones preferred to do head cloths; since it did not take so long to finish a head cloth, they received payment for it sooner. And Inem's mother supported her family by putting batik designs on head cloths. She got the cloth and the wax from her employer, the Idjo Store. For every two head cloths that she finished, she was paid one and a half cents. On the average, a woman could do eight to eleven head cloths a day.

Inem's father kept gamecocks. All he did, day after day, was to wager his bird in cockfights. If he lost, the victor would take his cock. And in addition he would have to pay two and a half rupiahs, or at the very least seventy-five cents. When he was not gambling on cockfights, he would play cards with his neighbors for a cent a hand.

Sometimes Inem's father would be away from home for a month or half a month, wandering around on foot. His return would signify that he was bringing home some money.

Mother once told me that Inem's father's main occupation had been robbing people in the teak forest between our town, Blora, and the coastal town of Rembang. I was then in the first grade, and heard many stories of robbers, bandits, thieves, and murderers. As a result of those stories and what Mother told me, I came to be terrified of Inem's father.

Everybody knew that Inem's father was a criminal, but no one could prove it and no one dared complain to the police. Consequently he was never arrested by the police. Furthermore, almost all of Inem's mother's

---

2   **batik:** a type of design using wax to control where fabric is dyed
3   **sarongs:** long strips of fabric worn loosely as skirts or dresses

relatives were policemen. There was even one with the rank of agent first class. Inem's father himself had once been a policeman but had been discharged for taking bribes.

Mother also told me that in the old days Inem's father had been an important criminal. As a way of countering an outbreak of crime that was getting out of hand, the Netherlands Indies government had appointed him a policeman, so that he could round up his former associates. He never robbed any more after that, but in our area he continued to be a focus of suspicion.

When Inem's mother called on my mother, Inem was heating water in the kitchen. I tagged along after Inem's mother. The visitor, Mother, and I sat on a low, red couch.

"Ma'am," said Inem's mother, "I've come to ask for Inem to come back home."

"Why do you want Inem back? Isn't it better for her to be here? You don't have any of her expenses, and here she can learn how to cook."

"Yes, ma'am, but I plan for her to get married after the coming harvest."

"What?" exclaimed Mother, startled. "She's going to be married?"

"Yes, ma'am. She's old enough to be married now—she's eight years old," said Inem's mother.

At this my mother laughed. And her visitor was surprised to see Mother laugh.

"Why, a girl of eight is still a child!" said Mother.

"We're not upper-class people, ma'am. I think she's already a year too old. You know Asih? She married her daughter when she was two years younger than mine."

Mother tried to dissuade the woman. But Inem's mother had another argument. Finally the visitor spoke again: "I feel lucky that someone wants her. If we let a proposal go by this time, maybe there will never be another one. And how humiliating it would be to have a daughter turn into an old maid! And it just might be that if she gets married she'll be able to help out with the household expenses."

Mother did not reply. Then she looked at me and said, "Go get the betel set and the spittoon."[4]

So I went to fetch the box of betel-chewing ingredients and the brass spittoon.

"And what does your husband say?"

---

4 **spittoon:** a spit receptacle

"Oh, he agrees. What's more, Markaban is the son of a well-to-do man—his only child. Markaban has already begun to help his father trade cattle in Rembang, Tjepu, Medang, Pati, Ngawen, and also here in Blora," said Inem's mother.

This information seemed to cheer Mother up, although I could not understand why. Then she called Inem, who was at work in the kitchen. Inem came in. And Mother asked, "Inem, do you want to get married?"

Inem bowed her head. She was very respectful toward Mother. I never once heard her oppose her. Indeed, it is rare to find people who are powerless opposing anything that others say to them.

I saw then that Inem was beaming. She often looked like that; give her something that pleased her even a little and she would beam. But she was not accustomed to saying "thank you." In the society of the simple people of our neighborhood, the words "thank you" were still unfamiliar. It was only through the glow radiating from their faces that gratitude found expression.

"Yes, ma'am," said Inem so softly as to be almost inaudible.

Then Inem's mother and mine chewed some betel. Mother herself did not like to chew betel all the time. She did it only when she had a woman visitor. Every few moments she would spit into the brass spittoon.

When Inem had gone back to the kitchen Mother said, "It's not right to make children marry."

These words surprised Inem's mother. But she did not say anything nor did her eyes show any interest.

"I was eighteen when I got married," said Mother.

Inem's mother's surprise vanished. She was no longer surprised now, but she still did not say anything.

"It's not right to make children marry," repeated Mother.

And Inem's mother was surprised again.

"Their children will be stunted."

Inem's mother's surprise vanished once more.

"Yes, ma'am." Then she said placidly, "My mother was also eight when she got married."

Mother paid no attention and continued, "Not only will they be stunted, but their health will be affected too."

"Yes, ma'am, but ours is a long-lived family. My mother is still alive, though she's over fifty-nine. And my grandmother is still alive too. I think she must be seventy-four. She's still vigorous and strong enough to pound corn in the mortar."

Still ignoring her, Mother went on, "Especially if the husband is also a child."

"Yes, ma'am, but Markaban is seventeen."

"Seventeen! My husband was thirty when he married me."

Inem's mother was silent. She never stopped shifting the wad of tobacco leaves that was stuck between her lips. One moment she would move the tobacco to the right, a moment later to the left, and the next moment she would roll it up and scrub her coal-black teeth with it.

Now Mother had no more arguments with which to oppose her visitor's intention. She said, "Well, if you've made up your mind to marry Inem off, I only hope that she gets a good husband who can take care of her. And I hope she gets someone who is **compatible**."

Inem's mother left, still shifting the tobacco about in her mouth.

"I hope nothing bad happens to that child."

"Why would anything bad happen to her?" I asked.

"Never mind, Muk, it's nothing." Then Mother changed the subject. "If the situation of their family improves, we won't lose any more of our chickens."

"Is somebody stealing our chickens, Mama?" I asked.

"No, Muk, never mind," Mother said slowly. "Such a little child! Only eight years old. What a pity it is. But they need money. And the only way to get it is to marry off their daughter."

Then Mother went to the garden behind the house to get some string beans for supper.

Fifteen days after this visit, Inem's mother came again to fetch her daughter. She seemed greatly pleased that Inem made no objection to being taken away. And when Inem was about to leave our house, never to be a member of our family again, she spoke to me in the kitchen doorway, "Well, good bye, Gus Muk. I'm going home, Gus Muk," she said very softly.

She always spoke softly. Speaking softly was one of the customary ways of showing politeness in our small-town society. She went off as joyfully as a child who expects to be given a new blouse.

• • • • •

From that moment, Inem no longer lived in our house. I felt very deeply the loss of my constant companion. From that moment also, it was no longer Inem who took me to the bathing cubicle at night to wash my feet before going to bed, but my adoptive older sister.

Sometimes I felt an intense longing to see Inem. Not infrequently, when I had got into bed, I would recall the moment when her mother drew her by the hand and the two of them left our house. Inem's house was in back of ours, separated only by a wooden fence.

She had been gone a month. I often went to her house to play with her, and Mother always got angry when she found out that I had been there. She would always say, "What can you learn at Inem's house that's of any use?"

And I would never reply. Mother always had a good reason for scolding me. Everything she said built a thick wall that was impenetrable to excuses. Therefore my best course was to be silent. And as the clinching argument in her lecture, she was almost certain to repeat the sentences that she uttered so often: "What's the point to your playing with her? Aren't there lots of other children you can ask to play with you? What's more, she's a woman who's going to be married soon."

But I kept on sneaking over to her house anyway. It is surprising sometimes how a prohibition seems to exist solely in order to be violated. And when I disobeyed I felt that what I did was pleasurable. For children such as I at that time—oh, how many prohibitions and restrictions were heaped on our heads! Yes, it was as though the whole world was watching us, bent on forbidding whatever we did and whatever we wanted. Inevitably we children felt that this world was really intended only for adults.

• • • • •

Then the day of the wedding arrived.

For five days before the ceremony, Inem's family was busy in the kitchen, cooking food and preparing various delicacies. This made me visit her house all the more frequently.

The day before the wedding, Inem was dressed in all her finery. Mother sent me there with five kilos of rice and twenty-five cents as a neighborly contribution. And that afternoon we children crowded around and stared at her in admiration. The hair over her forehead and temples and her eyebrows had been carefully trimmed with a razor and thickened with mascara. Her little bun of hair had been built up with a switch and adorned with the paper flowers with springs for stalks that we call sunduk mentul. Her clothes were made of satin. Her sarong was an expensive one made in Solo. These things had all been rented from a Chinaman in the Chinese quarter near the town square. The gold rings and bracelets were all rented too.

The house was decorated with constructions of banyan leaves and young coconut fronds. On each wall there were crossed tricolor flags encircled by palm leaves. All the house pillars were similarly decorated with tricolor bunting.

Mother herself went and helped with the preparations. But not for long. Mother rarely did this sort of thing except for her closest neighbors. She stayed less than an hour. And it was then too that the things sent by Inem's husband-to-be arrived: a load of cakes and candies, a male goat, a quantity of rice, a packet of salt, a sack of husked coconuts, and half a sack of granulated sugar.

It was just after the harvest. Rice was cheap. And when rice was cheap all other foodstuffs were cheap too. That was why the period after the harvest was a favorite time for celebrations. And for that reason Inem's family had found it impossible to contract for a puppet performance. The puppet masters had already been engaged by other families in various neighborhoods. The puppet theater was the most popular form of entertainment in our area. In our town there were three types of puppet performance: the *wajan purwa* or shadow play, which recounted stories from the *Mahabharata* and the *Ramayana*, as well as other stories similar in theme; the *wajang krutjil*, in which wooden puppets in human shape acted out stories of Arabia, Persia, India, and China, as well as tales of Madjapahit times; and the *wajang golek*, which employed wooden dolls. But this last was not very popular.

Because there were no puppet masters available, Inem's family engaged a troupe of dancing girls. At first this created a dispute. Inem's relatives on her mother's side were religious scholars and teachers. But Inem's father would not back down. The dance troupe came, with its gamelan[5] orchestra, and put on a tajuban.[6]

Usually, in our area, a tajuban was attended by the men who wanted to dance with the girls and by little children who only wanted to watch—little children whose knowledge of sexual matters did not go beyond kissing. The grown boys did not like to watch; it embarrassed them. This was even more the case with the women—none of them attended at all. And a tajuban in our area—in order to inflame sexual passions—was always accompanied by alcoholic beverages: arrack, beer, whisky, or gin.

The tajuban lasted for two days and nights. We children took great delight in the spectacle of men and women dancing and kissing one another and every now and then clinking their glasses and drinking liquor as they danced and shouted, "Huse!"

And though Mother forbade me to watch, I went anyway on the sly.

"Why do you insist on going where those wicked people are? Look at your religious teacher: he doesn't go to watch, even though he is Inem's father's brother-in-law. You must have noticed that yourself."

---

5   **gamelan:** a group of traditional Indonesian instruments and vocalists
6   **tajuban:** a party of drinking and dancing used to celebrate rites of passage

Our religious teacher also had a house in back of ours, to the right of Inem's house. Subsequently the teacher's failure to attend became a topic that was sure to enliven a conversation. From it there arose two remarks that itched on the tip of everyone's tongue: that the teacher was certainly a pious man, and that Inem's father was undoubtedly a **reprobate**.

Mother reinforced her scolding with words that I did not understand at the time: "Do you know something? They are people who have no respect for women," she said in a piercing voice.

And when the bridegroom came to be formally presented to the bride, Inem, who had been sitting on the **nuptial** seat, was led forth. The bridegroom had reached the veranda. Inem squatted and made obeisance to her future husband, and then washed his feet with flower water from a brass pot. Then the couple were tied together and conducted side by side to the nuptial seat. At that time the onlookers could be heard saying, "One child becomes two. One child becomes two. One child becomes two."

And the women who were watching beamed as though they were to be the recipients of the happiness to come.

At that very moment I noticed that Inem was crying so much that her make-up was spoiled, and tears were trickling down her face. At home I asked Mother, "Why was the bride crying, Mama?"

"When a bride cries, it's because she is thinking of her long-departed ancestors. Their spirits also attend the ceremony. And they are happy that their descendant has been safely married," replied Mother.

I never gave any thought to those words of hers. Later I found out why Inem had been crying. She had to urinate, but was afraid to tell anyone.

reprobate:
villain;
scoundrel

nuptial:
marital;
conjugal

•••••

The celebration ended uneventfully. There were no more guests coming with contributions. The house resumed its everyday appearance, and by the time the moneylenders came to collect, Inem's father had left Blora. After the wedding, Inem's mother and Inem herself went on doing batik work— day and night. And if someone went to their house at three o'clock in the morning, he would be likely to find them still working. Puffs of smoke would be rising between them from the crucible in which the wax was melted. In addition to that, quarreling was often heard in that house.

And once, when I was sleeping with Mother in her bed, a loud scream awakened me: "I won't! I won't!"

It was still night then. The screams repeated again and again, accompanied by the sound of blows and pounding on a door. I know that the screams came from Inem's mouth. I recognized her voice.

"Mama, why is Inem screaming?" I asked.

"They're fighting. I hope nothing bad happens to that little girl," she said. But she gave no explanation.

"Why would anything bad happen to her, Mama?" I asked insistently.

Mother did not reply to my question. And then, when the screaming and shouting were over, we went back to sleep. Such screams were almost sure to be heard every night. Screams and screams. And every time I heard them, I would ask my mother about them. Mother would never give a satisfactory answer. Sometimes she merely sighed, "What a pity, such a little child!"

One day Inem came to our house. She went straight in to find my mother. Her face was pale, bloodless. Before saying anything, she set the tone of the occasion by crying—crying in a respectful way.

"Why are you crying, Inem? Have you been fighting again?" Mother asked.

"Ma'am," said Inem between her sobs, "I hope that you will be willing to take me back here as before."

"But you're married, aren't you Inem?"

And Inem cried some more. Through her tears she said, "I can't stand it, ma'am."

"Why, Inem? Don't you like your husband?" asked Mother.

"Ma'am, please take pity on me. Every night all he wants to do is wrestle, ma'am."

"Can't you say to him, 'Please, dear, don't be like that'?"

"I'm afraid, ma'am. I'm afraid of him. He's so big. And when he wrestles he squeezes me so hard that I can't breathe. You'll take me back, won't you, ma'am?" she pleaded.

"If you didn't have a husband, Inem, of course I'd take you back. But you have a husband . . ."

And Inem cried again when she heard what Mother said. "Ma'am, I don't want to have a husband."

"You may not want to, but the fact is that you do, Inem. Maybe eventually your husband will change for the better, and the two of you will be able to live happily. You wanted to get married, didn't you?" said Mother.

"Yes, ma'am . . . but, but . . ."

"Inem, regardless of anything else, a woman must serve her husband faithfully. If you aren't a good wife to your husband, your ancestors will curse you," said Mother.

Inem began crying harder. And because of her crying she was unable to say anything.

"Now, Inem, promise me that you will always prepare your husband's meals. When you have an idle moment, you should pray to God to keep him safe. You must promise to wash his clothes, and you must massage him when he is tired from his work. You must rub his back vigorously when he catches cold."

Inem still made no reply. Only her tears continued to fall.

"Well, now, you go home, and from this moment on be a good wife to him. No matter whether he is good or bad, you must serve him faithfully, because after all he is your husband."

Inem, who was sitting on the floor, did not stir.

"Get up and go home to your husband. You . . . if you just up and quit your husband the consequences will not be good for you, either now or in the future," Mother added.

"Yes, ma'am," Inem said submissively. Slowly she rose and walked home.

"How sad, she's so little," said Mother.

"Mama, does Daddy ever wrestle you?" I asked.

Mother looked searchingly into my eyes. Then her scrutiny relaxed. She smiled. "No," she said. "Your father is the best person in the whole world, Muk."

Then Mother went to the kitchen to get the hoe, and she worked in the garden with me.

• • • • •

A year passed imperceptibly. On a certain occasion Inem came again. In the course of a year she had grown much bigger. It was quite apparent that she was mature, although only nine years old. As usual, she went directly to where Mother was and sat on the floor with her head bowed. She said, "Ma'am, now I don't have a husband any more."

"What?"

"Now I don't have a husband any more."

"You're divorced?" asked Mother.

"Yes, Ma'am."

"Why did you separate from him?"

She did not reply.

"Did you fail to be a good wife to him?"

"I think I was always a good wife to him, ma'am."

"Did you massage him when he came home tired from work?" asked Mother probingly.

"Yes, ma'am, I did everything you advised me to."

"Well, then, why did you separate?"

"Ma'am, he often beat me."

"Beat you? He beat a little child like you?"

"I did everything I could to be a good wife, ma'am. And when he beat me and I was in pain—was that part of being a good wife, ma'am?" she asked, in genuine perplexity.

Mother was silent. Her eyes scrutinized Inem. "He beat you," Mother whispered then.

"Yes, ma'am—he beat me just the way Mama and Papa do."

"Maybe you failed in some way after all in your duty to him. A husband would never have the heart to beat a wife who was really and truly a good wife to him."

Inem did not reply. She changed the subject: "Would you be willing to take me back, ma'am?"

There was no hesitation in Mother's reply. She said firmly, "Inem, you're a divorced woman now. There are lots of grown boys here. It wouldn't look right to people, would it?"

"But they wouldn't beat me," said the divorcée.

"No. That isn't what I mean. It just doesn't look right for a divorced woman as young as you to be in a place where there are lots of men."

"Is it because there's something wrong with me, Ma'am?"

"No, Inem, it's a question of propriety."

"Propriety, ma'am? It's for the sake of propriety that I can't stay here?"

"Yes, that's the way it is, Inem."

The divorcée did not say anything more. She remained sitting on the floor, and seemed to have no intention of leaving the place where she was sitting. Mother went up to her and patted her shoulder consolingly. "Now, Inem . . . the best thing is for you to help your parents earn a living. I really regret that I can't take you back here."

Two tears formed in the corners of the little woman's eyes. She got up. Listlessly she moved her feet, leaving our house to return to her parents' house. And from then on she was seldom seen outside her house.

And thereafter, the nine-year-old divorcée—since she was nothing but a burden to her family—could be beaten by anyone who wanted to: her mother, her brothers, her uncles, her neighbors, her aunts. Yet Inem never again came to our house.

Her screams of pain were often heard. When she moaned, I covered my ears with my hands. And Mother continued to uphold the respectability of her home.

Translated by Rufus S. Hendron

After You Read

Critical Reading

1. On pages 602–603, the narrator's mother tells Inem to be a good wife by preparing her husband's meals, washing his clothes, and performing other tasks. Later, after hearing that Inem's husband beats her, the narrator's mother says that Inem may have "failed in some way" in her duties as a wife. Consider the **character** of Inem. Do you think that Inem failed in her duties? Support your answer with details from the story.

2. On page 596, the narrator notes "Indeed, it is rare to find people who are powerless opposing anything that others say to them." Cite one example from the text that supports this statement and one example that refutes it.

3. Compare and contrast the **character** of Inem before her marriage and after her marriage. Support your response with details from the story.

Literary Lens: Point of View

Analyze the **point of view** of the story. First, identify the point of view (first-person, third-person limited, or third-person omniscient). Then cite three quotations from the story that reveal the narrator's opinion of the events in the story. Lastly, infer Pramoedya Ananta Toer's purpose in choosing to tell the story through this point of view.

Point of view:	
Quotation 1	
Quotation 2	
Quotation 3	
Author's purpose in using this point of view:	

Focus on Research: Conduct Informal Research

In the story, the narrator's mother argues with Inem's mother about Inem getting married at age eight. Conduct research on the topic of arranged marriage or child marriage. Find two sources from varying points of view. Identify any faulty reasoning or cultural bias in the sources. Share with a partner what you learned from both of your sources.

The Literature of
Australia and New Zealand

Background

The Aboriginal population has lived in Australia for 50,000 years or more. Europeans began arriving in the 17th century. Starting in 1788, Britain tried to relieve its overcrowded prisons by sending criminals to settle Australia. Later, British colonists began to arrive voluntarily to settle the vast countryside.

Traditionally, much Australian literature has portrayed the rough life on Australia's farms and ranches. Such writings celebrate the outdoor virtues of rowdy cheerfulness and "mateship." For example, Nobel Prize-winning novelist Patrick White (1912–1990) wrote about survival and death in the dry "outback" in *Voss*. Recently, Australian writers have focused more on urban life.

About 1,200 miles southeast of Australia is the island country of New Zealand. Most of the country's literature is written in English. One of the best-known works from New Zealand is *The Whale Rider*, by Witi Ihimaera (1944–). His ancestors include both Europeans and Maoris, the native people of the islands.

Australia and the United States

In his 1851 novel *Moby-Dick*, American author Herman Melville described Australia as "that great America on the other side of the sphere." Indeed, the United States and Australia bear striking similarities. Both countries were colonized by England, and both of their literatures have been marked by a struggle for cultural identity.

During the 19th century, writers such as Melville strove to disprove Europeans' assumption that Americans were naive and culturally backward. Today, some Australian writers feel that they are battling the same prejudice. As the poet Mark Tredinnick (1962–) puts it, "Maybe it takes two hundred years to write in tune with a land you come to . . . It took that long in North America. . . . But it seems the time has come in Australia."

Research: Conduct Informal Research

Research the Aboriginal concept of "Dreaming" or "Dreamtime." In a short oral presentation, describe how this concept has been used in Aboriginal storytelling.

Eve to Her Daughters

Judith Wright

Before You Read

Judith Wright (1915–2000) was an Australian writer, conservationist, and activist for the rights of Aboriginal people. At the outbreak of World War I, she returned to her family home in New South Wales. "I knew then," she said, "how closely connected I was to that landscape. I began to write again, and the poems came closer to what I'd hoped for."

World Context

According to Judaism, Christianity, and Islam, Eve was the first woman, and Adam was the first man.

 LITERARY LENS Listen to the **voice** of Eve as you read. How would you describe it?

It was not I who began it.
Turned out into draughty caves,
hungry so often, having to work for our bread,
hearing the children whining,
I was nevertheless not unhappy.   5
Where Adam went I was fairly contented to go.
I adapted myself to the punishment: it was my life.

But Adam, you know . . . !
He kept on brooding over the insult,
over the trick They had played on us, over the scolding.   10
He had discovered a flaw in himself
and he had to make up for it.
Outside Eden the earth was imperfect,
the seasons changed, the game was fleet-footed,

he had to work for our living, and he didn't like it.   15
He even complained of my cooking
(it was hard to compete with Heaven).

So, he set to work.
The earth must be made a new Eden
with central heating, domesticated animals,   20
mechanical harvesters, combustion engines,
escalators, refrigerators,
and modern means of communication
and multiplied opportunities for safe investment
and higher education for Abel and Cain   25
and the rest of the family.
You can see how his pride has been hurt.

In the process he had to unravel everything,
because he believed that mechanism
was the whole secret—he was always mechanical-minded.   30
He got to the very inside of the whole machine

Bark painting depicting the aboriginal equivalents to Adam, Eve, and the serpent

exclaiming as he went, So this is how it works!
And now that I know how it works, why, I must have invented it.
As for God and the Other, they cannot be demonstrated,
and what cannot be demonstrated   35
doesn't exist.
You see, he had always been jealous.

Yes, he got to the center
where nothing at all can be demonstrated.
And clearly he doesn't exist; but he refuses   40
to accept the conclusion.
You see, he was always an egotist.

It was warmer than this in the cave;
there was none of this fallout.
I would suggest, for the sake of the children,   45
that it's time you took over.

But you are my daughters, you inherit my own faults of character;
you are submissive, following Adam
even beyond existence.
Faults of character have their own logic   50
and it always works out.
I observed this with Abel and Cain.

Perhaps the whole elaborate fable
right from the beginning
is meant to demonstrate this; perhaps it's the whole secret.   55
Perhaps nothing exists but our faults?

But it's useless to make
such a suggestion to Adam.
He has turned himself into God,
who is faultless, and doesn't exist.   60

After You Read

Critical Reading

1. What is the **setting** of the poem? How does the setting reveal the **theme** of the poem?

2. The **speaker** of the poem is Eve, a character from a biblical creation tale. Infer Wright's **purpose** for choosing this character as the speaker. Support your inference with details from the poem.

3. The poem states that Adam got to the inside of "the whole machine." What does the "whole machine" **symbolize**? Use details from the poem to support your response.

Literary Lens: Voice

An author's distinctive personality revealed through their writing is referred to as **voice**. Voice is often developed through the use of tone, imagery, and sensory details. Consider Wright's techniques. Describe each technique, and support your description with a quotation from the poem. Then describe the author's voice.

Technique	Description	Quotation
Tone		
Imagery		
Sensory details		

Focus on Research: Use Transitions

When drafting a research project, use appropriate transition words to help readers understand the relationship between your ideas and follow your train of thought. Here are some transition words:

also	finally	in conclusion	second
and	first	in contrast to	subsequently
besides	following	in other words	therefore
but	furthermore	lastly	too
clearly	however	moreover	undoubtedly
conversely	importantly	nevertheless	whereas
despite	in addition	particularly	

Pick a selection from this unit, or consider all the selections in this unit. Then write several paragraphs about your experiences reading this selection(s). Exchange your work with a partner. Have your partner circle all the transitional words in your paragraphs and make suggestions to change or add words to increase the readability of your writing.

American Dreams

Peter Carey

Before You Read

Peter Carey (1943–2010) was born in Australia, but also lived in New York. He wrote several prizewinning novels, including *Oscar and Lucinda*, *The Unusual Life of Tristan Smith,* and *Jack Maggs*. He often wrote about life in his native Australia and his country's history, which he described as "dismal." His most famous novel is probably *The True History of the Kelly Gang,* based on the life of the Australian outlaw Ned Kelly.

World Context

Carey is notable for fiction that contains elements of the bizarre, black humor, and satire. By including surreal elements, he forces readers to make judgments without their usual reference points. "American Dreams" is a double-edged satire about the growing influence of America as well as Americans' fantasies about the rest of the world.

LITERARY LENS As you read, notice the **connotations**, or shades of meaning, of key words.

No one can, to this day, remember what it was we did to offend him. Dyer the butcher remembers a day when he gave him the wrong meat and another day when he served someone else first by mistake. Often when Dyer gets drunk he recalls this day and curses himself for his foolishness. But no one seriously believes that it was Dyer who offended him.

But one of us did something. We slighted him terribly in some way, this small meek man with the rimless glasses and neat suit who used to smile so nicely at us all. We thought, I suppose, he was a bit of a fool and sometimes he was so quiet and grey that we ignored him, forgetting he was there at all.

When I was a boy I often stole apples from the trees at his house up in Mason's Lane. He often saw me. No, that's not correct. Let me say I often sensed that he saw me. I sensed him peering out from behind the lace curtains of his house. And I was not the only one. Many of us came to take his apples, alone and in groups, and it is possible that he chose to exact payment for all these apples in his own peculiar way.

Yet I am sure it wasn't the apples.

What has happened is that we all, all eight hundred of us, have come to remember small **transgressions** against Mr. Gleason who once lived amongst us.

My father, who has never borne malice against a single living creature, still believes that Gleason meant to do us well, that he loved the town more than any of us. My father says we have treated the town badly in our minds. We have used it, this little valley, as nothing more than a stopping place. Somewhere on the way to somewhere else. Even those of us who have been here many years have never taken the town seriously. Oh yes, the place is pretty. The hills are green and the woods thick. The stream is full of fish. But it is not where we would rather be.

For years we have watched the films at the Roxy and dreamed, if not of America, then at least of our capital city. For our own town, my father says, we have nothing but contempt. We have treated it badly, like a whore. We have cut down the giant shady trees in the main street to make doors of the school house and seats for the football pavilion. We have left big holes all over the countryside from which we have taken brown coal and given back nothing.

The commercial travellers who buy fish and chips at George the Greek's care for us more than we do, because we all have dreams of the big city, of wealth, of modern houses, of big motor cars: American Dreams, my father has called them.

Although my father ran a petrol station he was also an inventor. He sat in his office all day drawing strange pieces of equipment on the back of delivery dockets. Every spare piece of paper in the house was covered with these little drawings and my mother would always be very careful about throwing away any piece of paper no matter how small. She would look on both sides of any piece of paper very carefully and always preserved any that had so much as a pencil mark.

I think it was because of this that my father felt that he understood Gleason. He never said as much, but he inferred that he understood Gleason because he, too, was concerned with similar problems. My father was working on plans for a giant gravel crusher, but occasionally he would become distracted and become interested in something else.

There was, for instance, the time when Dyer the butcher bought a new bicycle with gears, and for a while my father talked of nothing else but the gears. Often I would see him across the road squatting down beside Dyer's bicycle as if he were talking to it.

We all rode bicycles because we didn't have the money for anything better. My father did have an old Chevy truck, but he rarely used it and it occurs to me now that it might have had some mechanical problem that was impossible to solve, or perhaps it was just that he was saving it, not wishing to wear it out all at once. Normally, he went everywhere on his bicycle and, when I was younger, he carried me on the cross bar, both of us dismounting to trudge up the hills that led into and out of the main street. It was a common sight in our town to see people pushing bicycles. They were as much a burden as a means of transport.

Gleason also had his bicycle and every lunchtime he pushed and pedalled it home from the shire[1] offices to his little weatherboard house out at Mason's Lane. It was a three-mile ride and people said that he went home for lunch because he was fussy and wouldn't eat either his wife's sandwiches or the hot meal available at Mrs. Lessing's café.

But while Gleason pedalled and pushed his bicycle to and from the shire offices everything in our town proceeded as normal. It was only when he retired that things began to go wrong.

Because it was then that Mr. Gleason started supervising the building of the wall around the two-acre plot up on Bald Hill. He paid too much for this land. He bought it from Johnny Weeks, who now, I am sure, believes the whole episode was his fault, firstly for cheating Gleason, secondly for selling him the land at all. But Gleason hired some Chinese and set to work to build his wall. It was then that we knew that we'd offended him. My father rode all the way out to Bald Hill and tried to talk Mr. Gleason out of his wall. He said there was no need for us to build walls. That no one wished to spy on Mr. Gleason or whatever he wished to do on Bald Hill. He said no one was in the least bit interested in Mr. Gleason. Mr. Gleason, neat in a new sportscoat, polished his glasses and smiled vaguely at his feet. Bicycling back, my father thought that he had gone too far. Of course we had an interest in Mr. Gleason. He pedalled back and asked him to attend a dance that was to be held on the next Friday, but Mr. Gleason said he didn't dance.

"Oh well," my father said, "any time, just drop over."

Mr. Gleason went back to supervising his family of Chinese labourers on his wall.

---

1 **shire:** an area similar to a county

Bald Hill towered high above the town and from my father's small filling station you could sit and watch the wall going up. It was an interesting sight. I watched it for two years, while I waited for customers who rarely came. After school and on Saturdays I had all the time in the world to watch the agonizing progress of Mr. Gleason's wall. It was as painful as a clock. Sometimes I could see the Chinese labourers running at a jog-trot carrying bricks on long wooden planks. The hill was bare, and on this bareness Mr. Gleason was, for some reason, building a wall.

In the beginning people thought it peculiar that someone would build such a big wall on Bald Hill. The only thing to recommend Bald Hill was the view of the town, and Mr. Gleason was building a wall that denied that view. The top soil was thin and bare clay showed through in places. Nothing would ever grow there. Everyone assumed that Gleason had simply gone mad and after the initial interest they accepted his madness as they accepted his wall and as they accepted Bald Hill itself.

Occasionally someone would pull in for petrol at my father's filling station and ask about the wall and my father would shrug and I would see, once more, the strangeness of it.

"A house?" the stranger would ask. "Up on that hill?"

"No," my father would say, "chap named Gleason is building a wall."

And the strangers would want to know why, and my father would shrug and look up at Bald Hill once more. "Damned if I know," he'd say.

Gleason still lived in his old house at Mason's Lane. It was a plain weatherboard house with a rose garden at the front, a vegetable garden down the side, and an orchard at the back.

At night we kids would sometimes ride out to Bald Hill on our bicycles. It was an agonizing, muscle-twitching ride, the worst part of which was a steep, unmade road up which we finally pushed our bikes, our lungs rasping in the night air. When we arrived we found nothing but walls. Once we broke down some of the brickwork and another time we threw stones at the tents where the Chinese labourers slept. Thus we expressed our frustration at this inexplicable thing.

The wall must have been finished on the day before my twelfth birthday. I remember going on a picnic birthday party up to Eleven Mile Creek and we lit a fire and cooked chops at a bend in the river from where it was possible to see the walls on Bald Hill. I remember standing with a hot chop in my hand and someone saying, "Look, they're leaving!"

We stood on the creek bed and watched the Chinese labourers walking their bicycles slowly down the hill. Someone said they were going to build a chimney up at the mine at A.1 and certainly there is a large brick chimney there now, so I suppose they built it.

When the word spread that the walls were finished most of the town went up to look. They walked around the four walls which were as interesting as any other brick walls. They stood in front of the big wooden gates and tried to peer through, but all they could see was a small blind wall that had obviously been constructed for this special purpose. The walls themselves were ten feet high and topped with broken glass and barbed wire. When it became obvious that we were not going to discover the contents of the enclosure, we all gave up and went home.

Mr. Gleason had long since stopped coming into town. His wife came instead, wheeling a pram down from Mason's Lane to Main Street and filling it with groceries and meat (they never bought vegetables, they grew their own) and wheeling it back to Mason's Lane. Sometimes you would see her standing with the pram halfway up the Gell Street hill. Just standing there, catching her breath. No one asked her about the wall. They knew she wasn't responsible for the wall and they felt sorry for her, having to bear the burden of the pram and her husband's madness. Even when she began to visit Dixon's hardware and buy plaster of paris and tins of paint and waterproofing compound, no one asked her what these things were for. She had a way of averting her eyes that indicated her terror of questions. Old Dixon carried the plaster of paris and the tins of paint out to her pram for her and watched her push them away. "Poor woman," he said, "poor bloody woman."

From the filling station where I sat dreaming in the sun, or from the enclosed office where I gazed mournfully at the rain, I would see, occasionally, Gleason entering or leaving his walled compound, a tiny figure way up on Bald Hill. And I'd think "Gleason," but not much more.

Occasionally strangers drove up there to see what was going on, often egged on by locals who told them it was a Chinese temple or some other silly thing. Once a group of Italians had a picnic outside the walls and took photographs of each other standing in front of the closed door. God knows what they thought it was.

But for five years between my twelfth and seventeenth birthdays there was nothing to interest me in Gleason's walls. Those years seem lost to me now and I can remember very little of them. I developed a crush on Susy Markin and followed her back from the swimming pool on my bicycle. I sat behind her in the pictures and wandered past her house. Then her parents moved to another town and I sat in the sun and waited for them to come back.

We became very keen on modernization. When coloured paints became available the whole town went berserk and brightly coloured houses blossomed overnight. But the paints were not of good quality and quickly faded and peeled, so that the town looked like a garden of dead flowers. Thinking of those years, the only real thing I recall is the soft hiss of bicycle tyres on the main street. When I think of it now it seems very peaceful, but I remember then that the sound induced in me a feeling of melancholy, a feeling somehow mixed with the early afternoons when the sun went down behind Bald Hill and the town felt as sad as an empty dance hall on a Sunday afternoon.

And then, during my seventeenth year, Mr. Gleason died. We found out when we saw Mrs. Gleason's pram parked out in front of Phonsey Joy's Funeral Parlour. It looked very sad, that pram, standing by itself in the windswept street. We came and looked at the pram and felt sad for Mrs. Gleason. She hadn't had much of a life.

Phonsey Joy carried old Mr. Gleason out to the cemetery by the Parwan Railway Station and Mrs. Gleason rode behind in a taxi. People watched the old hearse go by and thought, "Gleason," but not much else.

And then, less than a month after Gleason had been buried out at the lonely cemetery by the Parwan Railway Station, the Chinese labourers came back. We saw them push their bicycles up the hill. I stood with my father and Phonsey Joy and wondered what was going on.

And then I saw Mrs. Gleason trudging up the hill. I nearly didn't recognize her, because she didn't have her pram. She carried a black umbrella and walked slowly up Bald Hill and it wasn't until she stopped for breath and leant forward that I recognized her.

"It's Mrs. Gleason," I said, "with the Chinese."

But it wasn't until the next morning that it became obvious what was happening. People lined the main street in the way they do for a big funeral but, instead of gazing towards the Grant Street corner, they all looked up at Bald Hill.

All that day and all the next people gathered to watch the destruction of the walls. They saw the Chinese labourers darting to and fro, but it wasn't until they knocked down a large section of the wall facing the town that we realized there really was something inside. It was impossible to see what it was, but there was something there. People stood and wondered and pointed out Mrs. Gleason to each other as she went to and fro supervising the work.

And finally, in ones and twos, on bicycles and on foot, the whole town moved up to Bald Hill. Mr. Dyer closed up his butcher shop and my father got out the old Chevy truck and we finally arrived up at Bald Hill with twenty people on board. They crowded into the back tray and hung on to the running boards and my father grimly steered his way through the crowds of bicycles and parked just where the dirt track gets really steep. We trudged up this last steep track, never for a moment suspecting what we would find at the top.

It was very quiet up there. The Chinese labourers worked diligently, removing the third and fourth walls and cleaning the bricks which they stacked neatly in big piles. Mrs. Gleason said nothing either. She stood in the only remaining corner of the walls and looked defiantly at the townspeople who stood open-mouthed where another corner had been.

And between us and Mrs. Gleason was the most incredibly beautiful thing I had ever seen in my life. For one moment I didn't recognize it. I stood openmouthed, and breathed the surprising beauty of it. And then I realized it was our town. The buildings were two feet high and they were a little rough but very correct. I saw Mr. Dyer nudge my father and whisper that Gleason had got the faded "U" in the BUTCHER sign of his shop.

I think at that moment everyone was overcome with a feeling of simple joy. I can't remember ever having felt so uplifted and happy. It was perhaps a childish emotion but I looked up at my father and saw a smile of such warmth spread across his face that I knew he felt just as I did. Later he told me that he thought Gleason had built the model of our town just for this moment, to let us see the beauty of our own town, to make us proud of ourselves and to stop the American Dreams we were so prone to. For the rest, my father said, was not Gleason's plan and he could not have foreseen the things that happened afterwards.

I have come to think that this view of my father's is a little sentimental and also, perhaps, insulting to Gleason. I personally believe that he knew everything that would happen. One day the proof of my theory may be discovered. Certainly there are in existence some personal papers, and I firmly believe that these papers will show that Gleason knew exactly what would happen.

We had been so overcome by the model of the town that we hadn't noticed what was the most remarkable thing of all. Not only had Gleason built the houses and the shops of our town, he had also peopled it. As we tip-toed into the town we suddenly found ourselves. "Look," I said to Mr. Dyer, "there you are."

And there he was, standing in front of his shop in his apron. As I bent down to examine the tiny figure I was staggered by the look on its face. The modeling was crude, the paintwork was sloppy, and the face a little too white, but the expression was absolutely perfect: those pursed, quizzical lips and the eyebrows lifted high. It was Mr. Dyer and no one else on earth.

And there beside Mr. Dyer was my father, squatting on the footpath and gazing lovingly at Mr. Dyer's bicycle's gears, his face marked with grease and hope.

And there was I, back at the filling station, leaning against a petrol pump in an American pose and talking to Brian Sparrow who was amusing me with his clownish antics.

Phonsey Joy standing beside his hearse. Mr. Dixon sitting inside his hardware store. Everyone I knew was there in that tiny town. If they were not in the streets or in their backyards they were inside their houses, and it didn't take very long to discover that you could lift off the roofs and peer inside.

We tip-toed around the streets peeping into each other's windows, lifting off each other's roofs, admiring each other's gardens, and, while we did it, Mrs. Gleason slipped silently away down the hill towards Mason's Lane. She spoke to nobody and nobody spoke to her.

I confess that I was the one who took the roof from Cavanagh's house. So I was the one who found Mrs. Cavanagh in bed with young Craigie Evans.

I stood there for a long time, hardly knowing what I was seeing. I stared at the pair of them for a long, long time. And when I finally knew what I was seeing I felt such an incredible mixture of jealousy and guilt and wonder that I didn't know what to do with the roof.

Eventually it was Phonsey Joy who took the roof from my hands and placed it carefully back on the house, much, I imagine, as he would have placed the lid on a coffin. By then other people had seen what I had seen and the word passed around very quickly.

And then we all stood around in little groups and regarded the model town with what could only have been fear. If Gleason knew about Mrs. Cavanagh and Craigie Evans (and no one else had), what other things might he know? Those who hadn't seen themselves yet in the town began to look a little nervous and were unsure of whether to look for themselves or not. We gazed silently at the roofs and felt mistrustful and guilty.

We all walked down the hill then, very quietly, the way people walk away from a funeral, listening only to the crunch of the gravel under our feet while the women had trouble with their high-heeled shoes.

The next day a special meeting of the shire council passed a motion calling on Mrs. Gleason to destroy the model town on the grounds that it contravened building regulations.

It is unfortunate that this order wasn't carried out before the city newspapers found out. Before another day had gone by the government had stepped in.

The model town and its model occupants were to be preserved. The minister for tourism came in a large black car and made a speech to us in the football pavilion. We sat on the high, tiered seats eating potato chips while he stood against the fence and talked to us. We couldn't hear him very well, but we heard enough. He called the model town a work of art and we stared at him grimly. He said it would be an invaluable tourist attraction. He said tourists would come from everywhere to see the model town. We would be famous. Our businesses would flourish. There would be work for guides and interpreters and caretakers and taxi drivers and people selling soft drinks and ice creams.

The Americans would come, he said. They would visit our town in buses and in cars and on the train. They would take photographs and bring wallets bulging with dollars. American dollars.

We looked at the minister mistrustfully, wondering if he knew about Mrs. Cavanagh, and he must have seen the look because he said that certain controversial items would be removed, had already been removed. We shifted in our seats, like you do when a particularly tense part of a film has come to its climax, and then we relaxed and listened to what the minister had to say. And we all began, once more, to dream our American Dreams.

We saw our big smooth cars cruising through cities with bright lights. We entered expensive night clubs and danced till dawn. We made love to women like Kim Novak and men like Rock Hudson. We drank cocktails. We gazed lazily into refrigerators filled with food and prepared ourselves lavish midnight snacks which we ate while we watched huge television sets on which we would be able to see American movies free of charge and forever.

The minister, like someone from our American Dreams, reentered his large black car and cruised slowly from our humble sportsground, and the newspaper men arrived and swarmed over the pavilion with their cameras and notebooks. They took photographs of us and photographs of the models up on Bald Hill. And the next day we were all over the newspapers.

The photographs of the model people side by side with photographs of the real people. And our names and ages and what we did were all printed there in black and white.

They interviewed Mrs. Gleason but she said nothing of interest. She said the model town had been her husband's hobby.

We all felt good now. It was very pleasant to have your photograph in the paper. And, once more, we changed our opinion of Gleason. The shire council held another meeting and named the dirt track up Bald Hill "Gleason Avenue." Then we all went home and waited for the Americans we had been promised.

It didn't take long for them to come, although at the time it seemed an eternity, and we spent six long months doing nothing more with our lives than waiting for the Americans.

Well, they did come. And let me tell you how it has all worked out for us.

The Americans arrive every day in buses and cars and sometimes the younger ones come on the train. There is now a small airstrip out near the Parwan cemetery and they also arrive there, in small aeroplanes. Phonsey Joy drives them to the cemetery where they look at Gleason's grave and then up to Bald Hill and then down to the town. He is doing very well from it all. It is good to see someone doing well from it. Phonsey is becoming a big man in town and is on the shire council.

On Bald Hill there are half a dozen telescopes through which the Americans can spy on the town and reassure themselves that it is the same down there as it is on Bald Hill. Herb Gravney sells them ice creams and soft drinks and extra film for their cameras. He is another one who is doing well. He bought the whole model from Mrs. Gleason and charges five American dollars admission. Herb is on the council now too. He's doing very well for himself. He sells them the film so they can take photographs of the houses and the model people and so they can come down to the town with their special maps and hunt out the real people.

To tell the truth most of us are pretty sick of the game. They come looking for my father and ask him to stare at the gears of Dyer's bicycle. I watch my father cross the street slowly, his head hung low. He doesn't greet the Americans any more. He doesn't ask them questions about colour television or Washington, D.C. He kneels on the footpath in front of Dyer's bike. They stand around him. Often they remember the model incorrectly and try to get my father to pose in the wrong way. Originally he argued with them, but now he argues no more. He does what they ask. They push him this way and that and worry about the expression on his face which is no longer what it was.

Then I know they will come to find me. I am next on the map. I am very popular for some reason. They come in search of me and my petrol pump as they have done for four years now. I do not await them eagerly because I know, before they reach me, that they will be disappointed.

"But this is not the boy."

"Yes," says Phonsey, "this is him alright." And he gets me to show them my certificate.

They examine the certificate suspiciously, feeling the paper as if it might be a clever forgery. "No," they declare. (Americans are so confident.) "No," they shake their heads, "this is not the real boy. The real boy is younger."

"He's older now. He used to be younger." Phonsey looks weary when he tells them. He can afford to look weary.

The Americans peer at my face closely. "It's a different boy."

But finally they get their cameras out. I stand sullenly and try to look amused as I did once. Gleason saw me looking amused but I can no longer remember how it felt. I was looking at Brian Sparrow. But Brian is also tired. He finds it difficult to do his clownish antics and to the Americans his little act isn't funny. They prefer the model. I watch him sadly, sorry that he must perform for such an unsympathetic audience.

The Americans pay one dollar for the right to take our photographs. Having paid the money they are worried about being cheated. They spend their time being disappointed and I spend my time feeling guilty that I have somehow let them down by growing older and sadder.

After You Read

Critical Reading

1. The author tells this story from the **point of view** of a young man. Why does the author use this point of view? What effects does this point of view have on the readers?

2. Consider the **setting** (the place and the time). In what ways does this setting contribute to the plot of the story?

3. What **conflict** do the townspeople have with the miniature town in the story? Is this an internal or external conflict? Explain your answer and support it with details from the story.

Literary Lens: Connotation

The phrase "American Dream" is used several times in the story. Use a chart like the one below to analyze the connotations of this popular phrase. Identify two or more quotations from the story that reference this idea. Then describe what you think the connotative meaning is for each quotation.

Quotation	Connotative Meaning

Focus on Research: Consider Multiple Viewpoints

This story can be seen as a critique of the American Dream. Gather two or three editorials that focus on some aspect of American life. Choose newspapers or magazines published in countries other than the United States. Summarize the viewpoints of the articles. With a partner, discuss any examples of bias or faulty reasoning in the articles, for example, overgeneralizations or faulty analogies.

A Consumer's Report

Peter Porter

Before You Read

Peter Porter (1929–2010) left his native Australia to see England. He settled there, becoming an advertising copywriter. After publishing several volumes of poetry, he gave up the advertising world to become a full-time poet.

World Context

Porter is known for his commentary on modern consumer-oriented culture.

 LITERARY LENS Identify examples of verbal **irony** in the following poem.

The name of the product I tested is *Life*,
I have completed the form you sent me
and understand that my answers are confidential.

I had it as a gift,
I didn't feel much while using it,   5
in fact I think I'd have liked to be more excited.
It seemed gentle on the hands
but left an embarrassing deposit behind.
It was not economical
and I have used much more than I thought   10
(I suppose I have about half left
but it's difficult to tell)—
although the instructions are fairly large
there are so many of them
I don't know which to follow, especially   15

as they seem to contradict each other.
I'm not sure such a thing
should be put in the way of children—
It's difficult to think of a purpose
for it. One of my friends says   20
it's just to keep its maker in a job.
Also the price is much too high.
Things are piling up so fast,
after all, the world got by
for a thousand million years   25
without this, do we need it now?
(Incidentally, please ask your man
to stop calling me "the respondent,"
I don't like the sound of it.)
There seems to be a lot of different labels,   30
sizes and colours should be uniform,
the shape is awkward, it's waterproof
but not heat resistant, it doesn't keep
yet it's very difficult to get rid of:
whenever they make it cheaper they seem   35
to put less in—if you say you don't
want it, then it's delivered anyway.
I'd agree it's a popular product,
it's got into the language; people
even say they're on the side of it.   40
Personally I think it's overdone,
a small thing people are ready
to behave badly about. I think
we should take it for granted. If its
experts are called philosophers or market   45
researchers or historians, we shouldn't
care. We are the consumers and the last
law makers. So finally, I'd buy it.
But the question of a "best buy"
I'd like to leave until I get   50
the competitive product you said you'd send.

After You Read

Critical Reading

1. The author chooses words and phrases that could be considered "advertising language." Identify two or more examples of **word choice** that you think are advertising language. How does the word choice create humor?

2. In this poem, the speaker **juxtaposes** life alongside a consumer report. Why do you think the author chose to do this?

3. The speaker uses several common **figures of speech** in this poem, but uses them in a new way by applying them to the topic of life. Identify two or more figures of speech, and consider what **mood** these figures of speech reveal.

Literary Lens: Irony

Irony is the recognition and heightening of the difference between expectations and reality. The types of irony are **situational irony**, **dramatic irony**, and **verbal irony**. Cite two or more examples of irony in the poem. Identify the type of irony and then explain what makes the quotation ironic.

Quotation	Situational, Dramatic, or Verbal	Explanation

Focus on Research: Create a Visual Representation

Conduct research into the life of Peter Porter. As you conduct this research, identify when you encounter gaps in the information. For example, you might find information about when he was born and then later information about his adult success as an author, which means you are missing information about his education. When you encounter these gaps, change the focus of your research to fill in these gaps. When you are done, create a timeline showing major dates and events from Porter's life.

A Way of Talking

Patricia Grace

Before You Read

Patricia Grace (1937–) was born into the Maori culture. She often writes about relationships between New Zealand's indigenous Maoris and relative newcomers from Europe and Australia. She uses Maori dialect to emphasize her own traditions. Her collection of short stories, *Waiariki*, was the first ever published by a Maori female writer.

World Context

Though first to inhabit the islands of New Zealand, the Maori people make up only 8 percent of the population. During the 19th century, they were unable to fight off the invading Europeans and Australians. In a country dominated by whites, the Maoris struggle to preserve their culture.

 LITERARY LENS As you read, watch for the use of **dialect**, or distinctive speech patterns of people from a certain group or region.

Rose came back yesterday; we went down to the bus to meet her. She's just the same as ever Rose. Talks all the time flat out and makes us laugh with her way of talking. On the way home we kept saying, "E Rohe, you're just the same as ever." It's good having my sister back and knowing she hasn't changed. Rose is the hard-case one in the family, the kamakama[1] one, and the one with the brains.

Last night we stayed up talking till all hours, even Dad and Nanny who usually go to bed after tea. Rose made us laugh telling about the people she knows, and taking off professor this and professor that from varsity. Nanny, Mum, and I had tears running down from laughing; e ta Rose we laughed all night.

At last Nanny got out of her chair and said, "Time for sleeping. The mouths steal the time of the eyes." That's the lovely way she has of talking, Nanny, when she

---

1 **kamakama:** Maori for "eager" or "quick"

speaks in English. So we went to bed and Rose and I kept our mouths going for another hour or so before falling asleep.

This morning I said to Rose that we'd better go and get her measured for the dress up at Mrs. Frazer's. Rose wanted to wait a day or two but I reminded her the wedding was only two weeks away and that Mrs. Frazer had three frocks to finish.

"Who's Mrs. Frazer anyway," she asked. Then I remembered Rose hadn't met these neighbours though they'd been in the district a few years. Rose had been away at school.

"She's a dressmaker," I looked for words. "She's nice."

"What sort of nice?" asked Rose.

"Rose, don't you say anything funny when we go up there," I said. I know Rose, she's smart. "Don't you get smart." I'm older than Rose but she's the one that speaks out when something doesn't please her. Mum used to say, Rohe you've got the brains but you look to your sister for the sense. I started to feel funny about taking Rose up to Jane Frazer's because Jane often says the wrong thing without knowing.

We got our work done, had a bath and changed, and when Dad came back from the shed we took the station-wagon to drive over to Jane's. Before we left we called out to Mum, "Don't forget to make us a Maori bread for when we get back."

"What's wrong with your own hands," Mum said, but she was only joking. Always when one of us comes home one of the first things she does is make a big Maori bread.

Rose made a good impression with her kamakama ways, and Jane's two nuisance kids took a liking to her straight away. They kept jumping up and down on the sofa to get Rose's attention and I kept thinking what a waste of a good sofa it was, what a waste of a good house for those two nuisance things. I hope when I have kids they won't be so hoha.

I was pleased about Jane and Rose. Jane was asking Rose all sorts of questions about her life in Auckland. About varsity and did Rose join in the marches and demonstrations. Then they went on to talking about fashions and social life in the city, and Jane seemed deeply interested. Almost as though she was jealous of Rose and the way she lived, as though she felt Rose had something better than a lovely house and clothes and everything she needed to make life good for her. I was pleased to see that Jane liked my sister so much, and proud of my sister and her entertaining and friendly ways.

Jane made a cup of coffee when she'd finished measuring Rose for the frock, then packed the two kids outside with a piece of chocolate cake each.

We were sitting having coffee when we heard a truck turn in at the bottom of Frazer's drive.

Jane said, "That's Alan. He's been down the road getting the Maoris for scrub cutting."

I felt my face get hot. I was angry. At the same time I was hoping Rose would let the remark pass. I tried hard to think of something to say to cover Jane's words though I'd hardly said a thing all morning. But my tongue seemed to thicken and all I could think of was Rohe don't.

Rose was calm. Not all red and flustered like me. She took a big pull on the cigarette she had lit, squinted her eyes up and blew the smoke out gently. I knew something was coming.

"Don't they have names?"

"What. Who?" Jane was surprised and her face was getting pink.

"The people from down the road whom your husband is employing to cut scrub." Rose the stink thing, she was talking all Pakehafied.[2]

"I don't know any of their names."

I was glaring at Rose because I wanted her to stop but she was avoiding my looks and pretending to concentrate on her cigarette.

"Do they know yours?"

"Mine?"

"Your name."

"Well . . . Yes."

"Yet you have never bothered to find out their names or to wonder whether or not they have any."

The silence seemed to bang around in my head for ages and ages. Then I think Jane muttered something about difficulty, but that touchy sister of mine stood up and said, "Come on Hera." And I with my red face and shut mouth followed her out to the station wagon without a goodbye or anything.

I was so wild with Rose. I was wild. I was determined to blow her up about what she had done, I was determined. But now that we were alone together I couldn't think what to say. Instead I felt an awful big sulk coming on. It has always been my trouble, sulking. Whenever I don't feel sure about something I go into a big fat sulk. We had a teacher at school who used to say to some of us girls, "Speak, don't sulk." She'd say, "You only sulk because you haven't learned how and when to say your minds."

She was right that teacher, yet here I am a young woman about to be married and haven't learned yet how to get the words out. Dad used to say to me, "Look out girlie, you'll stand on your lip."

---

2 **Pakehafied:** like a white person; Pakeha is the Maori term for a white person

At last I said, "Rose, you're a stink thing." Tears were on the way. "Gee Rohe, you made me embarrassed." Then Rose said, "Don't worry Honey she's got a thick hide."

These words of Rose's took me by surprise and I realised something about Rose then. What she said made all my anger go away and I felt very sad because it's not our way of talking to each other. Usually we'd say, "Never mind Sis," if we wanted something to be forgotten. But when Rose said, "Don't worry Honey she's got a thick hide," it made her seem a lot older than me, and tougher, and as though she knew much more than me about the world. It made me realise too that underneath her jolly and forthright ways Rose is very hurt. I remembered back to when we were both little and Rose used to play up at school if she didn't like the teacher. She'd get smart and I used to be ashamed and tell Mum on her when we got home, because although she had the brains I was always the well behaved one.

Rose was speaking to me in a new way now. It made me feel sorry for her and for myself. All my life I had been sitting back and letting her do the objecting. Not only me, but Mum and Dad and the rest of the family too. All of us too scared to make known when we had been hurt or slighted. And how can the likes of Jane know when we go round pretending all is well. How can Jane know us?

But then I tried to put another thought into words. I said to Rose, "We do it too. We say, 'the Pakeha doctor,' or 'the Pakeha at the post office,' and sometimes we mean it in a bad way."

"Except that we talk like this to each other only. It's not so much what is said, but when and where and in whose presence. Besides, you and I don't speak in this way now, not since we were little. It's the older ones: Mum, Dad, Nanny who have this habit."

Then Rose said something else. "Jane Frazer will still want to be your friend and mine in spite of my embarrassing her today; we're in the fashion."

"What do you mean?"

"It's fashionable for a Pakeha to have a Maori for a friend." Suddenly Rose grinned. Then I heard Jane's voice coming out of that Rohe's mouth and felt a grin of my own coming. "I have friends who are Maoris. They're lovely people. The eldest girl was married recently and I did the frocks. The other girl is at varsity. They're all so *friendly* and so *natural* and their house is absolutely *spotless.*"

I stopped the wagon in the drive and when we'd got out Rose started strutting up the path. I saw Jane's way of walking and felt a giggle coming on. Rose walked up Mum's scrubbed steps, "Absolutely spotless." She left

her shoes in the porch and bounced into the kitchen. "What did I tell you? Absolutely spotless. And a friendly natural woman taking new bread from the oven."

Mum looked at Rose then at me. "What have you two been up to? Rohe I hope you behaved yourself at that Pakeha place?" But Rose was setting the table. At the sight of Mum's bread she'd forgotten all about Jane and the events of the morning.

When Dad, Heke, and Matiu came in for lunch, Rose, Mum, Nanny and I were already into the bread and the big bowl of hot corn.

"E ta," Dad said. "Let your hardworking father and your two hardworking brothers starve. Eat up."

"The bread's terrible. You men better go down to the shop and get you a shop bread," said Rose.

"Be the day," said Heke.

"Come on my fat Rohe. Move over and make room for your Daddy. Come on my baby shift over."

Dad squeezed himself round behind the table next to Rose. He picked up the bread Rose had buttered for herself and started eating. "The bread's terrible all right," he said. Then Mat and Heke started going on about how awful the corn was and who cooked it and who grew it, who watered it all summer and who pulled out the weeds.

So I joined in the carryings on and forgot about Rose and Jane for the meantime. But I'm not leaving it at that. I'll find some way of letting Rose know I understand and I know it will be difficult for me because I'm not clever the way she is. I can't say things the same and I've never learnt to stick up for myself.

But my sister won't have to be alone again. I'll let her know that.

After You Read

Critical Reading

1. In the first paragraph, the speaker says that her sister Rose has a "way of talking." What are the different ways of talking that Rose has? What does the story reveal about Rose's ways of talking?

2. The author describes the speaker using several **sensory details** over the course of the story. What do these details reveal about the speaker? Cite examples of sensory details in your answer.

3. Identify an **internal conflict** and an **external conflict** depicted in the story. How do these conflicts reveal the theme of the story?

4. Rose tells the narrator that it is "fashionable" for Pakehas (whites) to have Maoris for friends. Explain both the **connotative** and **denotative** meanings of the word "fashionable" in this context. Support your answers with details from the story.

Literary Lens: Dialect

Dialect is a regional variation of speech that includes differences in pronunciation, vocabulary, and grammar. Quote several examples of dialect from the story. For each example, infer how the use of dialect reveals the characters, the mood, or the conflict in the story. Then consider how the author's choice to use dialect affected the story overall.

Examples of dialect (Quotation from the story)	How does this reveal the characters, mood, or conflict?
How does the use of dialogue impact the story?	

Focus on Research: Revise for Word Choice and Sentence Structure

Find and read three or more sources about the Maori people. Write a five- to seven-sentence summary of the information you learn from these sources. Then exchange your summary with a partner. Identify any unclear or overused words in your partner's writing. Also make suggestions to improve sentence structure and variety. For example, you may find simple sentences that would be better written as a compound sentence with a conjunction that reveals relationships between details. Revise your paragraph according to your partner's suggestions.

East Asia and the Pacific Rim

Unit Review

Key Ideas and Details

1. Consider the autobiography *From Emperor to Citizen* and the poem "An Ancient Temple." What do you think the last emperor of China, Piu Yi, would think of the poem "An Ancient Temple"? Consider the **tone**, or attitude, both he and the speaker of the poem convey about the old days in China.

2. Look at the couples shown in the stories "The Tall Woman and Her Short Husband," "Tokyo," "Swaddling Clothes," and "Inem." What do you think contributes to the success or failure of their relationships? Look at the characters' personalities and social backgrounds and discuss how those things may influence them.

3. War has had a profound effect on many of the characters in these selections. Compare the way war is used as a theme in "Cranes," "Thoughts of Hanoi," "Tokyo," and "The Shadow." Think about the attitude the writers seem to convey about this subject and the variety of ways in which they explore human beings reacting to war.

Craft and Structure

4. Consider the use of **time** in many of the selections in this unit, for example, in Ha Jin's "Saboteur," Hayashi's "Tokyo," Toer's "Inem," and Carey's "American Dreams." Do these authors have time pass rapidly or slowly? Do they place all the actions and events in a single moment in time or in several different moments? Which selections use time differently and which use time similarly?

5. Consider all of the selections from the Pacific Rim countries of Australia and New Zealand. Are there any literary techniques that they share in common, such as **theme, syntax, figurative language,** or **tone**?

6. In "A Consumer's Report," Peter Porter makes fun of advertising language. Find three or four examples of language from print advertisements and write an analysis of the **word choice**. Do you see any claims the ad writer probably cannot support? Explain.

Integration of Knowledge and Ideas

7. The narrator in "A Way of Talking" says the character Rose has a way of talking—meaning both that sometimes Rose uses specific word choices or dialect and also that sometimes Rose "speaks out when something doesn't please her" (page 627). Consider someone you know who has a unique way of talking. This might mean that the person has a way of speaking in public or that the person uses dialect or uses certain words or language. The person can be a friend, family member, or even yourself. Write a letter to this person describing what you have observed and admire about this person's unique way of speaking.

Research Projects

Examine Arguments

Divide into two teams, affirmative and negative, and debate one of the following topics.

Topic 1: Royalty

Should royalty be abolished along with all other systems of hereditary privilege? Yes or no? Why or why not?

Topic 2: Arranged Marriages

Are arranged marriages a good way for people to find a spouse? Yes or no? Why or why not?

After the debate, examine the arguments presented during the debate for the following types of faulty reasoning: strawman, false dilemma, faulty analogies, and nonsequitur.

Multimedia Project

Find several sources on some aspect of East Asian art or music that interests you. Conduct research on the history of the art form and develop a multimedia presentation that includes text, images, video, and sound. Include a slide with your works cited information. Share your presentation with the class.

Identify Gaps in Research

Work with a partner to research the history of the novel in either Japan or China. Together, make a timeline showing the information you find. Then identify gaps in the information in your timeline and conduct research to try to find information to fill in these gaps.

Publishing a Research Report

Korea, Vietnam, China, New Zealand, and other countries represented in this unit have suffered painful political or cultural divisions. Write a three-page paper comparing and contrasting how three or four works from this unit portray the idea of division. Review your work to make sure your paper is appropriate for your audience (your fellow students). Consider adding images, such as photographs, timelines, charts, graphs, or maps to better engage your audience. Then publish your paper on an appropriate platform, such as a class website or other shared site. Invite your classmates to comment on your paper and respond to their comments.

Cultural Reflection

Pick one or more characters from this unit who expressed viewpoints on topics that differ from your own. Then write in your journal about these characters. Address the differences in your viewpoints and also describe your experience of reading about a viewpoint that is different from your own. Analyze how reading about a different viewpoint affected your way of seeing the world.

Research Handbook

Some investigations begin with questions that are literally a matter of life and death. *Who killed this murder victim? How can we cure this disease?* Others are born from an observation. *Why does this author write so much about orphaned children?* Some are sparked by your teacher's warning. *"Your research papers are due . . . ."*

Whatever your question, research skills can help you find information about any topic, from car stereos to the drum sounds in African poetry. But locating sources is just the beginning. Of course many sources-- perhaps too many sources--can be found online. There are over 1.5 billion websites on the Internet today. However, not all of these sites are reliable. It takes time to sort through what is real, what is fake, and what is true.

The vast amount of information available can feel overwhelming. But you can tame information overload. The handbook section on **Finding Information** will help you locate sources that are relevant to your topic. **Sharing Information** will help you select the best information and organize it so your audience finds it easy to understand.

Finding Information

What is my research topic?

If "a journey of a thousand miles begins with a single step," a research project begins with a single topic. The topic may be assigned by your teacher, or you may be allowed to research any subject that interests you. In either case, you need to decide what you're trying to find out about before you begin your research. Otherwise, you'll be wandering through the information jungle without a compass.

Suppose you're assigned to write about magic realism in Latin American literature. "I don't even know what magic realism is," you might mutter. There's your first question: *What is magic realism?* "Aren't the ideas of *magic* and *realism* contradictory?" you grumble. There's a second question: *How are these contradictions handled by Latin American authors?* That brings up another question: *Which Latin American authors have I read?* As you think about the different authors you've studied, you realize that you enjoyed one author more than all the others. Now you're starting to see how you might make this assigned topic fit your interests.

Suppose that you can choose any topic related to world literature. You may already have a question you want to research. Perhaps you're curious about diaries kept during the Holocaust, or you want to read more contemporary Arabic stories. On the other hand, you may find it hard to think of a topic. Looking over this book's Table of Contents or each unit's list of research projects might give you some ideas. You can also start with yourself instead of with the literature. For example, as you sit at your desk trying to think of a topic, you might be listening to music. As you start to tap out the rhythm to a song, you remember that Léopold Sédar Senghor wanted his poems to capture the complex rhythms of African music. As you start to wonder about the relationship between drums and Senghor's poetry, you realize that your interests have led you to a topic.

Finding a Topic	
Assigned Topic	**Self-Chosen Topic**
• Analyze key words in the topic • Identify what you already know • Relate the topic to your interests	• Think about your questions or interests • Make a list of topics you'd like to know more about • Choose a topic you want to explore

What questions do I have about my topic?

A saying among researchers and writers is that asking the right question is 90 percent of the answer. Ninety percent? Isn't that exaggerating the importance of questions? You'll have a chance to see for yourself as you do your research.

Now is a good time to start keeping track of your questions about your topic. You can use a log or research journal to record your initial questions and those that arise as you learn more about a topic. Your question log might look something like the one on the next page.

```
┌─────────────────────────────────────────────────────────────────────┐
│  Name                                                   Class, Period │
│                                                                       │
│                          Question Log                                 │
│                                                                       │
│  Topic: traditional African rhythms in Léopold Sédar Senghor's poems  │
│                                                                       │
│  Date     The first questions that come to my mind about this topic are │
│           What are some traditional African rhythms?                  │
│           How does Senghor use traditional rhythms?                   │
│           Why does he include them in his poems?                      │
│           What instruments does he use besides drums?                 │
│           What poems could I use for examples?                        │
│                                                                       │
└─────────────────────────────────────────────────────────────────────┘
```

At this point, the research questions are pretty broad. So it is good to start with sources that provide general background about the topic, such as encyclopedia articles or *Twentieth Century Literary Criticism*. One critic mentions that Senghor was influenced by the griots, or storytellers, the poet heard as a child. This helps answer the question about traditional African rhythms. However, you might have new questions.

```
┌─────────────────────────────────────────────────────────────────────┐
│  Jan 16    What are griots?                                           │
│            What rhythms do griots use in their stories?               │
│            How did the stories Senghor heard as a child shape his poetry? │
│                                                                       │
└─────────────────────────────────────────────────────────────────────┘
```

At the beginning of your research, each answer you find is likely to suggest more questions. These questions will give you new directions to explore. At the same time, they keep you from getting lost and disoriented given the vast amount of information that exists. You will probably learn that Senghor was the first president of Senegal. This is a significant achievement, but it doesn't relate to any of your questions. So you look for more information on griots instead of focusing on Senghor's political career.

But what if the new questions are more interesting than the original ones? Many people find that new questions suggest a whole new topic. That's why your teacher may want to go over your questions with you. At the beginning of your research process, it's easy to change topics. You just need to be sure that your new subject will fulfill the assignment. The more time and effort you have invested in a topic, the more important it is to talk to your teacher before changing your focus.

Once you feel that you're familiar with the basic background information about your subject, review your questions. Which are the most interesting? Most important? Most likely to be questions your audience will have too? Choose ten or so questions to be the focus of your research. These questions will help you and your teacher track your progress as you dig more deeply.

Where do I find information?

The best place to start your research depends on two things: the topic and the assignment. To research a current topic, you might start with the Internet. However, the Internet doesn't contain all information that is available and online search tools often do not even search all the information available online. If you're looking for reference books or back issues of magazines, you'll find more resources from your school or local library. Some of these resources may be available in print at the media center. However, digital copies of resources are often available through an online database. Many online databases are not free; your media center pays for a subscription to them, so to access them, you may need a password.

The assignment might also specify that you use particular kinds of resources, such as works of literary criticism or personal interviews. The chart on the next page shows some specialized resources for world literature and gives examples of different kinds of sources that your teacher might require. For example, say your teacher wants you to use at least two primary sources. *Primary sources* are firsthand information about a topic, such as eyewitness accounts, diaries, or historical documents. *Secondary sources* are materials based on firsthand sources, such as reference works and biographies. When you research literature, the works you study are considered primary sources. Critics' comments are secondary sources.

Type of Information	Best Place to Find
A quick overview of a subject	• General encyclopedias, such as *Encyclopaedia Britannica* • Specialized encyclopedias, such as *Cassell's Encyclopedia of World Literature*
Biographical information	• Reference works such as *Current Biography* or *Who's Who, International Edition* • Biography of one author (see your library catalog or a bookseller's website)
Critics' comments	• Reference series such as *Contemporary Authors, Poetry Criticism,* and *Contemporary Literary Criticism* • Reviews (*Book Review Digest* or *Book Review Index*) • The Internet Public Library • *New York Times Book Review*
Geographical information	• Atlases, such as *The Columbia Lippincott Gazetteer of the World* • The CIA's *World Factbook*
Literary terms and traditions	• Specialized reference works such as *A Handbook to Literature* and *Merriam-Webster's Encyclopedia of Literature*
Literary works	• *Granger's Index to Poetry* • *Play Index* • *Short Story Index*
News items or magazine articles	• *Readers' Guide to Periodical Literature* • Electronic databases
People to interview	• Acquaintances with firsthand experience of your subject • People who teach or write about your subject • Members of organizations related to your subject (see Gale's *Encyclopedia of Associations*)
Statistics	• Almanacs, such as *Information Please* • *International Index to Statistics*
Websites	• General search engines • Search engines specialized by subject

One important resource isn't on the chart: your public librarian or media center specialist. These expert guides can suggest sources and shortcuts you might not think of on your own. Also, they can help you request materials from other libraries through interlibrary loan.

What if I have trouble locating information?

Remember Juliet's question to Romeo: "What's in a name?" She and her beloved were from two rival families, but she didn't see why the names Capulet and Montague should keep them apart. When you're searching for information, Juliet's question is a good one to keep in mind. Digital information, whether in library catalogs or on the Internet, is retrieved by using *keywords* that describe your topic.

For example, you might decide to track down the quotation from George Herbert that begins *The Book of Sand.* Generally, it is best to be as specific as possible when using keywords. Searching for *george herbert* will yield many general sources on the writer, but you will have difficulty finding anything related to *The Book of Sand.* Typing in *george herbert book of sand quotation* results in a PDF of the first few pages of the book—with the quotation at the top. Another option is to find a preview of the book in order to find the opening quotation.

Try these strategies for finding information:

1. When using an online search engine, vary your keywords. If you don't find anything under *Jamaican literature,* try a word or phrase that has a similar meaning, such as *Caribbean literature.*
2. Try using Boolean operators (*and, or, not*) with your keywords to get closer to the results you need.
3. Try using a different search engine or a library research tool, such as JSTOR or EBSCOHOST.

How do I sort through this information?

It is possible to have too much information. People who have to deal with too much unorganized information suffer from what some have called "information fatigue syndrome."

One way to reduce information fatigue is to use a general-to-specific search strategy. Start by reading sources that give a broad overview of your topic. Then look for sources that provide more in-depth answers to your research questions. If several sources overlap, read them together and take notes from the most complete source first. For example, perhaps one of your sources contains much more about griots than the others. Since you have taken notes from that one first, all you have to do for the rest is record any new details you find.

Another way to reduce information fatigue is to be selective. "Junk information" is as common as junk food, but more dangerous. Eating one candy bar is not going to totally destroy your health. However, using even one biased or inaccurate source can ruin the credibility of your research project. You can use these criteria to screen your sources.

Criteria for Judging Sources

Timeliness	Is the information in this source outdated?
Completeness/ Accuracy	Does this source cover the topic thoroughly? How does information in this source compare to other sources on this topic?
Bias	Is this source objective? • Does the source stand to profit from taking this position (such as in a laboratory hired by a drug company to conduct pharmaceutical tests)? • Does this source include only evidence favorable to one side of a controversy? • Does this source reflect the views of a particular time in history, such as empire builders' attitudes toward native peoples?
Credibility	What evidence do I have that this source is knowledgeable and believable? • academic or professional credentials • documentation, such as lists of references • recognition as an authority

How you apply these criteria will depend on your topic. For example, Japanese haiku were first written in the 16th century, so new information is unlikely to replace what we already know about their origins. However, novels have not been an important part of Africa's literary tradition until recently. As African novelists continue to experiment with the genre, sources about the novel in African literature will quickly become outdated.

Judging credibility is especially important when using resources from the Internet. A search for Chinua Achebe's novel *Things Fall Apart* could turn up everything from a college student's book report to the works of W. B. Yeats (the poet who coined the title phrase) to a scholar's Chinua Achebe website. Sites associated with universities, libraries, and professional associations are generally more trustworthy than those created by individuals. Individuals' sites are more credible if they

- tell you who created the site and when it was last updated.

- are created by someone with expert knowledge.

- provide thorough coverage of the topic, with suggestions about finding additional information.

- are included in other sites' collections of recommended links.

How do I keep track of my sources?

The easiest way to keep track of your sources is to write information about each source on a 3" x 5" index card or in a computer file you can save. Record the author's name and publication information before you take a single note. Then you won't have to retrace your steps when you're trying to credit the sources you used for your presentation or paper.

What information do you need? Examples of how to cite some commonly used sources are shown below. If your teacher wants to follow the Modern Language Association (MLA) style, you can find more detailed examples in guides like the *MLA Handbook for Writers of Research Papers* or from MLA's online website. Styles change often so consult these guides before beginning your paper.

Source	Example of MLA Works Cited
Print book	Mahfouz, Naguib. *Karak Café.* Translated by Roger Allen. American University Press, 2007.
Print article	Simpson, Mona. "A Quiet Genius." *Atlantic Monthly,* Dec. 2001, pp. 126–136.

Source	Example of MLA Works Cited
Article from an online database	Ross, Robert L. "Seeking and Maintaining Balance: Rohinton Mistry's Fiction." *World Literature Today,* vol. 82, no. 6, April 2010, pp. 4–5. *EBSCO.* doi:10.1002/tox.20155. Accessed 29 Apr. 2020.
Online text	Le Clézio, Jean-Marie Gustave. "In the Forest of Paradoxes." *NobelPrize.org,* 7 Dec. 2008. www.nobelprize. org/prizes/literature/2008/clezio/25790-jean-marie-gustave-le-clezio-nobel-lecture-2008/. Accessed 20 April 2020.
Article in an online reference work	Robinson, W. Andrew. "Rabindranath Tagore." *The Encyclopedia Britannica.* www.britannica.com/biography/Rabindranath-Tagore. Accessed 30 Jan. 2020.
A page from a website	"Timeline." *Isabel Allende.* www.isabelallende.com/en/timeline#2019. Accessed 29 Feb. 2020.

It's a good idea to cut and paste links to your online sources into a computer file, along with the date you first accessed the information. As you see above, MLA format requires you to include an access date for websites. If you are working on your own computer, use the Bookmark function in your web browser to create a record of all your project's sources. Many online sources also provide citation information at the end of the web page or on a Cite tab at the top of the page.

How do I take notes?

Unless your teacher requires you to take notes a certain way, you can choose from several efficient ways to record and organize the information you need. For any of them, you need to record information in small chunks and include all the information you need to identify the source and any direct quotations. Breaking information into small chunks makes it easier to organize and write your final product. Identifying sources will help you give them proper credit within the paper and in the Works Cited page at the end of your paper.

The time-honored way to take notes is on 3" x 5" index cards, with a key word to identify the source and the page number (if available) at the top.

Here is a note card with a summary of a speech by Chinese playwright Gao Xingjian.

Nobel site (pars. 14–16)

Accepting the Nobel Prize in 2000, Gao Xingjian said:

"Because of where I was born and the language I use, the cultural traditions of China naturally reside within me." While acknowledging that Chinese traditions shape his work, Gao Xingjian believes that literature transcends issues of national identity. "As the creator of linguistic art there is no need to stick on oneself a stock national label that can be easily recognized."

Some people prefer to take notes on a computer. Information from electronic databases and websites can either be downloaded or cut-and-pasted into a document. Downloaded PDFs can be marked by using the highlighting and comments tools. However, eventually, you will want to put your notes into a single computer file. Taking notes on a computer makes it easy to group similar information together and then to arrange it in a logical order. Just remember these two additional steps: include information to identify the source and paraphrase instead of plagiarizing.

How can I avoid plagiarizing?

Writers have a saying, "Easy writing is hard reading." When a writer just dumps words onto paper, the burden of sorting out what's important falls on the reader. That's not where it belongs, and your grade is likely to show it.

Ethical and legal issues are also involved. Since no one understands everything there is to know about a topic, you'll need to use sources. But conclusions you make about the subject and the way you organize the material should be your own. Using other people's words and ideas without acknowledging them is called *plagiarism.* Best-selling authors who are accused of plagiarizing can wind up in court, being sued by the authors whose work they have stolen. Many teachers run students' work though plagiarism checkers. When students are caught, penalties depend on the school. They range from loss of credit for the assignment to failing the course to expulsion.

The best way to avoid plagiarism is to use your own words or quotation marks. Using your own words for someone else's ideas is called *paraphrasing*. You still need to credit the source from which you took the information, but you do not need to use quotation marks. When you copy someone else's words, you must use quotation marks to acknowledge that you are using not just ideas but exact words. Quote only ideas that are exceptionally well stated or views that you want to make clear. For example, if you are trying to disprove a critic's opinion, quoting the opinion will help your audience follow your argument.

While there's no question about when you need to use quotation marks, the line between plagiarism and paraphrase isn't as clear. You may have no intention of stealing someone else's words. However, if your paraphrase is too close to the original, you may find yourself slipping into *unintentional plagiarism*. That means you've kept too much of the author's wording or organization. These examples illustrate acceptable and unacceptable uses of this passage from Ruth Behar's review of Isabel Allende's *Eva Luna* stories:

> "And of Clay Are We Created" was inspired by the 1985 avalanche in Colombia that buried a village in mud. Among those trapped was Omaira Sánchez, a thirteen-year-old girl who became the focus of attention of news-hungry photographers, journalists and television cameras that fixed their curious and helpless eyes on the girl who kept her faith in life as she bravely met her death. In that horrid audience of onlookers, there was one man, a reporter, who made the decision to stop observing Omaira from the lens of his camera and lay down in the mud to offer her what comfort he could as her heart and lungs collapsed. Allende, who was obsessed by "the torment of that poor child buried alive," wrote her story from the perspective of a woman—and she was that woman—"who watches the televised struggle of the man holding the girl" (15).

Unacceptable paraphrase • uses words from the source without quotation marks • is too close to source's organization	"And of Clay Are We Created" was inspired by a 1985 avalanche in Colombia. A thirteen-year-old girl trapped in the mud, Omaira Sánchez, became the focus of attention of news-hungry photographers. Allende, who was obsessed by "the torment of that poor child buried alive," wrote her story as if she were the woman watching the reporter who tried to help the girl (Behar 15).
Unacceptable paraphrase • does use quotation marks but is too close to source's organization	"And of Clay Are We Created" is based on an actual event, a 1985 avalanche that buried a thirteen-year-old Colombian girl in mud. The girl "became the focus of attention of news-hungry photographers" and a "horrid audience of onlookers" (Behar 15).
Acceptable paraphrase • quotes any exact words taken from source • does not depend on source's organization • shows why material is included	One reason that the relationship between Rolf Carlé and Azucena seems so real is that "And of Clay Are We Created" is based on an actual event, a 1985 Colombian avalanche that left thirteen-year-old Omaira Sánchez trapped in mud. As journalists provided live coverage of her ordeal, one reporter put down his camera to try to ease her death. Viewing "the torment of that poor child being buried alive" moved Allende to write a story told by a woman "who watches the televised struggle of the man holding the girl" (Behar 15).
Acceptable paraphrase • uses quotation marks • works quotation smoothly into the paper by identifying the source and showing why the quotation is used	Allende's inspiration for "And of Clay Are We Created" came from the ordeal of a thirteen-year-old Colombian girl trapped in the mud after an avalanche. Reviewer Ruth Behar describes how watching television coverage of the 1985 disaster affected the author. "Allende, who was obsessed by 'the torment of that poor child buried alive,' wrote her story from the perspective of a woman . . . 'who watches the televised struggle of the man holding the girl' " (15).

How can I avoid unintentional plagiarism?

These note-taking tips will help you avoid being too dependent on your sources:

- Take time to understand the material.
    - Look up difficult words.
    - Break long sentences down into shorter parts.
    - State the main point of what you have just read in your own words.
- Cover up the source as you take your notes. Then check to be sure that
    - your notes contain all the information you think you'll need.
    - your notes are accurate.
    - you've used quotation marks to set off any words you've taken directly from the source.
    - you've identified the source and location of the information (page numbers for printed material; paragraph numbers for Internet sources).

Sharing Information

You'll know it's time to stop searching when you've answered your research questions and are finding less and less new information. You now have the best answers available to your research questions.

How should I organize my ideas?

Sometimes your subject may practically organize itself. For example, you might want to do research on Sylvia Ashton-Warner, an innovative New Zealand educator who wrote three autobiographies about her writing career and her work with Maori children. Start by organizing your presentation chronologically, beginning with her earliest work.

If your topic doesn't suggest a logical organization, you can think about questions your audience might have and answer those questions in the order that will best help your audience understand the topic. For example, you might have researched South African writers in order to see how they respond to apartheid. Begin by defining *apartheid* and showing how this systematic separation of blacks and whites operated. This will prepare your audience to understand why South African writers want to expose the injustice of apartheid.

You can also start by writing a *thesis statement*—one sentence that sums up the point you're trying to prove. For example, after researching Chinua Achebe's *Things Fall Apart*, you might summarize your argument in this thesis statement: "Okonkwo's death represents not just the downfall of a village leader but the disintegration of an entire traditional culture." Then present the information you have gathered as proof of your thesis statement.

How should I credit sources in my paper or presentation?

Here's a general rule for citing sources: When in doubt, give credit! To avoid plagiarism, you must acknowledge any words, facts, or ideas taken from other people's works. The only exceptions are facts or ideas that are so widely known they are considered *common knowledge*. For example, the statement that Alice Munro is a Canadian writer appears in many sources and does not need to be credited. However, a critic's comment like this one from writer Mona Simpson needs to be attributed: "The highest compliment a critic can pay a short-story writer is to say that he or she is our Chekhov. More than one writer has made that claim for Alice Munro" (Simpson 3). You should also give the source for any statistics you use.

Within your paper, acknowledge any source you use by giving the author's last name and page numbers inside parentheses following the quotation or idea you used in your paper. This is called *parenthetical documentation*. When you use the author's name to introduce the quotation, as in the quotation from Ruth Behar on page 645, you need only give the page number.

If your source is from the Internet or an electronic database and doesn't have traditional page numbers, just include the author's name. If there is no author, reference the title or a key word from the title.

Every source mentioned in parenthetical documentation should be included in a Works Cited page at the end of your paper. Center the heading "Works Cited" and list your sources in alphabetical order. You can find sample Works Cited pages in guides like the *MLA Handbook for Writers of Research Papers*. See also page 648 in this handbook for an example.

If you give an oral presentation, you can introduce your sources just as you would introduce a long quotation in a paper. On slides, you can include parenthetical documentation with the text you display. Your teacher may also ask you to submit a summary of your presentation that includes a list of works cited.

Why shouldn't I write a presentation the same way I write a paper?

The biggest difference between a presentation and a paper is that your audience will read one and hear the other. To express your ideas effectively in a presentation, you need to

- Establish rapport with your audience.
  - Make eye contact at the beginning of your presentation.
  - Give your audience a reason to listen.

- Help your audience follow along.
  - Avoid long, involved sentences.
  - Use verbal cues, such as *"At the beginning of the novel . . . ."* and *"The second theme I'm going to talk about . . . ."*

- Use visual aids to reinforce your key points.
  - Use only a few words and make them large enough to be easily readable from the back of the room.
  - Use bold colors that complement each other, especially in complex charts or graphs.
  - Use numbers or bullets to set off your most important points.
  - Avoid USING ALL CAPITAL LETTERS; this style is hard to read.

Works Cited

Behar, Ruth. "Excerpt from *In the House of the Spirits*." *Short Stories for Students*. Edited by Jennifer Smith. Vol. 11. Gale, 2001.

Nelson, Mark R. "We Have the Information You Want, But Getting It Will Cost You: Being Held Hostage by Information Overload." *ACM Crossroads Student Magazine*. 29 Apr. 2019. *xrds.acm.org/*. Accessed 13 Feb. 2020.

Simpson, Mona. "A Quiet Genius." *Atlantic Monthly*, Dec. 2017, pp. 126–136.

A Sample Research Paper

What makes a good research paper? Of course, it should have the same basic elements as other good writing: it should be clear, concise, and coherent. In addition, it should include accurate, pertinent, and well-documented information. The chart below lists traits to strive for in every research paper that you write.

Traits of an Outstanding Research Paper

Ideas	The text conveys a clear and original thesis statement with abundant supporting details and is well chosen for the purpose and audience.
Organization	The organization is clear with abundant transitions.
Voice	The voice sounds engaging and is appropriate for purpose and audience.
Word Choice	Words are specific, and all terms are explained or defined.
Sentence Fluency	Varied sentences flow smoothly.
Conventions	Punctuation, usage, and spelling are correct, and all commonly accepted rules of English are followed.

The research paper on the following pages focuses on one theme from Isabel Allende's short story, "And of Clay Are We Created." As you read it, evaluate it using the traits listed above. Identify where you think the paper is strong and in what ways the writer could improve it.

Confronting the Past in
"And of Clay Are We Created"

by Hank Strickler

Introduction ●   Often, people need to look at others to understand themselves. This is the core message of Isabel Allende's, "And of Clay Are We Created," one of the short stories in her book *The Stories of Eva Luna*. In this story, as in many of Allende's works, a strong female character provides the power for others to change for the better. The strong female in "And of Clay Are *f* We Created" is a dying thirteen-year-old girl, Azucena's. In the final three days of her life, a photographer named Rolf Carlé tries to comfort **Thesis Statement ●**   her. However, Azucena's strength causes Rolf Carlé to recall the suffering in his own childhood and to begin to confront and overcome his past.

Body: Main Topic I, ●   The author, Isabel Allende, was born in Lima, Peru, in
Background on the   1942, to Chilean diplomat Tomás Allende and his wife
Author   Dona. Throughout her childhood Allende lived in numerous countries, including Peru, Lebanon, Switzerland, and Chile. In her semi-autobiographical novel *My Invented Country*, Allende recalls that the constant changes left her feeling that she had no real home for much of her life, except for the few periods when she lived in Chile. As a young woman, she became a writer, creating humorous essays and books for children. In 1970, her uncle, Salvador Allende, was elected president of Chile. However, in 1973, General Augusto Pinochet staged a violent coup that overthrew the government. In 1975, Isabel was forced to flee the country. She spent the next 13 years in Venezuela, where she wrote for a newspaper in Caracas

(Isabel Allende). Starting in the 1980s, she began writing novels, short stories, and autobiographical works for adults. Books such as *The House of Spirits, My Invented Country,* and *Daughter of Fortune* made her one of the first female writers from Latin America to be praised by critics and read by millions around the world ("Timeline"). She has had her works translated into at least 28 languages and has sold well over 30 million copies of her books (Cortínez 1).

Allende's books often feature a girl or woman who shapes her own world or causes the changes that occur in other characters. Her interest in such characters began when she was very young. "Starting at the age of four, I dreamt that the whole world was feminist" (Satvio). Because Allende focuses on female characters and she writes in the style of magic realism, literary scholar Patricia Hart calls Allende's writing "feminocentric magic realism" or "magic feminism" (30). Some examples of the strong female characters in Allende's works include Alba in *The House of Spirits,* Inés Suárez in *Inés of My Soul,* Eva Luna in *Eva Luna,* and characters in several short stories in *The Stories of Eva Luna.*

According to Allende, *The Stories of Eva Luna* and most of her other stories "are based on real people and real things that have happened, events that I read in the newspaper or have seen on television, or things that people have told me" (Crystall 119). In an interview, Allende described the incident on which she based "And of Clay Are We Created": "In 1985 the Nevada Ruiz volcano [in Colombia] became active; the snow at the peak melted, and that caused an avalanche of mud and rock that buried a village below. Because 23,000 people died and rescuers couldn't recover the bodies, they declared the entire zone a cemetery ("1985"). A girl, Omaira Sánchez, died there buried in mud up to her armpits in the rubble of her house and the bodies of her family. It took her three whole days to die. The world press filmed her dying face. I saw it on Caracas television. Her big black eyes, filled with resignation and wisdom,

Body: Main Topic II, Background on the Story

still pursue me in dreams. Writing the story failed to exorcise her ghost" (Correas Zapata 76). The other main character in the story, Rolf Carlé, is also based on a real person, a man Allende interviewed in Hamburg, Germany, who was the son of a Nazi officer (Rodden 39).

Body: Main Topic III, The Beginning of the Story →

The story is told by Eva, who is Rolf Carlé's girlfriend. As the story begins, Azucena is trapped in the mud. Rolf Carlé is a photographer, and he is sent to cover the story. He is an intrepid reporter who never shies away from a dangerous situation, be it military action or a disaster site. He could view anything, no matter how frightening or horrible, as long as he saw it through his camera. According to Eva, "I believe that the lens of a camera had a strange effect on him; it was as if it transported him to a different time from which he could watch events without actually participating in them. When I knew him better, I came to realize that this fictive distance seemed to protect him from his own emotions" (Allende 118).

When Rolf Carlé sees Azucena, he decides to stay with her and try to save her. The girl seems stoic in the face of possible death: "she did not seem desperate, as if an ancestral resignation allowed her to accept her fate" (Allende 119). As they talk, "Her tone was humble, as if apologizing for all the fuss" (Allende 122). Most significantly, when Rolf Carlé begins to cry, she tells him, "Don't cry. I don't hurt anymore. I'm fine" (Allende 125).

Azucena might say she is fine, but Rolf Carlé can't pull her out of the mud, no matter what he tries. She is stuck, "held by the bodies of her brothers and sisters clinging to her legs" (Allende 119). Just as Azucena is literally trapped by her family, Rolf Carlé is figuratively trapped by his. Her situation becomes "a powerful metaphor for the torrent of memories that erupts and flows through Rolf Carlé as he confronts his past, equally buried behind his camera, yet exercising a firm grasp on his life" (Levin 80).

Rolf Carlé soon puts down his camera. This is the turning point in the story. When Rolf Carlé puts down the camera to try to help and comfort Azucena, he is taking off his armor. He has to be a part of the awfulness of this situation because there is no lens with which to distance himself. He has chosen to "emerge from behind the metaphoric lens that distances [him] from life and to open the sealed box that contains the memory of [his] past" (Levin 84). He tells Azucena about some of his adventures, but he also delves deep into the painful abyss of his repressed memory, which he does not tell the dying girl. Eva explains it this way: "Azucena had surrendered her fear to him and so, without wishing it, had obliged Rolf Carlé to confront his own. There, beside that hellhole of mud, it was impossible for Rolf Carlé to flee from himself any longer, and the visceral terror he had lived as a boy suddenly invaded him" (Allende 124). The reader finds out that in his youth, Rolf Carlé was forced to bury bodies in concentration camps during the Holocaust. He saw his mother humiliated by Russian soldiers. He suffered physical and psychological abuse from his father. He failed to protect his mentally retarded sister from their father. All the pain and suffering and guilt that he accumulated as a child begins to come out in a great rush under the influence of Azucena. So when he starts to cry, and Azucena tells him that she is fine, he responds that he is crying for himself (Allende 125).

●——— Body: Main Topic IV, The Effect on Rolf Carlé

On its surface, Isabel Allende's "And of Clay Are We Created" is about a man comforting a girl who is about to die. But the real story is about confronting the past. The hero is not the man who does the comforting—it is the girl. Rolf Carlé's past was dormant in his psyche for many years. When he saw Azucena trapped in the mud, he dropped his camera that was a shield from the reality confronting him. When he did, the dam suppressing the river of painful memories broke. Rolf Carlé emerged a better man, all because of his encounter with Azucena.

●——— Conclusion

Works Cited

"1985: Volcano kills thousands in Colombia." *BBC News: On This Day 1950–2005*, 13 Nov. 1985, news.bbc.co.uk/onthisday/hi/dates/stories/november/13/newsid_2539000/2539731.stm31. Accessed 3 Feb. 2020.

Allende, Isabel. "And of Clay Are We Created." *Reading the World*, edited by Andrea Stark, Perfection Learning, 2021, pp. 120–131.

Correas Zapata, Celia. *Isabel Allende: Life and Spirits*. Arte Público Press, 2002.

Cortínez, Verónica. "Isabel Allende." *Latin American Writers*. Charles Scribner's Sons, 2012.

Crystall, Elyse, et. al. "An Overwhelming Passion to Tell the Story." *Conversations with Isabel Allende*. Revised ed., University of Texas Press, 2004.

Hart, Patricia. "Magic Feminism in Isabel Allende's: 'The Stories of Eva Luna.' " *Contemporary Literary Criticism*, vol. 97, July–Dec. 2000, pp. 30–35. JSTOR, www.jstor.org/stable/26407248?seq=1. Accessed 25 Feb. 2020.

Levin, Linda. *Isabel Allende*. Twayne Publishers, 2002.

Rodden, John. "Introduction," *Conversations with Isabel Allende*. Revised ed., University of Texas Press, 2012.

Satvio, Anita. "A Teller of Tales: Isabel Allende." *The National Magazine of the Successful American Latino*. October–November 2002.

"Timeline." *Isabel Allende*. www.isabelallende.com/en/timeline#2019. Accessed 29. Feb. 2020.

A Glossary of Literary Terms

allegory a literary work in which characters, objects, and events stand for abstract qualities such as goodness, pleasure, or evil

alliteration the repetition of beginning consonant sounds

allusion a reference to an artistic, historical, or literary figure, work, or event

analogy a description of an unfamiliar object or idea made by comparing it to something familiar

anecdote a short incident or story that illustrates a point; usually has an informal storyteller's tone

antagonist a character who opposes the hero or main character of the story

anti-hero a protagonist who displays traits opposite to the qualities usually associated with a traditional hero

aphorism a short saying that teaches a lesson

appeal to emotion a persuasive technique that encourages others to act based on emotions rather than facts; see also *propaganda*

archetype an image, character, symbol, plot, or other literary device that appears so frequently in myths,

folktales, and other literary works that it becomes an important part of a culture

aside a short comment that departs from the main flow of a narrative; in drama, an aside is delivered to the audience and is not heard by the other characters

assonance the repetition of vowel sounds in a literary work, especially in a poem

asyndeton the omission or absence of a conjunction between parts of a sentence

autobiography a nonfictional account of the author's life

biography a nonfictional account of someone's life

blank verse (also called *unrhymed iambic pentameter*) unrhymed lines of ten syllables, each with the even-numbered syllables bearing the accents

burlesque a work that ridicules a topic by treating something exalted as if it were trivial or vice versa

catharsis from the Greek *katharsis*, which means to cleanse or purge. The term is used to describe the purging of emotions (pity, fear, and empathy) brought on by the death or downfall of the tragic hero.

character a person, animal, or imaginary being in a story

characterization the manner in which an author creates and develops a character using exposition, dialogue, and action

cliché a hackneyed or trite phrase that has become so overused that it has lost its meaning or value

climax the high point of a plot; sometimes coincides with the turning point or defining moment. Some stories do not have a clear climax.

colloquialism a local or regional expression

comedy a genre of drama in which characters avert disaster and enjoy a happy ending; a play that is humorous in nature

complex character a character that has multiple personality traits and usually changes throughout the story, also known as a round or a dynamic character

conceit an elaborate or unusual comparison—especially one using unlikely metaphor, simile, hyperbole, and contradiction

conflict the struggle between opposing forces; external conflict involves an outer force such as nature or another character, while internal conflict exists inside a person, say between a hero's sense of duty and desire for freedom

connotation the emotional associations surrounding a word

consonance a type of alliteration in which the repeated pattern of consonants is marked by changes in the intervening vowels, such as in the words linger, longer, and languor

couplet two consecutive lines of the same metrical length that end in a rhyme to form a complete unit

denotation the dictionary definition of a word

dénouement literally "the untying"; the part of a plot in which the conflict is "untied" or resolved; usually follows the climax

dialect the distinctive speech pattern of people from a certain group or region

dialogue conversation between characters in a literary work

drama a narrative involving conflict between a character or characters and some external or internal force; see *conflict*

dramatic irony see *irony*

elegy a poem dealing with death or sorrow

end rhyme the last syllables or words of a poem rhyme or have similar sounds

enjambment in poetry, the continuation of a sentence without a pause beyond the end of a line, couplet, or stanza

epic a poetic form that adheres to the following classic conventions: a long narrative about a serious subject; an elevated style of language; and a focus on the exploits of a hero or demigod who represents the cultural values of a race, nation, or religious group

epigram a short verse or motto often appearing at the beginning of a longer poem or on the title page of a novel; it establishes mood or raises thematic concerns

epigraph a short quotation or saying at the beginning of a book or chapter, intended to suggest its theme

epilogue a short passage at the end of a work, often designed to bring closure to a literary work

epiphany an event, sometimes mystical in nature, in which a character changes in profound ways due to the revelation of a simple yet powerful truth; also sometimes called a defining moment, moment of clarity, or moment of truth

epitaph an inscription carved on a gravestone; the final statement spoken by a character before his death

epithet a short descriptive phrase added to the name of a character or object, such as rosy-fingered dawn and grey-eyed Athene in Homer's epic poetry

eulogy a formal expression of praise, usually about the dead

euphemism a mild or gentle phrase used to conceal an embarrassing or painful truth

existentialism a philosophy that stresses a person's free will and responsibility to create his or her own order and meaning

exposition information about the background of a story's plot that is directly conveyed or explained, usually by the narrator

external conflict see *conflict*

fable a short story or tale that demonstrates a moral or truth; frequently contains fantasy elements such as talking animals

fairy tale a story involving fairies, elves, giants, and other make-believe characters

falling action the events of a plot that follow the climax; also referred to as the dénouement or resolution

fantasy fiction that contains characters, settings, and objects that could not exist, such as dragons or magic swords; often heroic in nature and sometimes based on myths and legends

farce a form of low comedy featuring exaggerated caricatures of people in improbable or silly situations

fiction literature created from the imagination, not presented as fact, though it may be based on a true story or situation

figurative language language that uses imagery, metaphor, simile, hyperbole, personification, or analogy to convey a sense that is beyond the literal meaning of the words

figure of speech an expression that conveys meaning or increases an effect, usually through figurative language

first-person point of view see *point of view*

flashback an interruption of the normal chronological order of a plot to narrate events that occurred earlier

foil a character that serves by contrast to highlight or emphasize opposing traits in another character

folktale a narrative, usually originating in an oral tradition, with a timeless and placeless setting and archetypal plot elements and characters; may contain elements of fantasy as well

foot the basic unit of meter in poetry; a foot is a group of syllables usually made up of one accented syllable and one or more unaccented syllables

foreshadowing the use of hints or clues about what will happen later in a plot

formal verse rhymed poetry that uses a strict meter (a regular pattern of stressed and unstressed syllables)

frame narrator a narrator who introduces or allows one or more other narrators to tell the main story (or stories) of a work, as in Chaucer's *The Canterbury Tales* (England, 1387). A more recent example can be found in "The Turn of the Screw" by Henry James (America, 1898).

free verse poetry based on the rhythms and pauses of natural speech rather than the artificial constraints of metrical feet

genre a distinctive type or category of literature such as the epic, science fiction, or mystery

gothic a type of writing that focuses on the macabre, grotesque, and mysterious

hero the main character in a story; often one who accomplishes exemplary deeds; also called the protagonist

hubris a negative term implying arrogance, excessive self-pride, or excessive self-confidence; in tragedy, hubris is often the protagonist's tragic flaw that leads to his or her downfall

humor a literary tool used to make the reader or audience laugh or to provoke amusement. Humor can be used to change the mood of a work. Humor-invoking devices include hyperbole, irony, wordplay, and puns.

hyperbole an overstatement or exaggeration used for both serious and comic effect, as in "My vegetable love should grow / vaster than empires and more slow." (Andrew Marvell, "To His Coy Mistress")

iambic pentameter a line of poetry composed of five iambic feet; an iambic foot is composed of one unaccented syllable followed by an accented syllable; see also *blank verse*

idiom an expression whose sense cannot be understood from the literal meaning of the words that form it; idioms are often peculiar to a group or locale

imagery vivid and striking descriptions of objects and details in a literary work, often through use of figurative language

inference a reasonable conclusion drawn by the reader based on clues given in a literary work

in media res literally, "in the midst of things"; refers to a plot that begins at a high point of the action and fills in background through exposition or other means

interior monologue the presentation in a literary work of the unspoken thoughts and feelings of a character; with some authors, may become stream of consciousness

internal conflict see *conflict*

internal rhyme rhyming of words or accented syllables within a line of poetry

interpretation an explanation of the meaning of a piece of literature, dependent in part on the perspective of the reader

irony a recognition and heightening of the difference between appearance and reality; situational irony occurs when events turn out differently from what is expected; dramatic irony occurs when the audience has important knowledge that a main character lacks; verbal irony occurs when what a character says is different from what he or she means

jargon specialized words and phrases used in an occupation, trade, or field of study

juxtaposition two or more things placed side by side, generally in an unexpected combination

lampoon a coarse or crude satire ridiculing a person, class, or style

legend a traditional story or group of stories told about a particular person or place

local color a style of writing that reveals the peculiarities of a specific place and the people who live there; see also *regionalism*

lyricism the state of expressing deep feelings or emotions in poetry or other works of literature. The writer shares a subjective and highly personal point of view.

magic realism also known as magical realism; a literary genre developed in Latin America during the 1960s in which magical or fantastic elements exist nonchalantly in an otherwise realistic setting. Authors in the movement include Isabel Allende (Chile), Jorge Luis Borges (Argentina), Laura Esquivel (Mexico), and Gabriel García Márquez (Colombia).

memoir an autobiographical sketch—especially one that focuses less on the author's personal life or psychological development and more on the notable people and events the author has encountered or witnessed

metaphor a figure of speech that implies a similarity between two unlike things

meter the pattern of stressed and unstressed syllables in poetry; see also *rhythm*

modernism an artistic and literary movement of the 20th century based in part on Freudian and Jungian theories of the unconscious and on the philosophy of existentialism. Modernists explored the notion that the individual is responsible for creating his or her own order and meaning out of the chaos of an indifferent universe. As such, they emphasized the internal experience of the individual artist over social structures. Notable writers of the modernist period include, among many others, James Joyce (Ireland), Virginia Woolf (England), T. S. Eliot and Ernest Hemingway (America), and Jean-Paul Sartre and Albert Camus (France).

monologue when a character shares his or her internal or emotional thoughts or feelings with an audience (in a play) or a reader (in a novel)

mood the overall atmosphere of a work

motif a recurring element in a story such as an object, image, or situation

motivation the reasons or forces that cause characters to act as they do

mysticism the belief that one can gain knowledge of God, truth, or reality through intuition or insight

myth a traditional story, often one that explains a belief or natural phenomenon

narrator a teller of a story; an unreliable narrator makes incorrect conclusions and biased assumptions; a naïve narrator does not fully understand the events he or she narrates; see also *frame narrator*

nonfiction story of actual people and events sometimes told with the dramatic techniques of a novel

novel a fictional prose work of substantial length

onomatopoeia words that sound like their meaning; used to reinforce meaning, dramatize events, and to add liveliness to writing; "pop," "squeak," and "whiz" are examples

oral tradition body of legends, folktales, or poems passed down through generations through oral storytelling or songs

oxymoron a contradiction that makes sense on a deeper level; jumbo shrimp is a simple example

parable a story or short narrative designed to reveal allegorically some religious principle, moral lesson, psychological reality, or general truth

paradox a statement or situation that seems contradictory but may in fact be true

parallel structure repetition of the same pattern of words or phrases within a sentence or across multiple sentences. For example, the three participles at the beginning of this sentence use parallel structure: Jumping, laughing, and skipping, the children ran across the playground.

parody a humorous imitation of a serious piece of writing

pathos an element of literature that evokes pity or compassion

personification a figure of speech in which human characteristics are given to nonhuman things

plot the events of a story that show the characters in action

poem a work written in verse

poetic devices elements of a poem that communicate meaning, including figurative language, rhyme, and meter

poetic license the freedom of a poet or other literary writer to depart from the norms of his or her craft or the literal or historical truth in order to create a special effect

poetic structure elements that make up the structure of a poem, including how the lines are grouped. Elements of poetic structure include lines, stanzas, and how words are placed on the page.

point of view the perspective from which a story is narrated: in first-person point of view, the narrator is a character in the story and uses the personal pronoun "I"; in third-person limited point of view, the narrator is outside the story but presents the story through the thoughts and feelings of one character; in third-person omniscient point of view, the narrator is outside the story, knows the thoughts and feelings of all characters, and can comment on any part of the story

postmodernism a contemporary literary and artistic movement that originated in the 1960s based on, yet extending beyond, modernism. Where the modernist sees the artist's role as creating order and meaning in the face of a chaotic universe, the postmodernist sees no point or possibility of creating a shared order or meaning and thus embraces the chaos. Various "deaths" mark the postmodern era, such as the death of the author and the death of the novel. This being said, the postmodern sensibility is playful, willing to juxtapose elements from different eras or cultures and to "deconstruct" artifacts to unveil hidden intentions or assumptions of the culture that produced it. Notable authors of the postmodern school include Thomas Pynchon, John Barth, and Kurt Vonnegut (America); Umberto Eco and Italo Calvino (Italy); and Harold Pinter and Tom Stoppard (England).

prologue introductory section before a work of fiction or nonfiction

propaganda writing that is designed to sway the reader or viewer to hold certain views or to take certain actions

prose any literary material that is not written in a regular meter

protagonist the main character of a story; see *hero*

proverb a succinct and pithy saying that is in general use and expresses commonly held ideas and beliefs

pun a play on two words similar in sound but different in meaning; for example, Shakespeare, in *Romeo and Juliet*, puns upon Romeo's vile death (vile = vial), the vial of poison Romeo consumed

quatrain a stanza or poem with four lines

realism a 19th-century literary movement that emphasized the objective depiction of people in everyday situations; a reaction against the excessive idealism and sentimentality of romanticism. Realism originated in America with William Dean Howells and Mark Twain; in England with George Eliot; in France with Honoré de Balzac.

refrain a repeated line or set of lines at the end of a stanza or section of a longer poem or song

regionalism literature with an emphasis on locale or other local characteristics such as dialect; see also *local color*

Renaissance the term Renaissance means "rebirth" and refers to the period in European history between the late 1400s to around 1660, during which time Europeans launched an unprecedented era of learning and discovery. The development of the printing press, the Protestant Reformation, the European encounter with the New World, the circumnavigation of the globe—these are but a few highlights of the era. One of the main influences behind this efflorescence was the rediscovery of classical literature and culture, with its emphasis on the arts and sciences and on the perfectability and glory of the individual. This newfound humanism, as the philosophy is called, was a reaction against the medieval spirit of humility and submission to the feudal social order. Whatever the cause, the age gave rise to some of the most influential artists in history, including Miguel de Cervantes (Spain), John Donne (England), Desiderius Erasmus (Netherlands), Ben Jonson (England), Christopher Marlowe (England), Sir Thomas More (England), Niccolò Machiavelli (Italy), François Rabelais (France), William Shakespeare (England), and Edmund Spenser (England).

repartee quick, witty exchanges of dialogue

repetition a technique in which words or phrases are repeated to stress a theme or to provide unity to a work

resolution the point at which the chief conflict or complication of a story is worked out

rhetoric the art of persuasive argument through writing or speech

rhyme scheme the pattern of end rhymes in the lines of a poem; usually represented by pairs of letters. In the scheme *aabb*; for example, the last syllables of the first two lines rhyme as do the last syllables of the last two lines

rhythm the pattern of sounds in speech or writing that is created by the careful arrangement of stressed and unstressed syllables; may create mood or emphasize ideas or themes

rising action the events leading up to the climax of a plot

romanticism an 18th- and 19-century literary movement that valued the individual and intuition over society's rules. The movement was a reaction against the mechanistic logic of neoclassicism. Romantic writers were given to using imaginative, figurative language, stressed the themes of spirituality and intellectual pride, and often displayed an attraction to the forbidden. Notable authors in the movement were William Blake, William Wordsworth, Samuel Taylor

Coleridge, Jane Austen, and Mary Shelley in England; Ralph Waldo Emerson, Henry David Thoreau, and Nathaniel Hawthorne in America.

saga a prose form based upon Scandinavian and Icelandic narratives concerning the exploits of historical kings and warriors

satire writing that uses humor or ridicule to point out human shortcomings and follies

scenario a plot outline; one of many ways in which a story could be worked out

sensory details descriptive elements based on the five senses: taste, touch, smell, sight, and hearing

setting the time and place of the action of a story

short story a work of narrative fiction that is shorter than a novel; may contain description, dialogue, and commentary but typically relies on plot to drive the art

simile a comparison of one thing to another that uses "like" or "as"

situational irony see *irony*

slant rhyme two or more words that have approximately, but not exactly, the same ending sound

soliloquy a monologue spoken by an actor at a point in the play when the character believes himself to be alone; frequently reveals a character's innermost thoughts, feelings, motives, or intentions; often provides necessary but otherwise inaccessible information to the audience

sonnet a lyric poem of fourteen lines, usually in iambic pentameter, with rhymes arranged according to certain definite patterns. It usually expresses a single, complete idea or thought with a reversal, twist, or change of direction in the concluding lines.

speaker in writing, the voice or persona behind the words. The speaker is not necessarily the writer.

stanza a set of lines of verse; in formal verse, stanzas will form a set pattern

stream of consciousness the flow of various impressions—visual, auditory, psychological, intuitive—that reveals the mind and heart of a character

subtext a hidden meaning, often symbolic or metaphorical, that must be inferred from the text

surrealism a literary and artistic movement emphasizing the expression of the subconscious, often through dreamlike imagery. Examples of surrealism can be found in the poetry of Charles Baudelaire and Arthur Rimbaud (France), of Frederico García Lorca (Spain), and Robert Lowell (America).

symbol an object that stands for, or represents, an abstract concept, such as an eagle for freedom or a rose for love

syllogistic fallacy a false conclusion based on incorrect or nonabsolute premises

symbolism (also known as the symbolist movement) a literary movement originating in France in the 1850s with the writer Charles Baudelaire. Baudelaire was influenced by the American author Edgar Allan Poe and sought ways to express the spiritual experience of the individual. The movement was a reaction against realism, with its emphasis on outer realities. The works in the school often have a dreamlike quality. Other authors in the movement include Stephane Mallarmé and Paul Verlaine.

theme the underlying meaning or message of a literary work

third-person point of view see *point of view*

tone the author or narrator's attitude toward the subject of a work; the attitude might be ironic, humorous, sarcastic, serious, deadpan, etc.

tragedy a dramatic form in which the protagonist, due to a tragic flaw, suffers a series of misfortunes leading to a final, devastating catastrophe

tragic flaw a flaw in the character of the protagonist of a tragedy that causes his or her downfall

transcendentalism a philosophical and literary movement of the mid-19th century, principally among the New England authors Ralph Waldo Emerson, Henry David Thoreau, and Nathaniel Hawthorne. Transcendentalists taught that wisdom comes in part from within oneself and emphasized intuition, self-reliance, the intellect, and living close to nature.

voice an author or character's distinctive manner of expressing himself or herself

Index of Titles and Authors

Acknowledgments

Text Credits

"Alone" by Tomas Tranströmer from *New and Collected Poems*, translated by Robin Fulton. Copyright © 1997 by Bloodaxe Books. Reprinted by permission of Bloodaxe Books.

"American Dreams" by Peter Carey from *The Fat Man in History*. Copyright © 1974, 1979 by Peter Carey. Reprinted by permission of International Creative Management on behalf of the author.

"An Ancient Temple" by Bei Dao, translated by Gordon T. Osing and De-An Wu Swihart from *Salt Hill*, Issue 5. Reprinted by permission of Gordon T. Osing.

"An Arab Shepherd Is Searching for His Goat on Mount Zion" by Yehuda Amichai, translated/edited by Chana Bloch and Stephen Mitchell from *The Selected Poetry of Yehuda Amichai*. Copyright © 1996 by The Regents of the University of California. Reprinted by permission of The University of California Press.

"And of Clay Are We Created" by Isabel Allende from *The Stories of Eva Luna*, translated by Margaret Sayers Peden. Copyright ©1989 by Isabel Allende. English translation, copyright © 1991 by Macmillan Publishing Company. Reprinted by permission of Scribner, a Division of Simon & Schuster, Inc.

"And Yet the Books" from *Collected Poems: 1931-1987* by Czeslaw Milosz. Copyright © 1988 by Czeslaw Milosz Royalties, Inc. Used by permission of HarperCollins Publishers.

"Another Evening at the Club" by Alifa Rifaat from *Arabic Short Stories*. Copyright © 1983. Reprinted by permission of Quartet Books.

"The Armenian Language Is the Home of the Armenian" by Moushegh Ishkhan. Reprinted by permission of Shaghzoyan Center, Beruit-Lebanon.

"At the Tourist Centre in Boston" by Margaret Atwood from *Selected Poems 1965–1975*. Copyright © 1976 by Margaret Atwood. Reprinted by permission of Houghton Mifflin Harcourt Publishing Company. All rights reserved.

Aztec Creation Story: "The Creation of Earth," *The Bedford Anthology of World Literature: The Early Modern World, 1450–1650*, edited by Paul Davis, et. al., vol. 3, pp. 715–716. Reprinted by permission of David M. Johnson.

"The Balek Scales" by Heinrich Böll from *The Stories of Heinrich Böll*, translated by Leila Vennewitz. Copyright © 1986 by Heinrich Böll. Reprinted by permission of Verlag Kiepenheur & Wirsch via The Joan Daves Agency of New York, Leila Vennewitz, and Northwestern University Press.

"Black Sheep" from *Numbers in the Dark and Other Stories* by Italo Calvino, translated by Tim Parks. Copyright ©1993 by Palomar S.r.l.e., Arnoldo Mondadori Editore, Milan. English translation copyright © 1993 by Tim Parks. Reprinted by permission of Houghton Mifflin Harcourt Publishing Company. All rights reserved.

"First Confession" from Collected Stories by Frank O'Connor, copyright © 1981 by Harriet O'Donovan Sheehy, Executrix of the Estate of Frank O'Connor. Used by permission of Alfred A. Knopf, an imprint of the Knopf Doubleday Publishing Group, a division of Penguin Random House LLC. All rights reserved.

"First Frost" by Andrei Voznesensky from *Antiworlds and the Fifth Ace: Poetry*, edited by Patricia Blake and Max Hayward. Copyright © 1963 by Encounter Ltd., renewed © 1966, 1967 by Basic Books. Reprinted by permission of Basic Books, a member of Perseus Books, LLC.

"Five Hours to Simla" by Anita Desai. Published by *Granta Magazine*, 1997. Copyright © Anita Desai. Reproduced by permission of the author c/o Rogers, Coleridge & White Ltd., 20 Powis Mews, London W11 1JN

from *Flights*: "Syndrome," "Cabinet of Curiosities," and "Purity of Blood" by Olga Tokarczuk; translation by Jennifer Croft, copyright © 2007 by Olga Tokarczuk; translation copyright © 2017 by Jennifer Croft; from Used by permission of Riverhead, an imprint of Penguin Publishing Group, a division of Penguin Random House LLC. All rights reserved.

from *From Emperor to Citizen: The Autobiography of Aisin-Gioro P'u Yi* by Aisin-Gioro P'u Yi. Copyright © 1964, 1965 by Foreign Languages Press. Reprinted by permission of Foreign Languages Press.

from *The Garlic Ballads* by Mo Yan by permission of Arcade Publishing, an imprint of Skyhorse Publishing, Inc.

"Girls Can We Educate We Dads?" by James Berry from *When I Dance*. Copyright © 1991 by James Berry. Reprinted by permission of Peters Fraser and Dunlop on behalf of the Estate of James Berry.

"The Guitar" by Federico García Lorca, translated by Elizabeth du Gué Trapier. Reprinted by permission of The Hispanic Society of America.

"The Handsomest Drowned Man in the World" from *Leaf Storm and Other Stories* by Gabriel Garcia Marquez. Copyright © Gabriel Garcia Marquez, 1972 and heirs of Gabriel Garcia Marquez.

"The Happy Man" by Naguib Mahfouz from *God's World*, edited by Akef Abudir and Roger Allen. Copyright © 1973, 1988 by Akef Abudir and Roger Allen. Reprinted by permission of Biblioteca Islamica, Inc.

from *Herzog* by Saul Bellow, copyright © 1961, 1963, 1964, renewed 1989, 1991, 1992 by Saul Bellow. Used by permission of Viking Books, an imprint of Penguin Publishing Group, a division of Penguin Random House LLC. All rights reserved.

"I Will Pronounce Your Name" by Léopold Sédar Senghor from *Black Orpheus*. Reprinted by permission of Editions du Seuil.

"Inem" by Pramoedya Ananta Toer from *Pramoedya Ananta Toer: Six Indonesian Short Stories*, translated by Rufus S. Hendron. Copyright © 1968 by Rufus S. Hendron. Reprinted by permission of the author's agent, Anna Soler-Pont, Pontas Literary & Film Agency, Barcelona, Spain.

Image Credits

Page v: © Burstein Collection/CORBIS. Page vi: © Scala / Art Resource, NY. Page xi: © Scala / Art Resource, NY; © 2002 Artists Rights Society (ARS), New York / ADAGP, Paris. Page xiv: © Penny Tweedie/CORBIS. Pages 2–3: Photodisc. Page 4: Amy Illardo/Photonica. Page 5: Rieder & Walsh/Photonica. Page 6: T, Octavio Paz, © The Nobel Foundation; B, Isabel Allende, AP Photo/Eric Risberg. Page 7: T, Margaret Atwood, AP Photo/Heribert Proepper; M, Derek Walcott, © The Nobel Foundation; B, Gabriel García Márquez, © The Nobel Foundation. Page 19: © Peter Turnley/CORBIS. Page 31: © Raphael Montpetit/Hollander York Gallery. Page 41: Amy Illardo/Photonica. Page 52: Fernando Holguin Cereceres. Page 71: © Burstein Collection/CORBIS. Page 77: Samere Tansley. Page 86: Angel Wynn/Native Stock. Page 92: Manu Sassoonian / Art Resource, NY. Page 113: © Steve Lindridge; Eye Ubiquitous/CORBIS. Page 124: Rieder & Walsh/Photonica. Page 134: © Hulton-Deutsch Collection/CORBIS. Page 135: © Royalty-Free/CORBIS. Page 136: T, Stevie Smith, © Hulton-Deutsch Collection/CORBIS; M, Seamus Heaney, © The Nobel Foundation; B, Heinrich Böll, © The Nobel Foundation. Page 137: L, Wislawa Szymborska, © The Nobel Foundation; R, Boris Pasternak, © The Nobel Foundation. Page 141: Dante and Virgil (oil on canvas, 102 1/2 × 67 1/8 in.), Corot, Jean Baptiste Camille (1796–1875) / Museum of Fine Arts, Boston / Gift of Quincy Adams Shaw, 75.2 / © 2009 Museum of Fine Arts, Boston. All rights reserved. / The Bridgeman Art Library International. Page 149: © Hulton-Deutsch Collection/CORBIS. Page 158: Photodisc. Page 161: © Royalty-Free/CORBIS. Page 167: Private Collection/Portal Gallery Ltd./Bridgeman Art Library. Page 170: © Smithsonian American Art Museum, Washington, DC / Art Resource, NY; © 2002 Artists Rights Society (ARS), New York / ADAGP, Paris. Page 180: © Herscovici / Art Resource, NY; © 2002 C. Herscovici, Brussels / Artists Rights Society (ARS), New York. Page 199: © Giraudon / Art Resource, NY; © 2002 Artists Rights Society (ARS), New York / ADAGP, Paris. Page 204: © Smithsonian American Art Museum, Washington, DC / Art Resource, NY. Page 212: George Tooker, Market, 1949, egg tempera on gesso panel, Collection of John P. Axelrod, Boston, MA, Courtesy DC Moore Gallery, New York, NY. Page 225: © Tate Gallery, London / Art Resource, NY; © Jasper Johns/Licensed by VAGA, New York, NY. Page 228: © Giraudon / Art Resource, NY. Page 241: James Gritz/Photonica. Page 252: © Scala / Art Resource, NY. Page 266: © Owen Franken/CORBIS. Page 267: © Hulton-Deutsch Collection/CORBIS. Page 268: T, Léopold Sédar Senghor, AP Photo/Remy de la Mauvinierre; M, Wole Soyinka, © The Nobel Foundation; B, Bessie Head, Vanda van Speyk/The National English Literary Museum, Grahamstown, South Africa. Page 269: T, Doris Lessing, AP Photo; B, Nadine Gordimer, © The Nobel Foundation. Page 282: Mmakgabo Mmapula Helen Sebidi/Everard Read Gallery. Page 291: © Manu Sassoonian / Art Resource, NY. Page 300: © Owen Franken/CORBIS. Page 313: Corel. Page 327: © Werner Forman / Art Resource, NY. Page 363: © Réunion des Musées Nationaux / Art Resource, NY. Page 371: © Hulton-Deutsch Collection/CORBIS. Page 376: Jed Share/Photonica. Page 377: © Ted Streshinsky/CORBIS. Page 378: L, Assia Djebar, AP Photo/Frank Rumpenhorst; R, Naguib Mahfouz, © The Nobel Foundation. Page 379: L, Yehuda Amichai, AFP/CORBIS; R, R. K. Narayan, AP Photo. Page 396: © Eduardo Garcia/Getty Images. Page 402: © Michael Boys/CORBIS. Page 419: © Robert Landau/CORBIS. Page 431: David Zaitz/Photonica. Page 442: © Jacqui Hurst/CORBIS. Page 459: © Scala / Art Resource, NY; © 2002 Artists Rights Society (ARS), New York / ADAGP, Paris. Page 462: Jed Share/Photonica. Page 473: Lynn Saville/Photonica. Page 488: © Ted Streshinsky/CORBIS. Page 500: © Bettmann/CORBIS. Page 501: © Jack Fields/CORBIS. Page 502: T, Ha Jin, AP Photo/Diane Bondareff; B, Pramoedya Ananta Toer, AP Photo/Dita Alangkara. Page 503: T, Yukio Mishima, AP Photo/Nobuyuki Masaki; B, Patricia Grace, AFP/CORBIS. Page 520: © Bettmann/CORBIS. Page 528: Collection International Institute of Social History, Amsterdam. Page 547: Guang Hui China Tourism Press.Xie/Getty Images. Page 554: Giraudon/Art Resource, NY. Page 580: © Anna Clopet/CORBIS. Page 586: National Archives. Page 597: © Jack Fields/CORBIS. Page 605: © Penny Tweedie/CORBIS. Page 626: © Paul Almasy/CORBIS.

Images not identified by page were provided by iStockphoto, Jupiter Images, Mary Evans Picture Library, Getty Images, or fotosearch.